fundamentals of electricity and magnetism

ARTHUR F. KIP
Professor of Physics
University of California, Berkeley

second edition

McGraw-Hill Book Company
New York   St. Louis   San Francisco   Toronto
London   Sydney

fundamentals of
electricity
and magnetism

Copyright © 1962, 1969 by McGraw-Hill, Inc. All Rights Reserved. Printed in the United States of America. No part of this publication may be reproduced, stored in a retrieval system, or transmitted, in any form or by any means, electronic, mechanical, photocopying, recording, or otherwise, without the prior written permission of the publisher.

Library of Congress Catalog Card Number 68-25655

34780

4567890 HDBP 7543210

editor's introduction

With the great developments in physical science that have occurred in the last thirty years, there has come a need for fundamental revision of the way in which the subject is presented in colleges and universities. In spite of the limited total time available in the curriculum of the four-year course leading to the bachelor's degree in liberal arts and in engineering, there is a growing recognition that fundamental physics requires two years, or at the very least three semesters, for a presentation that is adequate to the needs of those who are going on in any field of science, medicine, or engineering. Soon, it is to be hoped, the one-year without-calculus course, which has been for too long regarded as good enough for liberal arts and pre-medical students, will be a thing of the past.

Until recently, those who felt a desire to work out a new, modern approach were severely hampered in what they could undertake because of the generally low quality of the instruction in basic science and mathematics that was being offered in most high schools. But this obstacle is rapidly dissolving because of the intensive effort that has gone into the preparation of a better type of high school physics course through the splendid efforts of the Physical Science Study Committee and others; because of analogous developments in improving the high school course in mathematics, chemistry, and biology; because of the large-scale program of academic-year institutes and summer institutes sponsored by the National Science Foundation for improving the knowledge of high school teachers about the subjects they teach; and because of the development of organized plans for the improvement of science and mathematics teaching at the college level, also sponsored by the National Science Foundation.

Thirty years ago, and even more recently than that, there was a sharp dichotomy among physicists between those primarily interested in research (who were too often deplorably negligent about their teaching) and those primarily interested in teaching (who were too often deplorably negligent about keeping informed on current developments). And it was the teachers who were low on the pecking order of the academic status scale. Fortunately all that is changing now. Outstanding research physicists are devoting energies to improving teaching, and many college teachers are taking a much more active interest in current research progress than formerly.

The new trends, which are still gaining momentum, must be reflected in new approaches in the available textbooks. The present volume, on electricity and magnetism, by Prof. Arthur Kip, of the University of California at Berkeley, is one of a series planned as a unit for a modern presentation of physics suitable for men and women who expect to play an effective role, possibly as scientists or engineers, in a world in which genuine understanding of the principles and methods of physics has become so important. It is expected that this book will be used in the second semester of a three- or four-semester sequence, after a course covering mechanics, heat, and the kinetic theory of matter, which is presented in another volume of this set, *Fundamentals of Mechanics and Heat* by Hugh D. Young. Going beyond this volume are three others: one planned for a one-semester course in optics and wave motion, *Fundamentals of Optics*, by Arthur Beiser (in preparation), one planned for a one-semester course in atomic and nuclear physics, *Concepts of Modern Physics* by Arthur Beiser, and one for a combined course in optics and atomic physics, *Fundamentals of Optics and Modern Physics* by Hugh D. Young.

Consistently with the improved situation in mathematical instruction that now exists, these books make use of basic concepts of the differential and integral calculus and also of vector methods where needed. Also consistent with the fact that most students probably will not have delved deeply into these subjects, a minimum use of skill in "wangling" special results by such methods is made. Instead the emphasis is on the development of good physical understanding of physical concepts and the experimental basis underlying their acceptance, rejection, or growth by modification.

It is sincerely hoped that the series will make a genuine contribution toward helping teachers give their students the kind of clear perception of what physics is really about that is so needed for life in the world today.

E. U. CONDON
University of Colorado,
and Fellow of the Joint Institute
for Laboratory Astrophysics
of the National Bureau
of Standards and
the University of Colorado,
Boulder, Colorado

preface

This book is a first course in classical electric and magnetic theory. In such a course there must be a compromise between the need to present the phenomena of electricity and magnetism and the desire to develop and display the remarkable unity of the theory, at the level of the student's experience. Here compromise has been made on the basis of experience with second-year students in physics, engineering, and chemistry courses at the Massachusetts Institute of Technology and at the University of California.

The basic laws are related to experimental observations, and the theoretical development is connected with experimental phenomena at many points. On the theoretical side, considerable effort has been made to demonstrate the remarkable economy of description of the basic phenomena of electromagnetism made possible by the use of Maxwell's equations.

In the development of the subject matter in this course, a knowledge of only elementary calculus and of simple vectors has been assumed. The more complicated concepts required are built up as the course proceeds. When scalar and vector fields are introduced, care is taken to introduce the use of line and surface integrals and of scalar and cross products. To this second edition has been added a development of divergence and curl, including a demonstration of the use of vector operators, and a more thorough development of the use of complex numbers. These subjects are treated in such a way that they can be omitted or included, at the option of the instructor. Special sections in the early chapters emphasize the connection between mathematical descriptions and physical problems. Numerous examples are given, both in the body of the text and in many new problems at the ends of chapters, to help the student gain facility in applying mathematical techniques to physical problems.

Since most students come to this course with very little or very cloudy knowledge of all but the simplest phenomena of electricity, practical examples are given throughout the book. However, since this is a course in physics and not in engineering, practical or useful devices are discussed only to the extent that they help to clarify basic principles.

There are two ways in which this book goes beyond the goal of displaying the classical phenomenology and theory of electromagnetism. The first is the inclusion of some of the essential concepts of solid-state physics, where these ideas can aid in the understanding of such fundamental electric phenomena as electric conductivity in metals and semiconductors. Dielectric and magnetic properties of matter are treated in enough detail to prepare the way for the enlarged discussion of semiconductor devices and for later, more sophisticated handling in a solid-state course. The second is the introduction of some of the phenomena that illustrate the impact of quantum mechanics on classical electricity and magnetism and, in the new edition, the connection between special relativity and electromagnetism. In neither case can the treatment of these subjects be comprehensive at this level, but in both cases the student is prepared to appreciate the basic ideas involved. Fuller treatments of quantum-mechanical effects are given in two other volumes in this series, "Concepts of Modern Physics" by Arthur Beiser and "Fundamentals of Optics and Modern Physics" by Hugh D. Young.

In order to give some of the flavor of the historical development of the subject, short excerpts from original papers by Coulomb, Ampère, Faraday, and Maxwell have been included at appropriate places in the text.

Rationalized mks units are used throughout the book, but in

Chapter 17, connection is established between these units and the esu and emu systems of units. It seems clear that a single system of units should be used in any introductory course, though it is also apparent that most students must eventually become familiar with both systems.

Arthur F. Kip

description of
chapter contents

This brief description of the material covered in this book is intended to facilitate omission of material in situations where there is too little time to allow complete coverage. The starred sections in a number of the chapters indicate material which goes beyond the minimum level intended for the course. Some of the starred sections are not particularly complicated, but refer to certain important practical applications of the theory of electromagnetism. In addition, certain chapters go beyond the minimum basic needs of an introductory course and can be omitted. Details are discussed below.

Chapters 1, 2, and 3: These chapters constitute the basic introduction to electrostatics. Starting with Coulomb's law, the concepts of electric field and potential are introduced. Gauss' flux theorem is derived from Coulomb's law, and the concept of circulation of the electrostatic field is related to its conservative nature. Starred sections, which can be omitted without loss of continuity, discuss the differential form of

Gauss' flux theorem and the curl of the field. Appendixes A to D relate to the more advanced parts of those chapters.

Chapter 4:   This chapter introduces the concept of capacitance and provides the first discussion of energy stored in the electric field. Some practical aspects of the use of capacitors are discussed. In a short course, the three starred sections could be omitted, as well as parts or all of some of the remaining sections.

Chapter 5:   This chapter on dielectrics provides the basic introduction to the behavior of matter in an electric field. It is thus slightly out-side the formal theory of electricity and magnetism in a vacuum. However, unless students will have some other course on the inter-action of matter with electric fields, at least some of this material should be included in an introductory course. The first ten sections of the chapter, with perhaps the addition of Section 5.13, cover the most important concepts needed for understanding elementary dielectric phenomena.

Chapter 6:   Much of the material in this chapter on currents and circuits will serve for many students as a review of concepts already encountered in high school courses. The first five sections contain the basic concepts needed.

Chapter 7:   This chapter discusses the classical and quantum theory of conductivity in metals and semiconductors at a level suitable for an introductory course. The entire chapter could be omitted in a short course, though for many students it can serve as a useful introduction to an important sector of solid-state physics. Sections 7.2 to 7.4 give the necessary background for the discussion of semiconductor devices in Chapter 16.

Chapter 8:   This chapter introduces magnetism in terms of the force between current elements. Except for the starred sections, it is essential to any basic course on electricity.

Chapter 9:   Here the important new idea of Faraday induction is discussed. Sections 9.5 to 9.8 could be omitted from a shortened course, but they play an important role in strengthening the understanding of the consequences of Faraday induction. The behavior of self-inductance and mutual inductance is introduced in Sections 9.9 and

9.10. The remainder of the chapter gives more work with inductances and considers magnetic stored energy.

Chapter 10:   This chapter deals with the magnetic properties of matter and develops the contrast between **B** and **H**. Sections 10.9 to 10.15 discuss paramagnetism, diamagnetism, and ferromagnetism, and thus lie outside the minimum requirements of a short course. These magnetic properties of matter are, however, of great practical importance, and should be discussed if time permits.

Chapter 11:   This chapter provides an introduction to the various ways of understanding ac circuits. The behavior of isolated resistors, capacitors, and inductors under sinusoidal voltage excitation is related to their behavior in series and parallel combinations. Solutions of ac circuit equations are obtained graphically, through sinusoidal functions, and alternatively by using complex notation. A short introduction to complex notation is given in Appendix H. The complex-number treatment is highly recommended, but can be omitted without loss of continuity.

Chapter 12:   The concept of displacement currents is discussed here to allow the development of ideas about electromagnetic waves. Maxwell's equations are developed and shown in both integral and differential form. These equations are applied to a number of wave problems, including the transport of energy, reflections, and waves in waveguides.

Chapter 13:   This chapter describes the development of ideas leading up to special relativity and applies relativity to the relationship between electric and magnetic fields.

Chapter 14:   In this chapter a few illustrative problems involving the motion of charged particles in combined electric and magnetic fields are considered. In addition, the ideas of magnetohydrodynamics are given elementary consideration.

Chapter 15:   Some important examples of the intrusion of quantum mechanics on electric and magnetic phenomena are given here, with elementary explanations. These can form a useful introduction to some of the experimental origins of quantum mechanics. The entire chapter can be omitted in a short course.

Chapter 16:   This chapter on electronic devices gives a qualitative survey of vacuum tubes and semiconductor devices. The discussion of the latter leans heavily on the material on semiconductors in Chapter 7.

Chapter 17:   This chapter on units is primarily for reference. In it are discussed the relationships between the various commonly used systems of measurement of electrical quantities.

The Appendixes: These provide background and supplementary material for some of the subjects discussed in the text. They are referred to, as appropriate, in the body of the text.

contents

*fundamentals
of electricity
and magnetism*

1

electric charge, Coulomb's law of electrostatic forces

1.1 Introduction

A thorough investigation of the behavior of *electric charges* (or *electrostatic charges*) will lead us to the complete theory of electromagnetism, and although present theory, as we shall see, tends to place most emphasis on rather abstract quantities such as electric fields, potential, and lines of force, it is the demonstrable reality of electric charges that forms the basis of all our ideas concerning electromagnetism.

The most noticeable thing about electric charges is that the forces between them are extremely large. Compared with gravitational forces, for example, electric forces are many orders of magnitude larger. Electric forces are similar to gravitational forces in that they both obey an inverse-square law, but there is a remarkable difference in the fact that there are two kinds of electric charges but only one kind of gravitational mass. Thus like charges repel each other and unlike charges attract each other; whereas all gravitational masses attract each other.

The reason we are not normally aware of electric forces is that, to a remarkable degree, all matter is made up of almost exactly equal mixtures of both kinds of charge, so that there is usually no net elec-

1

tric force of consequence between separate bodies. The fact is, however, that electric forces hold individual atoms together, and also hold the groups of atoms together to form solid matter. Ours is indeed an electrical universe. A useful description of the world around us actually requires only two additional sets of ideas beyond those of electric and magnetic forces. The first relates to the extremely large forces which hold the components of atomic nuclei together (these are, however, effective over only very small distances, $\approx 10^{-14}$ m, decreasing much more rapidly than with the inverse square of the distance between particles). The second relates to quantum-mechanical principles which govern the electronic configurations of atoms and the building up of matter out of atoms. Familiarity with the electrical rules of behavior is thus essential for understanding much of nature.

In our treatment of electric charges we start with the simplest experimental facts and indicate how the present framework of ideas and methods of theoretical treatment has evolved. For simplicity we consider at first the idealized situation as it would occur if the charges were in a vacuum. Later we shall study the usually small perturbing effects of air and other matter on our simple results. The treatment of charges at rest will first concern us, and later we consider the effects of moving charges, that is, currents. The study of forces on currents is related to the phenomena of magnetism. Finally, we show that the propagation of energy by electromagnetic waves, as in, for example, radio waves and light, is to be understood on the basis of the phenomena we have already studied.

The knowledge of the existence of electrostatic charge goes back at least as far as the time of the ancient Greeks, around 600 B.C. We can repeat the observations of the Greeks by rubbing a rod of amber or hard rubber with a piece of fur. After this it will be found that small bits of paper or other light materials are attracted to the rod. No particular advance was made in the understanding of this phenomenon until about 1600, when William Gilbert, court physician to Queen Elizabeth, began a detailed study of the kinds of materials that would behave like amber. These he described as *electric* (from the Greek word for amber, *elektron*). Materials that Gilbert found unable to show this attractive force he called *nonelectrics*. We now call these two kinds of materials *insulators* and *conductors*.

The next important step in the development of ideas about charges came about 100 years later. Du Fay showed that there are two kinds of electrification. By rubbing various kinds of insulators together, he was able to show that under some conditions they repel each other. His results could be explained by postulating the two kinds of charge already noted: forces between bodies having like charge are found to be repulsive, while forces between unlike charges are attractive. The quantitative theory assigns a plus sign to one type of charge and a minus sign to the other, as was first suggested by Benjamin Franklin. Which sign is given to which kind of charge is arbitrary (and unimportant), but as we shall see, a sign convention allows us to make a very concise mathematical formulation of the experimental facts.

We now leave the qualitative discussion of electric charge and begin the study in quantitative form.

1.2 Electric Charge, Coulomb's Law of Force

It is remarkable that all the simple phenomena involving charges at rest can be described very well by the equation

$$F \propto \sum_i \frac{q_i q'}{r_i^2} \qquad \text{vector sum} \tag{1.1}$$

This rather concise statement contains the essence of the law of electrostatic forces. We owe its formulation to experiments by Priestley in 1767, repeated by Coulomb in 1785. Usually called Coulomb's law of force, it is one form of the law of electrostatics. The simple mathematical statement contains much more than appears explicitly. We list below the set of ideas that is implied in its formulation, and later discuss the experimental evidence which justifies each idea.

1. There is a quantity q (called *electric charge*) which may exist on matter. Its presence on two or more bodies is made evident by forces of attraction or repulsion between bodies containing charge.
2. There are two kinds of electric charge. The force between two *like* charges is *repulsive* and acts along the line joining them. Between two *unlike* charges the force is *attractive* and also acts along the line joining the charges. The charges are named *positive* and *negative* (quite arbitrarily).
3. It is further implied that charge is *conserved;* that is, if a charge q_1 and a charge q_2 are brought together, the result is a total charge q, where $q = q_1 + q_2$. The use of positive and negative charge not only by name, but in the mathematical sense, expresses the fact that the two kinds of charge are indeed opposite. That is, if we combine a charge $-q_a$ with a charge $+q_a$, the net charge is zero, according to the addition rule stated above, which in this case becomes $q_a - q_a = 0$. This remarkably simple

behavior, so concisely expressed by the use of positive and negative signs for charge, shows that, in calculating the force, we need consider only the *net charge* on a body, the excess of one sign of charge over that of the other sign.

4.   The force between a given pair of charges is inversely proportional to the square of the distance between them. [This discussion and Eq. (1.1) assume all charges to be on bodies having very small dimensions compared with distances to other charged bodies being considered. Thus a single length, say, *r*, describes accurately enough the distance between one charged body and another.] We speak of such charges as point charges.

5.   The force between a given pair of charges is directly proportional to the *quantity* of one charge multiplied by the *quantity* of the other.

6.   The total force on a given charge is obtained by computing the force due to each of the other charges separately, and adding the separate forces vectorially. This procedure implies that the force between any two charges is unaffected by the presence of other charges, or stated differently, the *total* force on a given charge is the (vector) sum of the individual forces due to all other charges. This result is often called the principle of *superposition*.

Before describing the experimental facts which justify these various statements about electric charges, let us with Fig. 1.1 show how

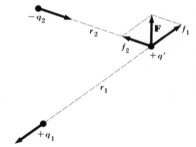

Fig. 1.1   *The force on $+q'$ is the vector sum of the forces of interaction with all other point charges.*

Eq. (1.1) is used and how it does indeed imply each of the statements made above.

We take the special case in which we wish to compute the net force on a charge $+q'$ of charges $+q_1$ and $-q_2$ at positions r_1 and r_2, as shown in the figure. For this case, Eq. (1.1) becomes

$$F \; \propto \; \left(\frac{q_1 q'}{r_1{}^2} + \frac{q_2 q'}{r_2{}^2}\right) \qquad \text{vector sum}$$

The first term involves the like charges q_1 and q', so that the mutual forces are repulsive as shown for f_1, while the second term involves

$-q_2$ and q', charges of opposite sign, giving attractive forces as shown for f_2. The net force on q' is then the vector sum of the two separate forces, as shown.

We now see how each of the six points discussed above has been involved in this use of Eq. (1.1):

1. We used the quantity q to characterize the *amount* of charge on each of the three bodies.
2. We took account of both positive and negative kinds of charge, and arranged the direction of the forces according to the stated rules.
3. Only if charge is a conserved quantity are we entitled to treat it as we did, using the various q's to indicate the *net* charge on each body.
4. We followed the inverse-square law when we computed the force between q' and each of the other point charges (by including $1/r_1{}^2$ and $1/r_2{}^2$).
5. We used $q'q_1$ and $q'q_2$, the products of the pairs of charges, in the calculation of the magnitude of the forces.
6. The final net force F is to be calculated in accord with the principle of superposition by the vector addition of the two forces f_1 and f_2 acting on q'.

One final step has been neglected for the time being. For, say, a given pair of charges a certain distance apart, there will be a certain force. But the equation as stated gives only a proportionality between force and the magnitude and relative positions of charges. We can replace the proportionality sign by an equal sign and a proportionality constant once we have defined units of measurement of charge, length, and force and have made appropriate measurement of actual forces between known amounts of charge.

We now discuss some simple experiments that help to clarify and give substance to these ideas. The first experimental step is to show that like charges repel each other.

The first step is to produce an excess of charge on some body, for example, by friction, as did the Greeks. We can then transfer some of this charge by contact to a small ball of paper. When we go through the same procedure several times, using different paper balls each time, we find easily measurable repulsive forces between the balls, indicating that the force between bodies holding similar kinds of excess charge is repulsive.

We now search for a possible different kind of charge by trying the frictional charging of rods of different materials. When we again charge other paper balls by contact with the new rods, we indeed find some combinations which give us attracting forces. An example would be a ball charged by contact with an amber rod (negative) previously rubbed with wool, which is attracted by a ball charged by contact with a glass rod (positive) rubbed with a silk cloth. (The former ball turns out to have an excess negative charge, and the latter an excess positive charge, by comparison with the sign of the charge on electrons, defined as negative.) In older books the charge on the glass is called *vitreous* electricity and that on the amber is called *resinous*.

A possible, though perhaps not very practical, way to verify statement 4 is given next. Later a much more satisfying argument will be given.

A demonstration of the validity of the inverse-square law of repulsion between like charges. Suppose we have like charges of equal magnitude on two pith balls of equal mass, suspended in equilibrium on insulating threads of negligible mass, as shown in Fig. 1.2. The equal charge

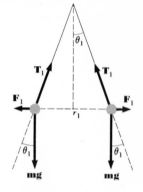

Fig. 1.2 Arrangement for measuring the force of repulsion between two equally charged pith balls. In equilibrium the net force on each pith ball is zero.

and mass requirement is not necessary, but is made here to simplify the calculation. Since the resultant of the electrostatic force **F** and the gravitational force **mg** must be equal and opposite to the tension force **T**,

$$\frac{F_1}{mg} = \tan \theta_1$$

When we shorten the suspending threads, the system takes up a new equilibrium position, with a new angle θ_2. The new repulsive electrostatic force will be given by $F_2/mg = \tan \theta_2$. Thus, by measuring θ_1 and θ_2, we can get the ratio F_1/F_2, since **mg** does not change. If we also measure the separations between the charges, r_1 and r_2, we can relate the ratio of forces to the ratio of separations. We find experimentally that $F_1/F_2 = r_2{}^2/r_1{}^2$. This result is consistent with statement 4 that

$$F \propto \frac{1}{r^2} \tag{1.2}$$

It is of interest to quote briefly from the original papers of Coulomb[1] part of his description of his quantitative measurements of the law of forces between charged particles. Coulomb had determined the law of torsion of wires, after which he applied the torsion method to the investigation of electrostatic forces. His torsion balance was arranged so that the force between two charged bodies resulted in a twisting of a fine suspension wire. He compared the amount of twisting for various separations between the charged bodies, and from this was able to induce the inverse-square law:

> In a memoir presented to the Academy in 1784, I determined by experiment the laws of force of torsion of a metallic wire. . . .
> I showed in the same memoir that by using this force of torsion it was possible to measure with precision very small forces, as for example, a ten thousandth of a grain. . . .
> I submit today to the Academy an electric balance constructed on the same principle; it measures very exactly the state and the electric force of a body however slightly it is charged. . . .
> . . . we go on to give the method which we have used to determine the fundamental law according to which electrified bodies repel each other.
> In the third trial the suspension wire was twisted through 567 degrees and the two balls are separated by only 8 degrees and a half. The total torsion was consequently 576 degrees, four times that of the second trial, and the distance of the two balls in this third trial lacked only one-half degree of being reduced to half of that at which it stood in the second trial. It results then from these three trials that the repulsive action which the two balls exert on each other when they are electrified similarly is in the inverse ratio of the square of the distances.

Statement 5, which says that the force between two charges is proportional to the product of the two charges involved, can be verified experimentally by inverse-square experiments. For example, the

---

[1] Charles Augustin de Coulomb, Mémoires sur l'électricité et le magnétisme, *Mem. Acad. Roy. Sci.*, pp. 569ff. (1788). The quotation is from the 1785 volume, published in 1788—there were delays in publishing in those days too!

ratios of charges on a whole set of balls could be determined by measuring the force between each charged ball and another fixed isolated charge. Then a series of force measurements between pairs of balls would verify the statement

$$F \propto q_1 q_2 \tag{1.3}$$

Statement 3 is the quantitative aspect of statements 1 and 2 regarding the existence of charge and of two "opposite" kinds of charge. The proof of statement 3 appears with the quantitative studies of statements 4 and 5. Only if charge is conserved as in statement 3 can we consider an inverse-square law and the product rule for the force between two charges.

Once the correctness of statements 4 and 5 is verified, the two ideas can be consolidated into the single equation

$$F \propto \frac{q_1 q_2}{r^2} \tag{1.4}$$

This simple statement also implies the legitimacy of the concept of quantity of charge as formulated in statements 1, 2, and 3.

There now remains only the verification of statement 6, the principle of superposition, which says that the *total* electric force on a charge, as given in Eq. (1.1), is simply the vector sum of the separate forces due to all the charges involved, each force being of the kind given in Eq. (1.4). The proof of this principle is relatively simple, since it requires only that we show by experiment that the total force on a charge is the vector sum of appropriate terms like that of Eq. (1.4).

Vector notation. It is useful to introduce one more kind of mathematical terminology that will aid in the description of the physical situation. We have noted that Eq. (1.4) is a vector equation, since it involves force, which is a vector quantity. In order to indicate that the right-hand side of the equation is also a vector quantity, we introduce the *unit vector* $\hat{\mathbf{r}}_{12}$, which has the direction of the vector (in this case, the direction of the radius vector $\mathbf{r}_{12}$ from q_2 to q_1) and a magnitude of unity.

Formally stated,

$$\hat{\mathbf{r}}_{12} = \frac{\mathbf{r}_{12}}{|\mathbf{r}_{12}|}$$

With this unit-vector notation we rewrite Eq. (1.4):

$$\mathbf{F}_1 \propto \frac{q_1 q_2}{r^2} \hat{\mathbf{r}}_{12} \tag{1.4a}$$

There is no change in the meaning of the equation, but we have made more explicit the vector nature of both sides. In illustration of this notation we first write out Eq. (1.1) explicitly as

$$F \propto \left(\frac{q_1 q_2}{r_{12}{}^2} + \frac{q_1 q_3}{r_{13}{}^2} + \cdots \right) \qquad \text{vector sum} \qquad (1.4b)$$

in which the terms on the right are vectors along $\mathbf{r}_{12}$, $\mathbf{r}_{13}$, . . . , and should be added as vectors. This expression written in vector form is

$$\mathbf{F} \propto \left(\frac{q_1 q_2}{r_{12}{}^2} \,\hat{\mathbf{r}}_{12} + \frac{q_1 q_3}{r_{13}{}^2} \,\hat{\mathbf{r}}_{13} + \cdots \right)$$

Here the unit vectors $\hat{\mathbf{r}}_{12}$ and $\hat{\mathbf{r}}_{13}$ have the directions of the lines from q_2 to q_1 and q_3 to q_1, respectively.[1]

We have now only one more task: to replace the proportionality sign in the equation with the more explicit equals sign. The usual method is to write the equation with a proportionality factor, which must then be evaluated. Thus Eq. (1.4) becomes

$$\mathbf{F}_1 = K \frac{q_1 q_2}{r_{12}{}^2} \,\hat{\mathbf{r}}_{12} \qquad (1.4c)$$

where K is the proportionality factor. The value of K depends on the choice of units for F, r, and q. If the units of F and r have already been adopted from a study of mechanics (as F in newtons and r in meters in the mks system), the value of K then depends solely on the choice of the unit of q. In the mks system we define the unit of q from totally different considerations, based on magnetic forces between electric currents; the unit is called the *coulomb*. In that case K becomes a quantity that has to be measured experimentally. For reasons that become clear later, it is customary to write K as $(4\pi\epsilon_0)^{-1}$; so the equation becomes

$$\mathbf{F} = \frac{1}{4\pi\epsilon_0} \frac{q_1 q_2}{r^2} \,\hat{\mathbf{r}} \qquad (1.5)$$

Subscripts can be omitted in cases where the meaning is clear.

---

[1] Another common way of handling the vector nature of equations like (1.4a) is to write it

$$\mathbf{F}_1 \propto \frac{q_1 q_2 \mathbf{r}_{12}}{r_{12}{}^3} \qquad (1.4b)$$

where $\mathbf{r}_{12}$ is now a vector with the magnitude of the distance r_{12}. The $r_{12}{}^2$ in the denominator has been changed to $r_{12}{}^3$ to compensate for this; so the meaning is identical with that of Eq. (1.4a). We shall use the unit-vector notation.

The quantity ϵ is called the *permittivity*. The subscript is attached to indicate that we refer to the force constant between point charges in a *vacuum*. ϵ_0 is thus the *permittivity of free space*. We learn later how the force between two charges is modified when the charges are immersed in matter. In this case ϵ_0 is replaced by ϵ, a quantity characteristic of the matter involved.

Equation (1.5) gives the force in newtons between point charges. When they are measured in coulombs, r is in meters, and ϵ_0, the permittivity of free space, is 8.854×10^{-12} coul²/newton-m², as determined by experiment. Since the 4π is included in the equation only for later convenience, it is useful to remember the equivalent number, $1/4\pi\epsilon_0 = 9 \times 10^9$ newton-m²/coul².[1]

In the cgs system of units, Coulomb's law provides the basis for defining the electrostatic unit of charge. K in Eq. (1.4c) is set equal to unity, and a unit charge is defined so that when q_1 and q_2 are each one cgs unit (often called esu, or statcoulomb), and r is one centimeter, F is one dyne. Comparing the two definitions, we find that 3×10^9 esu $= 1$ coul. The basic equations of electricity and magnetism are presented in the several common systems of units in Chap. 17.

For the force on q_0 due to a number of charges, we may write

$$\mathbf{F}_0 = \frac{1}{4\pi\epsilon_0} \sum_i \frac{q_0 q_i}{r_i^2} \, \hat{\mathbf{r}}_i \tag{1.6}$$

which amounts to the same thing as Eq. (1.1). A true understanding of this equation gives insight into a great deal of the physics involved in the concept of charges and of the forces between them.

A simple modification allows us to handle situations where the charge is spread over a region instead of being concentrated at particular points. Suppose we have a point charge q_0, which is near a region of continuous charge distribution, as indicated in Fig. 1.3, where we wish

[1] More accurately, this number is 8.9875×10^9.

Fig. 1.3 Calculation of the force on a charge q_1 due to a continuous distribution of charge. The forces due to each element dq at its distance r must be added vectorially. r points from dq to q_1, and $d\mathbf{F}_1$ is the contribution of the interaction between q and dq to F_1.

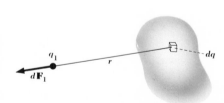

to calculate the total force on q_0 due to all the other charges. As suggested by our discussion so far, we shall need to make a vector sum of all the forces due to all the small charges dq distributed over the region. Thus we should write

$$\mathbf{F}_0 = \frac{1}{4\pi\epsilon_0} \int \frac{q_0\, dq}{r^2}\, \hat{\mathbf{r}} = \frac{q_0}{4\pi\epsilon_0} \int \frac{dq}{r^2}\, \hat{\mathbf{r}} \tag{1.7}$$

where $\hat{\mathbf{r}}$ is a variable unit vector that points from each dq toward the location of the charge q_0.

1.3   Charge Distributions

The simplest kind of charge distribution is an isolated *point* charge (that is, an amount of charge covering such a small region of space that we need not be concerned about its dimensions). Any charge which covers a space with dimensions much less than its distance away from a point of interest can be considered a point charge, for example, if there is a net charge on the earth, the earth can be considered a point charge when its electrical effects at the sun are considered.

When the finite size of the space occupied by a collection of charges must be considered, it is useful to consider the *density* of charge. The word density is used in three different ways. For simplicity we use

ρ (rho) for the charge per unit volume, the *volume* density
σ (sigma) for the charge per unit area, the *area* density
μ (mu) for the charge per unit length, the *linear* density

Thus we can write

$$\rho = \frac{dq}{dV}\ \text{coul/m}^3 \qquad \sigma = \frac{dq}{dA}\ \text{coul/m}^2 \qquad \mu = \frac{dq}{dl}\ \text{coul/m}$$

where V, A, and l are volume, area, and length, respectively.

In the special cases where density is uniform over a region, these expressions can be written

$$\rho = \frac{q}{V}\ \text{coul/m}^3,\ \text{etc.}$$

1.4   Examples

We give below a few examples of particular situations involving the ideas discussed so far. Certain parts of the work are dealt with only briefly, since more general methods will be applied to them in following chapters.

a *Force between two point charges.* Two point charges q_1 and q_2 are separated by a distance r, as shown in Fig. 1.4. Find the force acting

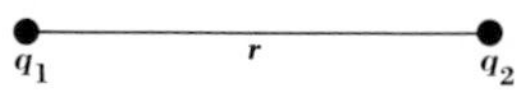

Fig. 1.4 Two point charges separated by a distance r.

on q_1 caused by q_2. This is clearly the most elementary case possible. In the mks system, we must have q_1 and q_2 in coulombs, r_{12} in meters, and F in newtons if we use

$$\mathbf{F} = \frac{1}{4\pi\epsilon_0}\frac{q_1 q_2}{r_{12}^2}\,\hat{\mathbf{r}}_{12} = 9\times10^9\,\frac{q_1 q_2}{r_{12}^2}\,\hat{\mathbf{r}}_{12}\text{ newtons}$$

This expression includes the fact that the force on q_1 acts along the line between the charges and is either attractive or repulsive depending on the relative signs of the charges.

b *Force on one charge due to two others.* For convenience we choose a simple right-angle geometry as shown in Fig. 1.5. This solution fol-

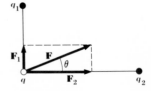

Fig. 1.5 Resultant force on q due to q_1 and q_2 obtained by vector addition of individual forces.

lows immediately if we remember the vector nature of force (and the implied independence of the force between two charges from the presence of other charges). We calculate $\mathbf{F}_1$ and $\mathbf{F}_2$, the forces on q, independently according to Coulomb's law, as in Example 1.4a, and then perform the *vector* addition. In this simple case, $\mathbf{F} = \mathbf{F}_1 + \mathbf{F}_2$ becomes

$$|\mathbf{F}| = \sqrt{|\mathbf{F}_1|^2 + |\mathbf{F}_2|^2}$$

The direction of $\mathbf{F}$ is given by $F_1/F_2 = \tan\theta$ or $\theta = \tan^{-1}(F_1/F_2)$.

c *Force due to linear charge distribution.* Imagine a long, thin stick (Fig. 1.6) with a uniform distribution of excess charge on it. Suppose the total excess charge on the stick is Q. What will be the force of these charges on a charge q at a distance a from the stick along a line

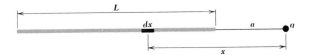

Fig. 1.6 *Calculation of force on a charge q due to a continuous linear distribution of charge.*

through the stick? This is a case requiring the use of an equation like (1.7), so that we can integrate over the entire charge distribution. Thus we must find an expression that allows us to sum up each differential piece of Q, keeping track of its distance from q. A convenient way is to establish a representative element of charge dQ at a distance x from q. The force on q due to this element will be[1]

$$dF = \frac{q}{4\pi\epsilon_0}\frac{dQ}{x^2}$$

In order to integrate this, we must relate the size of dQ to the element dx. This we do by using the linear density $\mu = dQ/dx$, or

$$dQ = \mu\,dx$$

This gives the amount of charge dQ in a length dx. The equation is now

$$dF = \frac{q\mu}{4\pi\epsilon_0}\frac{dx}{x^2}$$

which can be integrated. In the simple case of uniform density, μ is a constant, Q/l; so the integration is as follows:

$$F = +\frac{qQ}{4\pi\epsilon_0}\frac{1}{a(L+a)}\qquad\text{newtons}$$

The positive sign indicates that the force is repulsive when q and Q have the same sign. It is easy to show that this answer is reasonable.

---

[1] A word of explanation for those whose experience with simple calculus is limited: two simple steps must always be taken when setting up problems of integration like this one. The first is that a kind of element must be chosen such that all parts of the element (for an infinitesimal dx) are the same distance from the point (here, at q) at which its influence is to be calculated. Here the one-dimensional nature of the problem makes this almost automatically true. Later examples illustrate the problem. The second step is to express things in terms of the minimum number of variables (here, one). Thus the expression dQ/x^2 as given is correct, but no solution is possible until the two variables dQ and x are reduced to a single one. This is the point at which the appropriate linear surface, or volume density of charge, enters the calculation.

Suppose we let $a \gg L$; then the forces should approximate those between two point charges q and Q. But this is just our result if we neglect L, as would be justified if $a \gg L$. That is, the farther away q is from the stick, the more nearly the stick acts like a point charge.

Another comment should be made about this problem: We have chosen a particularly simple example in which the direction of the force from each element of charge is the same. This allows us to neglect the vector nature of the integration since the sum of a number of vectors all pointing in the same direction is the arithmetic sum of their magnitudes. In some later problems we shall study the more general case.

1.5 Electric Charge and Matter

As mentioned in the introduction, the behavior of all matter is understood through the laws of quantum mechanics and of electricity. If we accept the existence of the particles which make up the cores, or positively charged *nuclei* of atoms (protons and neutrons), and of the very strong nuclear forces which hold them together as nuclei, the atoms of matter are made up of nuclei and negatively charged electrons which are strongly held in the region surrounding each nucleus by the electric attractive forces between opposite kinds of charge. In principle, the configuration of electrons around the nucleus is understood by the rules of quantum mechanics. The ultimate problem of the existence of electric charge and of protons, neutrons, electrons, and all the other particles of physics is still with us. The fact of the *quantization* of charge—that the minimum amount of charge is fixed and is the same for all charged particles—is best regarded as a fundamental quantum characteristic of nature. But this hardly can be considered an explanation.

When atoms combine to form solids, it often happens that one or more of the electrons normally bound to each atom are liberated and can wander around more or less freely in the material. These are the *conduction electrons* in metals. When such freeing of the electrons does not occur, we speak of the material as an insulator, or dielectric. In such materials the electrons are not free to move around, and thus external forces cannot produce currents within the material. In some solid or liquid materials, ions of mass equal to that of atoms are able to move about and give rise to currents. Such materials are called *electrolytes*. In gases, conduction occurs because some of the neutral atoms or molecules become ionized by various external agents, thus producing free electrons and ions which can drift through the gas. We shall discuss electrical effects in dielectrics later, when we shall see that since the electric-charge centers are not tied down rigidly, their slight motion as they stretch their bonds under external forces causes a host of interesting and revealing dielectric effects.

A third category of solid in which some of the bound charges are free to move, and thus allow current to flow, is called a *semiconductor*. Bound charges can be freed by thermal vibrations within a semiconductor, by incident light, or by the application of externally produced electric fields.

The freeing of electrons from atoms at the surface of solids accounts for the charging of bodies by rubbing materials like amber and fur together. Of two different materials rubbed together, the one from which electrons are most easily separated tends to lose electrons and be left with a net positive charge, and the other one becomes negatively charged by collecting excess electrons.

One other aspect of the relation between matter and electrical theory should be introduced at this time. On the one hand, the essential feature of matter is that it is made up of atoms. On the other hand, much of our treatment of electricity ignores the fact that matter is made up of atoms and that there is a minimum size of charge, the charge of an electron or proton. Since the "graininess" of matter is on such a small scale, this neglect is of no significance for many situations. Electromagnetic theory alone cannot tell us the details of what happens on an atomic scale inside matter. Quantum theory is required to discuss matter on an atomic scale, and this subject is left largely untouched in this book. The most we can do with electrical theory inside matter is to investigate *average* values of electrical quantities.

The fact that charge can flow within metals and that charges which have been freed from the atoms of solids (or liquids or gases) can be placed on macroscopic bodies has allowed detailed study of electric (and magnetic) forces on a macroscopic scale. Such study has given rise to the present-day view of electricity and magnetism, which is the principal subject of this book. Because of the large size of electric and magnetic forces, electricity has developed into the most important entity involved in the conversion of stored energy into work and in the transmission of energy from one place to another. Add to this the central role of electricity in communications and its genesis in the atoms of matter, and we see the importance of its study in physics.

1.6   *Electrical Measurements*

One of the most satisfying aspects of the study of electricity is the ultimate simplicity of the few basic principles which allow one to understand its nature. Our main purpose is to show how a relatively few simple experimental facts, combined with the judicious use of moderately simple mathematics, lead us to a few all-encompassing ideas, easily expressed, from which all else follows. The beauty and simplicity of the theory must not make us forget that, as in all physics, everything starts with experimental observations. To this end we continually turn to experimental facts and give considerable emphasis to methods of measurement.

Since the measurement of force gives the most direct and convenient evidence of electricity, the most obvious electrical measuring instruments are those which measure force. We describe some simple ones below.

The electroscope.   This is not only a historically old instrument for detecting the presence of an excess charge, it is also simple to build and easy to understand. Two strips of gold foil are connected to an insulated metal rod as shown in Fig. 1.7. If an excess charge is placed

Fig. 1.7   *Sketch of a gold-leaf electroscope.*

on the rod, part of the charge flows to the foils, which then repel each other. The extent of the separation of the foils depends quantitatively on the amount of charge on the electroscope. This rather primitive indicator of charge is still used in demonstration experiments.

As a detector of charged bodies (or—it amounts to the same thing—for measuring potentials) it has been superseded by other devices, particularly the cathode-ray oscilloscope. The same principle of electrostatic repulsion between charges which we see in the action of an electroscope operates in an electronic vacuum tube. Thus the repulsion between negative charges on the control grid of a vacuum tube and the electron stream from the hot cathode inhibits the flow of charge and gives rise to the control action of the grid.

The cathode-ray oscilloscope (*CRO*). This is perhaps the most used device for detection of electric effects by means of electric forces. In this day of universal acquaintance with television, it is easy to describe how it works, in principle, if not in great detail.

The basic element is a large evacuated tube with a phosphor material on the inside of the large flat glass end, as shown in Fig. 1.8.

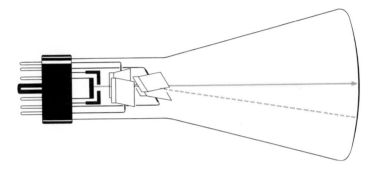

Fig. 1.8 Schematic drawing of a cathode-ray tube.

The phosphor emits light when struck by a beam of rapidly moving electrons. Thus from outside the tube the exact point on the end which is being hit by an electron beam is visible. On the other end is a heated "cathode" which emits a steady stream of electrons. (They are "boiled" off as a consequence of the thermal motions occurring in the solid at high temperature.) The electrons pass through a magnetic or electric focusing arrangement, and pass down the tube as a narrow beam. The electrons are speeded up to high velocity by the attraction of positive charges on appropriately placed and shaped metal electrodes (or, to use language which will be more appropriate after Chaps. 2 and 3, *potentials* have been applied to appropriate electrodes, producing *electric fields* which accelerate the electrons down the tube). So far we have a not very useful device for television or oscilloscope—a large vacuum tube with a phosphor on one end and a bright spot which lights up when proper batteries or voltages are applied. (Electric power is used to heat the cathode which emits electrons, just as the filament of an ordinary light bulb is heated by the electric current which flows through it.)

The element which transforms this device into a measuring instrument is a pair of plates near the cathode end of the tube, between which the electron beam passes. These plates are connected to terminals outside the tube. Connections to whatever is to be studied result in excess negative charge on one plate and excess positive charge on the other. The electrons in the beam are thus repelled by one plate and attracted to the other. As a result the beam bends, and the illuminated spot moves to a new position on the screen. Another pair of plates placed at right angles to the first pair permits vertical as well as horizontal movement of the beam. The two pairs allow two independent parameters to be observed simultaneously by noting deflections in two perpendicular directions on the screen. Most often circuits are provided which move the spot along one axis at an adjustable constant speed so that the other parameter can be studied as a function of time. Usually the spot is caused to move at a uniform velocity across the screen horizontally, and then is rapidly returned to the side, to repeat its sweep periodically.

As used in a television receiver, the spot moves across the screen horizontally many times per second (usually about 25), and each time is at a different vertical position. Simultaneously, the information transmitted by radio modulates the intensity of the beam to produce the light and dark areas of the picture. (In the usual television receiver, the electron beam is deflected by magnetic forces rather than by the electrostatic forces as described above.)

Perhaps the most important characteristic of the CRO is its ability to display the time rate of change of electric parameters with very high time resolution. The study of events occurring in much less than microsecond (10^{-6} sec) intervals is commonplace. This description has omitted all discussion of the electronic circuits, such as amplifiers, trigger circuits, etc., which are essential for practical measurements.

1.7   Charge Separation

We discuss below two devices for systematically bringing about a separation of charge. The first is the electrophorus apparatus, which is a simple and practical device for building up the excess charge on a body by doing mechanical work, and is also interesting as an example of charging by *induction*. The other is the Van de Graaff generator,

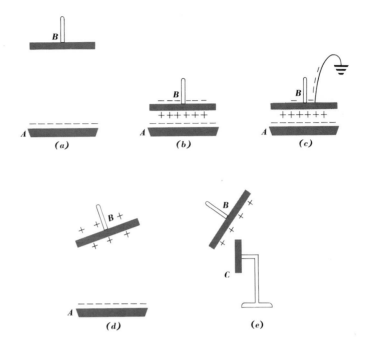

Fig. 1.9   *Plate A is an insulator, such as sealing wax, which can be charged on its surface by rubbing with, say, cat's fur. This charge remains fixed. Metal plate B is held by an insulating handle. We show how another metal electrode C, also insulated, can be charged to whatever extent desired by the use of plate B, repeatedly charged by induction. (a) Insulator A has been charged by friction. Insulated metal plate B is uncharged. (b) Plate B has been moved close to A. Force of charges on A attracts positive charge to lower side of B, leaving net negative charge at top surface. (c) Some of negative charge at top of B is allowed to escape through mutual repulsion of negative charges, by connecting top surface to ground through finger contact. (d) Plate B is pulled away from charge on A. Plate B has been charged by induction. (e) Charged plate B shares some of its charge with plate C by contact. The process can be repeated again and again until the required charge is built up on plate C. The energy needed to collect the charge on plate C has been provided by the mechanical work done in moving the charged plate B away from A against the mutual attractive forces of the opposite charges on A and B.*

in which electric charges are sprayed on a moving conveyor belt and carried to an insulated electrode, where they are removed. The importance of this machine is that potential differences of millions of volts[1] can be obtained, useful for accelerating charged particles for nuclear experiments.

The electrophorus.   This device, often used for demonstration purposes, illustrates the basic process of charging by induction. In Fig. 1.9 we show the successive steps by which charging by induction can be used to produce a net charge on any isolated system.

The Van de Graaff generator.   In this machine electric sparks produce charged gas molecules, and an insulating belt collects charges of one sign and moves them to the inside of an insulated hollow conductor, where they are collected. As in the electrophorus, the stored energy which results from the separated charges (as is discussed later) is provided by the work done by the motor turning the belt. In the electrophorus this work is done by the operator manually when he moves charges against the electric forces of other charges.

Attraction of neutral bodies by charged bodies.   As mentioned earlier, small bits of paper are found to be attracted to a charged rod. Since the paper is normally uncharged, this is at first surprising. It is easily explained when we realize that although the net charge on the paper is zero, under the influence of the charged rod the equal quantities of positive and negative charges on the paper will redistribute themselves much as they do on the metal plate of the electrophorus apparatus; thus a net attractive force is produced, as shown in Fig. 1.10. Such re-

[1] These terms are explained in Chap. 3.

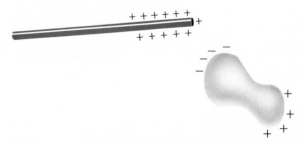

Fig. 1.10   Attraction of a neutral body by a charged rod.

distribution of charge, we shall see later, can take place even in an insulator.

If the bits of paper touch the charged rod, they tend to fly off at once. This results from the leaking of some of the charge on the rod onto the paper, thus bringing into play the mutual repulsion between the like charges on the rod and paper.

1.8   Comments on Chapter 1

This first chapter describes how, by experiments involving forces between bodies, we infer the existence of electric charges. It also develops the quantitative ideas which allow us to formulate the rules from which we can predict or calculate the forces between any groups of charges.

Most students will already be familiar with much of this material. The principal emphasis is on the experimental fact of two kinds of electric charge, and the (Coulomb) law of force between charges, which is described for all geometries of charge distribution by an inverse-square law of force between point charges. The fact that the inverse-square law between two point charges can be applied to assemblies of many point charges, or to continuous distributions of charges, rests on the validity of the rule of *superposition*, which states that the force between any two charges is uninfluenced by the presence of other charges. This experimental fact is necessary for the validity of the vector formulation.

The equation for the force between two point charges is

$$\mathbf{F}_1 = \frac{1}{4\pi\epsilon_0} \frac{q_1 q_2}{r_{12}^2} \, \hat{\mathbf{r}}_{12} \qquad \text{newtons} \tag{1.5}$$

or for the force $\mathbf{F}_0$ on a charge q_0 caused by a number of charges is

$$\mathbf{F}_0 = \frac{1}{4\pi\epsilon_0} \sum_i \frac{q_0 q_i}{r_{0i}^2} \, \hat{\mathbf{r}}_{0i} \qquad \text{newtons} \tag{1.6}$$

When transformed for use with a continuous distribution of charge, Eq. (1.6) becomes

$$\mathbf{F}_0 = \frac{q_0}{4\pi\epsilon_0} \int \frac{dq}{r^2} \, \hat{\mathbf{r}} \qquad \text{newtons} \tag{1.7}$$

in which $\mathbf{r}$ is the vector from dq to q_0.

The $1/4\pi\epsilon_0$ term is the experimentally determined scale factor which allows the equations to describe the actual force in newtons between two charges of a given amount at a certain distance apart. The 4π is explicitly included in order to simplify later equations, and the numerical value of ϵ_0, the susceptibility, depends on the choice of units of force, charge, and distance.

It is easy to remember that $1/4\pi\epsilon_0 = 9 \times 10^9$ newton-m²/coul². This is consistent with

$$\epsilon_0 = 8.85 \times 10^{-12} \text{ coul}^2/\text{newton-m}^2$$

the value of the permittivity of free space as defined.

Nothing in this chapter requires that electric charge be quantized. The existence of the unit negative charge of the electron and the similar unit positive charge of the proton became known rather late in the development of the ideas of electricity. Much of our work in this book is unaffected by whether or not charges are divisible into discrete quanta, as they are, in fact. The classical laws of electromagnetism had nothing to say about the particulate nature of charges. Only when we begin the consideration of matter is it necessary to take into account the fact of quantized charges. We do not understand why charges come in a unique size any more than we know why charges exist in the first place.

With an understanding of the meaning and implications of Coulomb's inverse-square law, we are now ready to turn to a more general formulation of the force law in terms of the electric field.

PROBLEMS

Applications of Coulomb's law:

*1.1A   Three point charges $+Q_1$, $-Q_2$, and $+Q_3$ are equally spaced along a line as shown in Fig. P1.1. If the magnitudes of Q_1 and Q_2 are equal, what must be the magnitude of Q_3 in order that the net force on Q_1 be zero?

Fig. P1.1 $+Q_1$ $-Q_2$ $+Q_3$

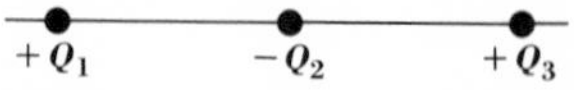

1.1B   Three identical point charges of Q coul are placed at the vertices of an equilateral triangle, 10 cm apart. Calculate the force on each charge.

*1.1C   *a*   Find the force on a point charge of $2Q$ coul at the center of a square 20 cm on a side if four identical point charges of Q coul are located at the corners of the square.

* Answers to starred problems can be found at the end of the book.

b Find the force on the charge at the center of the square when one of the corner charges is removed.

The following elementary problems are given to emphasize the connection between charge density and total charge. The second problem involves a varying density and requires integration.

1.2A A charge Q is uniformly distributed throughout a sphere of radius 2 cm.

    a What is the charge density ρ in coulombs per cubic meter in the sphere?

    b How much charge is there in the outer shell of radius from 1 to 2 cm in this sphere?

★1.2B The linear charge density on the rod shown in Fig. P1.2, 2 m long, is given by

$$\mu = \mu_0 + 2x \qquad \text{coul/m}$$

where x is the distance measured from one end of the rod. What is the total charge on the rod?

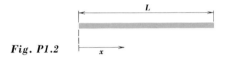

Fig. P1.2

Further calculations using Coulomb's law. The first problem requires integration over the charge distributed in the ring.

★1.3A A thin circular ring of 3 cm radius has a total charge of 10^{-3} coul uniformly distributed on it. What is the force on a charge of 10^{-2} coul at its center? What would be the force on this charge if it were placed at a distance of 4 cm from the ring, along its axis?

1.3B Two charges of Q coul each are placed at two opposite corners of a square. What additional charges q placed at each of the other two corners will reduce the resultant electric force on each of the charges Q to zero? Is it possible to choose these charges so that the resultant force on *all* the charges is zero?

This is the first problem involving the work done in moving a charge against coulomb forces:

★1.4A A point charge of Q_2 coul is located on the x axis a distance a m from another point charge of Q_1 coul, as shown in Fig. P1.3. Calculate the

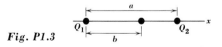

Fig. P1.3

force on Q_2 and then calculate the work to move Q_2 from a to a distance b from Q_1.

We compare magnitudes of electric and gravitational forces:

1.5A   Compute the ratio between the electrostatic repulsion and the gravitational attraction between two electrons. The charge on an electron is -1.6×10^{-19} coul, and its mass is 9.0×10^{-31} kg. The gravitational constant is 6.670×10^{-11} newton-m^2/kg.

A classical calculation based on Coulomb's law and classical mechanics gives a crude approximation of the hydrogen atom. Gravitational forces between proton and electron are insignificant compared with the electrostatic forces.

*1.6A   In a hydrogen atom the negative electron moves in an orbit around the (much heavier) positive proton, bound by the attractive coulomb force. Assuming that the orbit is circular and has a radius of 0.528×10^{-8} cm, calculate the number of revolutions per second made by the electron; calculate the angular momentum of the system. How large would the hydrogen atom be if it moved with the same angular momentum but was bound by gravitational attraction?

2

the electric field

2.1 *Introduction*

In this chapter we develop a somewhat more general way of handling the kinds of force problems discussed in Chap. 1. This involves use of the concept of the *electric field*.

In Chap. 1 we considered the force on one charge as being caused by the presence at some distance away of another charge. In the "field" formulation of the problem, as we discuss in detail in the next section, one charge is thought of as producing an "electric field" everywhere in space which accounts for the force on the other charge. Thus the perhaps troublesome idea of "action at a distance" involved in our first point of view is somewhat eased. The force on a given charge is regarded as caused by the electric field *at that point.*

If only static physical situations were of interest and everything was at rest, it would make little difference whether the field idea was introduced. The same answers are reached whether we compute the force, say, between two charges by a direct inverse-square computation or whether we first calculate the field at one charge due to the other charge and from this find the force on the first charge. The crucial distinction comes when charges are in relative motion. Here experiment shows that only by considering the field a property of space which propagates at a finite speed (the velocity of light) can we account for the actual forces on charges. That is, the finite speed at which information can propagate concerning the whereabouts of charges makes the field idea particularly appropriate.

A further argument for the "reality" of the electric field is the propagation of energy in an electromagnetic wave such as light. As is developed later, light waves are produced when charges are accelerated. Such electromagnetic waves carry energy and are, for example, responsible for our "seeing" stars which are light-years away. This propagation of energy through vast distances of empty space is hard to describe without the idea of self-propagating fields.

Once we have introduced the electric field, we discuss the use of *electric lines* and *flux*, and show how *Gauss' flux theorem* gives a generalized account of the inverse-square law of force between point charges.

2.2 Electric Field

The electric field is a vector quantity which gives, at every point in space, the force that would act on a unit positive charge that is placed at that point. Thus defined, the field, which we shall call $\mathbf{E}$, is related to the force $\mathbf{F}$, which acts on any charge q at any point, by the equation

$$\mathbf{E} = \frac{\mathbf{F}}{q} \quad \text{newtons/coul} \tag{2.1}$$

This is the basic definition of the electric field. The magnitude of this vector quantity is called the *magnitude*, or *intensity*, of the electric field.

In the case of electrostatics, where all charges are at rest, the value of $\mathbf{E}$ at each point in space can be obtained by the application of Coulomb's law. Thus the principle of superposition gave

$$\mathbf{F} = \frac{1}{4\pi\epsilon_0} \sum_i \frac{qq_i}{r_i^2} \, \hat{\mathbf{r}}_i \quad \text{newtons} \tag{1.6}$$

which by Eq. (2.1) gives

$$\mathbf{E} = \frac{1}{4\pi\epsilon_0} \sum_i \frac{q_i}{r_i^2} \, \hat{\mathbf{r}}_i \quad \text{newtons/coul} \tag{2.2}$$

A very simple illustration of the contrast between force and field calculations can be given using Fig. 2.1. Here the particular point of

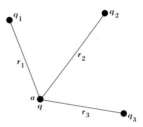

Fig. 2.1 Calculation of force on charge q due to charges q_1, q_2, and q_3. The electric field at a is the force per unit charge at a due to the charges q_1, q_2, and q_3.

interest is point *a*. The calculation of the force on a charge *q* at a point *a*, resulting from the fixed charges q_1, q_2, q_3, proceeds, as we have seen, by obtaining the vector sum

$$\mathbf{F} = \frac{1}{4\pi\epsilon_0} \left(\frac{qq_1}{r_1{}^2} \hat{\mathbf{r}}_1 + \frac{qq_2}{r_2{}^2} \hat{\mathbf{r}}_2 + \frac{qq_3}{r_3{}^2} \hat{\mathbf{r}}_3 \right) \qquad \text{newtons}$$

By contrast, the electric field **E** at the point *a* caused by q_1, q_2, and q_3 is found by

$$\mathbf{E} = \frac{\mathbf{F}}{q} = \frac{1}{4\pi\epsilon_0} \left(\frac{q_1}{r_1{}^2} \hat{\mathbf{r}}_1 + \frac{q_2}{r_2{}^2} \hat{\mathbf{r}}_2 + \frac{q_3}{r_3{}^2} \hat{\mathbf{r}}_3 \right) \qquad \text{newtons/coul}$$

That is, we have merely divided through by *q*. Our calculation now gives the force, not on *q*, but per *unit* charge at the point *a*.

For a continuous charge distribution we could write

$$\mathbf{E} = \frac{1}{4\pi\epsilon_0} \int \frac{dq}{r^2} \hat{\mathbf{r}} \qquad \text{newtons/coul} \tag{2.3}$$

where it is understood that each *dq* is divided by the square of the appropriate distance to the space point in question, and the sum of terms is vectorial.

The principle of superposition is being used here for the field just as it was for forces. The field at a given point is the vector sum of field contributions from all charges involved.

These simple equations for static situations must be seriously modified for fields resulting from moving charges. One kind of effect we shall be discussing is *magnetism*, that is, forces between moving charges, and another results from the finite velocity at which the electric and magnetic fields propagate in space. In any case, however, Eq. (2.1) is a correct statement of the meaning of the electric field. For the static situation, it does not matter in practice whether we think in terms of the force on a charge or the electric field. Since Eq. (2.1) is a vector equation, **E** and **F** are directed along the same line at all points in space, and are in the same direction if q is positive, but oppositely directed if q is negative. Actual problems can be solved with or without bringing in the electric field.

There is, however, an important improvement in generality if we think in terms of the electric field. **E** is a vector quantity which has a value at each point in space. It is a *vector field*. We can imagine a plot of the electric field in a region as a diagram like that in Fig. 2.2,

Fig. 2.2   The electric field is a vector field. To each point in space may be assigned a magnitude and direction.

which would tell us the magnitude and direction of the force per unit charge at every position in the region. We might think of the field as describing the condition of space in a given region. We are thus de-emphasizing the individual charges that cause the field and are instead thinking more about the effect of their presence on the space around them. We shall have much more to do with this vector field farther on. Here we examine only a few simple problems. It is interesting to note that the value of the electric field at particular points may well be zero. Also, the value of this new vector quantity is always finite (or zero) as long as we stay away from the immediate vicinity of any of the charges causing the field. If we get too close to any of these, **E** tends to infinity, since the distance r in q/r^2 tends to zero. In a major part of our study of electricity we avoid this difficulty by staying sufficiently far from electric charges. Since they are actually very highly localized—on electrons and protons, for example—this is easy to do without interfering with the usefulness of our study.

We now point out a necessary elaboration on our earlier definition of electric field. More accurately, we define the field thus:

$$\mathbf{E} = \lim_{\Delta q \to 0} \frac{\Delta \mathbf{F}}{\Delta q} \quad \text{or} \quad \mathbf{E} = \frac{d\mathbf{F}}{dq} \tag{2.4}$$

That is, the field is the limiting value of the force per unit charge as the test charge is made vanishingly small. This elaboration is needed because there are situations in which a finite test charge, by its presence, alters the distribution of charges causing the field. Suppose, for example, that the electric field is due to charges placed on conductors. When we bring up a finite charge, the other charges producing the field redistribute themselves as a result of the forces between them and the test charge. The field is thus modified by the presence of the test charge according to its size. The definition of Eq. (2.4) avoids this pitfall.

Equations (2.2) and (2.3) are extremely important in electrostatics. They provide the method by which it is always possible to calculate the electric field at a given point due to a static distribution of charges. We next show some examples of field calculation according to this scheme.

2.3   Examples, Calculation of Electric Fields

a   *Field of an array of point charges.*   Given point charges q_1 and q_2 as shown in Fig. 2.3 at distances a and b from the origin on the x and

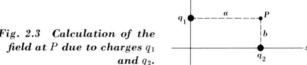

Fig. 2.3   Calculation of the field at P due to charges q_1 and q_2.

y axes, find the value of **E** at the position P (a,b). Using Eq. (2.2), we write

$$\mathbf{E} = \frac{1}{4\pi\epsilon_0}\left(\frac{q_1}{a^2}\,\hat{\mathbf{r}}_1 + \frac{q_2}{b^2}\,\hat{\mathbf{r}}_2\right) \qquad \text{newtons/coul}$$

Since for this case the two vectors are at right angles, the calculation of the field at P becomes

$$E = \frac{1}{4\pi\epsilon_0}\sqrt{\left(\frac{q_1}{a^2}\right)^2 + \left(\frac{q_2}{b^2}\right)^2} \qquad \text{newtons/coul}$$

and the angle θ, say, between the resultant field and the x axis is found by using

$$\frac{q_2/b^2}{q_1/a^2} = \tan \theta$$

b *Field out from a long, uniformly charged rod.* Contrast this with Example 1.3c, from which it differs by asking for the electric field rather than for the force on a certain charge. Also, in the present example, the point of interest is to the side of the line containing the charge distribution. This brings out the full complexity of the vector summation in the integral. As shown in Fig. 2.4, we calculate the elec-

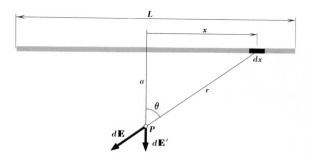

Fig. 2.4 **Calculation of the field due to a uniform linear array of charges.**

tric field **E** at the point P, a distance a along the perpendicular bisector of the rod. We let the linear charge density be μ as before. It is Q/L, where Q is the total charge on the rod.

The problem is simplified if we replace the variable x by the variable angle θ. We may then express the variable distances x and r in terms of θ and the fixed distance a.

The component of the field at P due to the element of charge $\mu\, dx$ is $dE = \dfrac{1}{4\pi\epsilon_0} \dfrac{\mu\, dx}{r^2}$ by Coulomb's law. Since $x/a = \tan \theta$ and $a/r = \cos \theta$, we have $dx = a \sec^2 \theta\, d\theta$ and $r = a/\cos \theta$. Substitution gives $dE = \dfrac{\mu}{a} \dfrac{1}{4\pi\epsilon_0}\, d\theta$. Since the various components $d\mathbf{E}$ from the various charge elements are not in the same direction, they must be added vectorially. The problem of taking the vector sum of these individual components turns out to be trivial when we use the obvious symmetry of the problem. That is, if the point P is opposite the center of the uniformly charged rod, the x components at P of each $d\mathbf{E}$ will cancel (since for each element at x there will be an equivalent at $-x$), whereas the y components along a will add. We therefore take the sum of the y components of each $d\mathbf{E}$ to obtain the required vector sum. We call such a component dE', given by

$$dE' = \frac{1}{4\pi\epsilon_0} \frac{\mu}{a} \cos\theta \, d\theta$$

The total field $\mathbf{E}'$ at P for a very long rod is then obtained from

$$E' = \frac{\textcircled{2}}{4\pi\epsilon_0} \frac{\mu}{a} \int_0^{\pi/2} \cos\theta \, d\theta = \frac{2\mu}{4\pi\epsilon_0 a} \qquad \text{newtons/coul}$$

If the rod is not very long, appropriate changes are necessary in the upper limit of integration. For a finite rod and for a point P not opposite the middle of the rod, we cannot use the simple symmetry property, and the solution is more difficult. Coulomb's $1/r^2$ law refers only to point charges. In this problem, for example, the field falls off in the ratio $1/a$ as we move away from a long rod.

c *Field of an electric dipole along axis and normal to axis.* A pair of equal and opposite point charges separated by a vector distance $\mathbf{a}$ is called a *dipole*. The vector $\mathbf{a}$ is drawn from the negative to the positive charge and is along the *axis* of the dipole. Calculation of the field of a dipole is an easy problem that does not involve integration because only point charges are concerned. It is an important problem because of the common occurrence of dipoles. A molecule made up of a positive and a negative ion is one example of an electric dipole in nature. Also, the dipole is often the most convenient first step in the description of more complicated arrays of charge.

We calculate the field of the dipole along its axis and perpendicular to the axis from the center of the dipole. Later we make the calculation for a general position. For convenience, we place the dipole along the x axis at the origin of the coordinate system, as shown in Fig. 2.5. By symmetry, results along the y and z axes will be identical; so we limit our discussion to the x and y axes.

We first discuss the field at P at a distance r_1 from the center of the dipole. This is given by

$$\begin{aligned} E_P &= \frac{1}{4\pi\epsilon_0} \left[\frac{q}{(r_1 - a/2)^2} - \frac{q}{(r_1 + a/2)^2} \right] \\ &= \frac{q}{4\pi\epsilon_0} \frac{2r_1 a}{(r_1^2 - a^2/4)^2} \end{aligned}$$

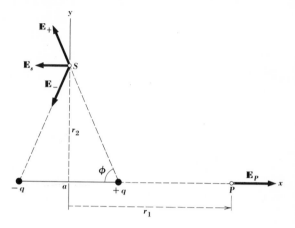

Fig. 2.5 *Calculation of field of a dipole of moment*
$$p = qa.$$

At S the fields due to $+q$ and $-q$ are designated as $\mathbf{E}_+$ and $\mathbf{E}_-$, respectively. Their y components cancel, while their x components add to yield the resulting field $\mathbf{E}_S$. Thus

$$E_S = |\mathbf{E}_+| \cos \phi + |\mathbf{E}_-| \cos \phi$$

or

$$E_S = \frac{1}{4\pi\epsilon_0} \left[\frac{q}{r_2{}^2 + (a/2)^2} + \frac{q}{r_2{}^2 + (a/2)^2} \right] \frac{a/2}{[r_2{}^2 + (a/2)^2]^{\frac{1}{2}}}$$

$$= \frac{q}{4\pi\epsilon_0} \frac{a}{[r_2{}^2 + (a/2)^2]^{\frac{3}{2}}}$$

These rather complicated expressions for the fields at points at a distance from a dipole along the two directions indicated can be simplified when the points of interest are far from the dipole compared with the dipole dimension a. In this limit, where $r^2 \gg a^2/4$, the term $a^2/4$ may be dropped in the denominators, to give the much simpler approximate expressions

$$E_P = \frac{1}{4\pi\epsilon_0} \frac{2p}{r_1{}^3} \qquad \text{newtons/coul} \tag{2.5}$$

$$E_S = \frac{1}{4\pi\epsilon_0} \frac{p}{r_2{}^3} \qquad \text{newtons/coul} \tag{2.6}$$

There is great practical importance to this approximation of the field around a dipole. In many situations in atomic, molecular, and solid-state physics we are interested in fields of dipoles at distances very large compared with the dimensions of atomic dipoles. This approximation is valid for all such cases. Fields at positions far away from dipoles relative to the dipole dimensions are usually called the *far fields* of the dipoles. Another terminology often used is to call the approximate expression the field of a *short* dipole.

We have written p, the *dipole moment* for qa. Thus, at places far away from a dipole relative to the separation a, the field of relatively large charges close together is the same as for smaller charges at larger separation. All that matters is the product: charge $\times$ separation. This is the reason for using the dipole moment in discussing dipoles. Instead of the $1/r^2$ dependence of the field due to an isolated point charge, the field of a dipole falls off as $1/r^3$.

A very important property of an electric dipole is the torque exerted on it by a uniform electric field. Figure 2.6 shows a dipole in

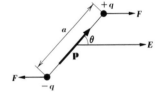

Fig. 2.6 *Torque on an electric dipole in a uniform electric field. Note positive direction of vector dipole moment $p = qa$.*

a constant field E. The torque τ is evidently given by

$$\tau = qaE \sin \theta \quad \text{newton-m}$$

where θ is the angle between the dipole axis and the field. Again we may replace qa by p, to give

$$\tau = pE \sin \theta \quad \text{newton-m} \tag{2.7}$$

The dipole moment of a short dipole may be treated as a vector quantity $\mathbf{p} = q\mathbf{a}$ directed from the negative to the positive charge. We see that the torque on the dipole due to the external electric field tends to align the dipole moment parallel to the electric field.

Equation (2.7) has the disadvantage that it does not state explicitly the sense of the torque for all relative orientations of p and E. It is more useful, therefore, to cast this equation into the vector form, which is completely explicit. Before doing so, however, we must take a small detour for the benefit of students who are not familiar with the *vector cross product*, which is needed in order to describe this physical situation and others we meet later.

MATHEMATICAL INSERT

The vector cross product.   This is a relationship between three vectors, written

A = B × C

where **A** is called the (*vector*) cross product of **B** and **C**. Its meaning is illustrated in Fig. 2.7. We show vectors **B** and **C** in the *xy* plane of a right-hand coordinate

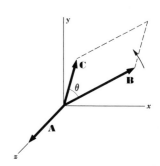

**Fig. 2.7   A is the vector cross product of vectors B and C:
A = B × C = BC sin θ. A is perpendicular to the plane of B and C, and its magnitude is equal to the area of the parallelogram built on B and C.**

system. The resultant vector **A** of the cross product **B × C** is perpendicular to both **B** and **C** and is therefore in the *z* direction. The sign of **A** is obtained by imagining the rotation of the vector given by the first term in the cross product, **B**, about its tail in the direction of the curved fingers of the right hand toward the second vector **C**, and taking for the direction of the resultant vector **A** the direction of the extended thumb. This gives the result shown in the figure. We see that **B × C** = −(**C × B**), since in the latter case **C** is rotated into **B** and the thumb will point along the negative *z* axis.

The magnitude of the resultant vector **A** is given by $BC \sin \theta$, where θ is the angle between the two vectors that form the cross product. This is easily remembered by noting that $BC \sin \theta$ is the magnitude of one vector times the component of the other vector *perpendicular* to the first vector. This quantity is the area of the parallelogram constructed, using the two vectors as adjacent sides as shown in Fig. 2.7. Thus the magnitude of the cross product of two vectors that are at right angles is the product of the magnitudes of the two vectors. The cross product of two parallel vectors is zero.

With this cross-product terminology Eq. (2.7) can be written

$$\tau = \mathbf{p} \times \mathbf{E} \qquad \text{newton-m} \tag{2.7a}$$

To make use of this vector relationship we must make the usual definition of the torque vector as a vector which points along the axis of rotation of the motion which would be produced by the torque and is positive in the direction of advance of a right-hand screw. Thus the torque in Fig. 2.6, being clockwise, is indicated by a vector pointing into the page away from the reader, as is given by **p × E**.

d *Field of an electric dipole in any direction.* The demonstration that the dipole moment is a vector quantity is given in Chap. 3. We use that fact here to obtain a general expression for the far field of a short dipole, not limited to two special directions as in Example 2.3c above.

We wish to calculate the field at a point S of a dipole **p**, as shown in Fig. 2.8. But the method we have developed for this calculation so

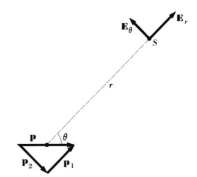

Fig. 2.8 Field components at S of dipole p calculated through use of component dipoles.

far can be applied only for directions parallel or perpendicular to the dipole. We get around this difficulty by substituting two perpendicular vectors $\mathbf{p}_1$ and $\mathbf{p}_2$ for the original dipole **p**. This is the step in which we use the vector property of the dipole moment. The two vectors are chosen so that one is oriented parallel and the other perpendicular to the line r to the point S.

Now using Eqs. (2.5) and (2.6), we can write directly in terms of these component dipoles the two field components E_r and E_θ parallel and perpendicular to r at S.

$$E_r = \frac{1}{4\pi\epsilon_0} \frac{2p_1}{r^3} \qquad E_\theta = \frac{1}{4\pi\epsilon_0} \frac{p_2}{r^3}$$

But we may substitute $p \cos\theta$ for p_1, and $p \sin\theta$ for p_2; so the field components become

$$E_r = \frac{1}{4\pi\epsilon_0} \frac{2p \cos\theta}{r^3} \qquad \text{and} \qquad E_\theta = \frac{1}{4\pi\epsilon_0} \frac{p \sin\theta}{r^3}$$

We now have developed explicit expressions for the field of a dipole at a distance r and in any direction as measured by the angle θ.

The field of a dipole has cylindrical symmetry about the dipole axis. These equations are derived in another way in Chap. 3.

e   *Field due to a plane distribution of charges.*   Suppose we have a plane area on which charges are distributed uniformly with a surface density σ coul/m². We wish to calculate the field at a point P a distance a from the plane as shown in Fig. 2.9. We assume that the dimen-

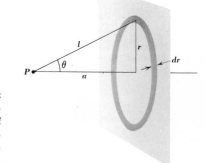

Fig. 2.9   *The electric field at P from a plane distribution of charge is obtained by integrating the contributions from concentric rings.*

sions of the plane are much greater than a. We use Eq. (2.3) to add up the vector contributions of all charges at the point P. We begin by calculating the contribution from the ring of charge of radius r and width dr and then integrate for all such rings that make up the total plane charge distribution. The calculation of the contribution of charges on the ring is really a two-dimensional integration problem, but because of the symmetry we can reduce it to a simple summation. The contribution of an element of charge on the ring to the field at P makes an angle θ with the x axis as shown on the figure. Because of symmetry, however, components of **E** perpendicular to the x axis cancel. Thus we need consider only the x components of **E** at P. Then using Eq. (2.3), we write for the field at P due to the ring of charge[1]

$$dE = \frac{1}{4\pi\epsilon_0} \frac{\sigma 2\pi r \, dr}{l^2} \cos\theta$$

[1] As explained in the footnote on p. 13, we have chosen a differential element such that all parts of it are the same distance from the point of interest P. In addition, the field contribution from each part of the ring-shaped element makes the same angle θ with the x axis.

In order to reduce this to a single variable, we substitute $a \tan \theta = r$ and $a/\cos \theta = a \sec \theta = l$. By differentiation we have $dr = a \sec^2 \theta \, d\theta$. Making these substitutions, we get

$$dE = \frac{\sigma}{2\epsilon_0} \frac{\tan \theta \sec^2 \theta \cos \theta}{\sec^2 \theta} d\theta = \frac{\sigma}{2\epsilon_0} \sin \theta \, d\theta$$

This is the contribution to the field at P from the ring we have chosen. To obtain the total field at P from all rings making up the plane charge distribution, we integrate this expression over the entire plane. The limits of integration are from $\theta = 0$ to $\theta = \pi/2$. Thus we find

$$E = \frac{\sigma}{2\epsilon_0} \int_0^{\pi/2} \sin \theta \, d\theta = -\frac{\sigma}{2\epsilon_0} [\cos \theta]_0^{\pi/2} = \frac{\sigma}{2\epsilon_0} \qquad \text{newtons/coul}$$

The resultant field is in the x direction and is independent of the distance from the plane as long as the plane is very large compared with a.

2.4   *Conductors and Electric Fields*

The free motion of charge within a conductor results in two characteristics of any static electric field in the vicinity of a conductor. The first is that the average field in a conductor must be zero, and the second is that if a field exists outside a conductor, it is normal to the surface at all points on the surface.

The zero value of the average field in a metal is easily understood on the basis that, if the field were not zero, the mobile charges present would move under the influence of the forces of the field and would continue to rearrange themselves until the field was canceled. Any change in the external charge arrangement brings about an appropriate charge rearrangement within the metal which keeps the average internal field zero. The question of whether there is in fact always possible a static charge arrangement within a conductor which can cancel any applied field is more complicated and is considered in Chap. 3. The answer is yes for any static field.

The other effect, that any field at the surface of a conductor must be normal to the surface, is a little more subtle, and we postpone the argument until later, in Chap. 3.

The property of zero average field within a metal is of great practical importance in any situation where effects of external fields are undesirable. Thus any region of space can be isolated from externally produced fields by surrounding the region by a conducting surface. If there are no excess charges placed inside such a metal *shield*, the field inside the volume will be zero, regardless of the motion of charges causing field changes outside the shield. Electric interactions between adjacent circuits in electronic devices are often prevented by metal shields placed around certain components or circuits.

Although the conclusions we have reached are satisfactory from a practical point of view, two factors have been neglected. The first is that we are considering only the static situation. With a rapidly varying field the situation is more involved. Second, the implied model of a conductor here is a grainless volume distribution of movable negative charge. This is satisfactory for present purposes, even though far from realistic, but in reality it is the actual graininess (due to its atomic nature) that accounts for many interesting properties of matter.

2.5 Electric Lines

The experimental fact of Coulomb's law of inverse-square forces between charges leads to a beautifully generalized statement regarding certain properties of the electric field. Basically, this is a purely mathematical idea, but we shall first discuss the situation in terms of the rather artificial idea of *electric lines* (called *lines of force* in many treatments). This allows a quasi-physical model by which to understand the implications of the mathematics, and is helpful, especially as an introduction to the ideas involved.

We first describe the idea of electric lines, then show some simple examples of the kind of reasoning they allow, and finally, discuss their connection with the inverse-square law.

In Sec. 2.6 we relate the ideas developed through electric lines to the more abstract ideas which develop from the inverse-square law.

In the case of electric forces, where an inverse-square law operates, electric lines provide a useful description of the behavior of the field. Electric lines describe the (vector) electric field in any region of space according to the following rules:

1. The *direction* of electric lines drawn in space is the same as the direction of the field at each point.

2. The *density* of lines in a given region is proportional to the magnitude of the field in that region. The density of lines means the number of lines per unit area cutting a surface perpendicular to the direction of the lines at any given point.

3. It is a direct consequence of the Coulomb inverse-square law that all possible static field configurations can be described by lines in the fashion

explained above, where all lines originate on positive electric charges and end on negative charges. Lines are thus continuous except at their *sources* and *sinks*[1] on positive and negative charges, respectively.

4.   The number of lines originating or ending on charges is proportional to the magnitude of each charge. We are free to choose any scale factor between the magnitude of the electric field and the density of lines used to represent that magnitude. The choice of scale factor determines the number of lines originating or ending on a unit charge.

We show in Fig. 2.10 the electric field in a region, using electric lines. The field points to the right and is more intense at the left, as

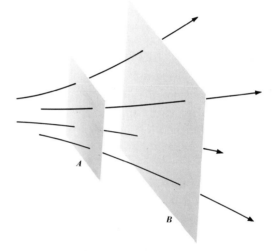

Fig. 2.10   An electric field shown by electric lines. The density of lines, and hence the field, is greater at A than at B.

shown by the higher density of lines at A than at B. At every point on a line the direction of the field is that of the line. In between lines, we determine the field direction by interpolating between the directions of adjacent lines. This description is very different from the simple vector representation of Fig. 2.2.

---

[1] The terms source and sink arise from the analogous description of fluid flow, in which fluid is described as coming from a source and flowing into a sink with mathematical similarity to the way electric lines originate on positive charge and terminate on negative charge.

Figure 2.11 shows a two-dimensional sketch of the electric lines around a dipole.

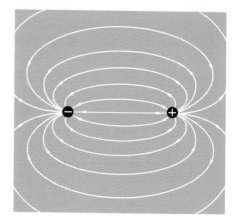

Fig. 2.11 A sketch in two dimensions of the electric lines around a dipole. The lines have cylindrical symmetry about the axis of the dipole.

Let us clarify the problem of choice of scale factor between field intensity and line density by the simple problem of depicting the field around an isolated point charge of magnitude q_0 couls. Some of the lines are sketched in Fig. 2.12.

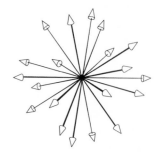

Fig. 2.12 Some of the radial electric lines originating at a charge q_0.

We establish the scale factor arbitrarily by setting unit density of lines (1 line/m²) as the measure corresponding to unit field intensity (1 newton/coul). We can then determine the required number of lines per unit charge, using the sketch and some quite simple reasoning. We draw (or imagine) a spherical surface of unit radius (1 m) around the charge as its center. From the symmetry of the geometric situation for an isolated point charge or from application of Eq. (1.5) we know that the field is directed everywhere radially outward from the point charge. This must mean that the electric lines here are radial straight lines. The density of these lines where they cut the spherical surface is uniform (by symmetry). The electric field E at the surface is calculated by $E = \dfrac{1}{4\pi\epsilon_0}\dfrac{q_0}{r^2}$, and the total area of the sphere is $4\pi r^2 = 4\pi$ m², since r is 1 m. Thus the field at the unit sphere surface is $q_0/4\pi\epsilon_0$, which is also the density of lines according to our definition. Multiplying this by the area of the sphere, we find the total number of lines originating at q_0 and cutting the spherical surface $= q_0/\epsilon_0$. Thus our unit field definition leads to $1/\epsilon_0$ lines of force per unit charge.

This is the result of a completely arbitrary though useful choice of scale factor. Since electric lines are not real, but just a useful way of describing the field, our choice of scale is inconsequential.

Electric lines provide a convenient qualitative description of the geometric properties of the electric field, but warning should be given on two scores. The first is that setting up a system which yields a certain number of lines from each charge looks as though it were producing quantized behavior of the field. That this is only the fault of the model is apparent when we realize that the scale factor between field intensity and number of lines is completely arbitrary. We choose a finite number of lines per unit charge only so that useful figures and models can be drawn. The second warning is that although most situations of interest are three-dimensional, we draw lines on a two-dimensional drawing. As a result it is easy to get the wrong impression about how the magnitude of the field varies with position.

The connection between electric lines and the inverse-square law can be shown as follows: Consider the case of the isolated point charge shown in Fig. 2.12. Let us calculate the field at a distance of 2 m, using the lines-of-force point of view. We have seen already that the density of lines at 1 m is $q_0/4\pi\epsilon_0$. As shown in Fig. 2.13, the area of spherical surface subtended by a bundle of lines originating on the point charge is four times greater for a surface 2 m away than for a surface at 1 m distance. Therefore the density of lines of force at 2 m is just one-quarter that at 1 m, in exact agreement with the result if calculated from the field equation. Thus, at least for an isolated point charge, the field at any point in its vicinity can be calculated equally well from the density of lines of force or from the inverse-square law. This result can be connected with the behavior of solid angles, as discussed in Sec. 2.6.

From this simple example we see that if the field of a point charge fell off at a rate different from an inverse-square law, it would be im-

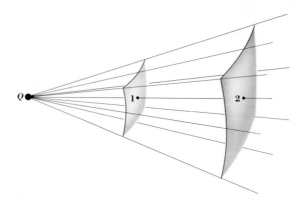

Fig. 2.13　*Elements of spherical surfaces inter-
sected by a bundle of lines of force originating
at a point charge.*

possible to represent the field in terms of continuous electric lines which start from and end on charges. We thus exhibit the close relation between the $1/r^2$ law and electric lines as they have been defined.

For a more general method of field determination, useful for situations of fairly high symmetry, we turn next to the formalism of Gauss' flux theorem.

2.6 Gauss' Flux Theorem

Gauss' flux theorem actually embodies nothing more than the validity of the electric-lines point of view, and is thus a direct consequence of Coulomb's inverse-square law. The theorem is stated mathematically as follows:

$$\iint_{cs} \mathbf{E} \cos \theta \, dS = \sum_i \frac{q_i}{\epsilon_0} \tag{2.8}$$

That is, the surface integral of the normal component of $\mathbf{E}$ over a closed surface equals the sum of the charges inside the enclosed volume divided by ϵ_0.

The meaning of this relation is easily understood in terms of electric lines. Let Fig. 2.14 represent a volume containing electric charges. Here we take the special case of a single point charge q_1 inside the volume. A small solid angle at q_1 subtends the area dS at the surface, at a distance r from q_1. The angle between the surface normal dS and its projection parallel to r is θ. (The vector $d\mathbf{S}$ is normal to the area dS

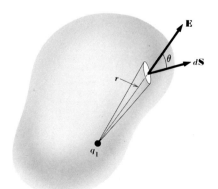

Fig. 2.14   A small solid angle
at the charge q_1 subtends
the surface area dS.

and has a magnitude equal to the area of dS.) The direction of the field **E** caused by q_1 is of course parallel to r.

The left-hand term in Eq. (2.8) is a surface integral, to be taken over the closed surface (CS) surrounding the volume. When integrated this gives just the number of electric lines which emerge from the volume. This quantity, the *net number of emerging lines*, is the important mathematical quantity, the *flux* through the chosen surface.

We could have defined this integral $\iint_{CS} E \cos \theta \, dS$ as the flux, without ever considering the concept of electric lines. However, many students find the connection between electric lines and the flux a useful one. This has been our principal reason for developing the ideas of electric lines.

It is easy to see that the flux integral is somehow related to the total number of emerging lines, since the integral is essentially a surface area times E. But E, the field intensity, is measured by the density of lines; so the integral is a line density times an area. It thus has the dimensions of (lines/area) $\times$ area = total lines.

Using Fig. 2.15, we can see in fact that the term $E \cos \theta \, dS$ is just the number of lines passing through the area element dS. Thus the magnitude of **E** measures the density of lines, and if dS is perpendicular to **E** (or the vector $d\mathbf{S}$ is parallel to **E**), then $E \, dS$ is the number of lines through dS. But if dS is tilted so that its normal makes an angle θ with **E**, we must multiply E by the projection of dS normal to the field in order to get the total number of lines. This projection is $dS \cos \theta$; so the number of lines through dS is $E \cos \theta \, dS$, as stated.

The right-hand term in Eq. (2.8) is simply the sum of all the charges *inside* the volume, multiplied by $1/\epsilon_0$. In our example we consider only a single point charge q_1.

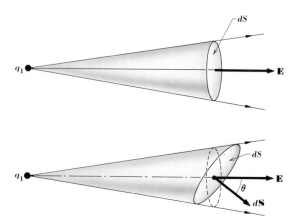

Fig. 2.15   The number of lines of E through dS is given by E cos θ dS.

In order to give a formal proof of Gauss' flux theorem we first define exactly what is meant by solid angle.

MATHEMATICAL INSERT

Solid angle.   In Fig. 2.16 we show an element of solid angle, identified as $d\Omega$. A solid angle is the three-dimensional equivalent of the ordinary two-dimen-

Fig. 2.16   The solid angle dΩ subtending the area dS from the point P depends on the projection of dS perpendicular to r. The solid angle is the ratio of this projected area to r^2; so $d\Omega = (dS \cos \theta)/r^2$.

sional plane angle. We see at once the necessary form of the expression for a solid angle if we think of it as a given cone in space, drawn from a given point: if r is the distance from the point P to the surface element dS, the element of solid angle $d\Omega$ must be

$$d\Omega = \frac{dS \cos \theta}{r^2}$$

The length r appears in the denominator as r^2 because, for a given solid angle, $dS \cos \theta$ is proportional to r^2. Thus, as is proper, the solid angle measures the cone and is independent of the length r. The $\cos \theta$ term allows for surfaces which are not taken normal to r.

The definition of solid angle puts no limitations on the *shape* of the cone. What matters is the area of the projected surface area, not the shape of the projected surface.

In two dimensions, the maximum plane angle is 360°, or 2π rad. Similarly, the complete solid angle around any point can be obtained by integrating $d\Omega$. If the unit solid angle is defined as that solid angle which, on a sphere of unit radius, will subtend a unit area on the surface of the sphere, the complete solid angle is seen to contain $4\pi R^2/R^2 = 4\pi$ unit solid angles. (The unit solid angle is called the *steradian*.) Just as in the plane-geometry case, the (solid) angle is a dimensionless quantity.

With the foregoing mathematical comments, it is easy to verify Gauss' flux theorem, as given in Eq. (2.8), no matter what the shape of the volume considered. Using Fig. 2.14, suppose for the moment that q_1 is the only charge in the volume being considered. We begin by writing $E \cos \theta \, dS$, the element to be integrated over the closed surface. We have seen that the meaning of this element is the number of electric lines, or flux, emerging through the surface subtended by the solid angle $d\Omega$ at the charge q_1. As suggested earlier, this interpretation in terms of lines, however, is not necessary for the mathematical proof, helpful as it may be for picturing the meaning. We may simply call this the flux through $d\Omega$ at the surface, without reference to electric lines. Since the field at the surface caused by q_1 is $\dfrac{1}{4\pi\epsilon_0} \dfrac{q_1}{r^2}$, the flux term can be written in terms of q_1 and integrated as follows:

$$\iint_{CS} E \cos \theta \, dS = \frac{q_1}{4\pi\epsilon_0} \iint_{CS} \frac{dS \cos \theta}{r^2} = \frac{q_1}{4\pi\epsilon_0} 4\pi = \frac{q_1}{\epsilon_0}$$

We have used the fact that, no matter what the shape of the volume involved, integration of the solid angle from any point inside it gives 4π. We have shown that for a *single* point charge in the volume, Gauss' flux theorem is true. By using the superposition principle we can generalize this result to cover any charge distribution whatsoever inside the volume. The result requires only that the point charge q_1 be somewhere inside the volume considered. Thus, for any distribution of charge whatsoever (suppose we had just two point charges q_1 and

q_2), we could add the flux terms due to each charge thus:

$$\iint_{cs} E \cos \theta \, dS = \iint_{cs} (E_1 \cos \theta_1 + E_2 \cos \theta_2) \, dS$$

$$= \frac{1}{4\pi\epsilon_0} \iint_{cs} \left(\frac{q_1}{r_1^2} \cos \theta_1 + \frac{q_2}{r_2^2} \cos \theta_2 \right) dS$$

Here r_1 and r_2 are the distances, respectively, from each charge considered to the surface element dS. These distances vary as we integrate over the entire surface, but over the closed surface each term gives $4\pi q$. Thus, for *any* charge configuration over *any* volume,

$$\iint_{cs} E \cos \theta \, dS = \sum_i \frac{q_i}{\epsilon_0}$$

and we have now formally derived Gauss' flux theorem, Eq. (2.8), and have thoroughly explored its dependence on the inverse-square law.

Using vector notation, and the *scalar*, or *dot*, product, this can be written

$$\iint_{cs} \mathbf{E} \cdot d\mathbf{S} = \sum_i \frac{q_i}{\epsilon_0}$$

MATHEMATICAL INSERT

Scalar, or dot, product. The surface integral is conveniently written

$$\iint_{cs} \mathbf{E} \cdot d\mathbf{S}$$

This is simply the vector equivalent of $\iint_{cs} E \cos \theta \, dS$. The dot, or scalar, product of two vectors $\mathbf{A}$ and $\mathbf{B}$, $\mathbf{A} \cdot \mathbf{B}$, is $AB \cos \theta$, a scalar quantity. As shown in Fig. 2.17, it is the magnitude of the component of vector A parallel to

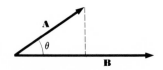

Fig. 2.17   The scalar, or dot, product of two vectors A and B is given by A • B = AB cos θ.

B, multiplied by the magnitude of B. In the integral expression above, the surface element $d\mathbf{S}$ is considered a vector quantity having the direction of the normal drawn outward from the enclosed volume at each point on the surface and having magnitude equal to the area of the surface element.

Finally, we rewrite Gauss' flux theorem in the general form, allowing its use when charge density (which may vary) is known throughout the volume:[1]

$$\int_{cs} \mathbf{E} \cdot d\mathbf{S} = \frac{1}{\epsilon_0} \int_V \rho \, dV \qquad (2.9)$$

The physical ideas involved in Gauss' theorem are the same as those involved when the ideas of electric lines are used. Take, for example, a closed surface which surrounds no charge but which has charges outside it. In this case the charge density ρ is zero in the volume under consideration; so Gauss' flux theorem gives

$$\int_{cs} \mathbf{E} \cdot d\mathbf{S} = 0 \qquad (2.9a)$$

Thus for a static electric field in regions containing no charge, no net flux emerges from any such region. In terms of the concept of electric lines, lines are continuous in regions containing no charge (Fig. 2.18).

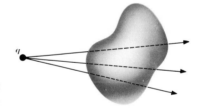

Fig. 2.18   The net number of lines emerging from a volume due to a charge outside the volume is zero. (The number of lines entering must just equal the number emerging.)

In addition, we have the quantitative rule for the amount of flux, or number of lines, which emerge from a region which contains a given amount of charge.

The usefulness of the concept of electric lines as an aid to thinking does not imply their reality as physical entities. They are merely a graphical way of picturing the mathematical facts resulting from the inverse-square law.

---

[1] In order to simplify the writing of integrals, surface integrals such as this one will be written with only one integral sign. It will be understood that when the integral is taken over an area $d\mathbf{S}$, the double integral is implied. Similarly, the volume integral $\iiint dV$ will be written $\int dV$, with the triple integral implied.

2.7* The Differential Form of Gauss' Flux Theorem

The formulation of Gauss' flux theorem we have written,

$$\iint_{cs} \mathbf{E} \cdot d\mathbf{S} = \frac{1}{\epsilon_0} \int_V \rho \, dV \qquad (2.9)$$

is called the *integral* form. It relates the net electric flux (number of lines) out of a volume to the net amount of charge contained within.

The other and completely equivalent form of Gauss' theorem, the *differential* form, is essential to advanced treatments, but is not used in this text. We state it, and show how it is obtained from the integral relationship by the use of the (mathematical) divergence theorem, discussed in Appendix A.

One way of writing this *differential* form of Gauss' theorem is

$$\text{div } \mathbf{E} = \frac{1}{\epsilon_0} \rho \qquad (2.10)$$

As explained in Appendix A, the divergence (div) of a vector is simply the limit of the flux, or number of lines, per unit volume, emerging from a volume, as that volume is shrunk to a point. That is,

$$\text{div } \mathbf{E} = \lim_{V \to 0} \left(\frac{1}{V} \iint_{cs} \mathbf{E} \cdot d\mathbf{S} \right) \qquad (A.1)$$

It is also shown in Appendix A that, in cartesian coordinates, the divergence can be written explicitly to give, according to Eq. (2.10),

$$\frac{\partial E_x}{\partial x} + \frac{\partial E_y}{\partial y} + \frac{\partial E_z}{\partial z} = \frac{1}{\epsilon_0} \rho \qquad (2.10a)$$

This statement[1] tells something about the nature of E at any point in space in terms of the charge density ρ at that point.

The mathematical theorem needed to derive the divergence equation is called the *divergence theorem*. It was established by Gauss, and is true for any vector field in space. In Appendix A it is shown that, for almost any vector field $\mathbf{F}$, we may write

$$\int_{cs} \mathbf{F} \cdot d\mathbf{S} = \int_V \text{div } \mathbf{F} \, dV \qquad (A.2)$$

This relates the flux of the vector field over a closed surface to the volume integral of the divergence, taken over the volume enclosed by

---

[1] The terms $\partial E/\partial x$, etc., signify *partial* derivatives of V. Their use indicates that although E is a function of x, y, and z, these derivatives are to be taken with respect to each variable while holding the other variables fixed.

the surface. If we let the vector field be **E**, the electric field, and compare this equation with Gauss' flux theorem as given in Eq. (2.8), we see that

$$\int \text{div } \mathbf{E} \, dV = \frac{1}{\epsilon_0} \int \rho \, dV$$

Since this relationship holds for *any* volume, it follows that at every point in space

$$\text{div } \mathbf{E} = \frac{1}{\epsilon_0} \rho \tag{2.10}$$

That is, the divergence of the field is a property of the field at each point in space, and it depends simply on the charge density ρ at each point in space. For example, div **E** is zero in any region in space having no net charge. The appearance of ϵ_0 in this equation is related to its appearance in Coulomb's law, and is just a result of our choice of units. It adjusts all the electrostatic equations to the fact that, given any pair of charges of a particular amount, at a particular separation, there will be a particular force between them in vacuum. Experiment, not theory, determines the value of ϵ_0, once units have been chosen for charge, force, and distance.

This simple relation makes possible the solution of many kinds of problems that might otherwise be complicated. It is equivalent to the integral form of Gauss' theorem, and thus depends on the validity of the inverse-square law. It is closely related to the elementary statement that electric charges act as sources and sinks of lines of electric field.

Finally, it is useful to write this form of Gauss' flux theorem using the vector operator form of the divergence, as discussed in Appendix D.

$$\boldsymbol{\nabla} \cdot \mathbf{E} = \frac{1}{\epsilon_0} \rho \tag{2.10b}$$

2.8   Examples, Use of Gauss' Flux Theorem

Gauss' theorem is important in two ways. In the first place, there are a number of kinds of charge distributions in space having high symmetry (spherical, cylindrical, and uniform-plane distributions) for which the theorem allows simple solution of otherwise difficult field-calculation problems. Second, Gauss' flux theorem provides a point of view which serves as a guide for more complicated problems. We give below some important examples of use of the theorem for situations of high symmetry.

a *Field of a uniform spherical shell of charge.* We suppose that there is a charge density σ coul/m² on a thin spherical shell of radius r_0. The total charge Q on the shell is $4\pi r_0^2 \sigma$. We use Gauss' theorem to find the field of this charge distribution both inside and outside the shell.

In order to use Gauss' flux theorem effectively, we must be able to determine the field from the flux. This is possible in cases for which a surface can be drawn such that the orientation of **E** with respect to the surface normal $d\mathbf{S}$ is everywhere known and the same, and for which **E** has a constant value over the entire surface. For example, in the present problem we apply Gauss' flux theorem to a spherical surface just outside the spherical charge shell, as shown in Fig. 2.19.

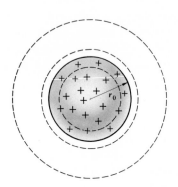

Fig. 2.19 Several different gaussian surfaces (indicated by dotted lines) placed around a spherical shell of charge to investigate the field produced by the charge.

For this *gaussian surface* symmetry considerations show that the field **E** has the same magnitude everywhere on the surface, and is parallel to the surface normal (or perpendicular to the surface) at each point on the surface. Using Gauss' flux theorem, we find for the total flux through the gaussian surface,

$$\int_{cs} \mathbf{E} \cdot d\mathbf{S} = \frac{1}{\epsilon_0} Q \qquad (2.8)$$

Because of the results of the symmetry argument, the flux can be written as $E \int_{cs} dS = E \cdot 4\pi r_0^2$. By comparison with Eq. (2.8) this gives

$$E = \frac{1}{\epsilon_0} \frac{Q}{4\pi r_0^2} \qquad \text{newtons/coul}$$

Thus the field at the surface of the shell is exactly the same as though all the charge Q were located at the center of the sphere defined by the shell. Also, by taking as gaussian surface a spherical surface of any radius greater than r, and noting that Eq. (2.8) is still valid, we see that for *any* point outside a uniform shell of charge, the field behaves according to Coulomb's law for the total charge Q at the center. This is indeed an important generalization. Even more generally, *any* spherically symmetric charge distribution has the same field outside it that would be given if all the charge were concentrated at the center.

What about the field *inside* the spherical shell of charge? This is readily shown to be zero at all points within r. We draw a spherical gaussian surface, this time, of any radius less than r of the charge shell, so that there is no charge within the volume; so by Gauss' flux theorem, the flux $\int_{cs} \mathbf{E} \cdot d\mathbf{S}$, is zero. But again by symmetry, whatever value $\mathbf{E}$ has, it is everywhere the same at the surface, and if it exists at all, it must (by symmetry) be perpendicular to the surface. The flux factor thus becomes $\mathbf{E} \int_{cs} d\mathbf{S} = \mathbf{E} \cdot 4\pi r^2 = 0$. Since $r \neq 0$, it must be that $\mathbf{E} = 0$ everywhere inside r_0.

Let us now turn to a situation which is very much like that of the charged spherical shell, that of a conducting (metal) sphere. We may argue at once that since, in a static situation, the average field inside a metal must be zero, as discussed in Sec. 2.4, any excess charge on a metal sphere must end up at its surface. We may phrase the argument for this in any of three different ways. The simplest is that if some net charge were to remain within the volume of metal, lines of $\mathbf{E}$ would originate on that charge and the field could not be zero. The second formulation, in terms of Gauss' flux theorem, is that with net charge inside the metal, $\int_{cs} \mathbf{E} \cdot d\mathbf{S}$ over a gaussian surface within the volume of the metal would not be zero, implying the existence of net flux, and therefore of electric field within the metal. Finally, if we chose to use the differential form of Gauss' theorem, we should argue that charge inside the volume would give div $\mathbf{E} \neq 0$, which again implies non–zero field.

These arguments are equivalent expressions of the idea of Gauss' theorem. The utility and economy of using them compared with using Coulomb's law, on which they depend, is evident.

Once the point has been made that all the excess charge on a conducting sphere must be distributed uniformly on its surface, the field calculation is seen to be identical with that for a spherical shell.

b *Field of a spherical charge distribution.* Suppose, as another simple example, we take a uniform charge distribution of density ρ coul/m³ contained in a sphere of radius R. In this case we might use Gauss' flux theorem in the form

$$\int_{cs} \mathbf{E} \cdot d\mathbf{S} = \frac{1}{\epsilon_0} \int_V \rho \, dV \tag{2.9}$$

The right-hand integral is just the total charge within the sphere. Its calculation is simple for the case of uniform charge density we have chosen, but we make the calculation to review the use of calculus and to make completely clear the meaning of the right-hand term. For convenience we choose spherical coordinates r, θ, and φ, as shown in Fig. 2.19. A volume element is given by $r \, d\theta \times r \sin \theta \, d\varphi \times dr$. Thus the volume integral becomes

$$\frac{1}{\epsilon_0} \int_{\theta=0}^{\pi} \int_{\varphi=0}^{2\pi} \int_{R=0}^{R} \rho r \, d\theta \, r \sin \theta \, d\varphi \, dr = \frac{\rho}{\epsilon_0} \iiint r^2 \sin \theta \, d\varphi \, d\theta \, dr$$

The density can be brought outside the integral because it is a constant in this problem.

The integration over $d\varphi$ is independent of the other terms and can be performed directly, yielding 2π. Thus the volume integral reduces to

$$\frac{2\pi\rho}{\epsilon_0} \iint r^2 \sin \theta \, d\theta \, dr = \frac{2\pi\rho_0}{\epsilon_0} \int r^2 \, dr \, [- \cos \theta]_0^\pi$$

$$= \frac{4\pi\rho_0}{\epsilon_0} \int r^2 \, dr = \frac{4\pi\rho_0}{\epsilon_0} [\tfrac{1}{3}r^3]_0^R = \frac{4\pi\rho_0}{3\epsilon_0} R^3 \qquad \text{coul}$$

Thus the integral becomes simply the volume of the sphere times the density ρ. But the same method allows us to solve the much more complicated problem of a radial charge distribution in which ρ is not uniform (Prob. 2.1I).

In any case, once the total charge is found, we are as before in a position to argue that $\mathbf{E}$ is everywhere uniform and normal to the surface, and to obtain the same value outside the sphere, as in Example 2.8a, if Q is replaced by $(4/3)\pi R^3\rho$.

c *Field in region of a charged cylindrical conductor.* This problem is that of a thin cylindrical shell of charge. It is the analogue, having cylindrical symmetry, of the spherical problem of Example 2.8a. We choose a long cylinder such as illustrated in Fig. 2.20, where the radius

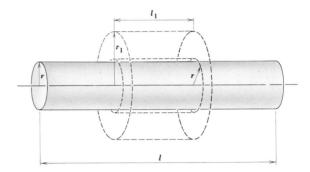

Fig. 2.20 *A charged cylindrical conductor having a surface charge density of σ coul/m², surrounded by gaussian surfaces for field determinations.*

r is much smaller than the length l. In order to avoid consideration of end effects we choose for a gaussian surface a cylinder of the same radius r as that of the shell of charge (so as to enclose the shell of charge) but of smaller length l_1 ($l_1 < l$). Our results will then apply to the entire charged cylinder, except near the ends. From the cylindrical symmetry we know that the electric field at the radial surface of the shell points uniformly radially outward and has the same value at all points on the radial (curved) surface (at a distance r from the axis).

Because the lines of **E** are parallel to the flat ends of the gaussian cylinder, the flux of **E** out of the ends is zero. We evaluate the total flux over the curved surface through Gauss' theorem. We define the surface density of the shell as σ coul/m². The total charge inside the gaussian surface is then $2\pi r l_1 \sigma$, and Gauss' theorem gives

$$\int_{cs} \mathbf{E} \cdot d\mathbf{S} = \frac{1}{\epsilon_0} 2\pi r l_1 \sigma$$

or

$$\mathbf{E} = \frac{1}{\epsilon_0} \frac{2\pi r l_1 \sigma}{\int_{cs} dS_1} = \frac{1}{\epsilon_0} \frac{2\pi r l_1 \sigma}{2\pi r l_1} = \frac{1}{\epsilon_0} \sigma \qquad \text{newtons/coul}$$

This result for the field at the surface of a cylindrical shell of charge is the same as was found for the field at the surface of a spherical shell.

To find how the field varies as we move out from the cylinder (for the spherical case the variation was inverse-square—as though all the charge were at the center), we proceed by constructing a new gaussian cylinder, this time with a radius r_1 greater than r.

Similar reasoning to that above gives for E,

$$E = \frac{1}{\epsilon_0} \frac{2\pi r l_1 \sigma}{2\pi r_1 l_1} = \frac{1}{\epsilon_0} \frac{\mu}{2\pi r_1} \qquad \text{newtons/coul}$$

Here μ is the charge on the shell per unit length of cylinder. This result is identical with our earlier result for the field out from a long line of charge. Taking a gaussian surface *inside* the cylindrical shell shows that the field inside the shell is zero, as found for the spherical case.

d *Field out from an infinite plane of uniform charge density.* Let the surface charge density be σ coul/m². Draw a pillbox-shaped surface of cross section A as in Fig. 2.21. The charge contained inside will be σA,

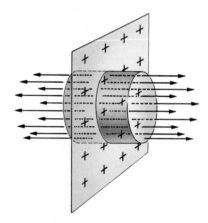

Fig. 2.21   *Calculation of field from uniform-plane distribution of charge. Pillbox-shaped gaussian surface.*

and by symmetry there will be no flux coming out of the curved surface (that is, $\int \mathbf{E} \cdot d\mathbf{S} = 0$ over the curved surface). Only the two flat ends contribute; so we find

$$E = \frac{1}{\epsilon_0} \frac{\sigma A}{2A} = \frac{\sigma}{2\epsilon_0}$$

This result is identical with our earlier calculation of Example 2.3e, in which the field was obtained by direct integration of contributions from each charge element. The much simpler calculation performed here illustrates the power of Gauss' law when symmetry conditions allow solution by this means.

e *Field near a metal plate, alternative use of Gauss' flux theorem and Coulomb's law.* We now discuss the problem of field calculation for the region near isolated charged plane sheets of metal. This will bring out alternative methods of arriving at the correct conclusions.

Consider first a single uniformly charged metal sheet as shown in Fig. 2.22a. We calculate the field at P due to the charge density

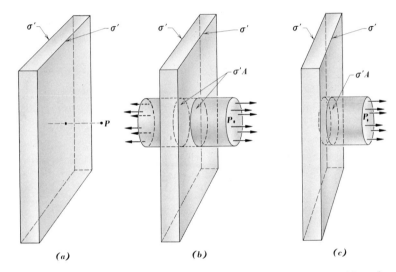

Fig. 2.22 *Alternative calculations of the field out from a uniformly charged conducting plate, charge density σ' on each surface.*

σ' coul/m² on each side of the metal. Using the result of Example 2.3c or of 2.7d, above, we add the contributions at P of each plane distribution:

$$E_p = \frac{\sigma' A}{2\epsilon_0 A} + \frac{\sigma' A}{2\epsilon_0 A} = \frac{\sigma'}{\epsilon_0} \qquad \text{newtons/coul} \qquad (2.11)$$

We have added the effect of the excess charge on both sides of the metal plate. We could arrive at this result starting from Coulomb's law directly or by using Gauss' flux theorem on both charge sheets, as we did for one sheet.

Alternatively, we could consider a gaussian surface surrounding both surfaces as in Fig. 2.22b, and with symmetry reasoning as in

Example 2.7*d*, write

$$E_p = \frac{2\sigma' A}{2\epsilon_0 A} = \frac{\sigma'}{\epsilon_0} \qquad \text{newtons/coul}$$

Here we use $2\sigma'$ to account for the plane charge densities on both surfaces, both of which are inside the gaussian surface used.

In both cases above we added the influence at P of each excess charge, and gave no attention to the fact that within a metal no net field exists. This emphasizes the point that in all cases Coulomb's law (or Gauss' flux theorem) gives correct answers if *all* excess charges are taken into account. We did *not* neglect the effect of the left-hand-plane distribution of charges, even though these charges are on the far side of the field-free metal sheets.

Another approach is possible in which the zero static field in the metal plate is acknowledged at the beginning. We show this argument, using Fig. 2.22c. Because of the zero-field condition, Gauss' flux theorem can be applied to the right-hand surface of the metal sheet to find the field at P. A cylindrical gaussian surface is drawn with one end inside the metal; so we know that no flux goes through this end. Gauss' flux law then gives the field at P:

$$E_p = \frac{\sigma' A}{\epsilon_0 A} = \frac{\sigma'}{\epsilon_0} \qquad \text{newtons/coul}$$

This result is the same as obtained above. The effect of the zero-field property of a metal is often remembered on the less fundamental but more graphic description of the shielding of lines by the metal.

The two approaches to the problem are reconciled by noting that the zero-field region requires equal charge densities on the two surfaces in order that the net field inside the metal be zero. Thus when we assume in Fig. 2.22c no flux through the left-hand gaussian surface, we are in fact taking into account the presence of the left-hand surface charge. The important thing is either to take *all* excess charges into account explicitly or else to put in the effects of some charges by means of the net zero-field regions which they account for.

The general result is that the uniform field in the region near an isolated uniform-plane charge distribution is $E = \sigma/2\epsilon_0$, but when the charges are at the surface of a conductor, the field is given by $E = \sigma/\epsilon_0$; the factor of 2 can be considered as due to the charges on the opposite surface of the metal or as resulting from the zero field within the metal.

f   *Field inside a hollow conductor.*   The experimental accuracy with which the inverse-square law is known is remarkably great. This satisfactory situation results from experiments done inside hollow conductors. It turns out that the field inside a hollow conductor is zero if, and only if, the law of force is accurately inverse-square.

We take the special case of a hollow conducting sphere. (Later, in Chap. 3, using a more sophisticated argument, we show that the field is zero inside an empty cavity of any shape in a conductor.)

The field at any point C inside a conducting spherical shell (Fig. 2.23), due to a charge density σ on the surface, is to be calculated.

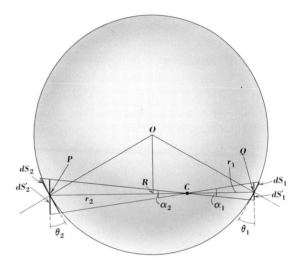

Fig. 2.23   *Construction showing absence of electric field inside a hollow spherical conductor.*

We must not initially invoke the concept of lines of force or any other consequence of the inverse-square law, since that is what we wish to investigate. We may, however, assume uniform charge distribution over the sphere, by using the argument of symmetry. The field at C is obtained by taking the vector sum of all the contributions at the point C. We may start by considering the contributions from the charges $\sigma\, dS_1$ and $\sigma\, dS_2$ subtended by the equal and opposite infinitesimal solid angles α_1 and α_2. From the properties of solid angles we know that

$$\frac{dS_2 \cos \theta_2}{r_2{}^2} = \frac{dS_1 \cos \theta_1}{r_1{}^2}$$

Furthermore, for small solid angles $\theta_1 = \theta_2$.[1] Thus

$$\frac{dS_2}{r_2{}^2} = \frac{dS_1}{r_1{}^2}$$

or

$$\frac{\sigma \, dS_2}{r_2{}^2} = \frac{\sigma \, dS_1}{r_1{}^2}$$

If the inverse-square law holds, the components of the field at C are just

$$dE_1 = \frac{1}{4\pi\epsilon_0} \frac{\sigma \, dS_1}{r_1{}^2} \quad \text{and} \quad dE_2 = \frac{1}{4\pi\epsilon_0} \frac{\sigma \, dS_2}{r_2{}^2}$$

and these are in opposite directions. With this law the contributions by the pair of equal and opposite elements of solid angles to the field just cancel to give a net value of zero. Since the remaining surface of the sphere can be similarly broken up into areas subtended by pairs of equal and opposite solid angles, it follows that the total contribution to the field at C is zero, if, that is, the inverse-square law is correct.

The experimental proof of this, as carried out by Maxwell, involved placing a concentric conducting sphere inside another one and insulated from it. Starting with no net charge on either sphere, a large charge was then placed on the outer sphere, and a field was looked for in the space between the two spheres. As we shall see in the next chapter, if a radial electric field were present between the spheres, a *potential difference* would be set up between them. Only if *no* field is produced inside the outer sphere is the potential difference between the spheres zero. No potential difference was found, and Maxwell was able to state that in his experiments the power 2 in the inverse-square law was accurate to at least 1 part in 21,600. Modern experiments involving the same principles have increased the accuracy of this to 1 part in 10^9.

2.9   *Comments on Chapter 2*

The principal idea of this chapter has been to introduce the *electric field*. The field concept centers our attention on the nature of the situation at each point in space, as would be determined by placing a test

---

[1] This may be shown as follows: dS_1' and dS_2' are $\perp PQ$.

Draw $OR \perp PQ$.

OR is also the bisector of $\angle POQ$.

$\therefore \theta_2 = \angle ROP, \; \theta_1 = \angle QOR$

$\therefore \theta_1 = \theta_2$

charge there. Since the electric field at any point in space is defined as
the force per unit positive charge, its calculation is closely related to
the force calculations of Chap. 1. For a distribution of point charges,
we have

$$\mathbf{E} = \frac{1}{4\pi\epsilon_0} \sum_i \frac{q_i}{r_i^2} \hat{\mathbf{r}} \qquad \text{newtons/coul} \tag{2.1}$$

and for a continuous distribution of charge,

$$\mathbf{E} = \frac{1}{4\pi\epsilon_0} \int \frac{dq}{r^2} \hat{\mathbf{r}} \qquad \text{newtons/coul} \tag{2.2}$$

The equation that defines the electric field at a point is

$$\mathbf{E} \text{ (on } q \text{ at } p) = \frac{\mathbf{F} \text{ (at } p)}{q} \text{ newtons/coul} \tag{2.3}$$

in which it is implied that the value of $\mathbf{E}$ is not disturbed by the magnitude of the test charge q.

In principle, either one of the statements [Eq. (2.1) or (2.2)]
about how the electric field results from the superposition of inverse-
square terms provides all that is necessary for solving problems in
electrostatics. But there is much to be gained in simplicity and generality if the consequences of the inverse-square law are formulated in
other terms. The first of these formulations discussed in Chap. 2 is the
concept of electric lines, which provides a pictorial method of handling
the consequences of the inverse-square law. The idea of lines originating on positive charges and ending on negative charges, and else-
where being continuous, is a fruitful one, especially for qualitative
considerations. This picture of lines is, however, artificial and in some
respects misleading.

The mathematical equivalent of the lines-of-force idea is Gauss'
flux theorem. We can think of Gauss' flux theorem in terms of lines of
force, though it is in no way dependent on this. But it does rest on the
validity of the inverse-square law.

The integral form of Gauss' flux theorem is

$$\int_{cs} \mathbf{E} \cdot d\mathbf{S} = \frac{1}{\epsilon_0} \int_V \rho \, dV \tag{2.9}$$

The left-hand surface integral, called the flux, can be associated with
the number of lines of force emerging from a given volume. Gauss' flux
theorem simply relates this flux to the total charge within the volume.

We saw that, for certain cases of high symmetry, this law provides a simple method for obtaining the field.

In a charge-free volume, the relation becomes

$$\int_{cs} \mathbf{E} \cdot d\mathbf{S} = 0 \tag{2.9a}$$

This chapter also includes some optional material leading to a differential form of Gauss' flux theorem. The differential form has the advantage that it provides information about the field at a point rather than over a finite surface. It can be expressed as

$$\text{div } \mathbf{E} = \frac{1}{\epsilon_0} \rho \tag{2.10}$$

which can be written in terms of the vector operator ∇ (del) (see Appendix D) as

$$\nabla \cdot \mathbf{E} = \frac{1}{\epsilon_0} \rho \tag{2.10b}$$

In cartesian coordinates this can be written

$$\frac{\partial E_x}{\partial x} + \frac{\partial E_y}{\partial y} + \frac{\partial E_z}{\partial z} = \frac{1}{\epsilon_0} \rho \tag{2.10a}$$

Thus we see that the divergence is the sum of spatial first derivatives of the components of the field. We shall not have much concern with this differential form of Gauss' flux theorem in this book, but it is important to become acquainted with it since it is a starting point for more advanced treatments. Similarly, the divergence theorem discussed in Appendix A, and used in obtaining the differential form of Gauss' flux theorem, is commended to the reader as a valuable mathematical result of importance in many fields of physics.

An introduction was given to the properties of an electric dipole, a pair of equal charges, $+q$ and $-q$, separated by a distance a. The dipole moment is a vector quantity

$$\mathbf{p} = q\mathbf{a} \qquad \text{coul-m}$$

where the vector points from $-q$ to $+q$. Further work on the dipole follows in the next chapter.

A dipole in a uniform field E is subject to a torque whose magnitude is given by

$$\tau = pE \sin \theta \qquad \text{newton-m} \tag{2.7}$$

where θ is the angle between the dipole direction **p** and the field **E**. The vector form of the torque equation,

$$\tau = \mathbf{p} \times \mathbf{E} \qquad \text{newton-m} \qquad (2.7a)$$

has the advantage that it gives the direction, or sense, of the torque for all situations.

The chapter concludes with some field problems solved by means of Gauss' flux theorem and some considerations of metals as electric conductors. In a static situation the mobility of the conduction electrons dictates that the average electric field inside a metal be zero, and that any external field be always normal to a metal surface.

PROBLEMS

Calculation of E using Coulomb's law: These problems are closely related to those of Chap. 1, which required the force on a given charge. The field E is the force per *unit* charge. The problems involving continuous charge distributions require integration. Problem 2.1G can be solved very simply by using the principle of field superposition.

2.1A Eight identical point charges of Q coul each are placed at the corners of a cube whose sides have a length of 10 cm.
   a Find the electric field at the center of the cube.
   b Find the electric field at the center of a face of the cube.
   c Find the field at the center of the cube if one of the corner charges is removed.

★2.1B A charge of Q coul is at the center of a sphere of radius 2 m.
   a How many electric field lines originate on the charge?
   b How many electric field lines emerge through an area of $\frac{1}{2}$ m^2 of the surface of the sphere?
   c What is the density of electric field lines for unit electric field?
   d What is the field at the surface of the sphere?

2.1C A total charge of Q coul is uniformly distributed along a rod 40 cm in length. Find the electric field intensity 20 cm away from the rod along its perpendicular bisector, as shown in Fig. P2.1.

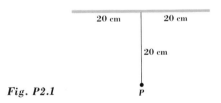

Fig. P2.1

*2.1D A total charge of Q coul is uniformly distributed over the volume of a sphere of 20 cm radius. Find the electric field intensity
  a At the center of the sphere
  b At a point 10 cm from the center of the sphere
  c At a point on the surface of the sphere
  d At a point 50 cm from the center of the sphere

2.1E A semicircular rod as shown in Fig. P2.2 is charged uniformly with a total charge of Q coul. Find the electric field intensity at the center of curvature.

Fig. P2.2

*2.1F A thin hemispherical cup (an insulator) of radius R bears a charge Q uniformly distributed over its surface. Find the electric field at the center of the flat surface of the hemisphere.

2.1G A thin circular ring of radius 20 cm is charged with a uniform charge density of μ coul/m. A small section of 1 cm length is removed from the ring. Find the electric field intensity at the center of the ring.

*2.1H A circular disk of 10 cm radius is charged uniformly with a total charge of Q coul. Find the electric field intensity at a point 20 cm away from the disk, along its axis.

2.1I Consider a charge Q distributed through a sphere of radius R with a density

$$\rho = A(R - r) \qquad 0 < r < R$$

where ρ is in coulombs per cubic meter. Determine the constant A in terms of Q and R. Calculate the electric field inside and outside the sphere.

This simple solid-angle exercise requires only an understanding of its definition.

*2.2A Find the solid angle in steradians, subtended at the center of a sphere of 2 m diameter by a 100-cm² area on its surface.

These problems involve Gauss' flux theorem, formulated in terms of electric lines.

2.3A Five thousand lines of force enter a certain volume of space, and three thousand lines emerge from it. What is the total charge in coulombs within the volume?

2.3B Lines of force emerge radially from a spherical surface and have a uniform density over the surface. What are the possible distributions of charge within the sphere?

The work to move a unit charge from one place to another requires evaluation of the line integral of the field over the distance involved. This idea will be related to potential difference in Chap. 3.

★2.4A Two identical point charges of $+Q$ coul are separated by a distance of 10 cm, as shown in Fig. P2.3. Calculate the work per unit charge to

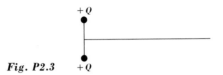

Fig. P2.3

bring up another charge from far away along the perpendicular bisector of the line joining the two charges to the point midway between the two charges.

2.4B If one of the two charges in Prob. 2.4A is changed from $+Q$ to $-Q$, calculate the work per unit charge to bring up a charge to the same position as in Prob. 2.4A.

The far field of a dipole is easily calculated through the vector sum of two perpendicular components.

★2.5A Use the equations for the far field of a dipole to calculate E_r, E_θ, and the resultant E at point A in Fig. P2.4. Show the approximate direction of

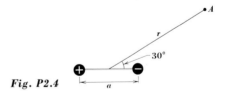

Fig. P2.4

E in a sketch. Express results in terms of the dipole moment p and the distance r.

A uniform electric field exerts a torque on a dipole, but no net force. A dipole in a nonuniform field is subject to a net force.

2.6A A dipole having a dipole moment $p = Qa$ coul-m makes an angle θ with the direction of a uniform electric field E, as shown in Fig. P2.5.

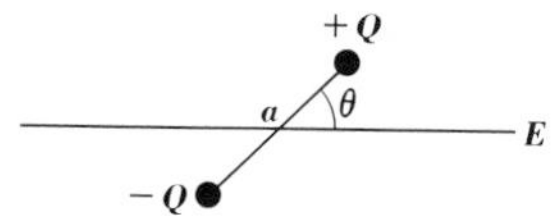

+Q

a   θ

———————————————— E

Fig. P2.5   −Q

a   Calculate the torque on the dipole.

b   Find the work necessary to reverse the position of the dipole from its equilibrium position along the field to the opposite direction.

c   For small amplitudes of oscillation about its equilibrium position, calculate the period of oscillation of the dipole if it has a moment of inertia I about its center.

★2.6B   A dipole of moment $p = Qa$ coul-m is aligned parallel to an electric field along the x axis. The field is nonuniform and varies in magnitude linearly along the x axis with a rate of change $dE/dx = K$. Find the force on the dipole.

More complicated distributions of charge, such as a quadrupole, have fields which fall off more rapidly with distance than that of a dipole.

2.7A   A pair of electric dipoles such as shown in Fig. P2.6 is called a *quadrupole*. Find the electric field at a point P along the axis of the quadrupole at a distance r $(r \gg a)$ from its center.

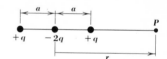

Fig. P2.6

3

the electric potential

3.1 Introduction

In this chapter we investigate the ideas of potential energy and potential in connection with problems involving static electric fields. The ideas will be familiar to most students from their study of mechanics; so our treatment serves primarily as a review, special attention being given to the application of potential to electrical problems. The close relationship between potential, a scalar quantity, and the electric field, a vector quantity, is demonstrated, and some examples are developed which show the usefulness of the potential as a means for learning about the electric field. Integral and differential forms of useful generalizations about the nature of static electric fields are developed with the help of the potential function. Some general rules regarding the spatial variation of potential are determined.

3.2 Work and Potential Energy

Wherever a suitable force field exists (and we show that a static electric field is "suitable"), it is possible and often useful to discuss the potential energy of a body in terms of the external work necessary to move it from place to place against the forces of the field.

Let us consider that some arbitrary array of fixed charges produces an electric field in some region, and ask about the external work required to move a test charge from one place to another. If the work we must do against the forces of the field is independent of the path taken between the initial and final positions, we can speak of the work done in terms of the difference in potential energies of the test charge in the two positions. Under these conditions we shall have stored the energy used to change the position of the test charge, since we can get back the energy by allowing the charge to return to its initial position. The potential energy of a charge in an electric field measures the stored energy it has by virtue of its position in relation to the charges which give rise to the field.

We start by making a simple calculation of the work necessary to move a charge from a position A to a position B against the force of an electric field $\mathbf{E}$, along a path such as shown in Fig. 3.1. (In this

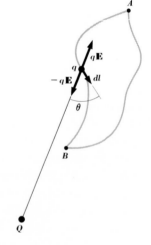

Fig. 3.1 Line integral for calculation of external work done against the field of a point charge Q in moving charge from A to B. For a conservative field the work done by any path is the same. The external force is
$$\mathbf{F} = -q\mathbf{E}.$$

example, the field is that due to a single fixed charge Q, as shown.) The calculation amounts to an evaluation of a *line integral*, whose element can be written

$$dW = F \cos \theta \, dl \qquad (3.1)$$

The meaning of this expression is illustrated in Fig. 3.2. $F \cos \theta$ is the

*Fig. 3.2   Use of line integral
for the calculation of work.
Element of work
dW − F cos θ dl.*

projection element of the external force along dl, and dl is the element of distance along the direction of motion. Thus dW is the element of external work done. If the displacement of the charge from A to B in Fig. 3.1 is performed *quasi-statically*, that is, if the external force is directed opposite to the force of the field, and is only infinitesimally larger than that force,[1] we may write

$$\mathbf{F} = -q\mathbf{E} \tag{3.2}$$

Under this condition all the work done by the external force is used in getting the body from its original position to the final one, and none goes into kinetic energy.

3.3   The Conservative Nature of the Electric Field

With the ideas introduced above, it is easy to show that a static electric field is *conservative*, that is, one for which the work done in moving a charge from one to another position is independent of the path chosen, and for which therefore the potential energy can be uniquely defined and is therefore a useful quantity. Clearly, if the work done should depend on the path taken, no unique definition of potential energy can be made, and some other mode of description would be necessary.

We use Fig. 3.1 to illustrate, first, the argument that if the field in the region is due to only a single fixed charge Q, the work to move a test charge q from A to B is independent of the path taken. After this we generalize the argument to apply to any static electric field, caused by any fixed-charge distribution.

The argument is continued by writing the integral of the work element, Eq. (3.1), and substituting for $\mathbf{F}$ the condition $\mathbf{F} = -q\mathbf{E}$, required for a quasi-static displacement. This gives us an expression

---

[1] The quasi-static process, in which the net force (here, $|F| - |qE|$) is vanishingly small, allows the displacement of charge to occur without speeding up the body being moved, thus avoiding the additional term of kinetic energy. In principle, the quasi-static displacement would take infinitely long to occur. This is no disadvantage since we have only to talk about it, not to do it.

for the total work which must be done against the field forces in order to move the test charge q from A to B.

$$W = \int_A^B F \cos \theta \, dl = -q \int_A^B E \cos \theta \, dl$$

From the figure we see that $\cos \theta \, dl = dr$, the change in the distance r between the two charges when we move q along dl. Making this substitution and replacing E by the law of force, we get

$$W = -\frac{qQ}{4\pi\epsilon_0} \int_A^B \frac{1}{r^2} \, dr = \frac{qQ}{4\pi\epsilon_0} \left(\frac{1}{r_B} - \frac{1}{r_A} \right)$$

This result shows that the work necessary to move q from A to B is independent of the particular path taken, and depends only on the positions A and B. If the force due to the field had been a function of velocity or had varied with time, or had the force on q not been directed along the line between Q and q, the work done would not have been independent of the path chosen.

We have shown that the electric field due to a single point charge, here Q, is conservative. It follows from the principle of superposition that any field configuration made up of the fields of any arbitrary distribution of point charges will also give a conservative field. This can be argued in detail. Work is a scalar quantity, so that the total work done in moving the charge q from A to B against the fields of a distribution of charges is just the sum of individual terms such as we have calculated for the field of the point charge Q. Since each term is independent of the path taken, the sum of all terms is also independent of the path.

We state this result more formally by writing for the external work in a quasi-static displacement

$$W = -q \int_A^B \mathbf{E} \cdot d\mathbf{l}$$

Here $\mathbf{E} = \mathbf{E}_1 + \mathbf{E}_2 + \cdots + \mathbf{E}_n$, in which $\mathbf{E}$ is the resultant field of any number of charges $Q_1, Q_2, \ldots, Q_n$. Putting these together shows formally that W is the sum of a set of terms of similar form. The negative sign results from the fact that we are talking about the *external* work done *against* the field $\mathbf{E}$. Since q is constant, the condition we have proved for the electric field is that

$$\int_A^B \mathbf{E} \cdot d\mathbf{l} = \text{const} \qquad \frac{\text{newton} - \text{m}}{\text{coul}} \text{ or } \frac{\text{joules}}{\text{coul}} \qquad (3.3)$$

for any path between A and B. That is, this line integral, for any path taken between any two given points, has the same value. This is true in any conservative field, and in particular in any static electric field. The line integral thus has a value which depends only on the positions at which it begins and at which it ends.

An equivalent statement of the conservative nature of an electrostatic field is

$$\oint \mathbf{E} \cdot d\mathbf{l} = 0 \tag{3.4}$$

that is, the line integral around a *closed* path[1] equals zero. This quantity is called the *circulation* of the vector $\mathbf{E}$, terminology which comes historically from the mathematics of fluid motion. The fact that the circulation is zero for any closed path in a static field follows at once, since, if we take a charge q from A to B and then return along an alternate path as shown in Fig. 3.1, the work done going from B to A must be just the negative of the work from A to B; so the total work around any closed path must be zero in a quasi-static process.

3.4*   *Circulation Related to Curl*

There is another way to express the lack of circulation in a static electric field. We show in Appendix B the meaning of *Stokes' theorem*, which says

$$\oint \mathbf{F} \cdot d\mathbf{l} = \int_S \operatorname{curl} \mathbf{F} \cdot d\mathbf{a} \tag{B.5}$$

In words, this means that the line integral of a vector field around a closed path, or circulation, is equal to the surface integral of another vector called the *curl* of the vector over any area bounded by the closed path involved in the line integral. The meaning of the curl is explained in detail in Appendix B. It is a vector quantity, and its component in any direction is the limit of the *ratio* of the circulation ($\oint \mathbf{F} \cdot d\mathbf{l}$) around an elementary area normal to the chosen direction, to the magnitude of that area, as the area shrinks to zero. In rectangular coordinates this new vector quantity, the curl, is written

$$\operatorname{curl} \mathbf{F} = \hat{\mathbf{x}} \left(\frac{\partial F_z}{\partial y} - \frac{\partial F_y}{\partial z} \right) + \hat{\mathbf{y}} \left(\frac{\partial F_x}{\partial z} - \frac{\partial F_z}{\partial x} \right) + \hat{\mathbf{z}} \left(\frac{\partial F_y}{\partial x} - \frac{\partial F_x}{\partial y} \right)$$
$$\tag{B.6}$$

[1] The symbol $\oint$ is used to indicate integration around a closed path.

With this much background we can easily see the consequences of the conservative nature of a static electric field. That is, if the electric field **E** is conservative, we have

$$\oint \mathbf{E} \cdot d\mathbf{l} = 0 \tag{3.4}$$

over any path we may choose. But according to Stokes' theorem, this means that the surface integral of curl **E** is zero over *any* area bounded by *any* closed path. This is only possible if, everywhere,

$$\text{curl } \mathbf{E} = 0 \tag{3.4a}$$

We thus arrive at the conclusion that the conservative nature of a static electric field results in an absence of circulation, which can be expressed in a microscopic sense by the zero value of the curl at all points. The real importance of this formulation comes when we later deal with electric and magnetic fields which are *not* conservative.

3.5* *Examples, Circulation Used for Field Studies*

a *Circulation in a nonstatic field.* An interesting problem involving the circulation may now be discussed briefly, and in greater detail later (under induced electromotive force). Suppose we have an electrostatic field produced by one or more charges and ask what happens after a wire loop has been placed in the region, as shown in Fig. 3.3. Since in

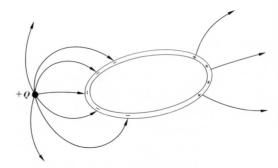

Fig. 3.3 *A conducting loop is placed in a static field, for which the circulation,* $\oint \mathbf{E} \cdot d\mathbf{l}$, *is zero over all paths. Static rearrangement of mobile charges can produce zero field within the wire only if the circulation is zero, as it is in any static electric field.*

equilibrium there can be no field within a metal, the mobile conduction electrons must arrange themselves on the wire so that they and the remaining positively charged atoms produce an average field which just cancels the electrostatic field originally present. That this is possible is allowed by the fact that the circulation, $\oint \mathbf{E} \cdot d\mathbf{l}$, around the wire, as on any closed path, is zero. But suppose the original field were *not* purely electrostatic (and we discuss such situations later), so that the original $\oint \mathbf{E} \cdot d\mathbf{l}$ was not zero. Then *no* static arrangement of charges on the wire can cancel this field, and no static equilibrium can exist. A continuous current, that is, a flow of charge in the direction of the applied circulation, would result.

b   *Field inside a cavity in a conductor.*   At the end of Chap. 2 we showed, for the special case of a spherical cavity in a conductor, that the inverse-square law leads to zero field inside the cavity as long as no net charge is placed in it. We now show that this is true for any shape of cavity, using the more sophisticated but simple argument based on Gauss' flux theorem and the zero circulation of any static electric field.

Suppose, using Fig. 3.4, that we imagine a closed gaussian surface A, surrounding an empty cavity of arbitrary shape completely

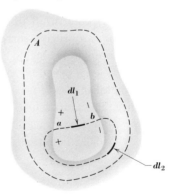

Fig. 3.4   A conductor with empty cavity cannot contain an electric field within the cavity, as shown by the requirement of zero circulation in a static field. Segment dl_1 is an element of the path through the cavity between a and b, and dl_2 is a path element from b to a through the metal.

within a conductor. Since the closed surface is within the conductor in which the average field $\mathbf{E}$ is everywhere zero, there can be no net flux crossing the surface. Therefore, by Gauss' theorem, the net charge inside the surface A is zero. But let us suppose that equal positive and negative charges reside on the surface of the cavity. Electric lines, or flux, must exist between these charges, though no flux originates inside the empty cavity. Let us take the circulation of the field, moving first in the cavity between points a and b and then within the metal from

b to a. The line integral $\int_a^b \mathbf{E} \cdot d\mathbf{l}$, if we travel along lines of $\mathbf{E}$ in the cavity, cannot be zero unless $\mathbf{E}$ is everywhere zero inside the cavity. But the line integral $\int_a^b \mathbf{E} \cdot d\mathbf{l}$ through the conductor must be zero since $\mathbf{E}$ is zero in the conductor. However, we know that the circulation $\oint \mathbf{E} \cdot d\mathbf{l}$, which is the sum of these two integrals, is zero around the complete path; so the only possible value of $\mathbf{E}$ within the empty cavity is identically everywhere zero. This means that the postulated separation of surface charge into equal positive and negative groups cannot occur in equilibrium. The simplicity of this argument illustrates the practical importance of the concept of circulation.

The argument would not hold if, instead of being empty, the cavity contained a net insulated charge. If a charge were introduced inside the cavity, its presence would induce an equal and opposite surface charge on the cavity surface. The zero field inside the metal would thus be maintained. As long as the charge is held away from the cavity surface, there would indeed be a field within the cavity, caused by the flux originating on the isolated charge. But with flux originating within the cavity, a field within the cavity is compatible with zero value of the line integral from a to b. Thus the circulation can be zero even though the field is not zero in the cavity.

The striking result of this argument leads to the important conclusion that any region surrounded on all sides by a closed conducting sheet is completely shielded from any external electrostatic field. This is also true in a practical sense for time-varying fields. As a result the use of metal *shields* to isolate sensitive circuits is of great practical importance. The most sensitive test of the accuracy of the inverse-square law for laboratory-scale dimensions investigates the accuracy to which the cavity field is actually zero in a cavity, as stated at the end of Chap. 2.

3.6 Potential Energy in a Fixed Field

We now begin to exploit the concepts of work and energy in order to arrive at a new and often useful way of describing an electric field. We ask about the amount of work necessary to bring a test charge[1]

---

[1] We are not concerned here with another problem, the amount of work necessary in the first place to assemble a charge q from its component parts dq. The existence of the electron and other elementary charged particles involves a self-energy term which relates to this work.

to a particular position in space against the forces of a fixed electric field caused by some arbitrary array of charges. The conservative nature of the static electric field allows us to discuss this problem in terms of a potential energy which depends only on the final position of the test charge, and not on the path by which it was brought there. When a charge q is moved a distance $d\mathbf{l}$ in a field $\mathbf{E}$, the change in its potential energy U may be written

$$dU = -q\mathbf{E} \cdot d\mathbf{l} \qquad \text{joules} \tag{3.5}$$

As before, the negative sign results from our consideration of external work *against* the field forces. If the charge is moved a finite distance, say, from a point A to a point B, the change in potential energy is

$$U_B - U_A = -\int_A^B q\mathbf{E} \cdot d\mathbf{l} \qquad \text{joules} \tag{3.6}$$

This gives the external work to move the charge quasi-statically from A to B against the electric forces. Since this is a difference expression, only *differences* in potential energy can be calculated. Absolute values have no meaning.

These considerations have now led us to the new way of describing the electrical situation in any space. We have already seen that we can describe the electrical situation by means of a *vector electric field* $\mathbf{E}$, which gives magnitude and direction of the force per unit charge at each point in space. But now we are able to describe the same situation in terms of a *scalar* quantity, the amount of work necessary to move a given charge quasi-statically between any two points in space.

3.7   *Potential Difference and Potential*

It is convenient to discuss the difference in potential energy in terms of work on a *unit* positive charge. Thus Eq. (3.5) for an infinitesimal change of position can be written

$$\frac{dU}{q} = -\mathbf{E} \cdot d\mathbf{l} \qquad \text{joules/coul, or } \textit{volts} \tag{3.7}$$

or for a finite change of position

$$\frac{U_B - U_A}{q} = -\int_A^B \mathbf{E} \cdot d\mathbf{l} \qquad \text{joules/coul, or volts} \tag{3.8}$$

This external *work per unit charge* is called the *potential difference* between points A and B. Its unit is the volt in both the mks and practical systems of units (Chap. 17). Potential difference is often written as V_{AB} or $V_B - V_A$. Note that both $\mathbf{E}$ and V relate to effects on a unit charge. The electric field $\mathbf{E}$ gives the force on a unit charge, and the potential difference V_{AB} gives the external work necessary to move a unit charge from one position to another. With this definition of potential difference, Eqs. (3.7) and (3.8) become

$$dV = -\mathbf{E} \cdot d\mathbf{l} \qquad \text{volts} \tag{3.9}$$

$$V_{AB} = -\int_A^B \mathbf{E} \cdot d\mathbf{l} \qquad \text{volts} \tag{3.10}$$

Although it is only the *difference* in potential between two points that has fundamental significance, it is often convenient to choose, arbitrarily, infinity as a reference point for zero potential. When this is done, the *potential V* at a given point is defined as the external work necessary to bring a unit positive charge from infinity to the point in question. Thus the potential at a point P is given by

$$V_P = -\int_\infty^P \mathbf{E} \cdot d\mathbf{l} \qquad \text{volts} \tag{3.11}$$

In this sense the *potential* at a point is the potential difference between that point and a point at infinity.[1]

Since potential difference is related to the line integral of $\mathbf{E}$, there is a simple graphical relationship between V and $\mathbf{E}$. We show this for the case of the field around a spherical shell of charge as in Fig. 3.5. In the graph below the sketch a plot of E against distance is drawn. From Eq. (3.10) it follows that the potential difference between points A and B is simply the area under the curve of E versus r, between A and B. The potential of a point on the surface of the charged sphere is just the area under the E curve from infinity to the surface at r_0. In this simple example, $\mathbf{E}$ is parallel to the path we take between A and B. In cases where this is not true, account must be taken of the angle between the field direction and the path, as required by the scalar product involved in the line integral. For example, if a straight-line path taken between the points A and B made a constant angle θ

---

[1] If, as in some idealized problems, the charge does not go to zero at infinity, as with an infinitely long charged wire (Prob. *e*, Sec. 3.9), the choice of zero potential at infinity is not useful.

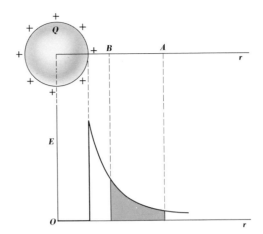

**Fig. 3.5   Plot of electric field
of a uniform charge distribution on a spherical shell.
Area under E curve between
points A and B measures
the potential difference
between the two points.**

with the field direction, the potential difference would be given by the
area under the curve of $E \cos \theta$ versus r between the two points.

3.8   The Superposition Principle Applied to Potential

It has been shown that the superposition principle applies to electric
fields. We now show that it also applies to potentials. This is not quite
an obvious result since superposition of fields means the *vector* addition
of separate contributions to the field. In contrast, since potential is related to work, and is therefore a scalar quantity, superposition of potentials means the *scalar* addition of contributions to the potential.

   The equivalence of these two aspects of the superposition principle is easily shown with the aid of Fig. 3.6. Let P be a point in space
for which the field from one charge (not shown) is $\mathbf{E}_1$ and from another
is $\mathbf{E}_2$. By superposition, the field at P is just the vector sum $\mathbf{E}_1 + \mathbf{E}_2$.
Now we ask for the change in potential when we move a small dis-
tance along the arbitrary direction $d\mathbf{l}$. According to Eq. (3.9), the potential difference involves the line integral $\mathbf{E} \cdot d\mathbf{l}$. Superposition of the
two fields gives us for the potential difference

$$dV = -(\mathbf{E}_1 + \mathbf{E}_2) \cdot d\mathbf{l} \qquad (3.12)$$

where $\mathbf{E}_1 + \mathbf{E}_2$ = vector sum of two fields. But this is mathematically
equivalent to adding the potential differences caused by the two fields
separately; that is,

$$dV = -(\mathbf{E}_1 \cdot d\mathbf{l} + \mathbf{E}_2 \cdot d\mathbf{l}) \qquad (3.13)$$

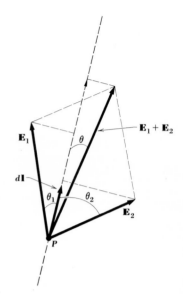

Fig. 3.6 Potential difference along $d\mathbf{l}$**, caused by fields** $\mathbf{E}_1$ **and** $\mathbf{E}_2$**. This graphic illustration of the equality of** $\mathbf{E}_1 \cos \theta_1 + \mathbf{E}_2 \cos \theta_2$ **and** $(\mathbf{E}_2 + \mathbf{E}_1) \cos \theta$ **justifies the application of the superposition principle to potentials.**

It makes no difference whether we add the vectors $\mathbf{E}_1$ and $\mathbf{E}_2$ first, and take the component of this resultant vector along $d\mathbf{l}$, as in Eq. (3.12), or whether we take the components of each field along $d\mathbf{l}$ separately, as in Eq. (3.13). The equality of these two expressions justifies the conclusion that, as in Eq. (3.13), the potential difference is the scalar sum of terms coming from each charge. We show an example of the simplicity of the scalar addition of potentials in Example 3.9d, below.

3.9   Examples, Calculation of Potential

a   *Potential difference between two points in the region of a point charge* Q (Fig. 3.7). We found in Sec. 3.3 that the work to move a charge q

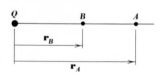

Fig. 3.7   Calculation of the potential difference between points B **and** A **due to the point charge** Q**.**

from A to B against the field of a charge Q was

$$W_{AB} = \frac{qQ}{4\pi}\left(\frac{1}{r_B} - \frac{1}{r_A}\right) \qquad \text{joules}$$

Since

$$V_{AB} = \frac{W_{AB}}{q}$$

we find

$$V_{AB} = \frac{Q}{4\pi\epsilon_0}\left(\frac{1}{r_B} - \frac{1}{r_A}\right) \qquad \text{joules/coul, or volts}$$

b   *Potential of a point P at a distance r from a point charge Q.*   We mean by this the work per unit charge to bring a test charge up to P from infinity. We calculate this by using the result of the preceding problem. Let the point P be at B and let $A \rightarrow \infty$. This gives $V_P = Q/4\pi\epsilon_0 r$ volts for the potential at a point P, r m from a point charge. Thus the potential due to a point charge falls off as $1/r$. That the potential is spherically symmetrical around the point charge follows from the similar symmetry of the electric field. The result $V_P = Q/4\pi\epsilon_0 r$ is also valid for the potential outside any spherically symmetric charge distribution according to the reasoning given in Example 2.8a.

c   *Potential of a charged metal sphere.*   This problem is essentially the same as Example 3.9b, but we work it out separately to emphasize the argument. Suppose a metal sphere has a radius r_0 and a net charge Q, as shown in Fig. 3.8. Since the average static field inside a metal is

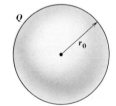

Fig. 3.8   Metal sphere of radius r_0 with net charge Q on its surface.

zero, the charge must reside on the surface. We saw in Chap. 2 that the field outside a spherical charge distribution is the same as though all the charge were at the center. Therefore, in calculating the potential, we may use the expression for the field of a point charge. The potential calculation proceeds:

$$V_r = -\int_\infty^{r_0} \mathbf{E} \cdot d\mathbf{r} = -\frac{1}{4\pi\epsilon_0}\int_\infty^{r_0}\frac{Q}{r^2}\,dr = \frac{Q}{4\pi\epsilon_0 r_0} \qquad \text{volts}$$

We have chosen $V = 0$ at infinity, as is the usual practice, and find indeed that this answer is identical with the previous answer for

the potential at a point a distance r from a point charge. The similarity results from the identical field distributions from r to infinity
in the two problems.

d *Potential due to several point charges.*   Here, for the first time in
our treatment of potential problems, we must add explicitly the effects
of two charges. We utilize the results of the discussion in Sec. 3.8, and
apply the potential superposition principle. Suppose we calculate the
potential at the origin due to charges q_1 at y_1 and q_2 at x_2 as shown in
Fig. 3.9. The contribution to the potential at the origin of each charge

*Fig. 3.9   Calculation of the
potential at 0 due to several
point charges. The potential
is the scalar sum of terms
due to individual charges.*

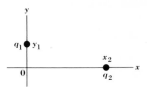

q_1 and q_2 is available from Example 3.9b. The two scalar terms add to
give

$$V_0 = \frac{1}{4\pi\epsilon_0}\left(\frac{q_1}{y_1} + \frac{q_2}{x_2}\right) \qquad \text{volts}$$

Thus the general expression for the potential at a given point in space
due to a distribution of point charges is

$$V = \frac{1}{4\pi\epsilon_0}\sum_i \frac{q_i}{r_i} \qquad \text{scalar sum} \tag{3.14}$$

where the contribution from each charge q_i is weighted according to
the reciprocal of its distance to the point in question.

Similarly, if the distribution is continuous, we may express the
same idea in terms of a density of charge ρ, which may vary from
point to point. The expression for the potential then becomes

$$V = \frac{1}{4\pi\epsilon_0}\int_{\text{vol}} \frac{\rho\, dv}{r} \tag{3.15}$$

where ρ is in coulombs per cubic meter, dv is the element of volume,
and r is the variable giving the distance from each point in the charge
distribution to the point where the potential is being calculated. Equation (3.15) can be used only when explicit expressions for charge density
and position for the entire charge distribution are available.

e   *Potential difference between two points out from an infinite uniform line of charge.*   We proceed as before, using our earlier result that the field is given by $E = \mu/2\pi\epsilon_0 r$ (Example 2.3b). Then, if B is the point closest to the line of charges, we write

$$V_{AB} = - \int_A^B \mathbf{E} \cdot d\mathbf{r} = - \frac{\mu}{2\pi\epsilon_0} \int_A^B \frac{dr}{r} = \frac{\mu}{2\pi\epsilon_0} \ln \frac{r_A}{r_B} \tag{3.16}$$

Now, if we attempt to calculate the potential with respect to ∞ by letting r_A go to ∞ as in Example 2.3b, we find that V anywhere in the region of the linear distribution (r_B finite) goes to infinity. This is correct, and results from the fact that our assumption of a uniform and finite charge density over the infinitely long line really amounts to assuming an infinite amount of charge. It is not surprising that the sum of finite contributions from each part of an infinite amount of charge leads to an infinite potential. The same situation occurs for the potential extending out from an infinite plane with a uniform density, which would also require an infinite charge. Since in practical problems we are interested in potential *differences* between finitely separated positions, and never in absolute potentials, this causes no trouble. Our choice of infinity for the point of zero potential was for convenience; any problem we solve by the use of potential will give the same physical answer regardless of our choice of reference for zero potential. Potential is defined only within an arbitrary additive constant; so only potential differences have any real significance.

3.10   Potential Related to Electric Field, the Gradient

We have seen that the potential difference between two points is related to the line integral of a vector (the electric field) between the two points. It is useful to study this relationship by considering again

$$dV = -\mathbf{E} \cdot d\mathbf{l} \tag{3.9}$$

This means that the potential difference dV between two points dl apart is the negative of the scalar product $\mathbf{E} \cdot d\mathbf{l} = E \cos \theta \, dl$. This relationship may be rewritten

$$-E \cos \theta = \frac{dV}{dl} \tag{3.17}$$

This form brings out the fact that the electric field is a kind of spatial derivative of the potential. We call it a *directional derivative*. As shown

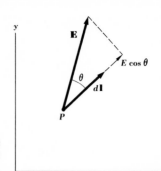

Fig. 3.10 *E* cos θ *at a point*
P is the component of E
along dl.

in Fig. 3.10, $E \cos \theta$ is the component of the (vector) electric field parallel to the displacement $d\mathbf{l}$. Suppose, for example, that we arbitrarily take $d\mathbf{l}$ along the x direction and call θ_x the angle between $\mathbf{x}$ and $\mathbf{E}$. Then the term $E \cos \theta_x$ is the component of $\mathbf{E}$ along the x direction. We could similarly write components of $\mathbf{E}$ along y or z or any other direction. The negative sign in Eq. (3.17) comes from the fact that we are discussing the work per unit charge which must be done *against* the force of $\mathbf{E}$ in a quasi-static displacement.

The magnitude of the rate of change of V with position depends on the direction of the displacement. For example, dV/dl has the largest magnitude along the direction of the field, and is zero in any direction perpendicular to the field.

Since a vector is the vector sum of its components, and since we can express the components of $\mathbf{E}$ along x, y, and z axes in terms of directional derivatives of the potential as in Eq. (3.17), we can easily develop an expression for $\mathbf{E}$ in terms of the potential derivatives. That is, we write for $\mathbf{E}$,

$$\mathbf{E} = \hat{\mathbf{x}} E_x + \hat{\mathbf{y}} E_y + \hat{\mathbf{z}} E_z$$

where we label the three mutually perpendicular directions by means of the unit vectors $\hat{\mathbf{x}}$, $\hat{\mathbf{y}}$, and $\hat{\mathbf{z}}$. But each of the components of $\mathbf{E}$ can be written through Eq. (3.17) as

$$E_x = -\frac{\partial V}{\partial x}$$

$$E_y = -\frac{\partial V}{\partial y}$$

$$E_z = -\frac{\partial V}{\partial z}$$

or

$$\mathbf{E} = - \left(\hat{\mathbf{x}} \frac{\partial V}{\partial x} + \hat{\mathbf{y}} \frac{\partial V}{\partial y} + \hat{\mathbf{z}} \frac{\partial V}{\partial z} \right) \tag{3.18}$$

The expression in parentheses involving space derivatives of the *scalar* quantity V is thus related to the *vector* field **E**.

This expression is called the *gradient* of the potential, and is more usually written

$$\operatorname{grad} V \equiv \hat{\mathbf{x}} \frac{\partial V}{\partial x} + \hat{\mathbf{y}} \frac{\partial V}{\partial y} + \hat{\mathbf{z}} \frac{\partial V}{\partial z} \tag{3.19}$$

Thus the potential-field relationship can be written

$$\mathbf{E} = - \operatorname{grad} V \tag{3.18a}$$

By its definition, the gradient, which means slope, is the *maximum* value of the spatial rate of change of V, and is obtained by evaluating dV/dl along the direction of the field vector itself. Thus, using Fig. 3.11, the gradient of V is a vector pointed opposite to the vector **E**. It

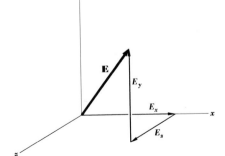

Fig. 3.11   The vector E is the sum of three mutually perpendicular vectors $\hat{x}\mathbf{E}_x$, $\hat{y}\mathbf{E}_y$, and $\hat{z}\mathbf{E}_z$.

follows that over a surface containing directions perpendicular to **E**, the gradient of V is zero and V is a constant. Such a surface is called an *equipotential surface*. Equipotential surfaces are everywhere perpendicular to the electric field direction. If the electric field is uniform in a region of space, the equipotential surface is a plane. Thus if the field **E** is uniform and pointed in the x direction, yz planes are equipotential surfaces. This follows from Eq. (3.18): since **E** is in the x direction, $\partial V/\partial y = \partial V/\partial z = 0$, and V does not change with any displacement $d\mathbf{r}$ in a yz plane. That is, $\partial V/\partial r = 0$ for any $d\mathbf{r}$ in a yz plane.

We have seen earlier that in a static situation a metal has no electric field component parallel to its surface. It follows that a metal surface is an equipotential surface.

Examples of the relationship between fields and potentials are given in the next section.

3.11   Examples, Field versus Potential

a   *Field obtained from potential of a point charge Q.*   This very simple example illustrates the method. Using Fig. 3.12, we write directly from

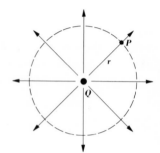

Fig. 3.12   The field at P due to a point charge Q can be obtained from $-dV/dr$.

the result of Example 3.9*b* the potential at a point P a distance r from the charge Q:

$$V_P = \frac{1}{4\pi\epsilon_0} \frac{Q}{r} \qquad \text{volts}$$

We know the direction of $\mathbf{E}$ in this simple case is along $\mathbf{r}$, but if we did not we could see from the equation for V_p that V changes most rapidly for a displacement along $\mathbf{r}$ and not at all for one perpendicular to $\mathbf{r}$. Therefore we write

$$|\mathbf{E}| = -\frac{dV}{dr} = \frac{1}{4\pi\epsilon_0} \frac{Q}{r^2} \qquad \text{volts/m}$$

in agreement with the earlier result. We have written a scalar expression although $\mathbf{E}$ is a vector quantity.

Since, when we move along r, we are going in the direction of maximum rate of change of V, dV/dr is the gradient of V, or $-\mathbf{E}$.

Choosing instead to take the rate of change of V perpendicular to the radial direction, we find $dV/r\,d\theta = 0$, as we should expect, since the potential has a constant value as we move along a direction perpendicular to **E**. Note that the elementary displacement along this direction perpendicular to **r** is given by $r\,d\theta$, where r is held constant.

b *Field of a dipole obtained from the potential.* Using the relationship between potential gradient and electric fields, we are now able to find the field at any general point in the vicinity of a dipole. Using Fig.

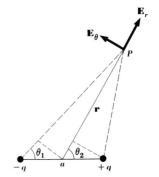

Fig. 3.13 *Calculation of potential and field around a dipole.*

3.13, we can write the expression for the potential at point P directly, using the expression for the potential due to point charges.

$$
\begin{aligned}
V_P &= \frac{1}{4\pi\epsilon_0}\left\{\frac{q}{[r-(a/2)\cos\theta_1]} - \frac{q}{[r+(a/2)\cos\theta_2]}\right\} \\
&= \frac{q}{4\pi\epsilon_0}\frac{a\cos\theta}{[r^2-(a^2/4)\cos^2\theta]}
\end{aligned}
$$

In the last expression we have made the approximation that

$$\theta = \theta_1 = \theta_2$$

When P is far enough away from the dipole so that $r \gg a$, this approximation is valid. We may also neglect the term $a^2/4$ compared with r^2 in this situation. This is the same far-field approximation we made in our earlier investigation of the field of a dipole. Using $p = qa$ for the dipole moment, we then have

$$V = \frac{1}{4\pi\epsilon_0}\frac{p}{r^2}\cos\theta \tag{3.20}$$

We do not have an explicit expression giving us the direction of **E**; so we cannot obtain **E** from the gradient of V at once. We can get around this difficulty, however, by obtaining the components of **E** in two perpendicular directions. The magnitude and direction of the total field can then be obtained by simple vector addition of the two perpendicular components. Thus we can find

$$E_r = -\frac{\partial V}{\partial r} = \frac{1}{4\pi\epsilon_0}\frac{2p}{r^3}\cos\theta \tag{3.21}$$

and

$$E_\theta = -\frac{\partial V}{r\,\partial\theta} = \frac{1}{4\pi\epsilon_0}\frac{p}{r^3}\sin\theta \tag{3.22}$$

This problem can be solved alternatively in terms of $\hat{x}$ and $\hat{y}$ coordinates, in the plane of the paper. The field is confined to the plane of the paper by the symmetry of the problem.

Equations (3.21) and (3.22) are identical with those of Sec. 2.3d, which were derived by assuming that the dipole moment is a vector quantity. Here we have derived the expressions for the field from the potential, and have not used the vector nature of the dipole moment.

These results for two perpendicular components of the field around a dipole can be combined to give an expression for the total field at any point, using the description of angles as shown in Fig. 3.14. θ is defined

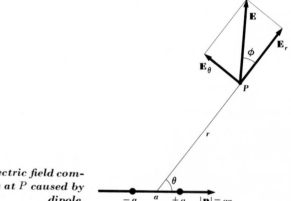

Fig. 3.14 Electric field components at P caused by dipole.

as the angle between the forward direction of the dipole moment vector (pointing from $-q$ to $+q$) and the radius vector from the dipole to the point P where the field is to be determined. It is left as a problem to show by simple vector addition that the resultant field is given by

$$E = \frac{1}{4\pi\epsilon_0}\frac{p}{r^3}(3\cos^2\theta + 1)^{\frac{1}{2}}$$

The angle ϕ is given by

$$\tan \phi = \tfrac{1}{2} \tan \theta$$

The vector nature of the dipole moment is clearly indicated by Eq. (3.20). Thus the potential at P of a set of dipoles, one of which is shown in Fig. 3.14, is the sum of terms containing $p \cos \theta$ from each dipole, added according to the superposition principle, just as would vectors having magnitude p and directions at an angle θ from the line connecting the dipoles to a point P. In other words, Eq. (3.20) can be written in the form

$$V = \frac{1}{4\pi\epsilon_0} \frac{\mathbf{p} \cdot \hat{\mathbf{r}}}{r^2} \tag{3.20a}$$

without any change in its meaning. The vector $\mathbf{p}$ is defined as of magnitude qa, and its direction, as indicated in Fig. 3.14, is along the dipole axis, pointed from $-q$ to $+q$. In Prob. 3.5A the student is asked to show explicitly that the expression for the potential of two dipoles differently oriented at a given position is identical with the expression for the potential of a third dipole which is the vector sum of the first two dipoles. This exercise provides a more formal proof of the vector nature of the electric dipole moment. The importance of this becomes apparent in Chap. 5, where we treat dielectric materials, which are really large collections of dipoles.

We also write without derivation the vector form for the field around a dipole from which x, y, and z components of the field may be obtained, in contrast to the radial and perpendicular components E_r and E_θ we found above. The expression is obtained from Eq. (3.20a).

$$\mathbf{E} = \frac{3(\mathbf{p} \cdot \mathbf{r})\mathbf{r} - r^2 \mathbf{p}}{r^5} \tag{3.23}$$

This is often the most convenient starting point (as, for example, in calculating the contributions of an ordered array of dipoles around a particular point).

These dipole equations, which are generally applicable to many real physical problems, are actually only approximations, valid far from the dipole involved, or expressed differently, valid only for "short" dipoles, where r is much greater than a.

3.12 Charge Clusters, Monopoles, Dipoles, Quadrupoles, Etc.

We now turn to a general description of the field at distances far from an arbitrary collection of charges. Suppose that charges producing a field are localized in a cluster having linear dimensions which are small compared with the distance r between the charge cluster and points where the field is to be determined. We wish to discuss the way in which the field varies with distance away from the charges.

In Chap. 2 we found that if the total collection of charge, Σq, has some nonzero value, the field at large distances falls off as $1/r^2$. But we have, in the preceding section, the further result that in a simple dipole arrangement, where there is no net charge in the collection, or $\Sigma q = 0$, the field is not zero, but falls off as $1/r^3$, more rapidly with distance than from a *monopolar* charge, where $\Sigma q \neq 0$.

Similarly, by placing two equal dipoles in opposite orientations, such as in the examples in Fig. 3.15, we can produce a cancellation of

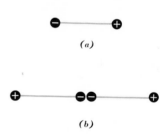

(a)

Fig. 3.15 Two arrangements of equal dipoles whose fields at a distance cancel to first order, producing a net quadrupole moment having a field which falls off as $1/r^4$.

(b)

these dipole fields so that that part of the field which falls off as $1/r^3$ is zero. This leaves a finite field, however, which falls off even more rapidly with distance than does a dipole field. This higher-order charge configuration is called a *quadrupole*. It can be shown that the field falls off from a quadrupole as $1/r^4$.

The field out from any arbitrary charge configuration can be accounted for by a series of terms involving successively higher-order distributions of charge. The field can be written

$$E = \frac{1}{4\pi\epsilon_0}\left(\frac{A}{r^2} + \frac{B}{r^3} + \frac{C}{r^4} + \cdots\right)$$

where the term containing A refers to the monopolar distribution, or net charge Σq, the term containing B refers to the dipolar part of the distribution, and the term with C, to the quadrupolar part, etc. Similarly, the expression for the potential at distance r from a localized array of charges would be given by an expression like

$$V = \frac{1}{4\pi\epsilon_0}\left(\frac{A'}{r} + \frac{B'}{r^2} + \frac{C'}{r^3} + \cdots\right)$$

as we could show by using the relation between the field and the potential. Only the monopolar term gives a field with spherical symmetry; so the quantities B, C, . . . and B', C', . . . are different in different directions away from the charge region.

This way of characterizing charge distributions has importance on an atomic scale as well as in the description of macroscopic charge distributions. Thus electric dipole moments of molecules are responsible for some special properties of dielectric materials, which we study in Chap. 5, and the quadrupole moments of nuclei of atoms making up solids can have important physical consequences in nuclear-resonance experiments, mentioned in Sec. 15.7.

3.13* Poisson's and Laplace's Equations

The general solution of potential problems is greatly simplified by use of a more sophisticated statement of the consequences of Coulomb's inverse-square law. We shall not have much to do with this work except to show (in Appendix C) how the generalized rules can be obtained, and to describe their use very briefly.

In Appendix C it is shown that Gauss' flux theorem (and therefore Coulomb's law, from which it comes) leads directly to the following requirement on the potential V. That is, V in the region of a point in space must satisfy

$$\frac{\partial^2 V}{\partial x^2} + \frac{\partial^2 V}{\partial y^2} + \frac{\partial^2 V}{\partial z^2} = -\frac{1}{\epsilon_0}\rho \qquad (3.24)$$

where ρ is the charge density at the point in question. In Appendix D we show that this can be written in the short notation of vector operators as

$$\nabla^2 V = -\frac{1}{\epsilon_0}\rho \qquad (3.24a)$$

(read as "del-squared" V). Either of these two equivalent forms is known as *Poisson's equation*.

When there is no charge in a given region, ρ becomes zero, and Poisson's equation reduces to *Laplace's equation.*

$$\frac{\partial^2 V}{\partial x^2} + \frac{\partial^2 V}{\partial y^2} + \frac{\partial^2 V}{\partial z^2} = 0 \qquad (3.25)$$

or

$$\nabla^2 V = 0 \qquad (3.25a)$$

These equations greatly simplify the solving of a whole class of electrostatic problems, called *boundary-value* problems, and in Appendixes E and F they are used in some simple illustrations of their utility.

Basically, these equations are simply another expression of the inverse-square law. They follow directly from the differential form of Gauss' flux theorem, which tells us that the electric flux per unit volume originating in any infinitesimal volume is proportional to the charge density in that infinitesimal region. The fact that the Poisson and Laplace equations are expressed in terms of potential should not obscure this simple idea. The advantage of using this potential form is that it is particularly appropriate for solving a large class of problems.

3.14 The Evaluation of the Electronic Charge

We earlier remarked (Chap. 1) that the classical laws of electromagnetism have nothing to say about the existence of the electron. Indeed, Maxwell published in 1865 his basic theory of electromagnetism (page 439), while it was not until 1897 that J. J. Thomson described his first experiments, which proved the existence of the electron with its unique mass and charge. In Chap. 8 we discuss experiments that evaluate the ratio of charge to mass, e/m, for various kinds of ions and for electrons. At the time of the discovery of the electron, however, there was no accurate method of evaluating m; so there was great need for an experiment that measured the electronic charge e directly. Efforts in this direction were brought to a successful conclusion in the period 1909–1913 by R. A. Millikan. In the experiment, very small oil drops were injected into the space between horizontal plates, across which an electric field could be varied by adjusting the voltage difference between the two plates. A microscope was arranged so that the vertical motion of the oil drops could be observed. An x-ray source was arranged so that x-rays could be used to ionize the oil drops, giving them one or more units of charge. Two steps were required in the experiment. The first was to observe the motion of an oil drop charged by exposure to x-rays and to adjust the electric field so that the vertical motion was arrested. Under this circumstance, the electric force on a drop with n units of electronic charge, neE, just balances the force of gravity as modified by the buoyant force of the air in which the drops are immersed. The net downward force is given by $\frac{4}{3}\pi r^3 g(\rho_0 - \rho_a)$, where ρ_0 is the density of the oil, g the acceleration of gravity, and ρ_a the air density. The radius r could not be measured accurately by observing its size in the microscope, since the drops were small (of the order of 10^{-4} cm); so a second step was taken to determine their size.

The method used was to turn off the electric field, by electrically connecting the two plates together, and to measure the terminal velocity of the downward-falling drop. A result from fluid dynamics, called *Stokes' law*, gives the terminal velocity of a falling sphere in a viscous medium like air in terms of the net force acting, the radius of the sphere, and the viscosity of the medium. Hence the net force with no field applied can be equated to the terminal-velocity expression of Stokes to give

$$\frac{4}{3}\pi r^3 g(\rho - \rho_a) = 6\pi\eta r v \tag{3.26}$$

where η is the viscosity of the medium (air), and v is the terminal velocity. Thus, after finding the electric field E for which a given drop is held in balance, so that

$$neE = \frac{4}{3}\pi r^3 g(\rho - \rho_a) \tag{3.27}$$

the radius of the drop is obtained by measuring its velocity in free fall according to Eq. (3.26).

By means of a large number of such observations, the charge ne on each of many drops could be measured. Examination of the results showed that in all cases the charge on the drop was given by an integral number times a particular charge e, where

$$e = -1.602 \times 10^{-19} \text{ coul}$$

Thus, in the first place, the experiment showed that the electronic charge is unique; in the second place, it gave its value to great accuracy. The principal limitation on the accuracy of the experiment was the difficulty in the separate determination of the viscosity of air.

3.15   The Electron Volt

Since the potential difference V_{AB} gives the work per unit charge to move a charge between two points, A and B, the energy gained by a charged particle which is accelerated by the electric field between two points is given by

$$dU = qV_{AB} \qquad \text{coul-volts, or joules} \tag{3.28}$$

In many situations a particle of charge equal to the charge e of an electron is involved; so a useful expression for energy is the *electron volt*. This is the energy gained by a particle of one electronic charge which is accelerated through one-volt potential difference. Since the electronic charge is -1.602×10^{-19} coul, an electron volt is, from Eq. (3.28), -1.602×10^{-19} joule.

It is useful to have some feeling for the size of this new energy unit, the electron volt. Suppose we ask how much energy in electron volts any particle, say, an electron, a proton, or some molecule, has on the average when it is in equilibrium with any system at room temperature. As an approximation we may use kT as this energy, where $k = 1.6 \times 10^{-23}$ joule/°K is the Boltzmann constant, and $T = 300$ is room temperature in degrees Kelvin. Comparison of kT with the electron volt gives $1/40$ electron volt for the rough value of the average energy at room temperature.[1]

3.16 Comments on Chapter 3

The principal point of this chapter has been to develop the ideas of potential. It was shown that a static electric field is conservative, which means that the work to move a charge from one position to another against the force of the field is independent of the path taken. A further consequence is that the circulation, that is, the line integral of the field taken around any closed path, is always zero. Thus we showed

$$\oint \mathbf{E} \cdot d\mathbf{l} = 0 \tag{3.4}$$

This property of zero circulation provides a useful method of characterizing the conservative nature of the static electric field, and is a powerful conceptual tool for solving certain kinds of problems.

Once the conservative nature of the electric field is understood, the usefulness of the concept of potential can be validated. In a fixed electric field the potential difference between two points is the work

---

[1] Readers with some background in thermodynamics will recognize that for a free particle with only translational degrees of freedom the average particle kinetic energy would be $\frac{3}{2}kT$, corresponding to the general rule of $\frac{1}{2}kT$ for each degree of freedom.

per unit positive charge to move a test charge from one to the other position. This work is measured in the mks system in joules per coulomb, or *volts*. Only *differences* of potential have fundamental meaning, though often the potential is defined in terms of an arbitrarily chosen zero potential at infinity.

The superposition principle which applies to electric fields was shown to apply to potentials. That is, the potential at a given point is simply the arithmetic sum of the potentials at that point of each charge producing the field.

One important use of the potential is in the calculation of electric field configurations. The field can be expressed in terms of the spatial variation of the potential in terms of the relation[1]

$$\mathbf{E} = -\operatorname{grad} V = -\left(\hat{\mathbf{x}}\frac{\partial V}{\partial x} + \hat{\mathbf{y}}\frac{\partial V}{\partial y} + \hat{\mathbf{z}}\frac{\partial V}{\partial z}\right) \tag{3.18}$$

This relation defines the meaning of the *gradient*, here written in cartesian coordinates. Thus, if we calculate V at a point, as caused by the set of charges which produce the field, we can obtain the field $\mathbf{E}$ at that point by obtaining the derivatives of V in three mutually perpendicular directions. This is made easy by the fact that V is a scalar; so the effects of all charges are the simple sums of effects of each individual charge. The derivative method of calculation of the field through the potential was used for obtaining expressions for the field around an electric dipole in Example 3.7*b*.

Because of its importance in nature, we repeat here the result of the far-field dipole calculation. For positions far from a dipole, where $r \gg a$, the potential is

$$V = \frac{1}{4\pi\epsilon_0}\frac{p\cos\theta}{r^2} \tag{3.20}$$

Differentiation of this expression gives, for the radial component E_r and the component perpendicular to it, E_θ,

$$E_r = \frac{1}{4\pi\epsilon_0}\frac{2p\cos\theta}{r^3} \tag{3.21}$$

$$E_\theta = \frac{1}{4\pi\epsilon_0}\frac{p\sin\theta}{r^3} \tag{3.22}$$

An essential feature of the dipole configuration of charges is that the far field falls off as $1/r^3$ rather than as $1/r^2$ for a point charge or a

---

[1] Using the operator notation given in Appendix D, grad V can be written ∇V.

spherical charge distribution. More complicated distributions of charge have fields which fall off still more rapidly with distance. For example, a *quadrupole*, consisting of oppositely directed but not exactly super-posed equal dipoles, has a field which falls off as $1/r^4$.

In contrast to this, it was shown that the field out from a linear or cylindrical array of charge falls off as $1/r$ when the length of the charge array is much greater than r, while out from a plane of charge, the field is *independent* of the distance away (for a plane which is large compared with its distance away).

The relation between the electric field and the gradient of the potential leads naturally to the idea of *equipotential surfaces* associated with electric fields in space. To move a test charge along directions everywhere normal to the gradient of the potential, no external work is required. The locus of such paths is thus an equipotential surface in space. If the field in some region is uniform, all **E** lines will point in the same direction, and the equipotential surfaces will be planes. Since the electric field must be normal at a metal (conducting) surface, metal surfaces are equipotential surfaces.

The change in energy of a charged particle which has been ac-celerated or decelerated by passing through a potential difference is most easily characterized by the work done on it by the field. Thus a common unit of energy is the *electron volt*, the amount of energy given an electron (or proton) which has gone through a potential difference of one volt.

Some of the material in this chapter requires for its complete understanding the optional material in Appendixes B and C. For those who have studied these appendixes we add here a brief summary of the more advanced material.

It is shown in Appendix B that the zero value of the circulation over any closed path in a conservative field can be converted to a point relation involving the mathematical *curl*. Using this result, we found that in a static electric field at any point,

$$\text{curl } \mathbf{E} = 0 \tag{3.4a}$$

An explicit expression for the curl of any vector is given in Eq. (B.6) in Appendix B.

We display this differential form of the conservative field criterion and its equivalent vector notation form, $\mathbf{\nabla} \times \mathbf{E} = 0$ (Appendix D), to serve notice of its existence and of its importance in more advanced work.

Coulomb's inverse-square law is shown in Appendix C to limit the spatial variation of the potential according to the relation

$$\frac{\partial^2 V}{\partial x^2} + \frac{\partial^2 V}{\partial y^2} + \frac{\partial^2 V}{\partial z^2} = -\frac{1}{\epsilon_0}\rho \qquad (3.24)$$

or using the vector notation of Appendix D,

$$\nabla^2 V = -\frac{1}{\epsilon_0}\rho \qquad (3.24a)$$

where ρ is the charge density. The use of this relationship (called Poisson's equation or, when $\rho = 0$, Laplace's equation), goes somewhat beyond the level of this book, but is of great importance in solving potential problems, as illustrated in some examples in Appendixes E and F.

PROBLEMS

The potential energy of a system of point charges is the work required to bring the charges to their final positions from far away.

$\star$3.1A   Two equal positive charges Q are a distance a m apart.

    a   Calculate the work to bring them to this position from far away, using $W = -Q \int_{\infty}^{a} \mathbf{E} \cdot d\mathbf{l}$, where $\mathbf{E}$ is the field of one of the charges.

    b   What is the potential energy of this pair of charges?

3.1B   *a*   Calculate the total stored energy of the configuration of point charges shown in Fig. P3.1. The charges are of equal magnitudes Q and are separated by a distance a m.

    b   What is the potential energy of this array of charges?

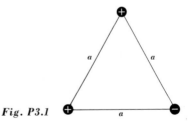

Fig. P3.1

The potential at a point in space is the external work per unit charge required to bring a positive point charge to that point from far away. The potential difference between two points is the external work per unit positive charge to move a charge from one point to the other.

3.2A   *a*   Repeat Prob. 3.1A(*a*) using $W = QV$, where V is the potential at the position of one of the charges with that charge absent.

         b   Find the potential at the center of Fig. P3.1.

★3.2B   A dipole of charge $\pm q$ and separation l (dipole moment $p = ql$) is placed along the x axis as shown in Fig. P3.2.

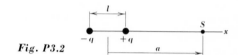

Fig. P3.2

   a   Using the expression for the potential V of a point charge, calculate the work necessary to bring a charge $+Q$ from far away to a point S on the x axis, a distance a from the center of the dipole. What is the potential V_s of the point S (in the absence of the charge Q)?

   b   Write a simple approximate expression for V_s, good for $a \gg l$. Use the expression for V_s to find the magnitude and direction of the electric field at the point S.

   c   Find the orientation of the equipotential surface at the point S.

3.2C   In Fig. P3.2, find an equipotential surface that is a plane. Find the value of the potential in this plane.

★3.2D   A uniform charge density of ρ coul/m³ is in the shape of a sphere of radius R. Find expressions for the potential V and field E at distances r from the center, for points inside and outside the sphere.

3.2E   Find the work necessary to move a charge q from a point A to a point B in the field of a point charge Q, as shown in Fig. P3.3.

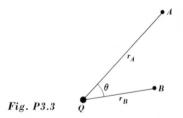

Fig. P3.3

★3.2F   A metal sphere has a radius R and is isolated from all other bodies. Express the potential of the surface of the sphere as a function of the charge placed on it. Integrate this expression to determine the work necessary to charge the sphere up to a potential V.

3.2G A spherical conductor of radius a has a charge Q_1 placed on it. This is surrounded by a thin spherical conducting shell of radius b, as shown in Fig. P3.4. The shell is connected to ground through a battery of potential difference V_1.

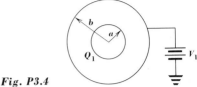

Fig. P3.4

  a Find the total charge on the outer surface of the shell and on the inner surface of the shell.
  b Find the field and potential at a radius r from the center of the sphere, where $r < a$, $a < r < b$, $r > b$.

★3.2H A long cylinder of radius a has a charge of Q couls/m. Find the potential difference between two points at distances r_1 and r_2 from the axis of the cylinder.

3.2I Two identical water drops are charged to the same potential V_1. Find the new potential if the two drops coalesce into one drop.

★3.2J Charges of $+\frac{4}{3} \times 10^{-8}$ coul and $-\frac{1}{3} \times 10^{-8}$ coul are placed along the x axis at the points -10 and 0 cm, respectively.
  a Make a plot of the potential as a function of x at any point along the x axis and also as a function of position on a line perpendicular to the x axis and passing through the point $x = 10$ cm.
  b At what points on the x axis is the potential 300 volts? Is the electric field intensity the same at these points?
  c At what point would a third charge be in equilibrium? Would it be stable equilibrium?

The electric field **E** is the negative of the gradient of the potential [Eq. (3.18)].

3.3A A conducting sphere of radius r has a net charge $-Q$.
  a Write the expression for the potential V at its surface.
  b From this expression, find the field **E** just outside the surface of the sphere.
  c What is the value of **E** just inside the surface?

★3.3B The potential at points in a plane is given by

$$V = \frac{ax}{(x^2 + y^2)^{3/2}} + \frac{b}{(x^2 + y^2)^{1/2}}$$

where x and y are the rectangular coordinates of a point, and a and b are constants. Find the components E_x and E_y of the electric intensity at any point.

3.3C   The potential at points in a plane is given by

$$V = \frac{a \cos \theta}{r^2} + \frac{b}{r}$$

where r and θ are the polar coordinates of a point in the plane, and a and b are constants. Find the components E_r and E_θ of the electric intensity at any point.

3.3D   The graph of Fig. P3.5 shows the way in which the potential varies along the x axis. Plot a curve of the x component of the electric field

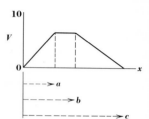

Fig. P3.5

E_x along the x axis. Explain why the two areas obtained for the E_x versus x plot should have equal magnitudes.

3.3E   The maximum electric field that can be supported in air (without producing ionization of the air and allowing charge to flow) is about 10^6 volts/cm. Using this criterion, find the maximum potential to which a conducting sphere of radius $R = 10$ cm can be charged in air.

The work done by an electric field on a charged particle: A charged particle q, accelerated by an electric field, has its energy increased according to $U = q(V_A - V_B)$, where V_A is the potential at its initial position, and V_B is the potential at its final position.

★3.4A   What is the velocity of an electron that has been accelerated through a potential difference of 100 volts? What is its energy in joules? In ergs? In electron volts?

3.4B   Some of the electrons which are emitted at low velocities from a hot wire (cathode) go through a small hole in a plate that is at a potential of 1,000 volts with respect to the cathode. What is the velocity of the electrons when they are passing through the hole? A second plate is parallel to the first and 20 cm beyond it and is at a potential of $-2,000$

volts with respect to the cathode. Describe the motion of electrons in the region between the two plates.

★3.4C   Electrons accelerated from rest through a potential difference of V_0 volts (having a kinetic energy of eV_0 electron volts) enter the middle of the vacuum region between two parallel plates of separation d and length b, as shown in Fig. P3.6. The potential difference between the

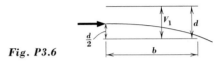

Fig. P3.6

two plates is V_1. Find the value of V_1 for which electrons just miss the edges of the plates. Assume $d \ll b$.

The vector nature of the dipole can be shown through the use of the expression for the potential at a distance r from a dipole [Eq. (3.20)].

3.5A   Calculate the potential at S in Fig. P3.7 by adding the potentials of dipoles $\mathbf{p}_1$ and $\mathbf{p}_2$ at S. Show that this has the same value as the potential at S of $\mathbf{p}_3$, the vector sum of $\mathbf{p}_1$ and $\mathbf{p}_2$. This can be done graphically.

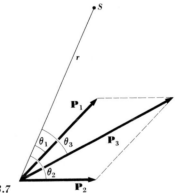

Fig. P3.7

An expression for the magnitude and direction of the field of a dipole can be obtained by adding the two perpendicular components E_θ and E_r, as given by Eqs. (3.14) and (3.22).

★3.6A   Use Fig. 3.14 to find the magnitude of the field E of a dipole, given r and θ. Also find the relation between the angle ϕ which E makes with the radial vector $\mathbf{r}$, and θ, the angle between $\mathbf{r}$ and $\mathbf{p}$, the dipole vector.

The conservative nature of an electrostatic field leads directly to its zero circulation, or equivalently, to curl $E = 0$.

3.7A Using the path suggested in Fig. P3.8, show that any central field, that is, one directed radially from a point charge, which has a magnitude depending only on r, is conservative.

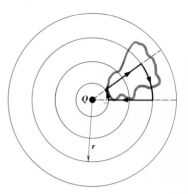

Fig. P3.8

4

capacitance

4.1 Introduction

In Chap. 3 we began by assuming an arrangement of charges in space which produced some electric field configuration. We then discussed the work per unit charge to move a test charge from one place to another, that is, the potential difference between two points in the given field. In this chapter we are interested in the charge configuration itself and in the work necessary to establish it. In particular, we are concerned with arrangements of one or more metal bodies on which charges can be placed. Such systems of equipotential surfaces are important practically, and also have the virtue that the relationship between the amount of charge on each body and its potential is remarkably simple. The arrangement of most practical importance is that involving two conducting bodies, the usual form of a new circuit element, the *capacitor* (or *condenser*).

We begin with a description of the properties of systems of isolated conductors, and discuss some general methods of finding charge distributions giving required field distributions. We then discuss the question of the work involved in charging one or more bodies. This

leads to considerations of stored electrostatic energy. Finally, we discuss the characteristics and applications of capacitors.

4.2   Description of a System of Charged Conductors

Our goal here is to learn how to relate the net charge on each of a
set of conductors to the resulting potentials of each conductor. A set
of several conducting bodies is shown in Fig. 4.1. We make the follow-

*Fig. 4.1   A system of con-
ducting bodies in other-
wise empty space. We
relate the potential of
each body to the charges
on it and on each of the
other bodies.*

ing statements about this static system, some of which are applicable
to any set of conductors and some of which are arbitrary and made
here to define our point of view:

    1.   All charges considered are those at the surface of each conducting
body. Thus the only electric fields are those resulting from the charged
equipotential surfaces of each body. If the bodies are in fact so close to
the earth that the field distribution is affected by the earth, we consider
the earth as one of the conducting bodies involved, and should ordinarily
assign it zero potential.

    2.   The charge on each body distributes itself so as to produce a uniform
potential over each body, a property of conductors.

    3.   Any distribution of charges which gives the required potential dis-
tribution (here, the required potential on each conductor) is the *only*
distribution which will do so. This *uniqueness theorem* is a basic property
of any static electric field.[1] It leads to the following criteria for obtaining

---

[1] The uniqueness theorem derives from the properties of Laplace's equation. We
do not show the proof here in spite of its very important role in electrostatic
problems.

the charge distribution which produces a given geometry of field or potential:

a The charges must give the required equipotential surfaces having the required values (including zero potential at infinity).

b. The potential must satisfy Laplace's equation, $\nabla^2 V = 0$,[1] everywhere outside of the conductors.

Requirement *b*, as discussed in Chap. 3, simply ensures that the solution is consistent with Gauss' flux theorem, and therefore is a consequence of the inverse-square Coulomb's law. In Appendixes E and F some simple examples of the use of these ideas in practical problems are given.

4. The potential V of each body depends *only* and *linearly* on the excess charge Q on *each* conductor. This means that the potentials V_1, V_2, and V_3 for the three-body system can be expressed in terms of the charges on each body as follows:

$$V_1 = a_{11}Q_1 + a_{12}Q_2 + a_{13}Q_3$$
$$V_2 = a_{21}Q_1 + a_{22}Q_2 + a_{23}Q_3 \qquad\qquad (4.1)$$
$$V_3 = a_{31}Q_1 + a_{32}Q_2 + a_{33}Q_3$$

where the coefficients depend only on the shape and size of each body and their relative positions. This result follows from the principle of superposition and the uniqueness theorem. (We omit a detailed argument.) The above relationship can be inverted to solve for the charges:

$$Q_1 = b_{11}V_1 + b_{12}V_2 + b_{13}V_3$$
$$Q_2 = b_{21}V_1 + b_{22}V_2 + b_{23}V_3 \qquad\qquad (4.2)$$
$$Q_3 = b_{31}V_1 + b_{32}V_2 + b_{33}V_3$$

Here *each* coefficient *a* (or *b*), say, a_{11}, depends on the presence of *all* bodies, since each one perturbs the field of each of the others, and the potential is affected by the shape and size of the electric field. However, as long as *all* bodies are fixed geometrically and we consider only charges on the conductors, the geometric constants *a* and *b* completely characterize the system.

Equation (4.1) or its equivalent (4.2) is the expression of a most important property of a system of conductors. It states the *linear* relationship between conductor potential and charges on each conductor. It is the basis for the entire discussion which follows on capacitance and capacitors. Our discussion of the ideas which lie behind these equations has been extensive, if partially without detailed proof, because of their great importance for the material which follows.

[1] In cartesian coordinates we found that this is written explicitly

$$\frac{\partial^2 V}{\partial x^2} + \frac{\partial^2 V}{\partial y^2} + \frac{\partial^2 V}{\partial z^2} = 0 \qquad\qquad (C\text{-}2)$$

4.3   The Simplest Case, a Single Isolated Conductor

We begin the discussion of the work required to charge a system of conductors by considering a single isolated body, as shown in Fig. 4.2.

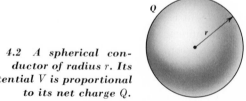

Fig. 4.2   A spherical conductor of radius r. Its
potential V is proportional
to its net charge Q.

We calculate the external work to charge the body to some potential V by placing on it a total charge Q.[1] Since the body is a conductor, its surface is an equipotential, and V depends linearly on Q according to a simplified version of Eq. (4.1). Considering only the one body on which charge is to be placed, we can write

$$V = aQ \qquad (4.3)$$

Since each charge dQ brought up to the body will change its potential, the total work is calculated by integrating $V \, dQ$ from 0 to Q. That is, the work to bring up a charge dQ is the potential, at the time a particular charge dQ is brought up, times the charge dQ. Thus, as the charge on the conductor increases, V also increases, and the work to bring each additional dQ up from a place of zero potential increases. The total work to charge the body is then

$$W = \int_0^{Q_1} V \, dQ$$

But by Eq. (4.3) we have

$$W = \int_0^{Q_1} aQ \, dQ = \tfrac{1}{2}aQ_1{}^2 = \tfrac{1}{2}Q_1 V_1 \qquad \text{joules} \qquad (4.4)$$

It would be possible to charge the conductor in a different series of steps. We could, for example, collect subgroups of charges and bring up the subgroups simultaneously or in sequence. But the work done is

[1] In our calculation of stored energy resulting from the work done to assemble the charges Q on the conductors, we are not concerned with the stored energy in the electrons themselves. Our concern is only with the work to bring up isolated electrons from far away. As we shall see, the amount of energy involved in a given amount of charge, say, an electron, depends critically on the (microscopic) distribution of that charge; so we cannot determine directly the stored energy in an electron simply by knowing its charge.

independent of the steps by which the initially isolated charges are brought to the final distribution on the conductor, since we are dealing with a conservative system. Our calculation via infinitesimal steps dQ thus gives the actual amount of work required, even if the actual charging process is quite different from that described. Equation (4.4) is a correct statement of the work necessary to collect a charge Q on a conductor which attains a potential V, no matter how the charging process occurs. And again, because of the conservative nature of the electric field, the equation also describes the energy stored by virtue of the assembled charge.

It is easy to calculate the relation between the charge Q on the conducting sphere and its potential, that is, the value of a in Eq. (4.3). We found in Chap. 3 that the potential at an isolated charged spherical conducting surface is given by

$$V = \int_\infty^r \mathbf{E} \cdot d\mathbf{l} = \frac{1}{4\pi\epsilon_0} \frac{Q}{r} \qquad \text{volts} \tag{4.5}$$

For this case, then, the constant a in Eq. (4.3) is

$$a = \frac{1}{4\pi\epsilon_0 r}$$

Except for the factor $1/4\pi\epsilon_0$, which depends on the units used, the coefficient a depends only on the radius of the sphere. If other conducting bodies were in the region, however, a would depend on their location and shape as well. This example demonstrates our earlier statement that the amount of stored energy involved in a collection of charge depends not only on the amount of charge, but on its configuration. Equation (4.4) shows that the stored energy depends on QV, and for this case of an isolated spherical conductor we can now express the stored energy in terms of Q or V alone, using Eq. (4.3) and the calculated value of the coefficient a.

4.4 Capacitance

We have seen that general expressions like Eq. (4.1) or (4.2) give the relationships between charges and potentials on a system of conductors. Usually, however, we are interested in a system consisting of one, two, or a few bodies and in the rather simple question of how much charge must be placed on a given body to change its potential by a given amount. The parameter which measures this is called the *capaci-*

tance, and is directly related to the geometric coefficients mentioned above. Capacitance is defined as

$$C = \frac{Q}{V} \quad \text{coul/volt, or } farads \tag{4.6}$$

The capacitance measures the amount of charge necessary to increase the potential of a conductor by one volt. Any system of conductors may be called a *capacitor.* Usually a capacitor consists of two conductors so close together that the field between them is little affected by other bodies. V is the potential difference between the two conductors.

In the case of the isolated sphere discussed above, C is $1/a$, or

$$C = 4\pi\epsilon_0 r \quad \text{farads} \tag{4.7}$$

The farad turns out to be a very large unit; so we often find it useful to deal with microfarads (μfd $= 10^{-6}$ farad), picofarads (10^{-9} farad), or micromicrofarads ($\mu\mu$fd $= 10^{-12}$ farad).

4.5 Capacitance in a System of Conductors

In a complicated system such as shown in Fig. 4.3, we must define the variables carefully before inquiring about the capacitance. Thus, sup-

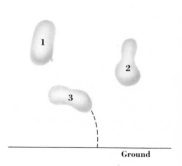

Fig. 4.3 A system of conductors. The capacitance of one body of a system of conductors, say, body 1 in the figure, depends on the physical arrangement of the other conductors and on whether they are isolated or connected to ground or to each other. Thus the capacitance of body 1 is modified if the dotted connection is made between body 3 and ground.

Ground

pose the earth is represented by the bottom line and we want to find the capacitance of a conductor 1 with bodies 2 and 3 isolated so that no charge is removed from or added to body 2 or 3 when we add charge to body 1. The capacitance of body 1 under these conditions is measured by the change in charge Q_1 on body 1 which results in unit change of potential of body 1. But if body 2 or 3 or both were connected by a wire to ground, the capacitance of body 1 would be different, since then Q_2 or Q_3 or both would change with Q_1 in order that body 2 or 3 stay at ground potential. Whatever the boundary conditions on the bodies auxiliary to the body whose capacitance is being investigated, the capacitance of the body is determined by the values of the appropriate coefficients in Eqs. (4.1) and (4.2).

The system of most practical importance is the two-body system, and one of its simplest forms is that of the parallel-plate capacitor, shown schematically in Fig. 4.4. We denote the area of each plate by A

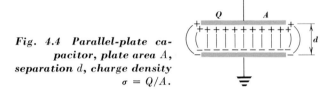

**Fig. 4.4 Parallel-plate ca-
pacitor, plate area A,
separation d, charge density
$\sigma = Q/A$.**

and the separation between plates by d. Let us begin by connecting one plate to ground. This will hold that plate at zero potential. To keep the problem simple we assume that the dimensions of the plates are large compared with the distance between them.

What happens when a charge Q is placed on the upper isolated plate? We wish to show that essentially all the charge moves to the bottom surface of the plate, and that an equal and opposite charge appears on the lower plate, as shown in the figure. The equal and opposite charges on the lower plate appear because of the zero-field requirement inside a conductor. These charges allow the electric flux to terminate at the surface of the conductor. But this excess charge thus pulled to the upper surface of the lower plate will attract the excess charge on the upper plate to its lower surface. Expressed differently, the mutual repulsion between the excess charges on the upper plate which tends to distribute the charges equally on both sides of the plate is countered by the mutual attraction of the opposite charges on the lower plate. When the plates are relatively close together compared with their dimensions, the field produced by the excess charge is almost wholly confined to the space between plates.

With the lower plate connected to ground, the charge density on its lower side must be close to zero, since this charge would produce a field incompatible with an equipotential situation between ground and the lower plate.

We have thus shown that, with electrodes relatively close together, the charge on a two-electrode capacitor lies on the inner surfaces of the two electrodes. The calculation of the capacitance between the pairs of plates is now straightforward. It involves the determination of the potential difference V resulting from a given charge Q on each plate. We may use the result found in Example 2.7c or calculate the field and then the potential difference directly. Working directly from Gauss' flux theorem, we find the field (which is uniform between the plates) to be

$$E = \frac{1}{\epsilon_0}\sigma = \frac{\sigma A}{\epsilon_0 A} = \frac{Q}{\epsilon_0 A} \qquad \text{volts/m}$$

where σ = charge density, coul/m^2
  A = area of either plate, m^2
  Q = charge on either plate, coul
Then the potential difference is

$$V = -\int_0^d \mathbf{E} \cdot d\mathbf{x} = \frac{Qd}{\epsilon_0 A} \qquad \text{volts}$$

where d is the separation between plates in meters. The capacitance of the parallel-plate capacitor follows directly from Eq. (4.6).

$$C = \frac{Q}{V} = \frac{A\epsilon_0}{d} \qquad \text{farads} \tag{4.8}$$

The capacitance increases linearly with the area of the electrodes and is *inversely* proportional to the plate separation.

The calculation of capacitance involves integration of the electric field between two equipotential surfaces to obtain the potential difference. This is then related to the charge responsible for the potential difference. From this point of view, the isolated sphere that was the first equipotential surface studied may be considered as one electrode of a capacitor, the other electrode of which is at infinity. We have in effect assumed that the second electrode is so large and of such shape that the excess charge density at any point on it is trivial compared with the charge density on the sphere.

4.6 Examples, Calculation of Capacitance

a *Capacitance between concentric spherical conductors.* Consider the outer sphere of radius b grounded as shown in Fig. 4.5. Place a charge

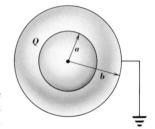

Fig. 4.5 Two concentric metal spheres forming a capacitor.

Q on the inner sphere (through a small hole in the outer sphere). Then an equal charge $-Q$ will be induced on the inner surface of the outer sphere (this follows from Gauss' flux theorem). A field exists only between the two spheres. The potential difference V_{ba} is given by integrating the field:

$$V_{ba} = - \int_b^a \mathbf{E} \cdot d\mathbf{r} = \frac{-Q}{4\pi\epsilon_0} \int_b^a \frac{dr}{r^2} = \frac{Q}{4\pi\epsilon_0}\left(\frac{1}{a} - \frac{1}{b}\right)$$

Then

$$C = \frac{Q}{V} = \frac{4\pi\epsilon_0}{1/a - 1/b} = 4\pi\epsilon_0 \frac{ab}{b-a} \qquad \text{farads}$$

Since we have already calculated the potential of a conducting sphere of radius r to be $V = \dfrac{1}{4\pi\epsilon_0}\dfrac{Q}{r}$, we can make this capacitance calculation alternatively by taking the difference between the potentials of the two spheres directly, instead of integrating the field over the distance between spheres. We would then write

$$C = \frac{Q}{V_{ba}} = \frac{Q}{(1/4\pi\epsilon_0)(Q/a - Q/b)} = 4\pi\epsilon_0 \frac{ab}{b-a} \qquad \text{farads}$$

It is left as a problem for the student to show that the capacitance between two coaxial cylinders is given by

$$C = \frac{2\pi\epsilon_0 L}{\ln(b/a)}$$

where a and b = radii of inner and outer cylinders
L = their length
ln = natural logarithm

b *Capacitance of a conducting sphere surrounded by an isolated thick spherical conducting shell.* This rather artificial arrangement is useful

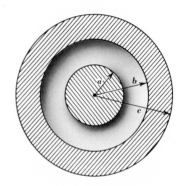

Fig. 4.6 Thick conducting shell surrounding a spherical conductor.

to fix clearly the ideas of field and potential (Fig. 4.6). The thick outer shell is isolated and considered to be initially uncharged. A charge $+Q$ is to be placed on the inner sphere. By Gauss' flux theorem we see at once that a negative charge $-Q$ is induced on the inner surface of the shell. This leaves a charge $+Q$ on the outer surface of the shell. Thus outside the metal shell the field is identical with the field due to a point charge $+Q$ at the center. We can therefore calculate the potential V_c at the surface by integrating the field from ∞ in the usual manner. Within the metal shell (between c and b) the field must be zero; therefore V_b is the same as V_c (since $\mathbf{E}_r = 0 = -\partial V/\partial r$). The field between b and a is also that of a point charge $+Q$; so the increase in potential at a over the value at b is obtained by integration from b to a. Then the potential at a, V_a, is given by

$$
\begin{aligned}
V_a &= -\int_\infty^c \mathbf{E} \cdot d\mathbf{r} - \int_c^b \mathbf{E} \cdot d\mathbf{r} - \int_b^a \mathbf{E} \cdot d\mathbf{r} \\
&= -\frac{Q}{4\pi\epsilon_0} \int_\infty^c \frac{dr}{r^2} - 0 - \frac{Q}{4\pi\epsilon_0} \int_b^a \frac{dr}{r^2} \\
&= \frac{Q}{4\pi\epsilon_0 c} + \frac{Q}{4\pi\epsilon_0} \left(\frac{1}{a} - \frac{1}{b} \right)
\end{aligned}
$$

The capacitance can be obtained in the usual fashion.

4.7 Combinations of Capacitors

It is often of practical importance to know how to connect two or more capacitors together to obtain a new capacitance value. The two most common arrangements involve direct connections of the capacitors in *series* or in *parallel*. We give the simple arguments that allow calculation of the capacitance of such combinations. Figure 4.7 shows

Fig. 4.7   *Two capacitors connected in parallel.*

two capacitors connected in parallel. Since the electrodes are connected directly by conductors, the potential difference between the pairs of plates must be equal. The expression for this potential difference in terms of the capacitance and charge on each capacitor is

$$V_{ab} = \frac{Q_1}{C_1} \qquad V_{ab} = \frac{Q_2}{C_2}$$

The capacitance of the equivalent single capacitor is obtained by comparing the total charge $Q_1 + Q_2$ with the potential difference V_{ab}. Thus

$$C = \frac{Q_1 + Q_2}{V_{ab}}$$

But since $C_1 = Q_1/V_{ab}$ and $C_2 = Q_2/V_{ab}$, $C = C_1 + C_2$. In general, for any number of capacitors in parallel, the resultant capacitance is given by

$$C = \sum_i C_i \qquad\qquad (4.9)$$

Figure 4.8 shows three capacitors in series. We start off with no charge on any of the capacitors and apply a voltage V across the top

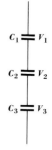

Fig. 4.8   *Three capacitors in series.*

and bottom leads to the three capacitors. It is easy to show that the net charge which appears on each capacitor is the same. Thus suppose a charge $+Q$ moves onto the top plate of C_1. An equal and opposite charge must be induced on the lower plate of C_1, and this leaves an equal positive charge on the top plate of C_2. Similar reasoning shows that each capacitor in the series has the same charge $+Q$ and $-Q$ on its plates.

Since $V_1 = Q/C_1$, $V_2 = Q/C_2$, etc., the total voltage across the set, which is given by $V = V_1 + V_2 + V_3$, is

$$V = Q \left(\frac{1}{C_1} + \frac{1}{C_2} + \frac{1}{C_3} \right) \tag{4.10}$$

and the equivalent capacitance is given by $1/C = 1/C_1 + 1/C_2 + 1/C_3$, or in general for series connections,

$$\frac{1}{C} = \sum_i \frac{1}{C_i} \tag{4.11}$$

That is, in series the reciprocal of the equivalent capacitance is the sum of the reciprocals of the capacitances.

4.8 Electrostatic Stored Energy

We showed in Sec. 4.3 that the work to bring up small increments of charge from a place of zero potential to a place of final potential V is given by the expression

$$W = \tfrac{1}{2}QV \quad \text{joules} \tag{4.4}$$

where Q and V are the final net charge and potential of the body involved. Using the definition of capacitance, $C = Q/V$, this work equation can be expressed in the equivalent forms

$$W = \tfrac{1}{2}CV^2$$

or

$$W = \frac{1}{2} \frac{Q^2}{C} \quad \text{joules} \tag{4.12}$$

Which of these forms is the most convenient depends entirely on the particular situation, as is shown in the problems at the end of the chapter.

We have already argued that the work done in the charging process goes into stored energy U in the system. We can therefore express the potential energy of a charged system in the three alternative forms

$$U = \tfrac{1}{2}CV^2 = \tfrac{1}{2}QV = \frac{1}{2} \frac{Q^2}{C} \quad \text{joules} \tag{4.13}$$

Where is this energy stored? In a very real sense we can say that we have collected some charge together against the forces of mutual repulsion; so the energy is stored by virtue of the potential energy of the collection of charges. There is an equivalent way of looking at the stored energy—one which emphasizes the reality of the electric field by asserting that in the act of creating an electric field, as for instance between the plates of a charged capacitor, energy has been stored. From this point of view the energy is actually stored in space by virtue of the presence of an electric field. For many purposes, it makes no difference which point of view we adopt; the same physical results can be explained either way. Later we find a similar situation with a magnetic field.

In one kind of physical situation, however, the stored energy in the field is the *only* way of understanding the energetics of the situation. This is the case of an electromagnetic wave, say, in a vacuum. This is discussed at some length later, but here we simply point out that an electromagnetic wave is a self-propagating, time-varying electric and magnetic field, which carries no charge but which can transport energy from one place to another, as with light or radio waves, for example. This would seem to argue conclusively that in a very elementary sense, electric and magnetic fields involve stored energy.

It remains only to develop a quantitative statement of the energy per unit volume in a given field. Once we assume that the presence of a field implies stored energy, we could almost guess the functional form of the relation between stored energy and $\mathbf{E}$. It is obvious that energy must involve an even power of $\mathbf{E}$, since otherwise we could change the sign of the energy by reversing the direction of $\mathbf{E}$. We might even guess that U was proportional to E^2, and indeed we can easily show that this is true. Suppose we turn again to an isolated metal sphere of radius R, carrying a net charge Q. We have shown that the total stored energy in this situation is

$$U = \tfrac{1}{2}QV = \frac{1}{2}\frac{Q^2}{4\pi\epsilon_0 R} \tag{4.14}$$

where the final expression is obtained through application of Eq. (4.5). We now compare this expression with the total energy expression obtained if we assume the stored-energy density to be proportional to E^2 per unit volume over all space. Let us see if a constant k times $\int E^2\, dV$ over all space is equal to U in Eq. (4.14). We take a volume element for integration consisting of a thin shell of thickness dr and area $4\pi r^2$. We find

$$k \int_\infty^R E^2 \, dV = k \int_\infty^R \frac{Q^2}{(4\pi\epsilon_0)^2 r^4} \, 4\pi r^2 \, dr$$

$$= k \frac{Q^2}{4\pi\epsilon_0^2 R}$$

Comparison with Eq. (4.14) shows that if $k = \epsilon_0/2$, the two expressions are the same. That is, the field energy can be expressed as

$$U = \tfrac{1}{2}\epsilon_0 \smallint E^2 \, dV \tag{4.15}$$

where the integration is over all space.

We have shown that the detailed expressions for stored energy based on work done and on E^2 are identical, except for a numerical constant. This verifies the assumed E^2 field dependence of the stored energy.

In the static case it is possible to write for the energy density (energy per unit volume)

$$\frac{U}{\text{vol}} = \tfrac{1}{2}\epsilon_0 E^2 \tag{4.16}$$

in any region. We leave as a problem the calculation of the energy density in the uniform-field region between the plates of a parallel-plate capacitor. It can be shown that Eq. (4.15) is also the expression for the electric field energy in an electromagnetic wave. In the case of electromagnetic waves, only Eq. (4.15) for the *total* energy in the field can be rigorously proved, though we tend to assume that the idea of energy density implied by Eq. (4.16) also is tenable in the case of waves.

4.9* Self-energy of Electric Charges

The expression for the energy stored in an electric field derived above allows us to investigate the self-energy of electric charges in more detail. Suppose we have two isolated charges, say, electrons, which are far apart. The self-energy of each electron, which results from the coulomb field of each charge, is given by Eq. (4.15). If the two charges are brought close enough together so that there is an appreciable overlap of the fields, the total stored energy will be given by the same expression, where $\mathbf{E}$ is the vector sum of the fields $\mathbf{E}_1$ and $\mathbf{E}_2$ from the individual charges. We may thus write for the total energy

$$U = \frac{1}{2}\epsilon_0 \int (\mathbf{E}_1 + \mathbf{E}_2)^2 \, dv$$
$$= \frac{1}{2}\epsilon_0 \int E_1^2 \, dv + \frac{1}{2}\epsilon_0 \int E_2^2 \, dv + \frac{1}{2}\epsilon_0 \int 2(\mathbf{E}_1 \cdot \mathbf{E}_2) \, dv$$

The first two terms are simply the self-energies of the two separate electrons, while the third term is the extra energy resulting from the overlapping of the two fields. It is possible to show that this third term is equal to $e^2/4\pi\epsilon_0 r$, where r is the separation of the two charges and e is the charge on each electron. This is just the usual expression for the potential energy of one charge in the field of the other. This result illustrates the fact that, in calculating the work done to assemble a group of charges, we neglect the self-energy terms.

4.10* Force between Capacitor Plates, Virtual Displacement

The calculation of the force between charged capacitor plates can be used conveniently as an illustration of the utility of ideas of energy conservation. Of course, the calculation *can* be done by summing the forces on the charges on one plate caused by the charges on the other plate. But the use of energy considerations is a much simpler way.

The method is called that of *virtual displacement*. We simply equate the external work necessary to make an infinitesimal quasi-static change in the spacing between the plates to the change in stored energy. Thus, if F is the electric force between the plates, the work done is

$$dW = -F \, dx$$

in a displacement which increases the plate separation by an amount dx. The negative sign results from the fact that we apply an external force opposite and equal to the internal electric force F. But this displacement changes the stored energy by an amount dU, which can be calculated. So the electric force F can be found by the equation

$$-F \, dx = dU$$

In order to evaluate dU, we take a parallel-plate capacitor of area A and separation x. It is simpler to consider the plates isolated with a charge Q on each. Then, using for the energy stored

$$U = \frac{Q^2}{2C} = \frac{Q^2 x}{2\epsilon_0 A}$$

the change in energy for a displacement dx, holding Q constant, is

$$dU = \frac{Q^2}{2\epsilon_0 A} \, dx = -F \, dx$$

or

$$F = -\frac{Q^2}{2\epsilon_0 A} \qquad \text{newtons}$$

The negative sign indicates that the electric force between the plates is opposite to the displacement dx, giving attraction between the plates. We use this same point of view for some similar kinds of force problems, later.

4.11* Electrostatic Problems, the Method of Images

Although the general methods of solution of electrostatic potential problems are mostly neglected in our work (two examples are given in Appendixes E and F), a few kinds of problems are particularly interesting and deserving of special mention. One kind of problem can be solved by the method of *images*, and we give an example here.

The problem is to find the force on a charge Q placed a distance r from a large conducting plate, as shown in Fig. 4.9. We are led to ex-

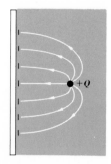

Fig. 4.9   Induced charges on
a conducting plate caused
by point charge $+Q$.

pect this force because of the charges induced at the conducting surface by the charge Q. These charges must be induced to allow the field inside the conductor to remain zero in the presence of the charge Q. The problem could be solved by determining the distribution of induced charge on the plate and then applying Coulomb's law to find the net force on Q. But by taking advantage of the uniqueness principle we can arrive at the solution in a very easy way. Our procedure is to show the similarity between the field of a point-charge conducting-plane configuration and that of a simple dipole.

We show in Fig. 4.10 a dipole having separation $2r$ between charges $+Q$ and $-Q$. The plane which cuts through the center of

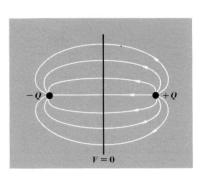

Fig. 4.10   The field of a dipole. The configuration of the field to the right of the zero potential plane is identical with that of the point and conducting plate shown in Fig. 4.9.

the dipole is an equipotential plane. The similarity between the right-hand side of this dipole and the field outside and to the right of the conductor in Fig. 4.9 is obvious. In both cases there is a point charge separated from an equipotential plane by a distance r. We should expect, and in fact the uniqueness theorem guarantees, that the two situations are identical electrically. As a result we know the exact field configuration outside a conducting plane when a point charge is placed nearby.

We now calculate this force between the charge Q a distance r away from a grounded plane. The grounding ensures that the only net charge on the conducting plane is that induced by the charge Q. As seen by the charge Q, the induced charges on the metal plane produce exactly the same field as would a point charge $-Q$ placed a distance $2r$ away (a distance r behind the front of the plane conductor), if the entire plane with its induced charges were removed. We can call the effective charge $-Q$ the *image charge*. This reasoning makes it easy to calculate the force between Q and the induced charges on the plane. The result, obtained by applying Coulomb's law between Q and the image charge, $-Q$, is

$$F = \frac{1}{4\pi\epsilon_0} \frac{Q^2}{(2r)^2} \quad \text{newtons} \tag{4.17}$$

This method of images, or image charges, can be used in a number of similar situations. We have shown only the simplest example of this often very useful technique.

4.12   Use of Capacitors in DC and AC Circuits

Quantitative study of capacitors in circuits is more appropriate after we have discussed circuits in general. Figure 4.11a represents a battery

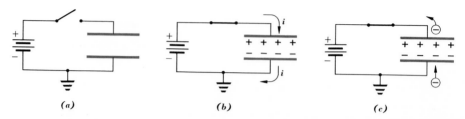

(a)   *(b)*   *(c)*

Fig. 4.11   (a) Uncharged capacitor before closing switch to battery; (b) capacitor while being charged by transient current, showing direction of current, and (c) showing direction of electron flow. Although current is toward and away from capacitor, no actual charge crosses gap between plates of capacitor.

connected by wire through a switch to a capacitor C. Starting with the capacitor uncharged, when the switch is closed (i.e., the two wires are connected), charge moves from the positive terminal of the battery until the upper capacitor plate has a net positive charge such that the plate is at the same potential as the battery terminal. An equal negative charge is induced on the lower plate of the capacitor, represented by the flow of charge away from the lower plate. Figure 4.11b shows the direction of positive charge flow, and Fig. 4.11c describes the same flow in terms of electron motion. When the potential difference across the capacitor reaches that across the battery, the flow ceases. During the transient period, while the charge is flowing, even though no actual charge flows across the space between capacitor plates, it is *as if* charge flowed across the space. Positive charge flows into the top capacitor plate and away from the bottom plate. On the other hand, in a steady-state situation, where there is a fixed source of potential difference in the circuit, no charge flows to or from either plate.

In the case of an ac circuit, as illustrated in Fig. 4.12, where the source of potential difference varies sinusoidally from positive to negative, a charge does flow into and away from the capacitor. This is

Fig. 4.12   An ac source of emf produces an ac current through a capacitor, though no charge crosses the gap between plates.

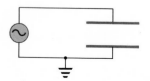

qualitatively like the transient situation described for the dc circuit above. Although a charge flows sinusoidally in one side of the capacitor and out the other, no actual charge crosses the gap between the plates.

We have indicated a connection to ground for both circuits, though this has no effect on the potential differences or charge flow in the circuit. It simply establishes zero potential on the bottom section of the circuit.

The property that capacitors allow ac current but do not allow dc current to flow gives rise to one of their very important uses. In any sort of ac amplifier, in which a time-varying electric signal (potential) is passed from one stage or section to the next, it is usually necessary to allow the ac signal to pass from the output of one stage at an average potential of one value to the input of the next stage which is at a different average potential. Insertion of a capacitance between stages allows the ac signal to be carried, but avoids the need to keep output and input at the same dc potential. Other essential functions of capacitors are discussed later.

4.13   Some Electrostatic Apparatus

The electroscope, potential measurement.   We have already seen in Chap. 1 that the separation of the foils of an electroscope results from the mutual repulsion of like charges placed on the foils. We can now see that the amount of charge depends on the potential placed across the electroscope, since the potential of the foils depends on the amount of charge on them. Thus the electroscope gives a direct measure of potential. The electroscope and similar electrostatic devices are particularly useful for measuring potential in certain applications since no current flow is required.

It is also possible to use the electroscope for determining small currents. Suppose the charge on a capacitor is leaking off very slowly (i.e., a very small current is flowing). An electroscope attached to the capacitor will measure the rate at which the potential decreases. If the total capacitance of the system is C and the original charge is Q, we have from Eq. (4.6) that the potential is given by $V = Q/C$. The rate of change of charge on the system can be related to the rate of change of potential by differentiating this equation, taking C as a constant. Thus we find

$$\frac{dV}{dt} = \frac{1}{C}\frac{dQ}{dt} = \frac{1}{C}i \qquad (4.18)$$

Here we have written i, the *current*, for dQ/dt. (We discuss current in Chap. 7.) Thus, if we know or can measure the capacitance of a system, measurement of dV/dt on an electroscope connected across the system will allow measurement of current.

Kelvin's absolute electrometer. The electrostatic force between charged parallel plates is used in an absolute electrometer as devised by Kelvin for measuring potential difference in absolute units. A pair of plates is connected as shown in Fig. 4.13, with the upper plate connected to a

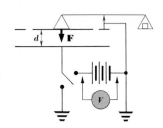

Fig. 4.13 Kelvin's absolute electrometer. Note use of guard ring to eliminate effects of fringing of field at edge of capacitor.

balance. An annular *guard ring* surrounds the circular upper plate. Its function is to keep the field uniform in the central region between the plates to avoid unwanted edge effects. There is fringing, or bulging, of the field lines at the outer radius of the guard ring, but this does not affect the field around the upper plate. After the balance is adjusted until the upper plate is just in the plane of the guard ring with no charge on the system (lower plate grounded), the lower plate is connected to the potential to be measured (shown as batteries in the sketch). Additional weights mg are then added to the balance until the upper plate is returned to its original position. Then, from Sec. 4.7, we have $F = mg = Q^2/2\epsilon_0 A$. Since $Q/A = \sigma$, $E = \sigma/\epsilon_0$, and $V = Ed$, we find

$$mg = \frac{1}{2}\frac{\epsilon_0 A}{d^2} V^2 \qquad \text{or} \qquad V = d\sqrt{\frac{2\,mg}{\epsilon_0 A}} \qquad \text{volts}$$

This device is now mostly of historical interest, but it provides an interesting application of the virtual-displacement method for calculating the force between collections of charge.

4.14 Comments on Chapter 4

This chapter has been concerned mostly with systems consisting of conductors on which charges can be placed. We found the important result that the potential of each conductor is linearly related to the excess charge on itself and on each of the other conductors. The discussion of this property of any system of conductors required the mention, which we gave without proof, of the uniqueness theorem which follows from Laplace's equation and the principle of superposition.

The general linear behavior of any system of conductors leads to the well-known proportionality between the charge on a conductor and its potential. The proportionality constant is known as the capacitance and is defined by the relation

$$C \text{ (farads)} = \frac{Q \text{ (coul)}}{V \text{ (volts)}} \tag{4.6}$$

The capacitance depends only on the geometric arrangement of conductors. It measures how much charge it takes to raise the potential of a given electrode by one volt.

The most important application of the idea of capacitance is to the two-conductor capacitor, a circuit element of great importance, especially in ac and transient circuits.

We also discussed the stored electrostatic energy in a charged capacitor and the association of stored energy in space with the electric field in that space. For an electrostatic field, we showed that the energy storage per unit volume in a vacuum is

$$\frac{U}{\text{vol}} = \tfrac{1}{2}\epsilon_0 E^2 \tag{4.16}$$

In a static situation the idea of energy stored in a field is not forced on us (we can instead ascribe the stored energy to the potential energy of the charge distribution). But because electromagnetic waves can transmit energy in a vacuum without transfer of charge, we must acknowledge the reality of field energy in that case.

We have used the stored energy in a capacitor to illustrate a generally applicable physical principle, that of virtual displacement. In any conservative system, whenever the change in stored energy can be calculated for a geometric displacement, the equation

$$dU = -F \, dx$$

can be used to find the internal force acting on the body displaced. This is often a powerful simplifying principle.

A short explanation is given of the sense in which current can flow through a capacitance even though no charge is transported from one conductor to the other. This idea is essential for our later work with ac circuits.

Space and time limitations have prevented all but the briefest mention of methods of solving any but the simplest electrostatic field problems. A particularly easy and powerful special technique, the method of images, is applied to the (simplest possible) case of a point charge out from a conducting plane. The uniqueness theorem gives the basic justification for this method. Appendixes E and F present slightly more general discussions of boundary-value electrostatic problems.

PROBLEMS

These problems involve the calculation of capacitance of various configurations of equipotential surfaces.

4.1A Find the capacitance of a pair of coaxial metal cylinders of radii a and b and length l, as shown in Fig. P4.1.

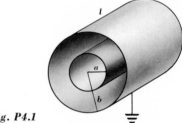

Fig. P4.1

★4.1B Figure P4.2 shows a metal sphere of radius a, surrounded by a spherical thick metal shell of inner and outer radii b and c. This shell is isolated electrically, with no net charge, and is surrounded by a grounded

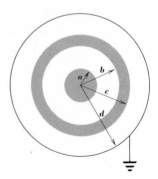

Fig. P4.2

spherical shell of radius d. Find the potential of the inner sphere when a charge Q is placed on it. What is the capacitance of the sphere?

4.1C   Find the capacitance of the earth (radius 4,000 miles).

⋆4.1D   A parallel-plate capacitor with plate separation d has a capacitance C_1. Find its new capacitance when an isolated metal slab of thickness a is placed between the plates.

4.1E   Calculate the capacitance of the multiplate capacitor shown in Fig. P4.3. The area of overlap of the plates is A, and the separation between

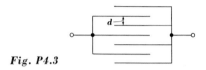

Fig. P4.3

consecutive plates is d. Tuning capacitors for radios, etc., are made in this fashion, by a mechanical arrangement that allows the area of overlap to be varied.

The effective capacitance of various combinations of capacitors is obtained through application of the basic equation for capacitance.

⋆4.2A   Find the capacitance of the combination of capacitors shown in Fig. P4.4.

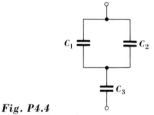

Fig. P4.4

4.2B   Find the capacitance of the combination of capacitors shown in Fig. P4.5.

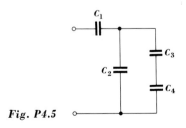

Fig. P4.5

★4.2C In the arrangement shown in Fig. P4.6, find the necessary relationship between the capacitances of the four capacitors in order that when a voltage is applied across terminals a and b, no voltage difference is set

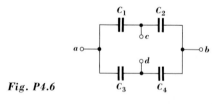

Fig. P4.6

up between terminals c and d. Would this arrangement work for the case of the voltage applied to terminals c and d to give no voltage across a and b?

This problem shows how the potential applied to a combination of capacitors is divided.

4.3A A potential difference of 200 volts is applied across a 2- and a 6-μf capacitor connected in series. What is the potential difference across each capacitor, and the charge on each?

With knowledge of the geometry of a capacitor, the potential applied to a capacitor is easily related to the field within it.

★4.4A What potential would be necessary between the parallel plates of a capacitor separated by a gap of 1 cm in order that the gravitational force on an electron would be balanced by an upward electric field? What potential would be required to balance the gravitational force on a proton?

This problem requires an understanding of the behavior of a field normal to a conducting surface.

4.5A A spherical capacitor has radii of inner and outer spheres a and b, respectively. The inner sphere bears a charge q. What total charge must be placed on the outer ($r = b$) sphere in order to confine the electric field to the space between the spheres $a < r < b$?

The energy stored in a charged capacitor can be accounted for in terms of the electric field produced by the charges.

★4.6A An isolated conducting sphere of radius R has a charge Q. What is the total stored energy? What is the radius r within which half the stored energy is contained?

4.6B A sphere whose radius is 0.2 m is charged to a potential of 30,000 volts.
   a What is its stored energy?

        b If it is connected by a very long wire to an identical uncharged sphere located at a very great distance, what is the final energy of this system?

★4.6C Two capacitors, one charged and the other uncharged, are connected in parallel. Prove that when equilibrium is reached, each capacitor carries a fraction of the initial charge equal to the ratio of its capacitance to the sum of the two capacitances. Show that the final energy is less than the initial energy, and derive a formula for the difference in terms of the initial charge and the capacitances of the two capacitors.

4.6D A parallel-plate capacitor has plates of area 500 cm², separated by a distance of 1.0 cm. A potential difference of 2,000 volts is applied between the plates, after which they are isolated.

    a What is the energy stored in the capacitor?

    b An uncharged sheet of metal 2.0 mm thick is placed between the plates and parallel to them. How much work is done by electric forces during the insertion of the metal sheet?

    c What is the potential difference between the capacitor plates after the sheet has been inserted?

★4.6E A parallel-plate capacitor of plate separation d is charged to a potential difference V_1 and isolated. The plate separation is increased to $2d$. What is the new potential V_2 between the plates? By how much is the energy stored in the capacitor increased? Where did this energy come from?

4.6F A crude idea of the size of an electron can be obtained from the following model. Assume the electron is a sphere of radius a, with its charge distributed uniformly over its surface. Calculate the total electrostatic energy involved in this charge distribution, and equate this to mc^2, where m is the mass of the electron and c is the velocity of light (3.0×10^8 m/sec). Use this to calculate the radius of the electron.

A straightforward integration gives the force of attraction between two charged plane conductors. Another approach is that of virtual displacement, as discussed in Sec. 4.10.

★4.7A Find the force of attraction between two parallel metal plates of area A separated by a distance d and charged to a potential difference V. Do this by calculating the force on a charge dq on one plate due to the field of the charges on the opposite plate. This can then be integrated to give the total force on all charges on the first plate.

5

dielectrics

5.1 Introduction

We have been considering the problems of electrostatics in the virtual absence of matter, except for the use of conductors to establish equipotential surfaces. We now begin our investigation of the effects of the presence of matter. In what would now be classed as an experiment in solid-state physics, Faraday in 1837 repeated independently the earlier experiments of Cavendish (in about 1770) showing that when the space between the plates of a capacitor is completely filled with insulating matter, called dielectrics,[1] such as glass or mica, the capacitance[2] is multiplied by a factor K greater than 1. This factor, which is called

---

[1] The term dielectric comes from the Greek *dia-* + electric, where *dia-* means through. Thus dielectric materials are those in which a steady electric field can be set up without causing an appreciable flow of current.

[2] It will be recalled from Chap. 4 that the capacitance C describes the excess charge required on a conductor to raise its potential by one volt. Thus $C = Q/V$. A farad is the capacitance of a conductor on which one coulomb of charge changes the potential by one volt. A capacitance of one farad is very large, from 1,000 to 10^6 or more times the size of capacitances usually found in the laboratory or in electronic circuits.

the *dielectric constant,* or *specific inductive capacitance,* is independent of the shape and size of the capacitor, but its value varies widely for different materials. Free space has the value 1 (by definition), various kinds of glass have values around 6, water has the value 81, and the value for air is 1.0006, so close to 1 that we ordinarily neglect its effect. The dielectric constant may not be the same if alternating voltages are applied instead of constant voltages. In fact, in general, the dielectric constant is a function of the frequency of the applied voltage. At the very high frequencies of optical electromagnetic waves, the dielectric constant of water is reduced to 1.77. Our purpose in this chapter is to find out the causes of the effect of matter on capacitance and to define the additional parameters that are used to describe it.

5.2 Polarization of Matter

The ultimate basis for understanding dielectric behavior lies in the electrical nature of matter. Although normally electrically neutral as a whole, in detail matter is made up of positive and negative charges in equal quantity. In dielectric materials these charges are not free to move far under the influence of an external electric field, as are the conduction electrons in a conductor. However, the forces of an external field do cause small relative displacements (on an atomic scale) of charges of each sign. The extent of such motion depends on the tightness with which the charges are held fixed. The displacement of charge resulting from an applied external field is called *polarization* of the material. The dielectric constant is a measure of the extent to which a given material is polarized by an external field. The parameter which directly relates the polarization of a material to the applied electric field is called the *electric susceptibility* of the material.

We may take as a crude model of a dielectric two interpenetrating arrays of charge, as shown in Fig. 5.1, where the representation is in two dimensions for simplicity. We can think of the positive array as being due to the nuclei of the atoms making up the solid, and the negative array as due to the average positions of the electrons associated with the atoms. In the absence of an external field we should expect the two arrays to be superposed, but the relative displacement of the charges under an applied field produces a separation of charge, as shown in the lower drawing. This model gives a crude idea of the situation within the polarized solid, though it cannot give exact information on an atomic scale. It is in fact useful to make an even rougher

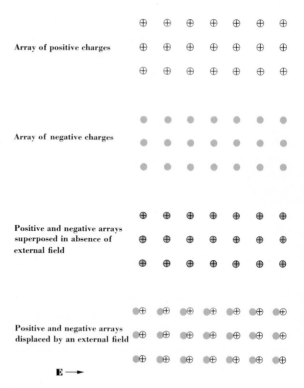

Array of positive charges

Array of negative charges

Positive and negative arrays
superposed in absence of
external field

Positive and negative arrays
displaced by an external field

E ⟶

Fig. 5.1   Simple model of polarization.

approximation of real matter by thinking of it as made up of two inter-penetrating *uniform* distributions of charge, forgetting all about the atomic nature of matter. This model has the great advantage of simplicity, and tells accurately the electrical effects of polarization external to the matter (since the atomic nature of matter is on such a fine scale that it is indistinguishable from a uniform "jelly" when viewed from outside). This model is also useful in its ability to tell us about *average* electric fields which are produced internally by the polarization of the charges by an external field.

This very crude continuum model is shown in Fig. 5.2. Here we have replaced the atomic arrays of positive and negative charges of Fig. 5.1 by smoothed out charge distributions showing their relative displacement (not to scale).

What can this model tell us about the effect of polarization of matter, both inside and outside the matter? Since in the absence of an applied field, the positive and negative charges are exactly superposed, there are no external effects of the charges in zero applied field. This follows from the exact cancellation of the superposed positive and negative charge distributions. But the relative displacements of the two charge distributions in an external field result in net charges at the two ends of the specimen, as shown in Fig. 5.2. The entire effect

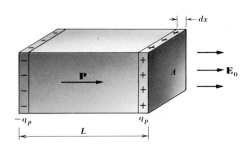

Fig. 5.2   Continuum model of polarization. Relative displacement dx of uniform positive and negative charges results in induced polarization charges $+q_p$ and $-q_p$ at surfaces. The polarization vector P is in the direction of relative displacement of positive charge.

of the polarization can be accounted for by the charges which appear on the ends of the polarized specimen. We call this charge the *polarization surface charge*. It is a net charge at the surface of a specimen, which, however, is bound and depends on the relative displacement of the charges making up the matter. The polarization charge is usually labeled q_p, and the resulting surface density of charge is called σ_p. Thus

$$\sigma_p = \frac{dq_p}{dS} \qquad \text{coul/m}^2 \tag{5.1}$$

where dS is an element of surface area.

Even if we go back to the atomic model of matter, as suggested in Fig. 5.1, the net effect of polarization is completely accounted for by the appearance of the polarization charge. In Fig. 5.3 we have emphasized this point by replacing the polarized specimen by its polarization charges. The net field is the (vector) sum of the externally applied

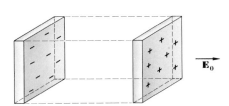

Fig. 5.3   A polarized dielectric block may be replaced by its induced surface charges for purposes of calculating the effect of the polarization on the field outside the block and on the average field within the block.

field E_0 and the field of the polarization charges. Inside the matter it is the average field which is given. The average field inside the matter is less than if no matter were present. The effect of polarization is always to reduce the average field inside matter.

On the atomic model, however, there is an alternative possible point of view. This is that, throughout the matter, each atom or molecule has been distorted to produce dipole moments where none existed before polarization. We can attribute the effect of polarized matter to the sum of the fields of all the dipoles. In many cases a calculation based on summing the effects of all dipoles might be quite difficult, but it is in principle entirely equivalent to working with the polarization charges which develop at surfaces.[1]

In making a calculation based on the dipoles we should take advantage of the vector nature of the electric dipole, as discussed in Chap. 3. Far from a region containing dipoles (say, outside a polarized specimen), two equal dipoles pointing in the same direction, either side by side, $\rightrightarrows$, or one in front of the other, $\rightarrow\rightarrow$, would give a field the same as from a single dipole of twice the magnitude. On this basis, a quantity of interest is the *dipole moment per unit volume* in matter. This quantity indeed is the standard one used to describe the state of polarization of matter. This dipole moment per unit volume, or *polarization* of matter, is a vector quantity $\mathbf{P}$ (since it is the vector sum of dipole vectors). In a region of uniform polarization, where all dipoles are pointed in the same direction,

$$\mathbf{P} = n\mathbf{p} \tag{5.2}$$

where $\mathbf{p}$ is the induced atomic dipole moment, and n is the number of dipoles per unit volume. The vectors $\mathbf{P}$ and $\mathbf{p}$ are in the direction of relative displacement of positive charge, that is, from negative to positive charge, as was defined for permanent dipoles.

Notice that the word polarization has two meanings: a qualitative one referring to any relative displacement of positive and negative charge, and this quantitative one, giving the resulting vector dipole moment per unit volume, $\mathbf{P}$.

---

[1] When the dielectric material is not homogeneous, so that the dipoles induced are not uniform, there is an additional effect from a volume distribution of polarization charges, ρ_p. This charge density represents incomplete cancellation of the ends of the individual dipoles. This complication does not occur when homogeneous matter is placed in a uniform or nonuniform applied field. We shall not discuss this effect further.

The polarization is closely tied to the atomic nature of matter, but as seen externally, its effects show up only in the polarization surface charges. In the next section we develop the connection between **P** and the polarization charge density σ_p.

5.3   Polarization Charge versus Dipole Moment per Unit Volume

There is a simple relationship between the induced dipole moment per unit volume in a dielectric specimen and the induced surface charge density. We can find this relationship, first in its simplest form, by referring to Fig. 5.2. Suppose the positive and negative charges making up the dielectric specimen consist of n charged particles of each sign per unit volume, each having a charge e. A relative displacement dx will then result in the appearance of dipoles, $p = e\,dx$. There will be n of these dipoles per unit volume. The vector sum of all the induced dipoles in a unit volume will be

$$P = np = ne\,dx \tag{5.3}$$

Alternatively, we can calculate the charge density σ_p induced at the ends of the specimen by the displacement dx. This is simply the amount of charge per unit area which is separated by the displacement from charge of the opposite sign, or

$$\sigma_p = ne\,dx \tag{5.4}$$

Comparison of these two equations gives

$$P = |\sigma_p| \tag{5.5}$$

The sign of the polarization surface charge is positive where P is directed out of the body and negative where it is directed inward.

The total dipole moment of the polarized specimen can now be calculated in two alternative ways. The first is by writing

$$p_{\text{total}} = \Sigma p = P \times \text{vol} = PAL \tag{5.6a}$$

The second method is to multiply the net charge at either end, $Q = \sigma_p A$, by the separation L between the ends.

$$p_{\text{total}} = QL = \sigma_p AL = PAL \tag{5.6b}$$

Actually, the example of Fig. 5.2 is somewhat special. More generally, we may use Fig. 5.4 to demonstrate the situation. Here the right-hand surface is not normal to the direction of polarization. If the charge displacement is dx, the thickness of separated surface charge, or effective displacement, is $dx \cos \theta$, where θ is the angle between the displacement direction (or **P**) and $\hat{\mathbf{S}}$, the unit vector drawn normal to the surface, outward from the dielectric into the vacuum. As a result, the surface charge density is

$$\sigma_p = ne \, dx \cos \theta = \mathbf{P} \cdot \hat{\mathbf{S}} = P_n \tag{5.7}$$

The sign of the induced surface charge is positive when $\mathbf{P} \cdot \hat{\mathbf{S}}$ is positive, as at the right-hand surface of Fig. 5.4, and negative when $\mathbf{P} \cdot \hat{\mathbf{S}}$ is negative, as at the left-hand surface.

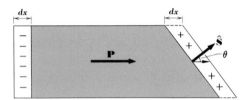

Fig. 5.4 Surface polarization charge related to polarization P. Actual relative displacement of charge on right is dx. Effective displacement is $dx \cos \theta$.

5.4 Electric Susceptibility and the Nature of the Polarization Vector

The simplest assumption we could make regarding the amount of polarization which will occur in a specimen in a given electric field **E** is that the relative displacement of opposite signs of charge is proportional to the *macroscopic* (or average) field. This would be the external applied field *as modified by* polarization surface charges. This is equivalent to saying that the induced dipole moments are proportional to the macroscopic field causing them. The induced dipole moment per unit volume, then, is

$$\mathbf{P} = \epsilon_0 \chi \mathbf{E} \tag{5.8}$$

where **E** is the average (macroscopic) field, and the constant χ (the Greek letter *chi*) is called the electric susceptibility of the material. The constant ϵ_0 is included only for the purpose of simplifying later relationships. The susceptibility is thus a property characteristic of each kind of matter and proportional to the ease of polarizing it. We might expect the value of χ to depend on the temperature, and it does in some situations.

This simple linear relationship turns out to be realistic for most materials, up to as large electric fields as usually can be applied to dielectric materials.

We can now investigate the properties of the polarization vector **P**. The linear **P** versus **E** relationship shows that **P** acts very much like **E**. Thus, using Fig. 5.5, we apply Gauss' flux theorem to a region

Fig. 5.5 Gaussian volumes inside and at surface of a polarized dielectric body. The gaussian volume at A is completely within the material; so the net charge is zero. Thus there is no net flux of E out of the volume chosen. But since the polarization vector P is proportional to E, it follows that there is no net flux of P from the volume. In the case of B, at an end of the body, there is a net polarization surface charge within the gaussian volume; so there is a net flux of E or P out of the volume. It is shown that the net flux of P is $-q_p$, the polarization charge within the volume chosen.

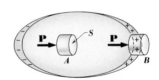

A, wholly inside a polarized dielectric specimen. Even though the material is polarized, there is no net charge inside the gaussian volume; so we may write for the net flux of **E** out of the volume

$$\int_{cs} \mathbf{E} \cdot d\mathbf{S} = 0 \qquad (2.9a)$$

But since $\mathbf{P} = \epsilon_0 \chi \mathbf{E}$, where ϵ_0 and χ are constants, we have

$$\int_{cs} \mathbf{P} \cdot d\mathbf{S} = 0 \qquad (5.9)$$

Thus we may think of the flux of **P** and see that, everywhere within the matter, "lines of **P**" are just like lines of **E** except for a constant factor.

If we now choose the gaussian volume B at the surface of the polarized specimen, we find a different situation. Since the gaussian volume has one surface which is inside the specimen where there are lines of **P**, and one surface outside the specimen where **P** is nonexistent, lines of **P** must terminate inside the volume; so the net flux of **P** is finite (and in this case negative). But since P_n and σ_P are equal to each other in magnitude, the surface integral is

$$\int_{CS} \mathbf{P} \cdot d\mathbf{S} = \int_{CS} P_n \, dS = - \int_{CS} \sigma_P \, dS = -q_P \tag{5.10}$$

This tells us that the flux of **P** is the negative of the charge q_P included in the gaussian volume. This is opposite to the case of the flux of **E**.

We may now make a general statement of Gauss' flux theorem applicable in a region with or without matter present, and including the possible presence of a dielectric surface. Since the effects of polarized matter can be ascribed to polarization surface charges, the electric field in any region can be related to the sum of both free and polarization charges. Thus Eq. (2.8) for a vacuum becomes more generally

$$\int_{CS} \mathbf{E} \cdot d\mathbf{S} = \frac{1}{\epsilon_0} (q_f + q_p) = \frac{1}{\epsilon_0} q_t \tag{5.11}$$

which states that the flux of electric field lines out of a given volume depends only on the total charge q_t, both free and polarization, inside that volume. Here the sign of the polarization charge is part of the symbol q_p. The polarization surface charge q_p always acts to reduce the field produced by the free charge. Equation (5.11) is a very important general relationship, but we must realize that it is not necessarily easy to go from this equation to a solution for the electric field configuration. However, there are cases where the problem is relatively easy to solve. The next section shows how in a simple case this generalized statement of Gauss' flux theorem can be used to find the field configuration and intensity in the presence of matter.

5.5   *Dielectric Theory Applied to Capacitors*

We now apply the ideas we have developed regarding dielectrics to the problem of a simple parallel-plate capacitor, filled between plates with a dielectric material. This will allow us to relate the susceptibility χ to the dielectric constant K, with which we introduced the subject of dielectrics (and the parameter which is most directly related to experiment). Figure 5.6a shows the capacitor in a vacuum, without a dielectric medium. We have called the mobile, or free-charge, density σ_f. The uniform field between the plates, as we have seen, has a value $E = \sigma_f/\epsilon_0$.

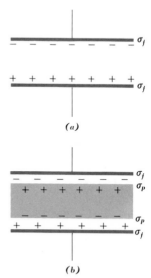

Fig. 5.6 *Effect of dielectric in capacitor. (a) Free charge density σ_f; (b) polarization charge density σ_p adds algebraically to effect of σ_f.*

In Fig. 5.6b the dielectric has been inserted so as to fill the entire space between the plates. As a result of the field originating from the free charges, the dielectric is polarized, and there appears a polarization charge of density σ_p on the two surfaces. To calculate the average field within the dielectric, we must take account of both σ_f and σ_p. We apply Eq. (5.11) to the plane distribution of charge on the plates of the capacitor and on the surfaces of the dielectric sample. Since the electric field is uniform out from a plane charge distribution, we can take **E** out of the integral and solve for it. This gives

$$E = \frac{1}{\epsilon_0}(\sigma_f + \sigma_p) \tag{5.12a}$$

where σ_f and σ_p are charge densities, obtained by dividing the total surface charge by the area of the gaussian surface, which we here take to be the area of the plates. This is just like the procedure for the vacuum capacitor, except for the inclusion of the polarization surface charge. Since σ_p is always of opposite sign to σ_f, the effect of the polarization surface charge is always to weaken the field as compared with the field in a vacuum. We discuss this in detail in Sec. 5.14, where we study the depolarization field.

The field E, as used in Eq. (5.12a) to describe the situation within a dielectric, is an *average* field. As we move from point to point on an atomic scale, the field varies widely in a periodic fashion. E here is simply the average value, which, when integrated, gives the true potential difference between the two plates of the capacitor.

We now calculate the capacitance of this capacitor filled with dielectric material, using, as in the vacuum case, $C = Q/V$. In this calculation we use for Q only the free charge, since we are concerned only with that charge which we can put on the plates. The polarization charge is, in effect, built into the dielectric material, and so is not under our direct control. The capacitance equation can then be written as

$$C = \frac{\sigma_f A}{Ed} \qquad (5.12b)$$

where $\sigma_f A$ is the free charge on each plate. Since E is on longer related to σ_f by the vacuum equation $\sigma_f = \epsilon_0 E$ because of the perturbing effects of σ_p, we find σ_f using Eq. (5.12), which takes account of the polarization charge. This gives $\sigma_f = \epsilon_0 E - \sigma_p$. If the macroscopic properties of the dielectric are characterized by its susceptibility [Eq. (5.8)], $-\sigma_p$ can be replaced by $\mathbf{P} = \epsilon_0 \chi \mathbf{E}$. This gives

$$\sigma_f = \epsilon_0(1 + \chi)E \qquad (5.13a)$$

Substituted into the capacitance equation, this gives

$$C = \frac{\epsilon_0(1 + \chi)A}{d} \qquad (5.13b)$$

Comparing this with the earlier result for the capacitance of a parallel-plate capacitor in vacuum, $C = \epsilon_0 A/d$, we see that $(1 + \chi)$ is the multiplicative constant K found by Faraday. Thus the dielectric constant is related to the susceptibility by

$$K = 1 + \chi \qquad (5.14)$$

The dielectric constant K is the obvious parameter to list for experimental purposes, since it represents the simple multiplying factor by which the capacitance is changed when dielectric materials are used between capacitor plates. Values of K vary widely, depending on the material used. Nominal values for a few materials are given in Table 5.1 (page 157).

Since the dielectric constant K measures the *ratio* of capacitances with and without dielectric material, it has the same value in all systems of units, and is dimensionless.

5.6 Permittivity and the Dielectric Constant

Another quantity which is sometimes used to characterize the dielectric behavior of matter is the *permittivity* ϵ. This is contrasted with the permittivity of free space ϵ_0. The relationship is defined by

$$\epsilon = \epsilon_0 K \tag{5.15}$$

The quantities P, K, χ, and ϵ are all measures of the extent of the polarization produced within a material by a given applied field. These quantities, however, are not simply related to the polarizability of the individual atoms or molecules of which the material is made. In order to relate dielectric properties to atomic polarizabilities, it is necessary to consider the *local* electric field at atomic sites, rather than the average or macroscopic field in the material. This problem is discussed in Sec. 5.15.

5.7 Practical Capacitors

The capacitor is of tremendous importance in the practical world and in electronics applications. The two most important specifications of capacitors are the capacitance C and the breakdown voltage, that is, the maximum voltage which can be applied across the terminals without causing an electric spark which will destroy the capacitor by allowing current to flow between the electrodes.

Since the capacitance increases as the spacing between plates is decreased, high capacitance and high breakdown voltage tend to have contradictory requirements. Thus capacitors for use in applications where, say, 5,000 volts will be placed across them are large for a given capacitance. A 0.1-microfarad capacitor (μfd $= 10^{-6}$ farad), which must not break down with 5,000 volts across it, is some $2\frac{1}{4} \times 3\frac{3}{4} \times 2\frac{3}{4}$ in. in size. But the same capacitance, rated for less than 400 volts, is contained in a cylinder 1 in. long and less than $\frac{1}{2}$ in. in diameter. Capacitors in this range are made of two long sheets of metal foil, separated by some dielectric material and rolled into a small cylinder. The *electrolytic* capacitor achieves effectively very close spacing between metal foils (at the expense of some leakage current, which in many applications is no disadvantage), and as a consequence very large capacitance can be packaged in a modest-sized package. A 500-μfd 12-volt electrolytic capacitor can be obtained in a cylinder $2\frac{3}{4}$ in. long of $1\frac{7}{8}$-in. diameter. For smaller values of capacitance, many capacitors, using high-dielectric-constant ceramic materials, are no larger than an aspirin tablet.

5.8   Electric Displacement D

It has been usual historically, and of some advantage practically, to introduce a new vector quantity, the *electric displacement* **D**, in problems involving dielectrics. The displacement is defined by the vector relation

$$\mathbf{D} = \epsilon_0 \mathbf{E} + \mathbf{P} \tag{5.16}$$

We treat only the case of isotropic dielectrics, in which the polarization **P** is always parallel to the field **E**. We also assume that **P** is proportional to **E**, that is, χ is a constant, independent of the magnitude of **E**. The use of **D** is a convenience, not a necessity. All the physics of dielectrics could be discussed without ever bringing in the displacement vector.

We may demonstrate the consequence of this definition of **D** by investigating Gauss' flux theorem using Eq. (5.16) and substituting earlier results for the flux of **E** and **P**. Thus, using results given in Eqs. (5.10) and (2.8),

$$\int_{CS} \mathbf{D} \cdot d\mathbf{S} = \epsilon_0 \int_{CS} \mathbf{E} \cdot d\mathbf{S} + \int_{CS} \mathbf{P} \cdot d\mathbf{S} = q_{\text{total}} - q_p = q_{\text{free}} \tag{5.17}$$

We find indeed that the displacement vector **D** is a quantity having sources only in free charges, even when dielectric material is present.

The vector **D** has certain obvious similarities to **E**. The two source equations

$$\int_{CS} \mathbf{E} \cdot d\mathbf{S} = q_t / \epsilon_0 \quad \text{and} \quad \int_{CS} \mathbf{D} \cdot d\mathbf{S} = q_f$$

are closely related. Also, just as we found that Gauss' flux law leads to div $\mathbf{E} = \rho_t / \epsilon_0$, Eq. (5.17) leads by the same reasoning to

$$\text{div } \mathbf{D} = \rho_f \tag{5.18}$$

But the field **E** obeys the circulation equation $\oint \mathbf{E} \cdot d\mathbf{l} = 0$ while the similar equation for the circulation of **D** is not generally true. Thus a knowledge of all sources q_f of **D** will not alone determine **D**, whereas **E** is completely determined if all sources q_t are known.

That is, in solving field problems we do not avoid the need for accounting for the behavior of the polarization vector **P** when we invoke the use of **D**. We now discuss the properties of **D** and its application to certain kinds of dielectric problems.

In regions *outside* dielectric materials, where only free charges are present, **P** $= 0$; so

$$\mathbf{D} = \epsilon_0 \mathbf{E} \tag{5.19}$$

Thus, outside of matter, **D** and **E** are identical, except for a constant factor ϵ_0.

In regions *inside* dielectric materials we can relate D and E by combining the definitions of D and χ. Thus we find

$$D = \epsilon_0 E + P = \epsilon_0 E + \epsilon_0 \chi E$$

or

$$\mathbf{D} = \epsilon_0 K \mathbf{E} \tag{5.20}$$

This assumes that the material is isotropic, so that **P** is parallel to **E**.

This new concept of displacement is now applied to the simple problem of a dielectric slab between the plates of a parallel-plate capacitor (Fig. 5.7). We have already seen, without using **D**, that the

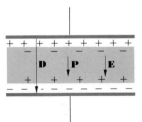

Fig. 5.7   Dielectric slab between capacitor plates.

field between the plates is diminished by a factor $1/K$. We now show it again by applying Gauss' flux theorem to **D**. Thus we use a gaussian surface at, say, the top electrode, and find **D** between the plates, using

$$\int_{cs} \mathbf{D} \cdot d\mathbf{S} = q_f$$

or since **D** is uniform,

$$D = \sigma_f$$

Inside the material we have $\mathbf{D} = \epsilon_0 K \mathbf{E}$ as shown on page 137; so we may solve for the average field.

$$E = \frac{D}{\epsilon_0 K} = \frac{\sigma_f}{\epsilon_0 K} \tag{5.21}$$

With no dielectric, the field between the plates would have been $E_0 = \sigma_f/\epsilon_0$. We have shown that the dielectric reduces the field by the factor $1/K$, or

$$E = \frac{1}{K} E_0 \tag{5.22}$$

In this simple special case the direction of $\mathbf{D}$ and $\mathbf{E}$ is unaffected by the presence of the dielectric, but this is not true in general.

Before going to some other illustrative examples to help fix these new ideas, we present an additional discussion of $\mathbf{E}$ and $\mathbf{D}$ that is sometimes helpful. Imagine again a parallel-plate capacitor filled with a dielectric. Let there be two cavities cut inside the material, as shown in Fig. 5.8. The left-hand cavity is coin-shaped, oriented with its faces

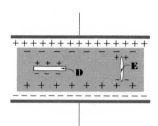

Fig. 5.8 Cavities in a dielectric slab between capacitor plates. The value of $\mathbf{D}$ in the left-hand coin-shaped cavity is the same as though no cavity were cut. Similarly, the value of $\mathbf{E}$ in the right-hand needle-shaped cavity is the average $\mathbf{E}$ in the dielectric material.

perpendicular to the field, and the right-hand cavity is a long needle-shaped cylinder, with its axis oriented along the field direction. We shall determine the field in the middle of these two contrasting cavities.

In the coin cavity the polarization surface charges which appear at the cavity surface produce a uniform field which exactly cancels the field of the polarization surface charges (of opposite sign) at the surfaces of the slab. Thus the field in the cavity is $E_c = \sigma_f/\epsilon_0$, just as it would be if there were no dielectric present, since in the empty space of the coin cavity $\mathbf{D}_c = \epsilon_0 \mathbf{E}_c$,

$$D_c = \sigma_f$$

This is the same value D has in the body of the dielectric.

In the needle cavity, the total induced surface change at the ends of the cavity is small, since the area of the cavity ends is small, so the induced surface charge on the cavity can be neglected. As a result, the the value of **E** in the needle cavity,

$$E_n = \frac{\sigma_f + \sigma_p}{\epsilon_0}$$

is the same as in the body of the dielectric.

We have arrived here, through a particular example, at an easily remembered and useful pair of boundary conditions for **E** and for **D** which we discuss later in more detail. If we generalize the results above, we have: (1) At the boundary of a dielectric, the component of **D** normal to the surface does not change as the boundary is crossed. (Thus **D** in the coin-shaped cavity is normal to the surface and has the same value inside and outside the cavity.) (2) At the boundary of a dielectric, the component of **E** parallel to the surface does not change as the boundary is crossed. (In the needle-shaped cavity **E** is parallel to the surface and is equal to its value in the body of the dielectric.)

5.9 Examples

a *Electric field in a parallel-plate capacitor filled with dielectric.* We discuss this simple case to show again the contrast between the use of **D** and **E**. It was shown in Sec. 5.5 that when Gauss' law is applied to the parallel-plate capacitor, the electric field is given by $E = (\sigma_f + \sigma_p)/\epsilon_0$. Substitution for σ_p in terms of K gave

$$E = \frac{1}{K\epsilon_0}\sigma_f \tag{5.21}$$

The alternative approach is to apply Gauss' flux theorem to the displacement vector **D** [Eq. (5.17)]. This gives

$$DA = q_f \quad \text{or} \quad D = \frac{q_f}{A} = \sigma_f$$

where $A = \int d\mathbf{S}$, the flat surface of the gaussian pillbox through which the lines of D emerge. Thus **E** may be obtained by expressing **E** in terms of both σ_f and σ_p; or, by dealing with **D**, the same result may be obtained without explicit use of σ_p. The capacitance can be obtained as before, by substitution of the value of **E** in Eq. (5.12).

b *Capacitance of a capacitor filled with two different dielectric slabs.*
Let the dielectric constants and thicknesses of the two slabs be K_1
and K_2 and a and b (Fig. 5.9). The lines of **D** are continuous from

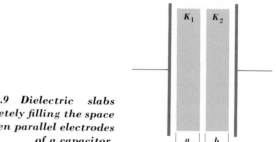

*Fig.   5.9   Dielectric   slabs
completely filling the space
between parallel electrodes
of a capacitor.*

one plate to the other, since lines of **D** originate only on *free* charges.
Application of Gauss' flux theorem to the interface between the two
dielectric slabs gives the same result. Then $D_1 = D_2$, or $K_1E_1 = K_2E_2$.

   We now find the capacitance from $C = Q_f/V$, where $V = E_1a +
E_2b$ (obtained from $dV/dx = -E$). Then $C = \sigma_f A/(E_1a + E_2b)$. For
parallel-plate geometry we have already seen that $D = \sigma_f$ from Gauss'
law; so we can write

$$C = \frac{A\epsilon_0}{a/K_1 + b/K_2}   \text{farads}$$

5.10   Boundary Conditions at a Dielectric Surface

We now show more rigorously the correctness of the boundary conditions discussed in Sec. 5.5. A plane boundary between regions of
different dielectric constant, K_1 and K_2, is shown in Fig. 5.10. We

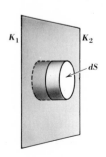

*Fig. 5.10   Gaussian surface
for calculation of boundary
condition for D across a
dielectric boundary. This
gives $D_{n1} = D_{n2}$. (The normal component of D is the
same on both sides of a dielectric boundary.)*

assume no collection of free charge at the surface. Gauss' flux theorem for **D** is now applied to a suitable gaussian surface. The net flux through the volume must be zero since there is no free charge inside the gaussian surface we have drawn. We can neglect the flux through the curved part of this surface, since this area can be made vanishingly small by reducing the distance between the flat surfaces. If we call the flat surface on the left-hand side S_1 and the flat surface on the right S_2, we may write

$$\int_{CS} \mathbf{D} \cdot d\mathbf{S} = \int_{S_1} \mathbf{D}_1 \cdot d\mathbf{S} + \int_{S_2} \mathbf{D}_2 \cdot d\mathbf{S}$$

$$= - \int_{S_1} D_{n1}\, dS + \int_{S_2} D_{n2}\, dS = 0$$

The sign for the integral on the left-hand side of the boundary is negative because the lines of **D** point *into* the gaussian volume. It follows directly from the equation above that

$$D_{n1} = D_{n2} \tag{5.23}$$

Thus *the normal component of* **D** *is the same on each side of the boundary.*

Figure 5.11 shows the argument needed regarding **E**. Here we in-

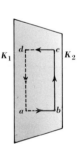

**Fig. 5.11   Line-integral cal-
culation of boundary con-
dition for E across a dielectric boundary. This gives
$E_{t1} = E_{t2}$. (The tangential
component of E is the
same on both sides of a dielectric boundary.)**

voke the conservation of energy in a static field. We apply the line integral $\oint \mathbf{E} \cdot d\mathbf{l} = 0$ to the path shown. The parts of the path perpendicular to the plane, ab and cd, can be made vanishingly small, so that the integral can be expressed as

$$\int_b^c \mathbf{E}_2 \cdot d\mathbf{l} + \int_d^a \mathbf{E}_1 \cdot d\mathbf{l} = \int_b^c E_{t2}\, dl - \int_d^a E_{t1}\, dl = 0$$

Since $bc = da$,

$$E_{t1} = E_{t2} \tag{5.24}$$

or *the component of* **E** *tangent to the boundary is the same on each side of the boundary.*

These two rules for the behavior of **D** and **E** at boundaries have now been derived generally. They are identical with those found from the special cases of coin and needle cavities in a continuous dielectric medium.

We may use these boundary conditions to show the effect of a dielectric boundary on the direction of an electric field that crosses the boundary. The dielectric materials are assumed isotropic. In such materials **P** is always parallel to **E**; so from Eq. (5.16), **D** is always parallel to **E**. Figure 5.12 shows two vectors corresponding to the

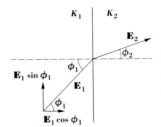

Fig. 5.12 Change of direction and magnitude of E at a dielectric surface.

directions of the electric field on the two sides of the boundary. We determine the necessary relationship between the angles ϕ_1 and ϕ_2. From the condition $E_{t1} = E_{t2}$ we find $E_1 \sin \phi_1 = E_2 \sin \phi_2$. From the condition $D_{n1} = D_{n2}$ we have $D_1 \cos \phi_1 = D_2 \cos \phi_2$. Combining results for D and E, we get

$$\frac{E_1 \sin \phi_1}{D_1 \cos \phi_1} = \frac{E_2 \sin \phi_2}{D_2 \cos \phi_2}$$

But since $D_1 = K_1 \epsilon_0 E_1$ and $D_2 = K_2 \epsilon_0 E_2$, our equation becomes

$$\frac{1}{K_1} \tan \phi_1 = \frac{1}{K_2} \tan \phi_2$$

or

$$\frac{\tan \phi_1}{\tan \phi_2} = \frac{K_1}{K_2} \tag{5.25}$$

This result did not really require the use of **D**. We have applied two simple conditions to the field. One is that since the field is conservative, the tangential components of **E** must be the same on both sides of the boundary, or $\oint \mathbf{E} \cdot d\mathbf{l}$ would not be zero. The other is that the normal component of **E** induces polarization surface charges which

modify perpendicular field components differently on the two sides of
the boundary.

5.11* Force between Charges in a Dielectric Medium

One of the important effects of a dielectric is the modification it produces in the force between charges. Let us consider the simple case of
two small spherical charged conductors (charges Q_1 and Q_2) placed in
an isotropic dielectric fluid, a distance r apart (Fig. 5.13). We calculate

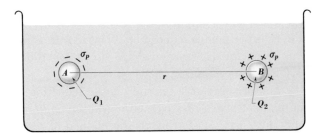

**Fig. 5.13   Two small spherical charged conductors
placed in a dielectric fluid, a distance r apart. The
field at B caused by Q_1 at A is decreased by the
polarization surface charge at A, but the polarization surface charge at B, being symmetrical about
B, exerts no force on it. The role of the two spheres
can be interchanged.**

the field at a distance r from Q_1, taking into account the polarization
charge at the dielectric surface surrounding Q_1, and from this find the
force on Q_2.

The simplest calculation involves finding D at a distance r from
Q_1 through Gauss' principle, $\int_{cs} \mathbf{D} \cdot d\mathbf{S} = Q_1$. We choose a spherical
gaussian surface of radius r around Q_1 and solve for D in the usual way:
We can take D outside the integral, since over the spherical boundary
of the dielectric, D has the same magnitude and is everywhere normal
to the surface. We thus obtain

$$D = \frac{Q_1}{4\pi r^2} = \epsilon_0 K E$$

Thus E (in the absence of the second charge Q_2) at a distance r is

$$E = \frac{1}{4\pi\epsilon_0} \frac{Q_1}{K r^2}$$

The second charge Q_2, when placed in the dielectric medium, will polarize the fluid in its vicinity, as did the first charge. But this polarizing effect produces a spherically symmetric polarization charge around Q_2 which does not affect the net force on Q_2. Therefore the total force on Q_2 is

$$F = Q_2 E = \frac{1}{4\pi\epsilon_0} \frac{Q_1 Q_2}{K r^2} \tag{5.26}$$

We have here assumed that both charges are contained in small volumes of radius much less than the separation distance r. Otherwise we should not expect the inverse-square law to hold, even in a vacuum. Our result for this limiting case is that the force between point charges in a dielectric fluid is reduced by a factor $1/K$, compared with vacuum. This is true for any size and shape of charges, though Eq. (5.26) is true only for point charges.

Another easy case to study is the reduction in the force between the parallel plates of a capacitor when it is immersed in a dielectric fluid (Fig. 5.14). Referring to the method of virtual displacement by

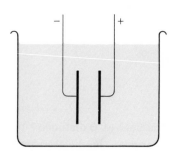

Fig. 5.14 A parallel-plate capacitor placed in a dielectric fluid. The force between the plates is reduced by the presence of the fluid, by a factor $1/K$.

which we calculated the force between charged isolated plates in a vacuum, we note from Sec. 4.8 that the vacuum equation for the energy stored in the field, Eq. (4.12), must be multiplied by $1/K$ to give

$$U = \frac{Q^2}{2C} = \frac{Q^2 x}{2\epsilon_0 A K}$$

so as to take into account the increased capacitance due to the dielectric fluid. Upon calculating the effect of the displacement dx, we find for the electric force

$$F = -\frac{Q^2}{2\epsilon_0 A K} \qquad \text{newtons}$$

which is again the vacuum result reduced by the factor $1/K$.

5.12* Forces in a Dielectric Fluid, a General Solution

In this section we illustrate the great power of the differential forms of the laws of electrostatics, as developed in Appendix D. Even without a study of the material leading up to and including Appendix D, the simplicity of the description made possible by the differential forms will emerge.

We found in the last section that a satisfactory solution could be found for two simple cases of charged bodies immersed in a dielectric body. For two point charges and for two parallel charged plates, we showed that the presence of the dielectric fluid reduces the electric forces by the same factor $1/K$, where K is the dielectric constant of the fluid. But what about some more complicated arrangement of electrodes? The approach used so far is applicable only for particular cases; so a general statement can be found only by induction, after trying many cases.

However, a general solution for the effect of immersion of charged bodies in a dielectric fluid can be found, using the results of Appendix D, which we quote as follows:

In a vacuum, the two laws of electrostatics in differential form are

$$\left.\begin{array}{c} \mathbf{\nabla} \cdot \mathbf{E} \\ \mathrm{div}\ \mathbf{E} \end{array}\right\} = \frac{\rho_f}{\epsilon_0} \quad \text{and} \quad \left.\begin{array}{c} \mathbf{\nabla} \times \mathbf{E} \\ \mathrm{curl}\ \mathbf{E} \end{array}\right\} = 0 \tag{5.27}$$

(The two equivalent forms for divergence and curl are given.) The first rule is a consequence of Coulomb's inverse-square law between point charges, and the second is a result of the conservative nature of the static field.

In an isotropic dielectric fluid with a susceptibility or dielectric constant which is independent of the magnitude of the field, we have, instead,

$$\left.\begin{array}{c} \mathbf{\nabla} \cdot (K\mathbf{E}) \\ \mathrm{div}\ (K\mathbf{E}) \end{array}\right\} = \frac{\rho_f}{\epsilon_0} \quad \text{and} \quad \left.\begin{array}{c} \mathbf{\nabla} \times (K\mathbf{E}) \\ \mathrm{curl}\ (K\mathbf{E}) \end{array}\right\} = 0 \tag{5.28}$$

The equation for the divergence follows from Eq. (5.18), div $\mathbf{D}$ = ρ_f, since $\mathbf{D} = \epsilon_0 K\mathbf{E}$ [Eq. (5.20)]. We can write curl $(K\mathbf{E})$ instead of curl $\mathbf{E}$ only because K is a constant, since a constant times the curl of a quantity is equivalent to the curl of that constant times the quantity.

Thus, for the simple case we are discussing, the general equations for $\mathbf{E}$ in a vacuum are identical with those for $K\mathbf{E}$ in a dielectric. In other words, given any distribution of free charges in a vacuum, leading to a field $\mathbf{E}_{\mathrm{vac}}$ over all the region, the same distribution of charges in a dielectric will give a field of value $\mathbf{E}_{diel}$, where everywhere

$$\mathbf{E}_{vac} = K\mathbf{E}_{diel} \tag{5.29}$$

Thus, in one simple argument, we have a general answer for all charge configurations! No matter what configuration of charges we have, immersion of the system in a fluid dielectric results in a decrease in the fields (and forces) by the same factor, $1/K$.

We conclude this discussion of fluid dielectrics with the comment that the state of affairs in solids is often more complicated. However, the reduction of force between charges in a dielectric is effective in solids, as is shown by the motion of free charges within a solid. An important example is the motion of a captured electron around a positively charged impurity atom in a dielectric material. Experiment indicates that such electrons are in much larger orbits than would be expected if they were in a vacuum. One of the reasons for the larger orbits is the reduced coulomb force between the electron and the positive charge, caused by the presence of the dielectric medium.

5.13   Stored Energy in a Dielectric Medium

We found in Chap. 4 that the stored energy per unit volume in a vacuum depends on the field and is

$$\tfrac{1}{2}\epsilon_0 E^2 \tag{4.16}$$

We wish to find how this expression is modified in a dielectric medium. We can determine this by comparing the stored energy in a capacitor with and without a dielectric between electrodes. We use the expression

$$U = \tfrac{1}{2}CV^2 \tag{4.11}$$

and will hold V, and therefore E, constant while we introduce the dielectric, thus modifying the capacitance C. For simplicity we may consider a parallel-plate capacitor, within which the field is uniform. If C_{vac} is the capacitance in vacuum, KC_{vac} is the capacitance with dielectric filling. Since the stored energy is $\tfrac{1}{2}CV^2$, the change in energy when a dielectric is inserted with V held constant (by adding more charge to the capacitor) is from $\tfrac{1}{2}C_{vac}V^2$ to $\tfrac{1}{2}KC_{vac}V^2$. Thus the stored energy changes from U_{vac} to KU_{vac} when dielectric is added at constant V. From Eq. (4.16) we then have for the energy density in a dielectric

$$\tfrac{1}{2}\epsilon_0 K E^2 \qquad \text{or} \qquad \tfrac{1}{2}ED \qquad \text{joules/m}^3 \tag{5.30}$$

The difference between the two cases arises from the extra work required to polarize the dielectric.

This comparison is on the basis of identical fields in vacuum and (on the average) in the dielectric medium. If, on the other hand, we charge a capacitor with a fixed charge Q and hold this Q constant while we add a dielectric medium, the stored energy becomes less. The argument follows using

$$U_{\text{vac}} = \frac{1}{2}\frac{Q^2}{C}$$

$$U_{\text{diel}} = \frac{1}{2}\frac{Q^2}{KC}$$

or

$$U_{\text{diel}} = \frac{1}{K}\,U_{\text{vac}} \qquad \text{for } Q = \text{const} \tag{5.31}$$

The contrast is due to the fact that if Q is held fixed, insertion of a dielectric lowers the field.

It is of interest to ask what happens to the stored field energy when we introduce a dielectric. In the constant-E case, the stored energy increases, and in the constant-Q case, it decreases. Where does the energy come from or where does it go? The principle of virtual displacement can be used to determine this, starting with the case of the isolated capacitor, holding V (or E) constant.

The equation which keeps account of all the energy and work terms is

$$dU = -F\,dx + V\,dQ \tag{5.32}$$

where F is the force exerted by the field on the slab. The term $V\,dQ$ is required because we must add charge in order to hold V constant. We can imagine that the capacitor is connected to a battery at voltage V. Then a displacement dx of the dielectric slab increases the capacitance, and at the same time the battery delivers a charge dQ at the voltage V.

We now need only to express dU and $V\,dQ$ in terms of a displacement dx to solve for F. To begin with, we choose the form $U = \tfrac{1}{2}VQ$, since V is constant and we can calculate Q in terms of V and the capacitance C. In fact, since $C = \epsilon_0 A/d + K\epsilon_0 A'/d$, where A is that part of the plate area without dielectric material inserted; A' is the plate area with dielectric inserted; and d is the plate separation, as shown in Fig. 5.15; we find

$$C = \frac{\epsilon_0 b}{d} (Kx + l - x)$$

where b is the width of the plates, and l the length.

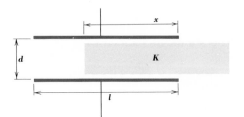

Fig. 5.15   Dielectric slab inserted between plates of a parallel-plate capacitor.

Now, since $Q = CV$, we have

$$Q = \frac{V \epsilon_0 b}{d} (Kx + l - x)$$

or

$$dQ = \frac{V \epsilon_0 b}{d} (K - 1)\, dx$$

and since

$$U = \tfrac{1}{2} VQ \qquad \text{or} \qquad dU = \tfrac{1}{2} V\, dQ$$

$$dU = \frac{1}{2} \frac{V^2 \epsilon_0 b}{d} (K - 1)\, dx$$

Eq. (5.32) becomes

$$F\, dx = -dU + V\, dQ$$

$$= -\frac{1}{2} \frac{V^2 \epsilon_0 b}{d} (K - 1)\, dx + \frac{V^2 \epsilon_0 b}{d} (K - 1)\, dx$$

or

$$F = \frac{1}{2} \frac{V^2 \epsilon_0 b}{d} (K - 1) \qquad \text{newtons}$$

Since F is positive, it is in the direction of increasing x. Hence the slab is being pulled *into* the capacitor by electrostatic forces. Half the work done by the battery goes into increasing the stored energy in the capacitor, and half appears as work pulling the dielectric slab into the space between the plates. This problem is of little practical importance since one seldom needs to know the force on a dielectric in the field of parallel-plate electrodes. However, it is a nice example of the effectiveness of the virtual-work method. One can imagine how difficult would be the conventional solution—to find the equilibrium position for all free and polarization charges and from this calculate the net force!

Another possible calculation is to consider the case in which the charge Q on the capacitor is held constant. In this case the stored energy is reduced by the presence of the dielectric. Thus we can expect that the work done by the field in pulling the dielectric slab into the capacitor is furnished by the decrease in stored energy. This is indeed the case, although since V is no longer constant, the calculation is a little more difficult. But we do not have to go through the calculation, since the following simple argument shows that the force is the same regardless of which process is imagined, constant V or constant Q.

The argument is as follows: Although our successful calculation involved work and energy ideas, in fact, the forces really depend directly on the real distribution of free and polarization charges on the electrodes and dielectric slab. For a given potential between plates and a given slab position, the distribution of these charges, whatever it may be, is surely independent of whether or not a battery at the same potential is connected to the electrodes. Therefore, for a given V and slab position, the force is the same, with or without a battery connected. If a more convincing argument is desired, the constant-Q problem is available at the end of this chapter. This may appeal only to the more skeptical and industrious students!

5.14* Depolarization Factor

We have emphasized the fact that when a dielectric body is placed in a field, the induced polarization charges always act to decrease the average field in the dielectric from the value it had before the material was introduced. In general, the polarization charges produce a nonuniform field; so the original field is modified differently at different regions in the dielectric body.

Let us limit the original field to a uniform one, choosing the special case of ellipsoidal dielectric bodies with a principal axis along the field direction. We find that the polarization charges produce in an isotropic dielectric a field which is uniform and exactly opposed to the original external field. In such cases and in those which approximate this shape, it is helpful to discuss the average field in terms of the original field less a *depolarizing* field, E_{dep}. E_{dep} depends on a geometric factor and on the magnitude of the polarization, P. We write this in the form

$$E_{\text{dep}} = \frac{1}{\epsilon_0} LP \tag{5.33}$$

where the geometric factor L, called the *depolarizing factor*, takes on possible values from 0 to 1, depending on the shape of the dielectric.

We give two examples of how the problem of average fields in a dielectric body can be expressed in terms of the effect of the depolarizing field. The first is the extreme case of a flat plate placed as shown in Fig. 5.16, with its plane perpendicular to the external field. We

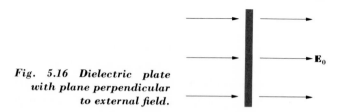

Fig. 5.16 Dielectric plate with plane perpendicular to external field.

approximate this geometry by a flat broad ellipsoid. The field within the plate will be approximately the same as in the flat ellipsoid, except at the edges of the plate, which we do not consider. We have already seen in our treatment of the parallel-plate capacitor that the field inside the plate is reduced from its original value E_0 to $(1/K)E_0$. What is the depolarizing field? We determine this by writing the field in the plate as

$$E_{\text{plate}} = E_0 - E_{\text{dep}}$$

or

$$E_{\text{dep}} = -E_{\text{plate}} + E_0 = (K - 1)E_{\text{plate}} = \chi E_{\text{plate}}$$

where we have used the relation $E_{\text{plate}} = (1/K)E_0$. But in the dielectric, $P = \epsilon_0 \chi E_{\text{plate}}$; so

$$E_{\text{dep}} = \frac{P}{\epsilon_0}$$

According to the defining equation (5.33), the depolarization factor L for the plate in this orientation is 1. This is the maximum value L can have, or we can say that this geometry gives the maximum depolarizing field for a given polarization of the body.

The other case is the opposite extreme, shown in Fig. 5.17, of a long thin dielectric rod, which we approximate by a long thin ellipsoid.

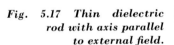

Fig. 5.17 Thin dielectric rod with axis parallel to external field.

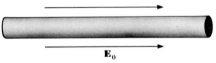

$\mathbf{E_0}$

The approximation is satisfactory everywhere except at the ends of the rod. If the rod is long and thin enough, the induced polarization charges at the end are small enough and far enough away so that the field in the middle section of the rod is negligibly modified from the original value E_0. Thus, for this case, $L \approx 0$.

In Appendix F it is shown that the depolarizing factor for a sphere (an important special case of the general ellipsoid) is $L = \frac{1}{3}$. Values of L for other shapes of ellipsoids can be worked out, but for our purposes, a knowledge of the shapes leading to the extreme values of 0 and 1 and the special case of the sphere are sufficient. The same kinds of considerations affect the magnetic fields in magnetic bodies, as we discuss in Chap. 10. As a result, the depolarization factor is also called the demagnetizing factor.

5.15* Atomic Polarizability

Of all the parameters of dielectrics studied, the susceptibility χ comes the closest to telling about the polarizability of the atoms in matter. Thus, in the equation $\chi = P/\epsilon_0 E$, the dipole moment per unit volume is related to the macroscopic field in the material. However, the macroscopic, or average, field is not a satisfactory measure of the *local field* producing the polarization of each atom. Let us call this local field E_{loc} and postpone its evaluation for the moment. We then define the *atomic polarizability* α by

$$p = \alpha E_{\text{loc}} \tag{5.34}$$

where p is the induced atomic dipole moment produced by the local field. We then write for the polarization

$$P = Np = N\alpha E_{\text{loc}} \tag{5.35}$$

where N is the number of atoms per unit volume, and we have assumed only one kind of atom in the dielectric material. Here we do not attempt to evaluate α from atomic properties, but we do indicate the problems involved in evaluating E_{loc}.

Let us take an ellipsoidal sample of dielectric placed in a uniform field E_0, as shown in Fig. 5.18. We center attention on some particular

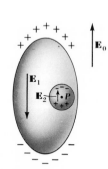

Fig. 5.18   Calculation of E_{loc} at a point P within an ellipsoidal dielectric placed in a uniform electric field. All dipoles outside the spherical boundary have effects that can be replaced by effects of induced surface charges. Charges within the spherical boundary must be treated as individual dipoles. Their effects cancel for crystals having cubic symmetry.

atom in the solid and inquire about the terms contributing to E_{loc} at the atomic site (excluding the atom itself, since it will not be polarized by its own field). The local field at the atom is just the external field plus the contributions of all the induced dipoles in the specimen. This represents the total effect of the external field at the atomic site. The idea involved here is simple, but the practical problem is somewhat complicated, since some of the dipoles are not far enough away to allow the usual approximation that substitutes for the effects of the array of dipoles, the field of the induced polarization charges. We get around this problem by discussing the problem in two parts. We place an imaginary spherical boundary around the atomic site in question, as in the figure. The sphere is made large enough so that all dipoles beyond it can be accounted for via the induced polarization surface charges. But inside the imaginary sphere we treat the dipoles individually.

Let us first consider all dipoles outside or far away from the arbitrary boundary. We can divide their contributions into two parts, $E_1 + E_2$. E_1 is just the depolarization field caused by the surface polarization charges on the specimen surface. Thus

$$\mathbf{E}_1 = -\frac{1}{\epsilon_0} L \mathbf{P}$$

where L is the depolarization factor, depending on the specimen geometry. The term $\mathbf{E}_2$ is also a depolarizing field. It arises from those charges at the imaginary spherical boundary which are the near ends of the dipoles just outside of the boundary. They correspond closely to the polarization surface charges which appear whenever a cavity is cut inside a dielectric medium. Because these charges are on surfaces with opposite symmetry from those at the outside of the specimen, they have opposite signs, and $\mathbf{E}_2$ is opposed to $\mathbf{E}_1$, as shown in Fig. 5.18. Using $L = \frac{1}{3}$ for the depolarization factor for the spherical boundary (as shown in Appendix F), we have

$$\mathbf{E}_2 = \frac{1}{3}\frac{\mathbf{P}}{\epsilon_0}$$

We are now left with the task of evaluating the local contribution of the set of dipoles in the sphere. It turns out, however, that if we take the rather common case of a lattice having cubic symmetry, the contributions of these nearby dipoles cancel out. Therefore we may write for the local field

$$\mathbf{E}_{\text{loc}} = \mathbf{E}_0 - \frac{L\mathbf{P}}{\epsilon_0} + \frac{1}{3}\frac{\mathbf{P}}{\epsilon_0}$$

where $\mathbf{E}_0$ is the external field. For a more complicated crystal structure, a further term may be required to account for the nearby dipoles. We need not take into account separately the polarization charges on the outer surface of the excluded sphere since these are already included in the contribution from the nearby dipoles.

Once we are able to relate E_{loc} to the applied field, as above, we are in a position to determine the atomic polarizability from experiment. There are three kinds of possible contributions to the polarizability. First, in all situations the application of an electric field causes some distortion of the atomic electronic cloud relative to the nucleus. We may call this the *electronic polarizability* (Fig. 5.19). Second, if we

No applied field   Applied field

E

Fig. 5.19 Schematic drawing of an atom, showing the displacement of the electronic cloud by an electric field, giving electronic polarization.

have a solid made up of ions, there is relative motion of positive and negative ions to produce *ionic polarizability* (Fig. 5.20). Finally, if

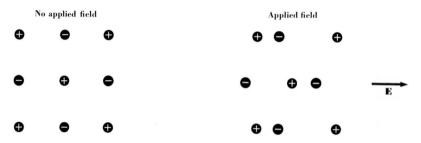

Fig. 5.20   Schematic drawing of an ionic solid, showing relative displacement of ions in an applied field, giving ionic polarization.

there are molecules with permanent dipole moments involved, as, for example, with water molecules, an external field tends to orient the otherwise randomly oriented dipoles so as to produce a net addition to the polarization. This last is called the *dipolar polarizability* (Fig. 5.21).

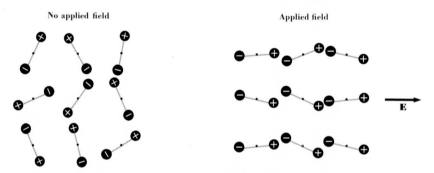

Fig. 5.21   Schematic drawing of a polar solid, showing orientation of permanent dipoles by an applied field, giving dipolar polarization.

These three types of response to electric fields may be somewhat sorted out by experiments in which the applied field is rapidly varied. As the frequency of the applied field is gradually increased, at first all three types of polarizability contribute. When frequencies up in the microwave range (say, 10^9 cps) are reached, the dipoles with their relatively slow response, because of their large moments of inertia, are not able to follow the rapidly varying electric field and their contribution to polarization ceases. Ionic polarization continues to act up to the infrared frequency range (say, 10^{13} cps), and electronic polarization continues up to the ultraviolet frequency range (say, 10^{15} cps). The low mass of the electron cloud gives it a small inertia, which allows it to respond to very rapidly changing fields.

Polarization from permanent dipoles is important in all liquids and gases whose molecules have permanent dipoles, and it also occurs in some solids. It is the damping out of this kind of response that accounts for the decrease in the dielectric constant of water from 81 for static- or low-frequency fields to 1.77 at optical frequencies. Since thermal vibrations tend to upset the orientation of permanent dipoles by an electric field, dipolar polarization decreases with increasing temperature.

5.16* Ferroelectric Materials

Certain types of dielectric materials become spontaneously polarized in the absence of external fields. This self-polarization results from the displacement of ions due to local electric fields. The local fields set up by ion displacement produce forces on the ions that are greater for small displacements than the elastic restoring forces within the crystal. As a result, the equilibrium position of the ions is such as to give a net polarization in the crystal. Such materials are called *ferroelectric* by analogy with the somewhat similar magnetic effects in ferromagnetic materials (Sec. 10.11). Ferroelectric materials often exhibit large susceptibility. They show hysteresis[1] in the polarization produced by external fields and lose their spontaneous polarization above some critical temperature. One of the best-known ferroelectric materials is barium titanate ($BaTiO_3$), which, because of its high dielectric constant, is often used in capacitors, especially where small size and large capacitance are required.

5.17 Comments on Chapter 5

In this chapter we investigated the electrical behavior of nonconducting matter. Even though the charges in such materials are not mobile, they are elastically held in position. The elastic forces allow electric

---

[1] Hysteresis means that the polarization depends not only on the test field presently applied, but also on the field applied earlier. We discuss the nature of hysteresis in ferromagnetic materials in Chap. 10.

fields to make small changes in the relative positions of the two kinds of charges; that is, an electric field polarizes a dielectric medium.

This polarization results in the appearance of polarization surface charges at dielectric boundaries. There is a simple connection between the induced dipole moment per unit volume, **P**, called the polarization, and the induced surface charge density, σ_P. This is expressed most easily by the equation

$$\mathbf{P} \cdot \hat{\mathbf{S}} = -\sigma_P \qquad \text{coul/m}^2 \tag{5.7}$$

where $\hat{\mathbf{S}}$ is the outward-drawn unit vector normal to the boundary of a dielectric body. Said differently, the induced surface charge density is numerically equal to the normal component of **P** at the surface. In the usual case, where **P** is proportional to **E**, we write

$$\mathbf{P} = \epsilon_0 \chi \mathbf{E} \tag{5.8}$$

where the constant χ is the electric susceptibility. Because of this linear relationship, Gauss' principle for **E** was shown to yield

$$\int_{cs} \mathbf{P} \cdot d\mathbf{S} = -q_P \tag{5.10}$$

where q_P is the polarization surface charge at any dielectric boundary contained within the gaussian volume being considered. The negative sign expresses the fact that lines of **P** terminate in volumes containing positive charge, and originate in regions of negative surface charge.

The electric field **E**, as given in Eq. (5.8), inside a dielectric body, is *not* the true field at each point, but the average value in the dielectric. The true field depends on the atomic arrangements and varies widely and periodically as we move from one atomic site to another.

The investigation of the properties of **P** leads us to a restatement of Gauss' flux theorem in the possible presence of a dielectric,

$$\int_{cs} \mathbf{E} \cdot d\mathbf{S} = \frac{1}{\epsilon_0} (q_f + q_P) = \frac{1}{\epsilon_0} q_{\text{total}} \tag{5.11}$$

The only change from the vacuum case is that here we acknowledge the fact that lines of **E** originate on both free and polarization charges.

A discussion of the modification made in the field of a charged parallel-plate capacitor filled with a dielectric leads to the relation

$$K = 1 + \chi \tag{5.14}$$

where K is the dielectric constant (or specific inductive capacitance).

Table 5.1   *Dielectric Constant K of Various Materials*
Room-temperature Values

Substance	Frequency, cps	
	60	2.5 × 10¹
Glass (Corning 001)	6.70	5.87
Quartz (fused)	3.78	3.78
Polystyrene	2.56	2.54
Teflon	2.1	2.08
Nylon	3.7	2.73
Bakelite	4.90	3.55
Wood (Douglas fir)	2.05	1.78
Ruby (⊥ optic axis)	13.27 (10⁴ cps)	
Ruby (∥ optic axis)	11.28 (10⁴ cps)	
Rutile (⊥ optic axis) (TiO₂)	86 (10⁸ cps)	
Rutile (∥ optic axis)	170 (10⁸ cps)	
Titanates (Ba, Sr, Ca, Mg, and Pb)	15–12,000	
Distilled water	78 (at 10⁸ cps)	
Benzene	2.28	2.28

K is defined as the factor by which the capacitance of a capacitor is multiplied when the space between electrodes is filled with a dielectric. Dielectric constant of various substances is given in Table 5.1.

Another parameter often used to describe dielectric behavior is the permittivity ϵ, related to the permittivity of free space ϵ_0 by

$$\epsilon = \epsilon_0 K \tag{5.15}$$

A new vector quantity $\mathbf{D}$ is related to $\mathbf{E}$ by the defining equation

$$\mathbf{D} = \epsilon_0 \mathbf{E} + \mathbf{P} \tag{5.16}$$

For isotropic materials, to which we limit our discussions, the three vectors $\mathbf{D}$, $\mathbf{E}$, and $\mathbf{P}$ are parallel. We show that Gauss' flux theorem can be applied to the vector $\mathbf{D}$, which is not surprising since we already know it applies to $\mathbf{E}$ and $\mathbf{P}$, to give the relation

$$\int_{cs} \mathbf{D} \cdot d\mathbf{S} = q_{\text{free}} \tag{5.17}$$

That is, lines of $\mathbf{D}$ have as sources and sinks only free charges, and not polarization surface charges. The microscopic equivalent to Eq. (5.17) is

$$\text{div } \mathbf{D} = \rho_f \tag{5.18}$$

where ρ_f is the free charge density at any point considered.

We find further, via Eq. (5.16), that at any point in free space, regardless of possible nearby dielectric bodies,

$$\mathbf{D} = \epsilon_0 \mathbf{E} \tag{5.19}$$

In other words, outside of matter, $\mathbf{D}$ and $\mathbf{E}$ are identical except for the multiplying constant ϵ_0. Inside matter, $\mathbf{D}$ and $\mathbf{E}$ are parallel in isotropic media, and the relation becomes

$$\mathbf{D} = \epsilon_0 K \mathbf{E} \tag{5.20}$$

The use of $\mathbf{D}$ is often a convenience, especially in the discussion of electromagnetic waves.

It is particularly useful to bring in $\mathbf{D}$ in the discussion of the behavior of the field at a dielectric boundary. The two rules which emerge are

$$D_{n1} = D_{n2} \tag{5.23}$$

and

$$E_{t1} = E_{t2} \tag{5.24}$$

These equations state that the normal components of $\mathbf{D}$ have the same value on both sides of a boundary and that tangential components of $\mathbf{E}$ have the same value on both sides. These equations allow easy determination of the relation between directions and between intensities of the electric field on the two sides of a dielectric boundary.

Arguments are given, one based on simple applications of the div and curl operators, to show that when charges are immersed in a dielectric medium, forces between charges are reduced by a factor $1/K$.

The presence of a dielectric medium is found to affect the energy stored in an electric field. The energy density, which in a vacuum is $\frac{1}{2}\epsilon_0 E^2$, is found to be

$$\frac{1}{2}\epsilon_0 K E^2 \text{ or } \frac{1}{2}ED \quad \text{joules/m}^3 \tag{5.30}$$

in the presence of matter. Thus more energy is stored in a given field in the presence of a dielectric than in a vacuum. The principle of virtual displacement is used to calculate the force on a dielectric slab in a field.

For bodies having ellipsoidal geometries, the effect of surface polarization charges can be expressed in terms of a depolarization factor. This is a handy method, even when we deal with bodies which are only roughly ellipsoidal.

A brief discussion shows how in principle calculations of the true field at an atomic site in matter can be obtained. This generally difficult problem must be solved to relate the bulk property of a dielectric, its dielectric constant, to the polarizability of the atoms or molecules of which it is made. A short description of ferroelectric bodies which spontaneously polarize under some conditions concludes this chapter, which is primarily concerned with the concepts useful for discussing fields in nonconducting matter.

PROBLEMS

The polarization charge density at the surface of a dielectric body depends on the magnitude of the polarization P and on its direction with respect to the surface normal.

5.1A   A dielectric block such as shown in Fig. P5.1 is uniformly polarized. The polarization is **P**. Find the polarization charge density σ_p on the faces 1, 2, and 3. (Find both magnitude and sign of the charge.)

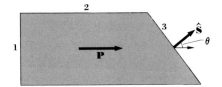

Fig. P5.1

★5.1B   A sphere of radius r is polarized uniformly and has a polarization **P** in the x direction. Write the expression for the surface polarization charge for a ring whose radius vector makes an angle θ with the x axis as shown in Fig. P5.2. Integrate this expression to get the total positive surface

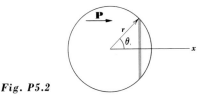

Fig. P5.2

polarization charge on the sphere. What is the net Q on the surface of the entire body?

The behavior of the displacement **D** at dielectric boundaries is a useful adjunct for field calculations.

5.2A At a boundary between two dielectric materials having different dielectric constants, show by means of a simple sketch that although *lines* of **D** are continuous, the *magnitude* of **D** is generally different in the two materials. Show by means of another sketch the special condition under which **D** has the same value in both materials.

*5.2B The angle of incidence of the electric field (the angle between the field direction and the surface normal) at a plane dielectric boundary outside the dielectric is 20°. Find the angle of refraction within the medium if the dielectric constant of the medium is 1.25. Assume vacuum outside the medium.

Capacitance is modified by the presence of a dielectric medium in a capacitor.

5.3A The capacitance of a capacitor is increased by a factor of 1.5 when it is completely filled with a certain dielectric material. Find the dielectric constant of the material and its electric susceptibility.

*5.3B Compare the capacitances of two identical capacitors with dielectrics inserted and having dielectric constants K_1 and K_2, as shown in Fig. P5.3.

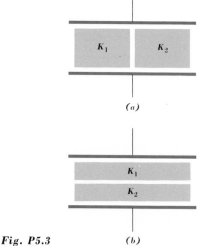

(a)

(b)

Fig. P5.3

5.3C Two capacitors of equal capacitance C are connected in parallel, charged to a voltage V_1, and then isolated from the voltage source, as shown in Fig. P5.4. A dielectric of dielectric constant K is inserted into one capacitor and completely fills the space between plates. Calculate the free charge transferred from one capacitor to the other and the final voltage V_2 across the capacitors in terms of C, V_1, and K.

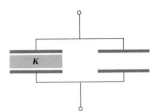

Fig. P5.4

---

*5.3D Discuss a metal as a polarizable body. What is the value of the polarization **P**? What is the susceptibility χ?

The stored energy in an electric field is modified by the presence of a dielectric medium.

*5.4A The voltage between parallel plates of a capacitor is V_1. The plates are isolated electrically. A dielectric slab of dielectric constant K is inserted between the plates and completely fills the volume between them. Find the new potential V_2. Compare the stored energy before and after inserting the slab. On the basis of this comparison, present an argument as to whether electrostatic forces pull the slab into the space between plates or tend to push it away.

5.4B Suppose the capacitor in Prob. 5.4A were connected to a battery so as to maintain constant voltage when the dielectric slab is inserted between the plates. Compare the stored energy in the capacitor before and after inserting the dielectric. On the basis of this comparison, can you argue about the direction of the force on the slab, as in Prob. 5.4A? Explain.

The effect of polarization surface charge on the average field within a dielectric body can be discussed in terms of the depolarizing field or of the depolarization factor. The problem given here is qualitative. In Sec. 5.14 there are quantitative arguments for certain extreme specimen shapes.

5.5A Two similar dielectric ellipsoids are placed in an electric field as shown in Fig. P5.5. For which orientation is the depolarization factor larger? Give qualitative reasons.

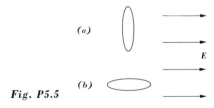

Fig. P5.5

6

current and circuits

6.1 Introduction

In this chapter we turn from considerations of electrostatic effects to a discussion of electric currents, and of the circuits in which the behavior of currents can be studied. It is a basic property of metals that electric currents can be caused to flow in them with relatively small expenditures of energy. The conducting properties of metals will be discussed in some detail in Chap. 7. In the present chapter we consider the experimental facts of current flow and the parameters that are useful in the description of currents in circuits.

Much of this material is relatively simple, and some students will be able to skim through most of the chapter very quickly on the basis of earlier studies. But electric circuits are of such great practical importance that it seems advisable to display carefully the rules of the game, even if only as review.

6.2 Electric Current

Electric current is the flow of charge. When there is a surface through which charges are flowing, such as a cross section cut through a wire, the current i is defined as

$$i = \frac{dq}{dt} \qquad \text{coul/sec, or amp} \tag{6.1}$$

A current of one coulomb per second is defined as one ampere in both the mks and the practical system of units (Chap. 17). The positive direction of current is taken conventionally as the direction of flow of positive charge. In a majority of cases, however, the current is produced by the flow of negative charge carriers. In such cases, the direction of current is opposite to that of the flow of the negative charges. We shall often use the common though redundant phrase *current flow* when charge flow or current is meant.

When the rate at which charge is flowing varies over the surface, we can more conveniently discuss the current density $\mathbf{j}$, which is related to the current by the equation

$$i = \int \mathbf{j} \cdot d\mathbf{S} \qquad \text{amp} \tag{6.2}$$

where $d\mathbf{S}$ is an element of the cross-section area A. The integral is taken over the cross section through which we are calculating the current. The unit of current density is the ampere per square meter. Use of vector notation allows the consideration of a cross-section area not perpendicular to the current flow. Thus, in Fig. 6.1, the integral allows

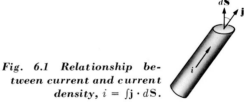

Fig. 6.1   Relationship between current and current density, $i = \int \mathbf{j} \cdot d\mathbf{S}$.

for the angle between $d\mathbf{S}$ and $\mathbf{j}$. The value of the integral is independent of the shape of surface taken, and thus gives the same current through the wire as long as the surface taken cuts completely across the region of charge flow. When the current density is uniform, Eq. (6.2) can be integrated to give

$$i = \mathbf{j} \cdot \mathbf{A} \qquad \text{amp} \tag{6.3}$$

When the area is taken perpendicular to the current density, this becomes $i = jA$, where A is the cross-section area of the conductor.

Current is due to the drift of charge carriers with a mean drift velocity **v**, each carrying a charge e and having a density of n carriers per unit volume; so

$$\mathbf{j} = ne\mathbf{v} \qquad \text{amp/m}^2 \tag{6.4}$$

or, if A is the cross-section area of the conductor,

$$\mathbf{i} = nevA \qquad \text{amp} \tag{6.5}$$

This is shown using Fig. 6.2. We ask for the rate at which charge crosses the area A. In a time dt a cylinder of charge of length $v\,dt$ and

Fig. 6.2   *Calculation of current in terms of drift velocity.*

area A passes through the surface we have chosen. This volume is $Av\,dt$, and it contains $nAv\,dt$ charge carriers. Since each carrier has a charge e, the total charge flow in the time dt is $dq = nevA\,dt$. Evaluation of $dq/dt = i$ gives the result of Eq. (6.5).

The detailed motion of charge carriers may be quite complex, but all that enters here is the average drift velocity. We shall later see that electrons in a metal move at high velocities ($\approx 10^8$ cm/sec) in random directions, usually for submillimeter distances between collisions with the metal lattice. Only the much slower average drift motion in a particular direction contributes to the current.

An important question, to which we shall postpone the answer for the present, is that of the measurement of current. The almost universal method of current measurement is magnetic; therefore the discussion is most appropriately delayed until our work on magnetism, in Chap. 8. There we shall learn convenient ways of describing the magnetic force on current-carrying conductors. This is the force which actuates most kinds of current meters. In the meantime we simply accept the fact that there are meters which measure current.

In order to produce current in a wire, an electric field must exist along the wire. This can be described by the potential difference which is maintained between the two ends of a wire. This is not the static situation described earlier, in which no net field exists in the conductor. Here we are dealing with a steady flow of charge, and not with a static situation. Usually, the magnitude of current flow in a conducting body is proportional to the voltage difference between the two ends. Under this condition we characterize the electrical behavior of the body by its *resistance R*, as defined by

$$V = iR \qquad \text{volts} \qquad\qquad (6.6)$$

where V = voltage difference, in volts, between the two ends

      i = current, amp

      R = a parameter called resistance, *ohms*

These are the units used in both the mks and the practical system. We later discuss the physical causes behind this relationship, well known as Ohm's law, but for the present we take it simply as an experimental fact. The resistance of a conducting body can have any value between wide limits (say, from 10^{-6} to 10^8 ohms or more), depending on the material and geometry of the body.

The resistance of a conducting body usually varies with temperature. Devices used in circuits to provide fixed resistance of known values are called *resistors*.

Electric energy is converted into heat when current flows through a resistor. Thus resistors are used as heater elements. They are also used to control current and voltage in circuits.

$$\frac{1}{R_4} = \frac{1}{R_1} \cdot \frac{L}{R_2}$$

6.3 Resistance, Resistivity, and Series and Parallel Resistors

Once it has been found experimentally that conducting bodies follow Ohm's law, that is, that the current through a given body from one terminal to another is proportional to the voltage between its terminals, it is possible to develop a more fundamental expression which separates the effects of size and shape of the body from effects due to its electrical properties. In addition, it is possible to determine the effects of combining resistors in series or parallel.

We begin by taking several identical resistors made of the same material and having the same size and shape. For simplicity we assume a uniform cylindrical geometry, having length L and cross-section area A, as shown in Fig. 6.3. We also assume that the connections at the ends across which a voltage is applied are of such design that the current density is uniform through the entire resistor. Suppose that each

Fig. 6.3 Resistor of uniform cross-section area A and length L. A current $I_1 = V_1/R$ will flow when a potential V_1 is applied.

resistor has a resistance R_1, so that when a voltage V_1 is applied, the current which flows is

$$I_1 = \frac{V_1}{R_1} \tag{6.7}$$

We now connect these resistors in various ways in order to find the effect of length and cross-section area on the total resistance.

First we connect two resistors in series as shown in Fig. 6.4. This combination simulates a single resistor of length $2L$. Since the total

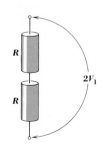

Fig. 6.4 Two resistors in series. The same current I_1 will flow when potential $2V_1$ is applied across the pair, giving V_1 across each resistor separately.

voltage across the two resistors is the sum of the voltages across each one, a voltage $2V_1$ applied across the pair gives V_1 across each. Therefore the same current I_1 will flow as before. Solving for the effective resistance R_s of the series pair, we find

$$I_1 = \frac{2V_1}{R_s} \tag{6.8}$$

which, by comparison with Eq. (6.7), gives

$$R_s = 2R_1 \tag{6.9}$$

If this argument is generalized, it leads to the conclusion that, with cylindrical geometry, the resistance is proportional to length.

We next connect two of the original identical resistors in parallel, as shown in Fig. 6.5. This combination simulates a single resistor of

Fig. 6.5 Two resistors in parallel. The same current I_1 will flow through each one when a potential V_1 is applied. Total current is the sum of individual currents. Current density in each resistor is unchanged.

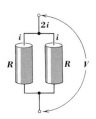

the original length but having twice the cross-section area. Application of Eq. (6.6) shows that for a voltage V_1 applied across the pair, a current I_1 flows in each resistor, to give a total current $2I_1$. In order to solve for the effective resistance R_p of this parallel combination, we write

$$2I_1 = \frac{V_1}{R_p} \qquad (6.10)$$

and using Eq. (6.7) again, we find

$$R_p = \frac{1}{2R_1} \qquad \frac{1}{R_s} = \frac{1}{R_1} + \frac{1}{R_2} + \frac{1}{R_3} \quad (6.11)$$

Generalization of this argument shows that the resistance of a body is inversely proportional to its cross-section area.

These two results for series and parallel arrangements of identical resistors allow us to write a general expression for resistance which includes the effect of length and cross-section explicitly. This is done by defining a quantity called the *resistivity* of the material of which the resistor is made. The resistivity, usually symbolized by ρ, may be defined as the resistance of a unit volume of material having unit length and unit cross-section area. Using the two results above, it is now possible to write an expression for the resistance of a resistor of any length L and any cross-section area A in the form

$$R = \rho \frac{L}{A} \qquad \text{ohms} \qquad (6.12)$$

Resistivity is measured in ohm-meters in the mks system.

Another way of looking at the resistance problem is to convert to what is called the *microscopic* form of Ohm's law. The discussion thus far involves measurement of current when a voltage is placed across a finite specimen of conducting material which has a total resistance R. But the effect of the applied voltage is best described by the electric field which it establishes within the material. It is this field which causes current to flow. It is therefore useful to discuss the current in terms of the electric field E, and to characterize the current, not by the total current flow i, but by the current density j. We expect to get a statement of how the current density anywhere in a specimen depends on the electric field in that region. This allows the local behavior in any microscopic region of the material to be described. This form of

Ohm's law can be written

$$j = \frac{1}{\rho} E \tag{6.13}$$

where ρ is the resistivity as defined above. The current density is proportional to the applied field. This relation can easily be derived from $V = iR$, as we now show. The total potential difference across the resistor is replaced by the field through the use of

$$V = EL$$

The current is replaced by the current density by using

$$i = jA \tag{6.3}$$

With these changes, the usual expression for Ohm's law is immediately shown to be equivalent to Eq. (6.13). Thus

$$V = iR$$
$$EL = \frac{jA\rho L}{A}$$

so

$$E = \rho j$$

or

$$j = \frac{1}{\rho} E$$

A useful change in this expression can be made by replacing the resistivity ρ by its reciprocal, the conductivity σ.

$$\sigma = \frac{1}{\rho} \tag{6.14}$$

Then the microscopic form of Ohm's law becomes

$$j = \sigma E \tag{6.15}$$

The conductivity is measured in units of (ohm-meter)$^{-1}$. For isotropic material, σ is a scalar quantity, since the current is everywhere parallel to the driving field.

The total resistance R of a cylindrical specimen of conducting material can now be written in either of the forms

$$R = \frac{1}{\sigma}\frac{L}{A} \quad \text{or} \quad R = \rho\frac{L}{A} \tag{6.16}$$

To summarize, the resistivity ρ, or the conductivity σ, character-

izes the property of the conductor which affects its resistance independent of its size and shape. The resistance of a conducting body
with constant cross section is proportional to its length and inversely
proportional to its cross-section area. To obtain this result we have
assumed that the current density in the conducting material is the
same throughout. This is true only with specimens having uniform
cross-section area and with material of uniform conductivity.

Once we have gone through the arguments above regarding the
influence of shape on resistance, we have really solved the problem of
the effect of combining resistances in series or in parallel. The series
case is shown in Fig. 6.6. A resistance R_{equiv} is to be found which has

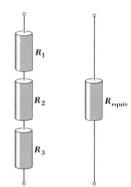

Fig. 6.6   Resistors in series.
$R_{equiv} = \Sigma R_i = R_1 + R_2 + R_3.$

the same effect as the several resistors in series. Since the total voltage
across the resistors shown is the sum of the voltages across each one,
and since the same current goes through each resistor when they are
connected in series, an equivalent single resistor would be one for which
the voltage drop is the same as the sum of the separate voltages, or

$$V_1 + V_2 + V_3 = i(R_1 + R_2 + R_3) = iR_{equiv}$$

The parallel case is shown in Fig. 6.7. Here the voltage across
each resistor is the same, and the total current through the array is
the sum of currents through each resistor; so the equivalent single
resistor is calculated by adding currents.

$$i_{total} = i_1 + i_2 + i_3 = \frac{V}{R_1} + \frac{V}{R_2} + \frac{V}{R_3} = V\left(\frac{1}{R_1} + \frac{1}{R_2} + \frac{1}{R_3}\right)$$
$$= V\frac{1}{R_{equiv}}$$

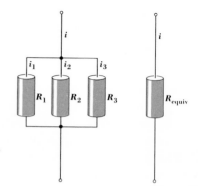

**Fig. 6.7 Resistors in paral-
lel.** $1/R_{\text{equiv}} = \Sigma_i(1/R_i) =
1/R_1 + 1/R_2 + 1/R_3.$

The two results may be written

$$\text{Resistances in series: } R_{\text{equiv}} = \sum_i R_i \tag{6.17}$$

$$\text{Resistances in parallel: } \frac{1}{R_{\text{equiv}}} = \sum_i \frac{1}{R_i} \tag{6.18}$$

When the cross section of a conducting body is nonuniform, the current density varies through the body and the problem of calculating its resistance becomes more complicated than in the case of a simple body of uniform cross section, where we can use $R = \rho L/A$ [Eq. (6.16)]. For all but the simplest shapes, the mathematical difficulties can become rather serious, but we shall take a very simple example to show the method of attack. The problem is mathematically identical with the calculation of heat flow through a thermally conducting body.

Consider the radial flow of current through a circular slab of conducting material from some radius a at a potential V_a to the outer radius b (Fig. 6.8). Let the conductivity of the circular slab be σ and its thickness be t. Since the cross section of this conductor perpendicular to the current flow is $2\pi rt$ at any radius r, and therefore varies as we move out from one end of the conductor to the other, we do not expect the voltage gradient or electric field to be uniform. However, the total current through any cross section is the same as that through any other cross section; so we can write an expression for the current,

$$i = jA = \sigma A E = -\sigma 2\pi rt \frac{dV}{dr} \tag{6.19}$$

where j is the current density at any radius r. When we solve this for

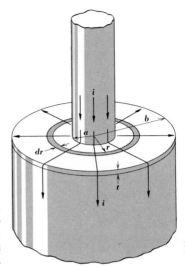

Fig. 6.8   Radial flow of current through a circular slab of conducting material. Flow is from radius a at V_a to radius b at V_b.

the potential drop dV across a ring of width dr, we get

$$dV = -\frac{i}{2\pi t\sigma}\frac{dr}{r}$$

The total voltage difference between the two ends of the conductor is

$$V_b - V_a = \int_a^b dV = -\frac{i}{2\pi t\sigma}\int_a^b \frac{dr}{r} = \frac{i}{2\pi t\sigma}\ln\frac{r_a}{r_b}$$

The resistance of the conductor is then given by

$$R = \frac{V_b - V_a}{i} = \frac{1}{2\pi t\sigma}\ln\frac{r_a}{r_b} \tag{6.20}$$

We have chosen a case in which it is easy to find the element of area that is perpendicular to the current flow. This is necessary in order to obtain i from jA as we did in Eq. (6.19). If the current is not perpendicular to the cross section chosen, we must use $i = \mathbf{j}\cdot\mathbf{A}$, which complicates the problem.

As we shall see in Sec. 7.2, the resistivity of metals varies with temperature and purity and is affected by imperfections in the crystal structure. In general, the resistivity in metals increases with increasing temperature, because of the shorter electron paths between collisions with the lattice. In the case of semiconductors, discussed in Sec. 7.1, the resistance generally decreases with increasing temperature. This results from the higher density of charge carriers in semi-conductors at higher temperatures.

Some materials and devices do not obey Ohm's law. For example, in a gas discharge tube, and in a diode vacuum tube (Sec. 16.2) or a crystal diode (Sec. 16.4), the current is *not* proportional to the applied voltage.

6.4 An Introduction to Circuits

An electric circuit is any arrangement of conductors in which current can flow around one or more closed conducting paths. Since in most circumstances the flow of current involves energy losses, a necessary component of any practical circuit is a source of energy, called an *electromotive force*, abbreviated *emf*. The energy to move current around a circuit cannot come from an electrostatic field, since, as we have seen, an electrostatic field cannot do net work on charge taken around a closed path back to where it started. Thus an emf must be a non-electrostatic source of energy. The measure of the emf ε in a circuit is in volts, since the emf describes the work done per unit charge.

In the case of a localized source, such as a chemical battery, the work on the charge is done within the source. In a battery, chemical forces cause a separation of positive and negative charges in spite of the mutual attraction between charges of opposite sign. As a result, a potential difference, say, V_0, is produced and maintained between the battery terminals. With no current flowing,

$$V_0 = \varepsilon \qquad \text{volts} \tag{6.21}$$

A discussion in Sec. 6.5 explains how the potential difference across a source of emf is reduced to a value less than ε when a current flows.

The part of the circuit to which energy is delivered is called the *load*. In it the electric energy is transformed into heat in a resistor, or mechanical energy in a motor, or light in an electric lamp, or chemical energy in an electroplating bath. Conducting wires provide the path for current to flow from the source of emf to the load and back to the source of emf. Usually, the loss of energy in the wires connecting source and load is minor compared with the energy transformation in the load.

In Chap. 11 we discuss the case of ac circuits, but in this chapter our concern is with circuits in which the current flow is steady. A steady-state circuit must provide a complete path which allows charge to move continuously, first through the energy source, where its potential energy is raised, then through the load elements, in which its potential energy is transformed, and finally back to its starting point, to repeat the process. We begin the discussion using Fig. 6.9, which

Fig. 6.9   Circuit connecting a source of emf to a resistance R. A potential difference V_0 appears between the terminals of the source. When the switch is open, no current flows, and there is a voltage difference V_0 across the switch.

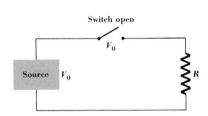

shows a source of emf and a load resistance connected by two wires to provide a closed loop for the flow of charge. A switch has been provided in the circuit which, when open as shown, interrupts the flow of charge.[1] We suppose that the resistive load R is, say, a light bulb or some other dissipative element through which we wish to pass current. The resistance of the wires connecting the source with the load is neglected here.

We first describe the situation prior to closing the switch. Suppose that the source of emf is a chemical battery. In this case chemical forces will have caused a separation of charge; that is, excess positive charge will have collected on the electrode connected to the upper terminal of the battery, and negative charge will have collected on the electrode connected to the lower terminal, as shown. Further charge separation ceases when the electric field built up within the battery by the chemical forces (Sec. 7.6) which cause charge separation is just enough to stop further separation. At this point the upper battery terminal and the wire connected to it have reached some potential V_0 above that of the negative terminal and the wire and resistor connected to it. This potential difference V_0 appears across the terminals of the switch.

When the switch is closed, the potential difference across the switch becomes zero, and current through the resistor R adjusts itself until the voltage V_0 provided by the emf is developed across the resis-

[1] A *closed* switch is one in which the gap is closed, allowing current to flow through it; an *open* switch presents a gap across which charge cannot flow.

tor. That is, the current i becomes

$$i = \frac{V_0}{R} \quad \text{amp}$$

We follow the flow of charge around the circuit starting from the negative terminal a of the source, as shown in Fig. 6.10. It is assumed

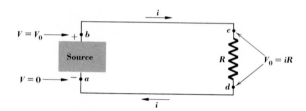

Fig. 6.10 *Circuit with switch closed. Current adjusts to a value such that iR across resistor equals V_0, the potential difference provided by the source of emf.*

for simplicity of description that it is positive charge which flows, although the same argument will hold for negative charge flowing in the opposite direction. The potential at point a is arbitrarily assumed to be zero. When the switch is closed, charge at a is forced by nonelectric forces in the source of emf up to the positive terminal at point b, which is at a potential V_0. The charge has been moved *against* the electrostatic field set up by the charge separation in the source. Neglecting the small voltage drop along the wire from b to c, the potential at point c is the same as at b. Similarly, because of the negligible resistance of the wire between d and a, the potential at point d is the same as that at a. Thus the entire potential difference V_0 across the source appears across the resistance R. The resulting electric field within R forces charge to move from a region of potential V_0 to the bottom of the resistor (point d) at zero potential. The charge then moves on back to point a. In moving completely around the circuit, the net work done on the charge by purely electrostatic forces is zero, in conformity with the principle of zero circulation.

$$\oint \mathbf{E} \cdot d\mathbf{l} = 0 \tag{3.4}$$

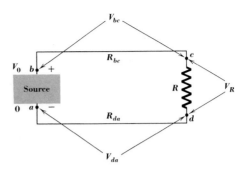

Fig. 6.11   Same circuit as in Fig. 6.10, taking into account the resistance of the wires connecting the source to the load resistor R. When the resistances of the connecting wires are small compared with R, they can be neglected.

If we choose not to neglect the resistance of the wires, the equation for current flow becomes, using the terminology of Fig. 6.11,

$$
\begin{aligned}
V_0 &= V_{bc} + V_R + V_{da} \\
&= iR_{bc} + iR + iR_{da} \\
&= i(R_{bc} + R + R_{da})
\end{aligned}
$$
(6.22)

If the resistances of the connecting wires, R_{bc} and R_{da}, are small compared with R, the voltages V_{bc} and V_{da} can be neglected, and $V_R \approx V_0$.

In the simple circuit just discussed, two fundamental circuit properties were used. The first property can be stated as follows: At any point in a circuit,

$$
\Sigma i = 0
$$
(6.23)

where the current coming into the point is considered positive, say, and that going away from the point is considered negative. This rule is the direct result of charge conservation, and means that at any point in a circuit the current coming into that point must equal the current leaving it. Thus, in Fig. 6.12a the current i_1 arriving at point a

Fig. 6.12   (a) The current-conservation rule requires that along any single conductor, as at point a, $i_1 = i_2$. Thus the current is the same at all points, such as at a and b. (b) Similarly, at any junction the current coming into the junction must equal that leaving the junction. Thus, here, $i_1 = i_2 + i_3 + i_4$.

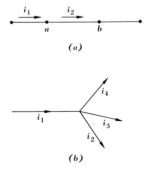

from the left must be equal to i_2 leaving the point and moving toward b. Formally stated, at any point a

$$i_1 - i_2 = 0$$

Thus the current passing through any point a on a single conductor must always be equal to that passing through any other point b. We invoked this rule when, in the circuit of Fig. 6.11, we assigned the same current i to both conducting wires and to the resistance R.

A slightly more complicated application of the charge or current conservation rule is shown in Fig. 6.12b. At the junction shown we can again interpret Eq. (6.23) to mean that the sum of the currents coming into the junction equals the sum of the currents leaving the junction, or

$$i_1 - i_2 - i_3 - i_4 = 0$$

Here again one sign is given to incoming current and the opposite sign is given to outgoing current.

The second property of any closed circuit is that the sum of emfs in a circuit is equal to the voltage drops in all resistances around the circuit, or

$$\Sigma\mathcal{E} = \Sigma iR \qquad \text{volts} \tag{6.24}$$

This is simply a consequence of Ohm's law applied around any loop. It follows directly from Eq. (3.4), $\oint \mathbf{E} \cdot d\mathbf{l} = 0$, and justifies Eq. (6.22), which we wrote for the simple circuit of Fig. 6.11. That is, starting at zero potential at point a, the nonelectrostatic forces of the source of emf lift the charge to point b at potential V_0. Equation (3.4) then requires that when the charge has gone around the circuit and back to its starting point a, it must arrive back at the original zero potential.

In order to deal with more complicated circuits we must establish sign conventions for both the emf and for voltage drops in resistances. In using Eq. (6.24), it is necessary to start at some point in the circuit and move completely around the circuit in one direction or the other, keeping track of the sign of each emf and of each change in potential iR through each resistor. The sign of each emf and each iR voltage change, or *voltage drop*, is related to the direction chosen for going around the circuit to make the summation. In the circuit of Fig. 6.11, for example, suppose it is decided to go around the circuit in the clockwise direction, a, b, c, d. If the direction of the path taken around the circuit is the same as the direction in which positive charge or positive current is pushed by the nonelectrostatic forces within a given source, we consider that emf positive. The sign of the iR drop in each resistor in the circuit is positive as written in Eq. (6.24) when the direction of travel is the same as the direction of the current. On this basis the equation obtained for the voltage and emf balance around the circuit of Fig. 6.11 is just Eq. (6.22) as we wrote it.

The two circuit equations

$$\Sigma i = 0 \tag{6.23}$$
$$\Sigma \mathcal{E} = \Sigma iR \tag{6.24}$$

are known as Kirchhoff's rules. Since these equations result from general properties of the electrostatic field, conservation of current, and Ohm's law, they must hold for any closed path taken around a circuit and back to the starting point. Their application to more complicated circuits is discussed later.

There is one class of circuits which provides more than one path for current, but which can be converted to an equivalent single-path circuit. We illustrate this class here, and reserve for Sec. 6.6 the discussion of circuits which cannot be simplified to single-path equivalent circuits. The circuit of Fig. 6.13 is used as an example here. It is as-

Fig. 6.13 *Circuit with two possible current paths. When the emf and all resistance values are known, the current i can be obtained by using the circuit equations. In this case the simplest way to obtain the current i is to replace the parallel combination of R_2 and R_3 by an equivalent resistance R_p.*

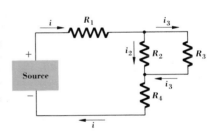

sumed that $\mathcal{E}$ and all resistances are known. The complication of this circuit is only that R_2 and R_3 are in parallel. Thus there are two possible paths for the current. The simple way to determine the current in this circuit is to replace R_2 and R_3 by an equivalent resistance R_p, as shown in Fig. 6.14. The value of R_p is calculated by means of the formula for parallel resistors, developed in the last section.

$$\frac{1}{R_p} = \frac{1}{R_2} + \frac{1}{R_3}$$

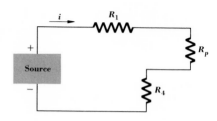

Fig. 6.14   Circuit of Fig. 6.13 in which R_2 and R_3 have been replaced by $R_p = R_2 R_3/(R_2 + R_3)$. The circuit equation now becomes $\varepsilon = i(R_1 + R_2 + R_4)$.

or

$$R_p = \frac{R_2 R_3}{R_2 + R_3}$$

Once this has been done, the second circuit equation,

$$\Sigma \varepsilon = \Sigma i R$$

can be applied to give

$$\varepsilon = i(R_1 + R_p + R_4) \tag{6.25}$$

which can be solved for the total current i. The division of current between R_2 and R_3 can be obtained by noting that the voltage drop across each resistor is the same; so

$$i_2 R_2 = i_3 R_3$$

It has been assumed in this section that the potential difference between the terminals of a source of emf is always ε volts. In fact, sources of emf characteristically give a potential difference which decreases to some extent when current is drawn from the source. It is shown in the following section that the voltage V between terminals can usually be described by the equation

$$V = \varepsilon - ir \tag{6.26}$$

where r is the effective *internal resistance* of the source. If the internal resistance is included, Eq. (6.25) becomes

$$\varepsilon = i(r + R_1 + R_p + R_4)$$

6.5   Energy Exchange in a Circuit

Let us take a simple circuit like that of Fig. 6.10 and find the work being done by the nonelectric source of energy in maintaining a constant current i. Since every amount of charge dq which is pushed against the electric field in the battery has an amount of work $dW = V_0\,dq$ done on it, the *rate* of work being done by the nonelectric energy source is

$$P = \frac{dW}{dt} = V_0\frac{dq}{dt} = V_0 i$$

$$\text{joules/coul} \times \text{coul/sec} = \text{joules/sec or watts} \qquad (6.27)$$

This rate of doing work is thus the power provided by whatever non-electrostatic source is maintaining the current.

Usually, the source of energy which maintains the current in a circuit is characterized by its *electromotive force* ε, as mentioned above. This is defined as

$$\varepsilon = \frac{dW}{dq} \qquad \text{joules/coul, or volts} \qquad (6.28)$$

Thus the emf ε is the work per unit charge done by the nonelectrostatic source of energy.

In the simple case of a localized source of energy in a circuit, as the battery in the circuit of Fig. 6.10, the emf ε is numerically equal to V_0, the potential difference between battery terminals, when no current is flowing.

We have now characterized the source of energy in any circuit in terms of the work per unit charge expended in maintaining the current. This amounts to a measure of the rate at which nonelectrical energy is being converted to electric energy. This *rate* of doing work, or power, is given by

$$P = \frac{dW}{dt} = \frac{dW}{dq}\frac{dq}{dt} = \varepsilon i \qquad \text{watts} \qquad (6.29)$$

Since the circuit is in a steady state, there must be a corresponding rate at which electric energy is being converted to some other form. In our simple circuit all this energy is being converted to heat energy in the resistor. We can calculate the rate of energy conversion simply, as follows: Because of the current, charge is continuously being transferred from a position at the top of the resistor in Fig. 6.10, where it is at a potential V_0, to a position at the bottom of the resistor, where it is at zero potential. But we may safely assume that the kinetic energy of all the charges making up the current is essentially constant; so the kinetic energy of the charges is the same at the top and bottom of the resistor. Where does the energy go which becomes available when charges are moved down from a potential V_0 to 0? The answer is that the energy is given up to the body of the resistor as the charges flow through it. This is the reason for the heating of any resistor when current flows through it. The rate of heat dissipation can be calculated without the need for a detailed model of the process which produces the losses. Thus the rate of conversion from electric to thermal energy is

$$P = \frac{dW}{dt} = \frac{V_0\,dq}{dt} = V_0 i \quad \text{watts} \tag{6.30}$$

Alternative and well-known expressions, obtained by application of Eq. (6.6), $V = iR$, are

$$P = iRi = i^2R \quad \text{watts} \tag{6.31}$$

and

$$P = \frac{V^2}{R} \quad \text{watts} \tag{6.32}$$

We can easily see that a purely electrostatic field cannot produce a steady current in a circuit. The nonzero resistance of materials in ordinary circuits implies energy dissipation by currents. But for any purely electrostatic field, the line integral of the field around any circuit, or circulation, $\oint \mathbf{E} \cdot d\mathbf{l}$, is zero; so such a field can do no net work in carrying a charge around an entire closed path. Some other agency which can provide the nonelectrostatic force is necessary.

In the case of a circuit in steady state (constant current) we can equate the nonelectrical work rate (power) to the rate of dissipation of electric energy into heat, to write

$$\mathcal{E}i = i^2R \tag{6.33}$$

Here we are assuming a simple circuit with only one path for the current (Fig. 6.10). The resistance R includes all the dissipative elements in the entire circuit.

In cases where the source of emf is localized, as in a battery, the losses in the circuit may be divided into losses *within* the source of emf and losses in the external circuit. Internal losses have the effect of lowering the potential difference between the terminals of a source of emf when current is drawn from the source. When this lowering is proportional to the current drawn, as is often the case, the behavior can be characterized by an *internal resistance r*. The graph of Fig. 6.15

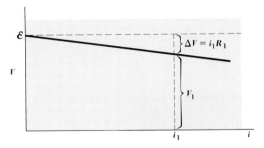

Fig. 6.15   *Output voltage of a source of emf versus current. At a current i_1 there is a resistive voltage drop $V = i_1 r_i$ within the source, leaving a potential difference V_1 between electrodes.*

shows an example of this behavior. For zero current the terminal voltage equals the emf ε. When current is drawn, the voltage is $\varepsilon - \Delta V$, where ΔV is proportional to current, or

$$\Delta V = ir \qquad \text{volts}$$

Internal resistance in a source of emf has the same effect on current in a circuit as an additional resistance in series with the source. Strictly speaking, only when there is a constant slope to the iV curve can the internal resistance be defined accurately. Chemical cells behave linearly over a fairly wide current range but with large current the linear relation no longer holds.

Within the range of currents which allow description of the output voltage of a power source in terms of an internal resistance, it is easy to find the behavior of a circuit having any given external resistance R. Thus we consider the emf ε in series with the sum $R + r$ of internal and external resistance, as in Fig. 6.16. Ohm's law then gives

$$\varepsilon = i(R + r) \qquad \text{or} \qquad \varepsilon - ir = iR \tag{6.34}$$

Fig. 6.16   *Schematic diagram showing internal resistance of a source of emf. Source shown is a chemical cell or battery. Battery terminals are at a and b.*

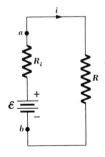

The potential difference across the source terminals or across the external circuit is given by $V = iR$; so we can write

$$V = \varepsilon - ir \tag{6.35}$$

for the voltage output. Equation (6.34) can now be written

$$V = iR$$

It says, simply, that the potential difference at the terminals of a source of emf maintains such a current i that the voltage drop iR equals the potential difference.

Even when the output voltage is not linearly related to the current passing through a source of emf, Eq. (6.35) may be used to characterize the relation between ε and V. The change of slope of the iV curve is accommodated by variation with i in the effective value of r, the internal resistance.

When the internal resistance of the source is negligible compared with the resistance in the external circuit, Eq. (6.35) may be approximated by

$$\varepsilon = V$$

as stated in the previous section.

Sources of emf are commonly classified as *constant-current* or *constant-voltage* sources. For example, a source having a very low internal resistance is approximately a constant-voltage source since the voltage supplied by the emf remains nearly constant for wide variation in the current drawn from it. A constant-current source is one in which the current supplied to a circuit, say, to a load resistor, is nearly independent of the value of the resistor. This behavior is characteristic of a source whose internal resistance is much larger than that of the load resistor. Both of these results are easily shown by means of the circuit equation.

More complicated sources of emf are built which use electronic controls to provide either constant current or constant voltage, despite changes in the load. Any source of emf can be made to give nearly constant current, independent of load, by inserting a large fixed resistance in series with the load resistance. The voltage available to the load will be reduced as a consequence by the amount of the iR drop across the series resistance.

6.6*   Kirchhoff's Rules

In Sec. 6.4 the two principles which apply to the behavior of circuits were explained and applied to simple circuits in which there is only one possible path for the current. Here we apply the same Kirchhoff rules to more complicated circuits with two or more alternative current paths. We consider the example shown in Fig. 6.17. Assuming

Fig. 6.17   Circuit contain-ing alternative current paths. Current can be de-termined by applying the Kirchhoff circuit equations to two loops. $\Sigma i = 0$ is ap-plied at the junctions, and $\Sigma \mathcal{E} = \Sigma iR$ is applied around each loop. One procedure is described here, and an-other in Appendix G.

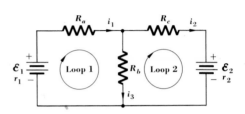

that all emfs and resistance values are known, we wish to apply the two circuit equations

$$\Sigma i = 0 \tag{6.23}$$
$$\Sigma \mathcal{E} = \Sigma iR \tag{6.24}$$

in order to determine the current in each branch. This allows calcu-lation of the voltage at all points in the circuit. Because of the presence of an emf in each of the loops of this circuit, it is not possible to reduce the circuit to a single loop. The procedure is to apply the two Kirch-hoff circuit equations to both loops. This gives two simultaneous equa-tions which can be solved to give the current in all parts of the circuit. There are two commonly used methods for obtaining the necessary equations, and we describe one of them here. Another, the Maxwell loop method, is described in Appendix G.

Figure 6.17 is used here to describe the method. Resistances r_1 and r_2 are included to describe the internal resistance of sources $\mathcal{E}_1$ and $\mathcal{E}_2$. The drawing adopts the usual symbol for chemical batteries to indi-cate the sources of emf. It is assumed that the values of all emfs and resistances are known. The steps to be taken are as follows:

1.   A direction and symbol is assigned to the current in each branch as shown. If in any case the assignment is wrong, the solution to the equa-tions will give a negative sign to those currents whose directions had been incorrectly chosen.

2.   Loops are identified, and a direction is assigned for adding up emfs and iR drops around each loop. There need be no concern to make the travel around two loops having a common section consistent. Thus, in the choice made in Fig. 6.17 for loop 1, the iR drop in R_b is taken from point a to b, while for loop 2 it is taken from point b to a. Not all loops need be considered. In the example given, the loop around the outside of the circuit adds no new information; so only two out of the three possible loops need be used.

3.   The relation between the labeled currents is obtained by applying the current conservation equation, $\Sigma i = 0$, at junctions. In the example, the junction at either a or b gives

$$i_1 = i_2 + i_3$$

4.   The final step is to apply the second circuit equation, $\Sigma \mathcal{E} = \Sigma iR$, around each loop in the direction chosen. Rules for assignment of sign to emfs and iR drops were given in Sec. 6.4. They are as follows:

a.   An emf is positive if the direction of progression around the loop is in the direction of the emf, from negative to positive within the source. Thus, in loop 1, $\mathcal{E}_1$ is positive and in loop 2, $\mathcal{E}_2$ is negative.

b.   An iR voltage drop is positive as in Eq. (6.24) if the direction of progression around the loop is the same as the assumed current direction in the resistance being considered. Thus the equations for the two loops are

$$\text{Loop 1:}\quad \mathcal{E}_1 = i_1 r_1 + i_1 R_a + i_3 R_b$$
$$= i_1(r_1 + R_a) + i_3 R_b$$
$$\text{Loop 2:}\quad -\mathcal{E}_2 = i_2 r_2 - i_3 R_b + i_2 R_c$$
$$= i_2(r_2 + R_c) - i_3 R_b$$

With the addition of the current equation

$$i_1 = i_2 + i_3$$

the three equations can now be solved for the current in each part of the circuit. In many cases it is possible to neglect the internal resistances of the sources of emf. After replacing the symbols by the known values of the resistances, the solutions to these simultaneous equations can be obtained by substitution or by the use of determinants.

The Maxwell loop method described in Appendix G is particularly useful for more complicated circuits.

When the resistance of a complicated network of resistors not connected to a voltage source is wanted, Kirchhoff's rules can be applied by assuming an arbitrary voltage V connected to the network terminals. Once the current through the two terminals is found, the effective resistance of the network is obtained by using

$$R_{\text{eff}} = \frac{V}{i}$$

See Prob. 6.5A for an example of this procedure.

6.7*   The Practical Use of Resistors

The role of resistors in electronic circuits is so important and so universal that study of their properties and uses is important. Students with even a little experience in electronics will find many of the ideas familiar, and may wish to skim over this material rather rapidly. The information is necessary, however, for anyone who wishes to move from the study of the abstract theory of electricity and magnetism to the laboratory use of real circuits.

We begin with a short discussion of the kinds of resistors available commercially and in common use. For applications in which the power dissipation in the resistor will be 2 watts or less, the most common resistor is one made of a composition of powdered graphite in clay. For higher-power applications, or where the appreciable variation of resistance with temperature, characteristic of the graphite resistors, is undesirable, wire-wound resistors are used. The resistance value and the accuracy with which it is known are color-coded on each resistor according to the code given and explained in Table 6.1.

In many applications variable resistors are used in circuits to provide manual control of circuit behavior (such as the volume control on a radio receiver). Variable resistors are made in both graphite and wire-wound varieties. They usually are made as three-terminal devices, with connections at either end and a third whose position can move from one end to the other. Figure 6.18 shows schematic drawings and sketches of such a variable resistor, one connected as a three-terminal device, usually called a *potentiometer* (the total resistance between A and C remains fixed, while the position of terminal B can be adjusted), and the other connected as a two-terminal variable resistor, often called a *rheostat*.

A common problem in electric circuits is the adjustment of a voltage supply source to the requirements of a particular load. Two possible methods involving resistors are suggested in Fig. 6.19a and b. One method simply inserts a resistance R_s in series with the load so that

Table 6.1   Standard Radio Industry Color Code

Color	As significant figure	As decimal multiplier	Tolerance, %
Black	0	1	
Brown	1	10	
Red	2	10^2	
Orange	3	10^3	
Yellow	4	10^4	
Green	5	10^5	
Blue	6	10^6	
Violet	7	10^7	
Gray	8	10^8	
White	9	10^9	
Gold			±5
Silver			±10
No color			±20

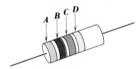

Band-A color indicates first significant figure of resistance in ohms.

Band-B color indicates second significant figure of resistance in ohms.

Band-C color indicates decimal multiplier.

Band-D color indicates tolerance in percent about nominal value.

Examples of Use of Code for Resistor Values

Resistance in ohms and tolerance	Band designation			
	A	B	C	D
3,200 ± 20%	Orange	Red	Red	No band
470 ± 10%	Yellow	Violet	Brown	Silver
1.5 megohms ± 5%	Brown	Green	Green	Gold

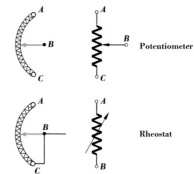

Fig. 6.18 Sketch and schematic drawings of a vari-
able resistor connected as
a three-terminal potenti-
ometer and as a rheostat.

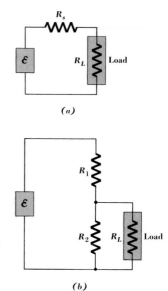

Fig. 6.19 (a) Series R_s used
to adjust voltage applied
to load R_L; (b) voltage di-
vider circuit used for the
same purpose.

the actual voltage applied to the load is correct. Another method,
shown in Fig. 6.19b, uses two resistors, R_1 and R_2, to divide the voltage. If the load resistance R_L is very large compared with R_1 and R_2,
the ratio of voltage drops across R_1 and R_2 is just the ratio of R_1 to R_2.
We leave as a problem the calculation of the voltage at the junction of
R_1 and R_2 when the current through R_L cannot be neglected in comparison with the current through R_2. The method of Fig. 6.19b has the
advantage that even if the load resistance were to vary appreciably
under changing conditions, the voltage applied to the load is essentially constant as long as R_L remains much larger than R_1 and R_2.

The *potentiometer* circuit of Fig. 6.20 uses the voltage-divider arrangement of Fig. 6.19*b*. The potentiometer circuit is used for com-

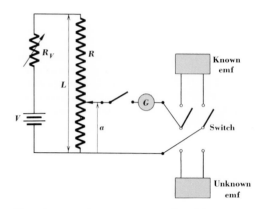

Fig. 6.20 Potentiometer circuit for null-method comparison of two emfs.

paring emfs of batteries or other sources of electric energy. This circuit measures the voltage across the terminals of a source of emf without drawing any current. Such a zero-current measurement is necessary in order to avoid the iR drop caused by the internal resistance of the source when a measure of its true emf is needed. The potentiometer circuit is used as a null device in the following way: V is an auxiliary source of voltage which has a power delivery capable of maintaining a *constant* voltage across its terminals under the load of $R_V + R$ for a long enough time to allow the required comparisons with other sources of emf. The resistance R_V is a variable resistor which allows adjustment of current through the resistance R (and hence of the voltage across R). Resistance R is a uniform-resistance wire. Because of the uniformity of the cross section and the resistivity of the wire of which it is made, the voltage at any point along its length is proportional to the distance along its length from the bottom end. A sliding contact allows connection to any point along the resistor. Thus, taking zero potential at the bottom of the resistor, the voltage V_a at the slide-wire contact is related to the voltage V_R across R by

$$\frac{V_a}{V_R} = \frac{(a/L)R}{R} = \frac{a}{L} \tag{6.36}$$

The sliding contact is connected through a key switch and a galvanometer to one output terminal of the device, and the end of the resistor R is connected to the other output terminal.

The potentiometer circuit is used to compare emfs as follows: A known source of emf is connected across the test terminals, and the current through R and the slide position a is adjusted to give no measurable current through the galvanometer when the switch key is depressed to connect the source of emf to the potentiometer circuit. If the slide-wire position is calibrated in convenient numbers, the position a of the slider can be set to correspond to the known emf of the standard cell, and R_V can then be adjusted to give the required balance of no current through the galvanometer. If this is done, the potentiometer circuit is now calibrated to measure unknown emfs directly. That is, the magnitude of any unknown emf connected to the test terminals is determined by adjusting the slider for null current through the galvanometer when the key switch is depressed. Under these circumstances the unknown emf being measured is read off directly on the calibrated position indicator. It is left as a problem to show that the emf of any source $\mathcal{E}_1$ is related to the emf of another source $\mathcal{E}_2$ with which it is being compared by the relation

$$\frac{\mathcal{E}_1}{\mathcal{E}_2} = \frac{a_1}{a_2} \tag{6.37}$$

where a_1 and a_2 are the null current positions of the slider with first one and then the other source connected.

The term potentiometer is used both to describe the variable-resistance element of Fig. 6.18a and also complete circuits like that of Fig. 6.20.

6.8*   *Measurement of Resistance; Current and Voltage Meters*
In principle, the magnitude of the resistance of a resistor is obtained by making two simultaneous measurements, one of current through the resistor and the other of voltage across it. Then, using Ohm's law, we find

$$R = \frac{V}{i} \quad \text{ohms}$$

The basic instrument for measuring both voltage drops and currents in a circuit is the *galvanometer*. This device measures current by means of magnetic forces. It is discussed in Chap. 8. When used for determining current, the galvanometer is commonly called an *ammeter*. When calibrated to measure current in units of 10^{-6} amp, the instrument is often called a *microammeter*, and when currents are measured in 10^{-3} amp units it is called a *milliammeter*. When used in such a way as to give information on the voltage difference between two points in a circuit, the galvanometer is called a *voltmeter*.

The same kind of basic current instrument is thus used for measuring both current and voltage. Let us first discuss the problem of measuring the current through the resistor R in Fig. 6.21a. Figure

Fig. 6.21 Ammeter placed in a circuit to measure current. r is the internal source resistance. The current will be modified when meter is connected to circuit, adding its resistance R_g. The fractional change in current will be small if $R_g \ll (R + r)$.

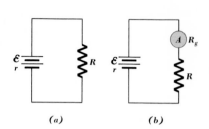

(*a*)   (*b*)

6.21b shows a galvanometer inserted in the otherwise unchanged circuit so that the current through R can be measured. The meter is labeled A to indicate that it is to be used as an ammeter. Since a galvanometer measures current, the meter measures the current passing through the resistor. But has the current the same value as it had prior to inserting the meter? The galvanometer has some internal resistance of its own, say, R_g; so the currents with and without the meter inserted can be compared. If the source of emf supplying the current has an internal resistance r, the circuit equation without the meter inserted is

$$\varepsilon = i_1(R + r)$$

and with the meter inserted,

$$\varepsilon = i_2(R + r + R_g)$$

Thus the fractional change in the current when the meter is inserted is

$$\frac{i_1 - i_2}{i_1} = \frac{R_g}{R + r + R_g} \tag{6.38}$$

as can easily be shown. The smaller R_g is, relative to the total resistance in the circuit, the smaller is the fractional change in the current when the meter is inserted. Furthermore, if the galvanometer has more current sensitivity than necessary in a particular application, the effective meter resistance can be further reduced by placing a *shunt,* or

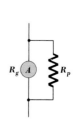

Fig. 6.22   Shunt resistance R_p placed in parallel with current meter. This lowers the effective resistance of the meter and thus minimizes its effect on the circuit. It also allows adjustment of the meter sensitivity.

shorting resistance, R_p, in parallel with the meter, as shown in Fig. 6.22. The effective meter resistance R'_g then becomes

$$R'_g = \frac{R_p R_g}{R_p + R_g} \quad \text{ohms}$$

Appropriate values of R_p can be used to adjust the meter sensitivity to any required value.

We next describe the use of a galvanometer as a voltage-measuring instrument. In Fig. 6.23 a galvanometer is shown placed across the

Fig.   6.23   (a)   Voltmeter placed across resistor to measure voltage drop will modify voltage. If $R_g \gg R$, the fractional change in voltage will be small; (b) use of a series resistance R_s in voltmeter circuit minimizes the change in voltage and also al ows adjustment of voltmeter sensitivity.

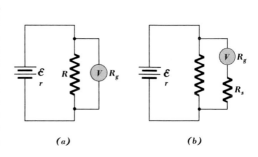

(a)   (b)

terminals of a load resistance R. Since the current in the galvanometer is proportional to the voltage difference between the resistor terminals, the meter can be calibrated as a voltmeter. However, we must ask how much the insertion of the meter in the circuit affects the voltage being measured. We now show that the larger the voltmeter resistance relative to the load resistor to which it is attached, the less will the voltage measured be affected. Without the meter connected, the voltage V_1 across R is obtained from the circuit equation

$$\mathcal{E} = i_1 r + i_1 R$$

where r is the internal resistance of the source of emf plus any additional series resistance in the circuit exclusive of R, and i_1 is the current when the meter is not attached. Thus

$$i_1 = \frac{\mathcal{E}}{R + r}$$

The potential V_1 across the resistor R with the meter not connected is

$$V_1 = i_1 R = \frac{\mathcal{E}}{R + r} R$$

With the meter connected, the resistance of the parallel combination of resistor R and meter with resistance R_g is given by

$$\frac{R R_g}{R + R_g}$$

according to the rule for adding resistances in parallel. The circuit equation now becomes

$$\mathcal{E} = i_2 r + i_2 \frac{R R_g}{R + R_g} = i_2 r + i_2 R A$$

where A stands for $R_g/(R + R_g)$. RA is the resistance of the parallel combination of R and R_g. The total current i_2 with the meter connected is

$$i_2 = \frac{\mathcal{E}}{r + R A}$$

and the voltage measured is

$$V_2 = i_2 R A = \frac{\mathcal{E}}{r + R A} R A$$

We can now calculate the fractional change in the voltage across R when the meter is connected.

$$\frac{V_1 - V_2}{V_1} = \frac{R/(r + R) - RA/(r + RA)}{R/(r + R)} \tag{6.39}$$

If $R_g \gg R$, A approaches unity, and when $A = 1$, we see that no change occurs in the voltage across R. Thus the higher the resistance of the meter relative to R, the less it affects the voltage being measured. If the meter has the necessary sensitivity, it is useful to add further resistance in series with the meter. Galvanometers used as voltmeters usually contain extra series resistance.

With these comments on the galvanometer as used for current and voltage measurements, we show in Fig. 6.24 two methods for the

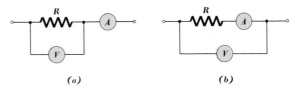

(a)   *(b)*

**Fig. 6.24   Two alternative methods for the simul-
taneous measurement of current through and
voltage across a resistor.**

simultaneous measurement of V and i in a resistor R. From the previous discussion we can see that the effect of the meters on the quantities being measured is negligible if the voltmeter internal resistance is much more than R and the ammeter resistance is much less than R. When the meters do not satisfy these criteria, accurate calculation of the value of R is possible if, in case a, the voltmeter resistivity is known, so that the current reading can be corrected for the current through the voltmeter, or if, in case b, the ammeter resistance is known, so that the voltage drop across it can be corrected for.

Another common method for determining values of resistors is Wheatstone's bridge (invented in 1833, probably by a man named Christie), shown in Fig. 6.25. This is also a null instrument using a

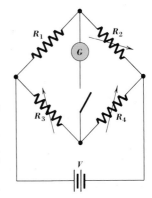

**Fig. 6.25   Wheatstone's
bridge, allowing measure-
ment by null method of an
unknown resistance R_1
in terms of three other
known resistances, R_2,
R_3, R_4.**

galvanometer to indicate "balance." R_1 is here the unknown resistance, and R_2, R_3, R_4 are known resistances, one or more of which are adjustable. No current flows when the switch in the galvanometer circuit is closed, provided that the resistances are related so that

$$\frac{R_1}{R_3} = \frac{R_2}{R_4} \tag{6.40}$$

This allows the unknown resistance to be calculated. This circuit is one example of many *bridge* circuits that allow null measurements to be made, giving high accuracy. This method does not require knowledge of or strict constancy of the voltage source V, and is the most common method of measuring resistance.

A common laboratory meter uses the same galvanometer with different scales and different series and shunt resistances to measure both voltages and currents in several ranges. Problems 6.7A*b* and 6.7A*c* discuss their design as voltmeter and ammeter. In addition, the device contains batteries, and can be connected to measure the current through a resistance connected externally, with the current meter calibrated to measure the resistance directly, as a direct-reading *ohmmeter*. The meter is also arranged to measure ac voltage and currents by means of a solid-state rectifier crystal which converts the ac to a dc signal, and which we shall discuss later.

In Chap. 11 we discuss a convenient method for measuring resistors of very high values from 10^6 to perhaps 10^8 ohms, where conventional current-voltage methods become difficult. The method consists of measuring the rate of discharge of a capacitor of known capacitance when one charged plate is connected to the other through the unknown resistor.

A final method we discuss for measuring resistances is particularly important in the case of low-temperature measurements, where most pure metals have very low resistivity. The problem is that if the resistance of a specimen is low, it is necessary to pass rather large currents through it in order to develop large enough voltage difference for easy measurement. But with large currents there is often difficulty in ensuring that essentially all the voltage drop occurs along the body of the specimen, and not at the contacts which carry the test current into and out of the specimen. It is very difficult even with soldered connections to avoid appreciable resistance in the contacts between a metal specimen and the wires connected to it. The circuit shown in Fig. 6.26 is used when accurate measurements are necessary. The volt-

*Fig. 6.26 Four-terminal
method for determining
the resistance of low-
resistivity specimens.
This method minimizes
errors caused by voltage
drops across high-current
density contacts to the
specimen.*

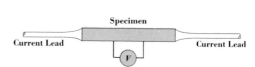

age measurement is isolated from the current leads. Only very small
currents flow in the voltage-measuring circuit; so the voltage drop
across the contacts is negligible. In the circuit shown, the resistivity
of the specimen material can be calculated from the current and voltage measurements, the size and shape of the specimen, and the spacing
between voltage-measuring contacts. The resistivity is the meaningful
quantity when we are studying properties of materials, since the resistance of a given specimen depends on both the material and its
shape and size.

Table 6.2 lists the resistivities at room temperature of a number
of metals in the order of increasing resistivity. The values listed in the
table are of practical importance (we see why copper wires are used as
electrical conductors) but often may be seriously affected by impurity
content. The noble metals copper, silver, and gold are easily purified,
to an extent that the room-temperature resistivities are very little influenced by the impurities normally present. By contrast, a metal like
beryllium is so difficult to purify that its position in the table would
presumably be much higher if it could be made purer.

An interesting sidelight on the use of aluminum wires for high-
voltage transmission lines is that, while the resistivity of aluminum is
less than that of copper, its density is so much less than that of copper
that for equal weights of wire, aluminum has a lower resistance for a
given length than copper. Since thermal effects can have much influence on electrical conductivity, resistivities of very pure specimens at
very low temperatures are needed for useful comparison of basic metallic properties. These matters are briefly discussed in the following
chapter.

6.9 Comments on Chapter 6

This chapter sets the stage for later treatment of many kinds of circuits. The familiar ideas of current and current density are defined.

Table 6.2 *Resistivities*
of Metals

[*At room temperature* (300°K);
listed in order of increasing resistivity]

Metal	Resistivity ρ, ohm-m†
Ag	1.4×10^{-8}
Cu	1.7
Au	2.4
Al	2.8
Na	4.3
W	5.3
Zn	5.7
K	6.1
Ni	7.0
Li	8.5
Fe	9.8
Pt	10.0
Be	10.1
Sn	11.5
Rb	11.6
Cr	12.9
Nb	14.5
Cs	19.0
Pb	19.8
Hg	95
Bi	119

† Many tables list resistivities in ohm-centimeters. In ohm-centimeters, the resistivity of Ag is 1.4×10^{-6}.

Current density, the rate of charge transport per unit area of cross section, can be defined as a vector $\mathbf{j}$, where

$$\mathbf{j} = ne\mathbf{v} \qquad \text{amp/m}^2 \tag{6.4}$$

and $\mathbf{v}$ is the drift velocity of the charge carriers.

Current is defined as the rate of total charge transport, integrated over the cross section of the entire conducting path. Thus we find

$$i = \frac{dq}{dt} = \int \mathbf{j} \cdot d\mathbf{s} \qquad \text{amp} \tag{6.2}$$

We need not necessarily express i in vector form. The positive direction of i is arbitrarily assumed, in accord with universal practice, to be that of the drift velocity of *positive* charge carriers.

If the current density is uniform over a cross-section area A, Eq. (6.4) becomes, when integrated,

$$i = nevA \qquad \text{amp}$$

The resistance R of a conductor is defined by

$$V = iR \qquad \text{volts} \tag{6.6}$$

where R (ohms) is the ratio of voltage applied across the ends of a conductor, and i is the resulting current in amperes.

Ohm's law can be written in the microscopic form, giving the current density $\mathbf{j}$ in terms of the field $\mathbf{E}$ in a region.

$$\mathbf{j} = \sigma \mathbf{E} \tag{6.15}$$

where the constant σ, the conductivity, measured in $(\text{ohm-meter})^{-1}$, describes the conducting property of the material involved, independent of its geometry. For simple uniform cross-section geometries, the resistance of a specimen can be calculated using

$$R = \frac{1}{\sigma}\frac{L}{A} = \rho\frac{L}{A} \qquad \text{ohms} \tag{6.16}$$

where the cross-section area is A, and the length is L. The resistivity ρ used above is the reciprocal of σ.

The effect of several resistors in series is seen to be additive, according to the rule

$$R_{\text{equiv}} = \sum_i R_i \tag{6.17}$$

Resistors in parallel combine according to reciprocals

$$\frac{1}{R_{\text{equiv}}} = \sum_i \frac{1}{R_i} \tag{6.18}$$

Some circuits involving more than one loop cannot be reduced to simple parallel and series combinations of resistances. Kirchhoff's rules provide the ideas necessary for determining currents in all branches when all emfs and resistance values are known. These rules involve conservation of current at all points in a circuit, written

$$\Sigma i = 0 \tag{6.23}$$

and, from the properties of a static field and Ohm's law,

$$\Sigma\mathcal{E} = \Sigma iR \tag{6.24}$$

The first equation, applied at all branch points in a circuit, fixes the relation between currents, and the second equation, applied around all closed loops, gives the additional relationships necessary to solve for actual values of all currents. One method of applying the two Kirchhoff rules to complicated circuits is given in Sec. 6.6, and in Appendix G the alternative method of Maxwell loops is outlined. This latter method is particularly useful for more complicated circuits.

The source of energy which produces the flow of charge around the closed path of a circuit is called an electromotive force, or emf, $\mathcal{E}$. The emf is defined by

$$\mathcal{E} = \frac{dW}{dq} \quad \text{joules/coul, or volts} \tag{6.28}$$

as the work per unit charge done by the energy source in carrying charge all the way around a circuit. From this definition it follows that the rate of doing work by the source of emf is given by

$$P = \mathcal{E}i \quad \text{watts} \tag{6.29}$$

where i is the current through the source. If the internal resistance within the source of emf is negligible, the power becomes equivalent to

$$P = Vi \quad \text{watts} \tag{6.30}$$

where V is the terminal voltage of the source emf.

Since an electrostatic field cannot do net work on a charge when it moves the charge away from a given point and back to its starting position, electrostatic fields cannot act as sources of emf. Such sources may be chemical, as in a battery, or mechanical.

Corresponding to the rate of expenditure of energy by sources of emf in a circuit is the rate of dissipation of energy in resistive components in a circuit. This rate at which electric energy is converted into heat in a resistance R can be expressed in the alternative forms

$$P = V_R i = i^2 R = \frac{V^2}{R} \tag{6.32}$$

where i is the current through the resistance, and V_R the voltage difference between its terminals.

We have said nothing about the factors which determine the resistivity of various materials. The entire discussion is based on the simple experimental fact that the current through conducting bodies is proportional to the voltage maintained across it. Later we develop the ideas which allow us to understand the physical reasons for this behavior.

There are usually significant energy losses within a source of emf which result in a lowering of the output voltage of the source when current flows. Often the lowering of output voltage is proportional to the current, in which case the losses can be described in terms of a series internal resistance r. For such cases, the output voltage V varies with current according to the equation

$$V = \varepsilon - ir \tag{6.35}$$

where ε is the emf of the source.

The final sections of the chapter discuss some simple practical problems involved in the use of resistors and in the measurement of resistance values using current and voltage meters.

PROBLEMS

These first problems are included to emphasize the meanings of current, current density, and drift velocity.

6.1A   The current density in a conductor of circular cross section of radius a varies with radius according to $j = j_0 r$. Find the total current.

★6.1B   A current of 10 amp flows through a wire of 1 mm² cross section. If the density of charge carriers in the wire is $10^{27}/\text{m}^3$, find the average drift velocity of the electrons.

6.1C   A point charge q is rotating in a circular orbit of radius r, with an angular velocity ω. What is the current produced by this moving charge?

★6.1D   An insulating disk of radius R, as shown in Fig. P6.1, has a uniform charge density σ on its surface. The disk rotates with an angular velocity

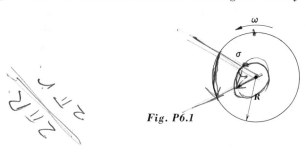

Fig. P6.1

ω. Find the total circulating current. (Write first the expression for the current from the moving charge on a thin ring of radius r and width dr.)

Current passing through a resistance results in the conversion of electric energy into heat.

6.2A   A source of emf causes a constant current i to flow through a resistance R. What is the work done during the time a total charge Q passes through the resistor? What is the rate at which work is being done? What is the rate of heat generation in calories per second in the resistor?

The resistance of simple shapes of material having uniform resistivity (or conductivity) and uniform current density is calculated on the basis of the geometric expression for R.

6.3A   Find the resistance of a block of copper of length 20 cm and cross-section area 2 cm². The conductivity σ of copper is 0.59×10^8 (ohm-m)⁻¹.

★6.3B   A thin square sheet of uniform material is connected to two low-resistance conductors along opposite sides, as shown in Fig. P6.2. If

Fig. P6.2

the sheet is 1 in. on each side, the resistance between the two conductors is 1 ohm. What would be the resistance if the same kind of arrangement were used with a sheet 2 in. on each side?

6.3C   A block of material 10 cm long and 2×1 cm in cross section has a resistance between ends of 10^{-4} ohm. What will be its resistance if it is deformed so as to be only 5 cm long and of uniform cross section, assuming no change in its resistivity?

The effective resistance of many complicated series and parallel combinations of separate resistors can be calculated through application of the series and parallel combination rules. The infinite-ladder problem (6.4D) is easily solved by noting that the resistance across ab is the same as across $a'b'$ with the first section removed.

★6.4A a Calculate the resistance between points A and B in Fig. P6.3. $R_1 = 2$ ohms, $R_2 = 3$ ohms, $R_3 = 4$ ohms, $R_4 = 6$ ohms, $R_5 = 5$ ohms.

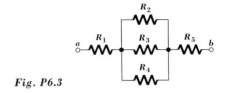

Fig. P6.3

    b   Calculate the power dissipation in each resistor if the potential
difference between *A* and *B* is held at 10 volts.

6.4B   Twelve resistors, each of resistance *R*, are joined to form the edges of
a cube. Find the equivalent resistance between two opposite corners
on a face of the cube.

6.4C   The resistor combinations shown in Fig. P6.4 are called delta and wye
circuits, respectively. With proper choice of R_1', R_2', and R_3', the resist-

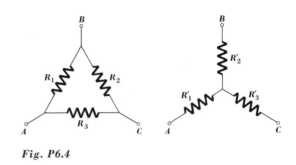

Fig. P6.4

ance between each pair of terminals in the wye circuit can be made the
same as in the delta circuit. Find R_1', R_2', and R_3' in terms of R_1, R_2, and
R_3 to give this equivalence.

★6.4D   Find the effective resistance (resistance between *a* and *b*) of an infinitely long ladder of resistors, as shown in Fig. P6.5, each having
resistance *R*.

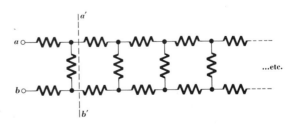

Fig. P6.5

6.4E In the circuit shown in Fig. P6.6 the internal resistance of the battery
(not shown) is 1 ohm. The resistance of each resistor in ohms is given

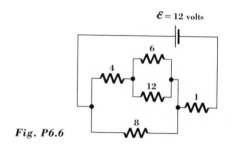

Fig. P6.6

in the diagram. Find
a The current in the battery
b The current in each resistor
c The power dissipation in each resistor and in the internal resistance of the battery

More complicated combinations of resistors cannot be separated into simple
series-parallel combinations. The more general method of Kirchhoff's rules is
required, as in the examples here.

★6.5A Find the current in each branch of the circuit shown in Fig. P6.7.
V_1 = 5 volts, V_2 = 2 volts, R_1 = 3 ohms, R_2 = 2 ohms, R_3 = 4 ohms.

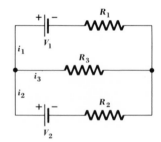

Fig. P6.7

6.5B In Fig. P6.8
a Find the equivalent resistance of the network between points a and
b in terms of R_1, R_2, R.
b Find the numerical value of the equivalent resistance if R_1 = 4,
R_2 = 2, R = 1.
c Compare (b) with the equivalent resistance when R is removed.

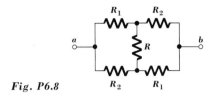

Fig. P6.8

The internal resistance of a source of emf is used to determine the voltage drop and power dissipation within the source itself.

★6.6A The internal resistance of a dry cell gradually increases with age, even though the cell is not used. The emf, however, remains fairly constant at about 1.5 volts. Dry cells are often tested for age at the time of purchase by connecting an ammeter directly across the terminals of the cell and reading the current. The resistance of the ammeter is so small that the cell is practically short-circuited.

    a The short-circuit current of a fresh No. 6 dry cell is about 30 amp. Approximately what is the internal resistance?

    b What is the internal resistance if the short-circuit current is only 10 amp?

6.6B In the circuit of Fig. P6.9 the internal resistance of the battery is R_i. Find the ratio of R_i/R_L to obtain maximum power dissipation in R_L, the load resistance.

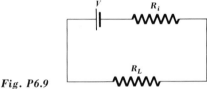

Fig. P6.9

Voltmeters and ammeters are constructed by adding appropriate series or parallel resistors to a galvanometer.

★6.7A *a* A galvanometer gives full-scale deflection when $i = 1$ milliampere (ma). It is desired to make it into a voltmeter giving full-scale deflection for 10 volts. The internal resistance of the galvanometer is 10 ohms. Tell how to do this. (Give diagram and necessary information.)

    b If it is needed, instead, as an ammeter to read full scale for 10 ma, how can this be done? (Give diagram and necessary information.)

6.7B Figure P6.10 shows the internal wiring of a three-scale voltmeter whose binding posts are marked 3, 15, and 150 volts, respectively. The internal

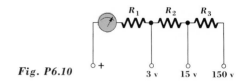

Fig. P6.10

resistance of the moving-coil galvanometer used is 15 ohms, and a current of 1 ma in the coil causes it to deflect full scale. Find the resistances and the overall resistance of the voltmeter on each of its ranges.

*6.7C The internal resistance of the moving-coil galvanometer in the ammeter shown in Fig. P6.11 is 25 ohms, and it deflects full scale with a current

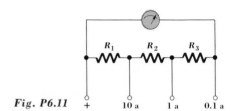

Fig. P6.11

of 0.01 amp. Find the magnitude of the resistances required to make a multirange ammeter deflecting full scale with currents of 10, 1, and 0.1 amp, respectively.

7

*the physics of conductivity

7.1* Introduction*

In this chapter we introduce the ideas which allow us to understand why metals conduct electricity and the various factors which influence conductivity. In addition, we extend our interest beyond metals and discuss the factors which cause some materials to be good conductors (metals), some semiconductors, and some insulators.

The most important guideline that can be laid down is that, although the simple idea of conductivity by conduction electrons in a metal can be explained qualitatively by means of classical physics, there is a large body of knowledge about metallic conduction which can be understood only on the basis of quantum mechanics. Quantum ideas have made possible the great strides in understanding the structure and behavior of atoms since early in this century. When we consider the complex behavior of semiconductors, we find it necessary, at the very beginning, to invoke quantum-mechanical ideas if we are to make any progress in understanding the observed phenomena.

Although the subject of electricity and magnetism is generally treated as classical, the study of electrical or magnetic effects in solids always forces attention on quantum-mechanical principles. This is not surprising, since quantum physics was developed by studying the behavior of atoms, and solids are simply assemblages of atoms. The subjects covered in this chapter are included because of the practical importance of matter in many electrical phenomena. We begin with a classical treatment leading to Ohm's law for conductivity. This is later modified to give a more useful model in quantum-mechanical terms.

7.2* *Conductivity in Metals, Classical Model*

A metal may be considered as a lattice of atoms in fixed positions and a large density of mobile electrons whose motion produces current. These *conduction* electrons come from the atoms of the metal, leaving the atoms as positively charged ions.

We have seen in Chap. 6 that the current which flows in a piece of metal is proportional to the voltage difference existing between the two ends. This was expressed formally as Ohm's law,

$$V = iR \tag{6.6}$$

where R is the resistance of the metal, a quantity depending on the nature of the metal and on its size and shape. We further found a more general expression for the same linear response of the current, but which eliminates the dependence of the current on specimen size and shape. This form of Ohm's law was written

$$\mathbf{j} = \sigma \mathbf{E} \tag{6.15}$$

where $\mathbf{j}$ = current density

σ = conductivity of material

$\mathbf{E}$ = field produced within material by applied voltage[1]

Our problem here is to understand the physics behind the experimental fact of Ohm's law. Having seen in Eq. (6.5) that the current in a conductor is proportional to the net drift velocity of the mobile carriers, we must understand how an applied field produces the drift motion.

Although the individual conduction electrons in a metal move at quite high velocities ($\approx 10^6$ m/sec), this motion in the absence of an externally imposed electric field is completely random and results in

---

[1] To bring out the close analogy of the generalized Ohm's law expression of Eq. (6.15) to $V = iR$, we could have chosen the form

$$\mathbf{E} = \mathbf{j}\rho$$

where ρ, the resistivity, is used in place of its reciprocal, σ, the conductivity.

no net flow of charge. We may think of this random motion as resulting from random elastic collisions between the electrons and the ions of the metal lattice. The average time between collisions is known as the *mean free time*, and the average distance traveled between collisions is called the *mean free path*. This same terminology is used in discussing the random motion of molecules in a gas. Because of the random nature of this motion, on the average no net charge is transferred. However, when an electric field is applied to the metal, the path of each electron is bent in its random motion in the direction of the force produced by the field. Figure 7.1 is a crude picture of the effect of the

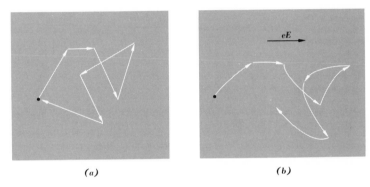

(a)   (b)

Fig. 7.1   *Effect of external electric field on random electron motion. (a) Typical random path without applied field, giving no net travel; (b) random path as modified by external field, giving net drift motion.*

external field in causing the electron paths to curve in the direction of the force to produce a net drift velocity. This curvature results from the acceleration of the charge between collisions. We may assume that on each collision with the lattice, the excess energy picked up by the electron in the external field is lost to the lattice. We now can associate the mean drift velocity **v** with the acceleration due to the externally applied electric field. Figure 7.2 shows a qualitative picture of the way in which the excess velocity produced by the external field varies with

Fig. 7.2   *Time variation of drift velocity produced by external field. The accumulated drift velocity goes to zero at each collision with the lattice.*

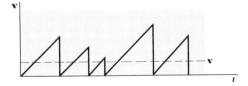

time. During each free path the electric field produces a uniform acceleration in the field force direction ($\mathbf{F} = e\mathbf{E}$). Each collision reduces the accumulated velocity produced by the external field to zero, after which the acceleration again causes a uniform velocity increase until the next collision with the lattice. The random nature of the collisions results in wide fluctuations in the time between collisions, as shown. The drift velocity is the time average of this motion caused by the accelerations in the field. This drift velocity is superposed on the much higher random velocity of the electrons.

Since the drift velocity is always much less than the random velocity[1] of the electrons, the mean time between collisions is independent of the applied field. Thus the only factor influencing the drift velocity is the acceleration due to the electric field force $\mathbf{E}e$ acting on the electrons. Since the current is proportional to the drift velocity, we have at once

$$i \propto E \tag{7.1}$$

which is the result we needed in order to understand Ohm's law. The current is proportional to the force imposed on the electrons by the electric field because of the effect of the collisions between electrons and lattice. The situation is similar to viscous flow, as, for example, the velocity of fall of raindrops in air under gravitational force. The raindrops fall with a constant velocity that depends upon the gravitational force acting on them. If, instead, the raindrops were in free fall, their velocity would increase continuously, as would the current in the absence of the viscous effect of collisions.

For the simple case of a conductor of uniform cross section and length L, an applied potential difference V between the ends gives rise to a uniform field $E = V/L$. For this conductor, we may replace the field E in the proportionality equation (7.1) by V/L to get

$$i \propto V$$

or

$$V = iR \tag{6.6}$$

where R, the resistance, gives the proportionality between V and i. This is the usual expression of Ohm's law, already discussed from an experimental point of view, in Chap. 6.

---

[1] The high random velocity of conduction electrons in a metal can be understood only from quantum-mechanical ideas. We discuss this in the next section.

Although electric fields in metals vanish in equilibrium, the present case is not one of equilibrium, but of steady state. That is, charge carriers (electrons, in the case of metals) are steadily moving under the influence of the field and are prevented from producing a zero field situation by the potential difference maintained between the two ends of the conductor.

We have seen that the drift velocity of conduction electrons in an applied field is affected by the mean free path, or the average time between collisions of the electrons with the lattice. It is possible to express the resistance R of a metal specimen in terms of the charge and mass of the conduction electrons and their *relaxation time*. In terms of the average drift velocity $\bar{v}$, the current density is given by

$$j = ne\bar{v} \qquad \text{amp/m}^2 \tag{6.4}$$

The external force which causes the electron drift is

$$\mathbf{F} = e\mathbf{E}$$

In order to determine the drift velocity produced by this force we may ask at some arbitrary time how long on the average it has been since each carrier suffered its last collision. If this average time interval is called τ, the relaxation time, then the average impulse $\int \mathbf{F}\, dt$ which has acted on the carriers at any time we choose to look is

$$\mathbf{F}\tau = e\mathbf{E}\tau \tag{7.2}$$

As a result, the average drift momentum acquired by carriers in a field $\mathbf{E}$ is

$$m\bar{\mathbf{v}} = e\mathbf{E}\tau$$

or

$$\bar{\mathbf{v}} = \frac{e\mathbf{E}}{m}\tau \tag{7.3}$$

We must pause briefly to note the consequences of the random nature of the collision process. Suppose we could look at the sequence of collisions for the whole assembly of moving electrons. If we looked at any arbitrary instant, τ would be the average time since the last collision, averaged over all the participating electrons. But because of the independence of each collision event on what has happened earlier, this time would also be the average time until the next collision, and perhaps even more surprising, τ would also measure the average time between collisions.[1]

The relaxation time has another equivalent interpretation. It measures the rate at which the current or current density changes when the applied field is suddenly turned off, turned on, or changed. Thus, if at $t = 0$, the field is suddenly turned off, the current follows the exponential law

$$i(t) = i_0 e^{-t/\tau} \tag{7.4a}$$

If we apply Eq. (7.3) to Eq. (6.4), we find

$$\mathbf{j} = ne\bar{\mathbf{v}} = \frac{ne^2}{m} \mathbf{E} \tag{7.4b}$$

By comparison with Eq. (6.30), we find the expression for the conductivity:

$$\sigma = \frac{ne^2\tau}{m} \quad \text{(ohm-m)}^{-1} \tag{7.5a}$$

or for the resistivity:

$$\rho = \frac{m}{ne^2\tau} \quad \text{ohm-m} \tag{7.5b}$$

This equation is useful in showing that the conductivity of a metal depends on the density of conduction electrons, their mass and charge, and on a relaxation time. However, there are many phenomena which show that the classical model is not satisfactory. We mention here one of the simplest, the effect of temperature on conductivity, especially in very pure metals. Resistance measurements on pure metals show a remarkable increase in conductivity as the temperature is reduced from room temperature to, say, the 4.2°K of liquid helium. A very pure single crystal of copper has, for example, shown a ratio of its conductivities at 4.2 and 300°K of more than 20,000, and for some other metals ratios four or five times larger than this

---

[1] This apparently strange result is easily understood when we examine the probability of another random process. What is the probability that an ace comes up when a single gaming die is thrown? Because the result of each throw is independent of what happened on the previous throw, if we start observations at any arbitrary time, six throws on the average will bring up the ace, and the average number of throws between aces will also be six. In addition, if we look at any arbitrary time, the average number of throws since the last ace came up will also be six.

have been found. Less pure metals or mixtures of metals show much less variation of conductivity with temperature. For example, brass, a mixture of copper and zinc, shows a conductivity ratio $\sigma_{4°}/\sigma_{300°}$ of only a factor of 4.

The cause of the drastic temperature dependence of conductivity is the variation of τ with temperature, as suggested by Eq. (7.5). But this variation in τ can only be explained by a quantum-mechanical argument, which is discussed in the next section.

7.3* The Physics of Conductivity, Quantum-mechanical Model

The conclusions from the quantum-mechanical study of conductivity will now be stated, and in the following section, the question of why some materials are metals, some semiconductors, and some insulators will be considered.

The crucial idea which allows us to explain the large effect of temperature on conductivity is the wavelike property of electrons. Conduction electrons in solids are described in quantum mechanics by *wave functions*, which describe their wave properties. The wavelike properties of particles on an atomic or subatomic scale were first demonstrated directly by Davisson and Germer in the United States and by G. P. Thomson in Great Britain in 1927. Thomson's experiment allowed a beam of monoenergetic electrons to fall on a photographic plate after passing through a thin metallic film. The electrons exposed the film where they hit, and the developed image which resulted showed the *diffraction rings* typical of waves propagated through a regular polycrystalline lattice. Such patterns were easily recognized because of experience with x-ray waves diffracted through crystalline matter. The Davisson and Germer experiments involved electrons diffracted by reflection from a metallic surface, a phenomenon very similar to the transmission through a lattice recorded by Thomson.

The meaning of a wave which is associated with a particle is a central problem of the quantum-mechanical description of nature. A useful point of view is to think of the amplitude of the wave at any point as determining the probability of finding the electron or other particle at that point. Actually, the probability is directly proportional to the *square* of the amplitude. Thus the wave function provides a recipe for determining the probability that an electron is at a particular place. The diffraction rings described above result from the diffraction of electron probability waves, which in turn dictate the probable positions of electrons in the beam after passing through the crystal lattice.

The wave property of conduction electrons provides the key to understanding the very long distances between collisions in nearly perfect crystals at low temperatures. The essential feature is that the wavelike character of the electron makes it sensitive to the entire array of ions through which it travels. If the ions of the crystal are regularly spaced, the classical collision between an electron and ion is unlikely to occur. Only to the extent that ions are misplaced from their regularly spaced positions can events like classical collisions occur. This is very much like the behavior of x-ray waves, which similarly can travel through crystalline matter with great ease. Mean free paths greater than a millimeter have been observed in some pure metal crystals at low temperatures. This means that electrons may travel for distances of more than 10^6 atomic spacings between collisions with the lattice ions.

This wave-lattice picture of electrons in a crystal explains the observed strong temperature dependence of the conductivity. We emphasize that the ease with which electrons slide through a lattice is strongly dependent on the perfectly regular spacing of ions in the lattice. Only with close to perfectly regular spacing can the wave-lattice interaction lead to the almost transparent behavior of the lattice. With this in mind, we can see the cause of strong temperature effects. Just as in a gas, where velocities of the gas molecules are related to the temperature, the vibrational motions of ions of a crystal are dependent on temperature. Only at very low temperatures does thermal agitation become negligible. The motion of each ion about a fixed point takes place very slowly compared with the time an electron is in its vicinity. Therefore the principal effect of thermal motion of the ions is to cause the crystal to look less regularly spaced than it would if the ions were at rest. But this is just the effect to cause drastic reduction of electron mean free paths.

Impurity atoms in a crystal have an effect similar to thermal vibrations. Such atoms affect electrons differently than the crystal atoms. Thus a crystal with impurities is less regular than a pure crystal, and this reduces the electron mean free paths. As a result, impure crystals have lower conductivity than pure crystals. The conductivity is also less temperature-sensitive since, even at very low temperatures, mean free paths are limited by the impurity irregularities.

Ordinary metals, as used in circuits and in many resistors, tend to have a small temperature dependence in the region of room temperature. It is common practice to describe this dependence in terms of the linear resistivity relationship

$$\rho_T = \rho_{20°C}(1 + \alpha \, \Delta T) \tag{7.6}$$

where ΔT is the difference between 20°C and the temperature T. The constant α is the fractional change in resistivity per degree. For most metals α lies in the range of 3.5 to 4 parts in 1,000 per degree centigrade. In certain alloys α is as low as 1 part in 10^5 per degree over an appreciable temperature range. Such alloys are particularly useful for making fixed resistances where variation with temperature is undesirable.

Equation (7.6) is valid over small fractional changes in the absolute temperature.

7.4*   Metals, Semiconductors, and Insulators

The classical model of metals, involving mobile electrons in a lattice, when modified to account for the crucial importance of lattice regularity that is characteristic of the quantum-mechanical electron wave, gives a useful picture of metallic conduction. The classical model, however, is of no use in predicting which substances behave as metals and which do not. This is indeed a rather complicated problem, but the quantum picture provides the basis for the answer. The quantum picture makes it easy to frame the criteria which distinguish the metals from insulators and semiconductors, though which materials should satisfy these criteria are not always easy to determine without actual tests. Finally, the model enables us to understand many of the remarkable properties of semiconductors, which nowadays are so important in electronic technology. We deal in this section with the quantum model as it is used to describe metal and nonmetal behavior, and again we invoke quantum concepts and results without proof.

We begin with an oversimplified model of conduction electrons in a solid, in order to describe some needed consequences of quantum ideas. This model replaces the solid by an empty box in which we imagine the electrons to be placed. The box is not quite empty since, if we placed the high density of electrons that exists in a metal in an empty box, their mutual electrostatic repulsion would pose a serious problem. So we imagine the positive ions of a crystal as spread out smoothly through the box so as to provide an electrically neutral system when the electrons are added. Unreal as it is, this model allows us to consider how the quantum rules affect the disposition of electrons.

The de Broglie relation relates the *wavelength* of the electron waves to electron momentum. If p represents the electron momentum and λ the wavelength, the relation is

$$p = \frac{h}{\lambda} \tag{7.7}$$

where h is the Planck constant, 6.63×10^{-34} joule-sec. Thus, if the energy or momentum of an electron is changed, the wavelength of the wave describing it also changes.

The second important idea we need is the Pauli exclusion principle. Electrons belong to the class of particles obeying the rule that limits the number of particles in each state of a system to one. The description of the state of an electron includes specification of its vector momentum and its angular momentum (spin) state. Since the spin of an electron may take two values, called $+\frac{1}{2}$ and $-\frac{1}{2}$, there is room for two electrons in every possible momentum state. Thus the allowed conduction electron states in a system are described by a set of momentum vectors with certain allowed lengths and directions. Each momentum state can accept two electrons having opposite spin. In order to simplify the discussion we can imagine a "one-dimensional" body in which all momenta are limited to a single direction. In such an artificial situation, Fig. 7.3 gives the relationship between energy,

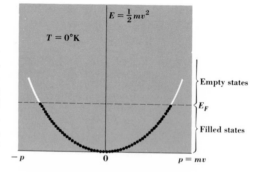

Fig. 7.3 *Energy-momen-tum curve for conduction electron states, free-electron model. Each point represents an occupied state. The Pauli exclusion principle limits occupa-tion of each distinct state to one electron.*

$\frac{1}{2}mv^2$, and momentum, mv. The parabolic curve shows the energy and corresponding momentum of each electron as a point. Negative momentum values correspond to electron motion from right to left. Let us assume that the box is near $0°K$, so that electrons tend to fall to the lowest energy states available. But since only one electron is allowed in each distinct state, as required by the exclusion principle, the more electrons there are in the system the higher are the highest energy occupied states. Each state is indicated schematically by a point on the curve in the figure. The upper states have high energies. In a typical metal, electrons of the highest energy are forced into states which have velocities as high as 10^6 m/sec.

The spacing between allowed states shown in Fig. 7.3 is unreal. The closeness of spacing between allowed momentum values of consecutive states is limited by the boundary conditions imposed on the electron waves by the box, that is, by the size of the specimen of metal. For any size of specimen greater than microscopic, the separation between allowed states is so small that the distribution may be considered essentially continuous.

In a real three-dimensional material, the allowed states can be described by plotting all allowed momentum vectors from some origin. These vectors will point in all possible directions and have all lengths allowed by the boundary conditions imposed by the shape and size of the specimen. The end of each vector arrow represents a momentum state which could be occupied by a pair of electrons having opposite spin. Such a plot provides a three-dimensional array of allowed states. The framework for this three-dimensional plot is called *momentum space*. At low temperatures electrons will seek the lowest unfilled states, and there will be a sharp division between filled and empty states. At higher temperatures there would tend to be some electrons promoted by thermal excitation from states near the top of the occupied states into unoccupied states just above the generally occupied ones. Thus, at higher temperatures, the sharp border between occupied and unoccupied states is somewhat smeared out. In the one-dimensional drawing of Fig. 7.3 the boundary between filled and empty states is shown at the energy E_F, called the *Fermi energy*. In the simplest three-dimensional case the border between filled and empty states is a sphere in momentum space, called the *Fermi surface*. States on the Fermi surface have the same energy over the entire surface. In more complicated situations the surface may be far from spherical.

A very important consequence of the complete filling of states brought about by the exclusion principle is that only those electrons at the top of the distribution can be effective in responding to external forces such as an electric field. This is the reason for the high random velocities of conduction electrons we spoke of earlier. Only the high-velocity electrons participate in the conduction process. The electrons in the lower or midenergy region are in effect unable to respond, since response to an external force involves modification of the electron's momentum, and for all but the electrons at the top in Fig. 7.3, electrons cannot change their states, since all the nearby states are occupied. Thus, in contrast to the classical model, only the electrons at the high-energy limit of the electron distribution are useful in conductivity, since only they can respond to external forces by moving into the nearby empty allowed states just above the occupied states.

The distribution of electrons in energy in a metal is called the *Fermi distribution*. As we have seen, it is characterized by the complete occupation of allowed states up to some maximum, called the *Fermi energy*, and a rapid falloff to zero occupation of higher energy states. The region of partially occupied states at the border between filled and empty states increases with increasing temperature and is of the order of kT in width, where k is the Boltzmann constant and T the absolute temperature. The reason for this is that kT is the measure of the average energy available from the thermal vibrational motions of the ions in the crystal lattice. There is a reasonable probability that conduction electrons will absorb amounts of energy in the range of kT and be boosted into higher-energy empty states above the Fermi surface.

It is a problem in statistical mechanics to work out the details of the thermal excitation of electrons in the energy region near the Fermi surface. Here we exhibit the qualitative nature of the calculations without details. The first step is to determine a parameter called the fractional filling f of states as a function of energy. This quantity depends on temperature, and a typical plot at some fixed temperature is shown in Fig. 7.4. When all available states are occupied by electrons, the

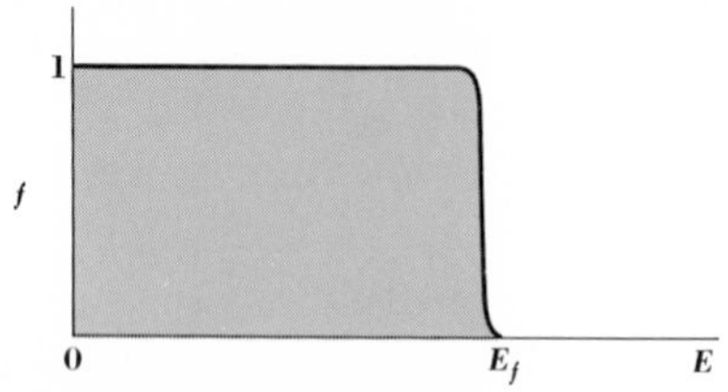

Fig. 7.4   Fractional filling of available electron states by conduction electrons.

filling is complete and $f = 1$. At energies far above E_F, there are no electrons; so $f = 0$. In between, in the region near E_F, there is a gradual transition from all filled to all empty states as we move up in energy through E_F. The Fermi energy is defined as that energy for which f is just ½, meaning that states are 50 percent occupied.

One more step is required after f is determined. The number of allowed states in a given energy interval, called the density of states, varies with energy. Thus the number of electrons in any interval is obtained by multiplying the density of states by the fraction f. A typical result for 0°K is shown in Fig. 7.5a, and at a high temperature in Fig. 7.5b.

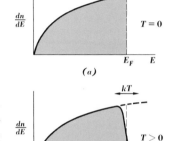

Fig. 7.5 Density of occupied conduction electron states. (a) At $T = 0$, occupied states cut off sharply; (b) at $T > 0$, cutoff is spread out slightly by thermal excitations.

The seemingly strange behavior resulting from the exclusion principle is perhaps easier to accept if we relate it to the similar behavior of electrons in atoms. The exclusion principle forces the electrons surrounding a nucleus into consecutive states to form the familiar shell-like occupation of states in atoms. A piece of metal in effect acts like a gigantic superatom, as far as the exclusion principle is concerned. This simply reflects the fact that the wave function which describes a conduction electron state in a metal exists over the entire metal volume.

To learn more, we must add an additional step to our model. We must realize that the electrons are not really free, but that there is a very special kind of interaction between the lattice and electrons which results from the regular spacing of ions in the lattice and the wave nature of conduction electrons. Namely, for certain wavelengths, interference effects between the electron wave and the lattice allow ions of the entire lattice to act in unison to change the momentum of the electron.

Once we get used to the idea that wave functions describe the behavior of electrons, it is easy to see how this new effect comes about.

It is exactly analogous to the phenomenon of x-ray diffraction by a crystal lattice. We describe the situation first in terms of x-rays incident on a crystal. There are certain angles of incidence of a given x-ray beam on a crystal for which each atom or ion in the crystal reflects the wave in the same way, so that the entire beam is reflected. The requirement for this massive reflection process in which multitudes of atoms participate is that the reflected wavelets from each atom add up to give a coherent wave in the reflected-wave direction, which is the sum of the wavelets reflected by each atom. The condition for the critical reflection condition is suggested in Fig. 7.6, where we show a

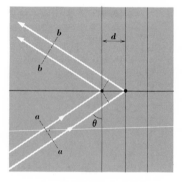

Fig. 7.6 Construction showing interference between reflected x-rays from successive layers of atoms in a crystal. If path difference is an integer times the wavelength, the waves add by constructive interference.

set of crystal planes as parallel lines spaced a distance d apart. aa is the wavefront of an x-ray beam incident on the crystal. We examine the reflections from two atoms, one on each of two crystal planes. One ray is incident on each atom. We ask whether or not a reflected wave exists, giving a wavefront bb as shown. As far as the two atoms are concerned, we can see that if the path lengths for the two rays from aa to bb differ in length by an integral number of wavelengths, the reflected waves at bb will be in phase, and the resulting wave will have an amplitude which is the sum of the reflections from the two atoms. But if this is true for these two atoms, it is also true for atoms in other planes, and indeed for all atoms upon which the x-ray beam is incident in the crystal.

This behavior of waves in regularly spaced lattices is called constructive interference. The criterion that the waves traveling by different paths end up in phase leads to the equation

$$2d \sin \theta = n\lambda \tag{7.8a}$$

where θ is the angle between the incident wave and the crystal planes, and n is an integer. This is the Bragg equation for x-ray diffraction. It also applies to electron waves in a crystal lattice. Of particular interest for the discussion to follow is the case of normal incidence, for which θ is 90° and the Bragg equation is

$$2d = n\lambda \tag{7.8b}$$

The effect of this wave-scattering mechanism is discussed here only in a qualitative way. We show a curve of the effect of this lattice-electron interaction on the one-dimensional energy-momentum plot for electrons in Fig. 7.7. What has happened is that the formerly smooth

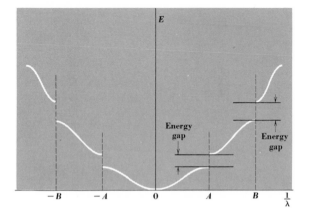

Fig. 7.7   *Energy-momentum diagram showing gap in allowed energy levels brought about by reflection of electron waves by the crystal lattice.*

energy-momentum parabola has been modified to produce some gaps in the curve within which no electron states are allowed. These energy gaps are closely involved in the metal-nonmetal characteristics of matter. Before discussing the effect of the gaps, let us see the qualitative reasons for their existence.

The electron wavelengths at the positions $\pm A$ and $\pm B$ are just those which satisfy the Bragg equation for normal incidence. This means that electrons which have this wavelength get scattered back and forth continuously by the entire crystal. This results in a standing wave, which means in effect that, at these critical places on the graph, electrons have zero velocity.

Suppose an electron wave is traveling through a crystal in a direction normal to a principal plane of the crystal and that the Bragg equation is not satisfied. For example, suppose that the electron momentum is such that, instead of Eq. (7.8), the wavelength satisfies

$$2d = \lambda(n + \tfrac{1}{2}) \tag{7.9}$$

As a result, wavelets reflected from atoms in successive planes will be just out of phase with one another. As a result, *no reflected wave appears.* The electron wave travels through unimpeded.

In contrast, suppose an electron wave exists which satisfies Eq. (7.8a), the Bragg reflection equation. In this case the reflected wavelets add in phase to give complete reflection. But then the reflected wave is reflected again, and this process of reflection and back reflection continues. Under these circumstances an electron wave cannot propagate through the crystal. The result is that a standing wave is set up.

In Fig. 7.7 this kind of multiple internal reflection takes place at values of momentum of $\pm A$ and $\pm B$. At these points on the momentum axis, electron wavelengths satisfy the Bragg equation, $2d = n\lambda$. Electrons at these points on the diagram are described by standing waves and therefore have zero velocity.[1] The quantum-mechanical solutions to the wave equation for electrons of these critical wavelengths are double-valued, and both solutions imply electrons at rest. One solution involves a high probability that the electrons are close to the positive ions, and the other that the electrons are more likely to be in the space between ions. The difference in energies results from the difference in electrostatic potential energies of these two contrasting situations. But for our needs, the important aspect of this result is the existence of bands of allowed energy states, separated by *energy gaps* within which no states can exist in a perfect crystal.

These results are easier to describe than to derive in detail, but once they are available, they are extremely useful. For example, in a simple crystal, such as copper, it turns out that the number of states in the lowest energy band is just sufficient to accommodate two electrons per crystal atom below the first energy gap. But copper atoms become singly ionized in a copper crystal; so each atom contributes one electron to the conduction electrons, and just half of the available levels below the gap are occupied by electrons. As a result electrons at

---

[1] It may seem surprising that electrons which have nonzero momentum have zero velocity. But the parameter we have plotted, $1/\lambda$, is proportional to the true momentum of an electron only if we are describing a free electron. In this critical situation, where the electron is continuously reflected by the lattice, the electron is far from free, and the momentum is really a measure only of the wavelength of the electron wave, and not a measure of its velocity.

the top of the distribution can be lifted into new momentum states by an applied external field, since unoccupied levels are available adjacent to the highest filled states. This allows the electrons in copper to respond to external fields and makes copper a conductor (metal). Figure 7.8 shows a simplified one-dimensional drawing of the occupation of

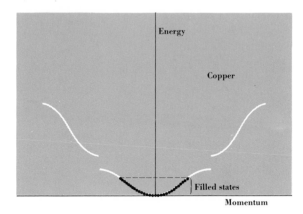

Fig. 7.8   Simplified one-dimensional energy diagram for copper, showing partially filled lowest energy band. The unoccupied states in this band allow conduction and make copper a metal.

states by conduction electrons in copper. Electrons fill the available states up to an energy E_F, and those close to E_F can be moved into other states above E_F by the energy provided by an external field. The number of electrons which can be accommodated in an energy band depends on the crystal structure; so information on structure, as well as on the number of electrons per atom contributed to the conduction states, is necessary to estimate the filling of available states.

Another example of a metal is aluminum, as shown in Fig. 7.9, in which the lowest band is completely filled and the second band is approximately half filled by the three electrons contributed by each atom making up the crystal. There is generally an added complication, which shows up here in aluminum. The position of the gaps is not always the same for waves traveling in different directions in a crystal. This is because the spacing between successive atoms is not the same in different directions. It would be necessary to draw different diagrams, like the one shown, for each possible direction in the crystal, to give a full description of the behavior of electrons. In some directions in aluminum, part of the third band is below the energy E_F

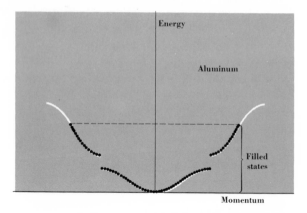

*Fig. 7.9 Simplified one-dimensional energy dia-
gram for aluminum. Lowest band is completely
filled, and does not contribute to conduction.
Next band is approximately half filled, allowing
conduction to occur.*

shown, and as a result there are some electrons in the third band. In
aluminum the first band is completely filled, the second band is partially filled, and a small fraction of the electrons are in the third band.

Although the electrons in the completely filled lowest band of
aluminum are not localized at the ions, they cannot take part in any
way in the process of electrical conductivity. This result follows at
once from the fact that *all* states up to the first energy gap are occupied; so the only way an electron can change its momentum state is to
trade places with another electron in a nearby state. But such an ex-
change of equivalent particles has no effect on the net charge momentum, so that conduction cannot occur in that band.

We now turn to the contrasting case of an insulator. In the case
of the diamond form of carbon crystal the highest filled band is completely filled, while the band above the energy gap is empty. The
width of the gap is 5.2 electron volts. Since the average thermal energy
at room temperature is only $\frac{1}{40}$ electron volt, the chance that an appreciable number of electrons would gain enough energy to jump across
the gap is understandably small. As in any completely filled band, the
electrons cannot be moved to new states by an external field, since no
empty states are available, so that conduction cannot occur. Pure
diamond is a good insulator, since its bands are either completely full
or completely empty, and are separated by a large forbidden energy
gap. Other crystalline forms of carbon, such as graphite, have differ-

ent crystal structures, and gap positions are such that there are partially filled bands. As a result, these other forms are not insulators.

Now turning to the crystals silicon and germanium, which also
have the diamond structure and are in the same group in the periodic
table of elements, we might expect, correctly, that the bands would in
both cases be completely empty or full as in diamond. But there is a
contrast, since the gaps in silicon and germanium are much smaller,
1.08 and 0.8 electron volts, respectively. The size of the gap depends
on the difference in energy between the two standing-wave solutions
of the critical wavelength at which the gap occurs. This energy difference depends on the details of the potential distribution around each
atom in the crystal. Its determination is a complicated problem. As a
result of the smaller gaps in germanium and silicon, both materials are
classed as semiconductors. In both cases statistical fluctuations in the
energies of individual electrons allow some of them to be excited into
the many available states in partially filled bands. In semiconductors,
gaps are small enough so that some electrons are always present in the
band above the gap, called the *conduction* band, leaving some empty
states in the otherwise filled lower band, called the *valence* band. In
Fig. 7.10 a one-dimensional plot is given of the distribution of electrons in a semiconductor.

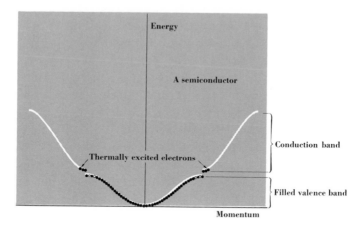

*Fig. 7.10   Simplified energy diagram for a semiconductor.
The highest completely filled band is called the valence
band. The energy gap to the next higher band, called the
conduction band, is small enough to allow some electrons
to be excited into it. Vacant states left behind in the
valence band are described as holes. Both holes and
excited electrons contribute to conduction.*

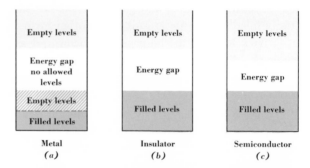

Fig. 7.11 Energy-band diagrams for crystalline
solids. (a) In a metal there are empty allowed
states adjacent to filled states; (b) in an insulator the highest filled band is completely filled
and other allowed states are separated by a
wide forbidden energy gap; (c) in a semiconductor the highest filled band is completely
filled but the forbidden gap is narrow enough
to allow thermal excitation to bring some electrons into the upper levels above the gap.

The contrast between the nature of metals, insulators, and semiconductors on the basis of quantum ideas is shown in Fig. 7.11. In a
metal there are empty states at energies between that of the filled
states and the region of the energy gap. This allows some electrons to
change their states, and thus to conduct under the influence of an externally applied electric field. In the insulator a band of states is completely filled with electrons up to a gap which is so wide that normally
no electrons can be excited up into an upper band. Since the mobile
electrons completely fill all the available states in the occupied band,
they cannot respond to an external field, and the material is a nonconductor, or insulator. In semiconductors, the relatively few electrons
excited into the upper band account for the conductivity. Electrons in
the lower band can also participate in the conduction process, by virtue of the empty states resulting when electrons are excited into the
upper band. Thus an electron in the valence band can move into an
empty state in that band, leaving its former state empty. By a series
of such interchanges between filled and empty states, the empty state
in effect can move from state to state and can thus be affected by an
external field. Conduction which results from this motion of empty
states in a nearly filled band is called *hole* conduction.

This model of a semiconductor allows us to understand many

properties of interest. We can easily explain why, in contrast to metals, electrical conductivity *increases* with temperature in semiconductors. Since at higher temperatures more electrons are excited into the conduction band and more holes are left behind in the valence band, it is merely the increase in mobile charge density which brings about the higher conductivity at higher temperatures.

We conclude this brief discussion of the theory of semiconductors with a discussion of the remarkable effect of small amounts of impurities on the electrical properties of semiconductors. These effects are described using germanium or silicon as an example. These elements are in group IV in the periodic table, and both form crystal structures like that of carbon in diamond. The special feature of the diamond lattice for our purposes is that each atom has four nearest neighbors. Each atom shares its four valence electrons with its four nearest neighbors, via a double electron bond between all nearest neighbor atoms, as shown schematically in Fig. 7.12. This model accounts

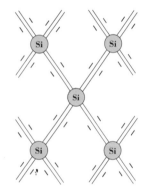

Fig. 7.12   Schematic representation of atoms in a silicon crystal, showing the four neighboring atoms next to each atom.   The true arrangement is three-dimensional. Bonding electron pairs are shown.

for all the valence electrons as being localized between pairs of atoms. The energy states of these electrons comprise the filled valence band of the material. The excitation of one of these electrons into a state in which it is no longer bound and the vacant state left behind by it constitutes the conduction-band electron and the hole in the valence band, respectively.

Consider the effect of two kinds of impurity atoms which, when they are introduced into the crystals, replace Si or Ge atoms in the lattice. First consider group V atoms such as P, As, or Sb. Since there are five valence electrons rather than four as in Ge or Si, one more electron will be required in the vicinity of the atom to maintain neutrality than is needed to fill the bonding positions. This extra electron is bound to the impurity atom only by the coulomb force of attraction to the nucleus, and is held much less tightly than the electrons that participate in the electron bonding between atoms. As a result, the *extra* electrons contributed by group V impurity atoms can be raised into the conduction band by the absorption of much smaller energies to overcome the coulomb force than those required for raising group IV electrons from a valence band into a conduction band. The situation is shown schematically in Fig. 7.13. The electronic levels pro-

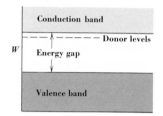

Fig. 7.13   Energy-band diagram of an n-type semiconductor.

duced by the impurity atoms are shown near the top of the forbidden energy gap. At low temperature, electrons occupy these levels, though relatively low energies of excitation lift them into the conduction band. These extra energy levels contributed by the impurity atoms are called *donor* levels, and material into which this type of atom has been introduced is called *n-type* (for negative) material.

When, instead, impurity atoms from group III of the periodic table, such as Al, Ga, or In, are introduced into sites normally filled by the Si or Ge atoms, the situation is reversed. That is, electrical neutrality requires one less than the four electrons needed to fill all the bonding positions between the impurity atom and its neighbors. It takes relatively little energy to remove a nearby bonding electron from the group IV atom and place it in the bonding position at the group III atom. In effect, such a removal of a bonding electron amounts to the production of a hole. This situation is shown in Fig. 7.14. When the

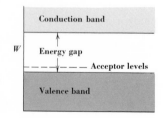

Fig. 7.14   Energy-band diagram of a p-type semiconductor.

acceptor levels of the impurity atoms are filled with excited electrons, holes are left in the valence band, and conductivity can occur via the holes. This kind of material is called *p-type* (positive).

We shall discuss the use of *n-* and *p-type* semiconductors in transistors in Chap. 16.

7.5* Superconductors

No practical discussion of the conduction of electricity in solids is complete without reference to that most exotic of all conductors, the superconductor. In the discussion of metallic conduction we saw that current in a conductor involves the dissipation of energy. Electric potential energy is converted to heat, according to the equation $P = i^2R$, which gives the rate at which heat is produced in a resistance R carrying a current i. Since the initial discovery in 1911 of the zero resistance of mercury metal at the temperature of liquid helium, this fascinating property has aroused the curiosity of both experimental and theoretical physicists. Only recently has substantial progress been made in really understanding the effect.[1]

The zero resistance of a superconductor implies that current flows with no expenditure of energy. Once a current is set up in a loop of superconducting material, it maintains itself indefinitely without the need for an emf to supply the energy.

Figure 7.15 shows an experimental curve of the manner in which

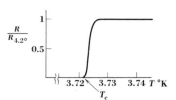

Fig. 7.15 *Rapid decrease in the resistivity of tin as its temperature is reduced to the critical temperature T_c, showing the zero resistivity in the superconducting state.*

the resistivity of metallic tin falls to zero in the region of 3.72°K. Some twenty-three elements show this kind of behavior, as do several hundred compounds. Critical temperatures T_c range from a fraction of 1°K to a maximum of 18.2°K (for Nb_3Sn). The other remarkable fact

[1] Good accounts at a reasonably elementary level are available as follows: B. T. Matthias, Superconductivity, *Sci. Am.*, November, 1957. J. E. Kunzler and M. Tanenbaum, High Field Superconductors, *ibid.*, June, 1962. W. A. Little, Superconductivity at Room Temperature, *ibid.*, February, 1965.

about the superconducting state is that any externally applied magnetic field[1] is always excluded from the body of a superconductor when it becomes superconducting. Magnetic fields of sufficient strength tend to destroy the superconducting state. This can be understood when we find that there is energy stored in a magnetic field, so that its exclusion from the body of a superconductor involves the expenditure of energy by the superconductor, which for high enough fields forces the material to return to the normal conducting state. An external magnetic field at the surface of a superconductor does not fall off to zero sharply within the material, but penetrates slightly into a thin layer at the surface.

Under some conditions a superconductor in a magnetic field will resolve into domains of thin lamina of superconducting states, alternating with normal material. The normal material allows the field to penetrate within it. The field also penetrates slightly into the surfaces of the superconducting regions. Thus, if many thin laminae of superconducting and normal regions are formed, the field is only partially excluded. As a consequence the energy expended in field exclusion is less, and superconducting paths can remain, giving zero resistance in very high applied fields. Recently, superconducting coils producing large fields, up to 100,000 gauss, have been constructed. Such sources of high fields, requiring no continuous expenditure of energy for their maintenance, will no doubt have very important practical applications, as they already have had for research purposes. A serious difficulty in their general use is the very low temperatures at which they must be held. The ability to produce and maintain magnetic fields of very high intensity without the expenditure of megawatts of power as is now necessary might make the production of the high fields required in nuclear particle accelerators, for example, much simpler.

A clear understanding of why under certain conditions conduction electrons can move completely freely through matter has developed only since 1957, although prior to that time many workers had developed clear and elaborately detailed knowledge of many interesting phenomena associated with the superconducting state. We saw in Sec. 7.3 that the exclusion principle affects the electron distribution to force electrons into high energy states when the lower states are already

---

[1] In Chap. 8 we begin the discussion of the magnetic fields, the force field which accounts for that part of the force between current elements or moving charges which is not electrostatic. In practice, magnetic fields are produced by coils carrying currents or by magnetized materials like iron.

occupied. It turns out that, in the superconducting state, electrons are acted upon by a weak attractive force which brings them together to form coupled pairs. The source of this attractive force is complicated to describe in detail, but it has to do with the small distortion of the lattice of positive ions by the motion of electrons through it. Now, for well-understood quantum-mechanical reasons, *pairs* of electrons are not forced to obey the exclusion principle; so each pair that is made can drop to a lower energy level. But the pair of electrons can suffer lattice collisions only if both members can be forced up into the higher energy state. This strange state of affairs allows the paired electrons to move without collisions if the temperature is kept sufficiently low. The successful and very detailed explanation of superconducting phenomena is a remarkable demonstration of the power of quantum-mechanical ideas.

7.6* *Electromotive Force of a Chemical Cell*

In Chap. 11 we discuss the conversion of mechanical to electric energy. One source of emf, the chemical cell, or battery, depends on the chemistry of metals in solution. There are many different types of batteries, but all depend on the same principles. Most students will have studied this problem in a chemistry course. The essential feature of a battery is that it sets up a potential difference between its two electrodes through the action of chemical forces. That is, chemical reactions tend to produce excess negative charge on one electrode and excess positive charge on the other, despite the electric forces which tend to equalize the charges through the mutual attraction of positive and negative charges. In the equilibrium situation, chemical separation of charges continues until the voltage difference, or emf, is just sufficient to prevent further separation of charge.

In order to understand the production of an emf by chemical forces, let us examine the experimental facts. If a piece of metal, say, copper, is placed in a dilute acid solution, there is a tendency for doubly charged copper ions (Cu^{++}) to leave the metal surface and go into solution. This tendency is called *solution pressure*, and results from the attraction of water molecules for the metal ions that overcomes the attraction of the metal surface for the ion. Each ion that goes into solution leaves its electronic charge behind, so that the potential of the metal with respect to the solution becomes increasingly negative. The metal continues to dissolve until an equilibrium state is reached.

This occurs when the rate at which ions escape from the metal is equal to the rate at which they come back to the surface from the solution. Since the rate at which ions come back and stick to the metal surface depends on the number that strike the surface per second, the equilibrium depends on the concentration of ions in solution (and also on the temperature, which affects their velocity). The equilibrium is also affected by the potential difference that has been reached as a result of the electronic charges left behind by the escaping ions. For a given concentration of ions of the metal in solution, each kind of metal comes to a characteristic negative potential upon reaching equilibrium. If we place two electrodes, say, Cu and Zn, in a solution, both some Cu^{++} and some Zn^{++} ions go into solution, leaving a net negative charge on both electrodes. But because of its greater solution pressure, the Zn becomes more negative than the Cu. In this situation, the more negative Zn electrode attracts Cu^{++} ions, which are deposited as Cu atoms and take up some of the net negative charge on the Zn electrode. The equilibrium potential on the Zn electrode is maintained if, on the average, for each Cu^{++} ion captured, a Zn^{++} escapes. Thus there is a plating of Cu on the Zn, and Zn^{++} ions will come into the solution. The equilibrium situation involves a very low Cu^{++} ion concentration and a high Zn^{++} ion concentration.

Suppose the two electrodes are connected together externally, say, through a voltmeter. The equilibrium is thus upset, and electrons flow from the more negative Zn to the Cu electrode. This decreases the negative potential of the Zn electrode, allowing more Zn^{++} ions to go into solution. The Cu electrode tends to become more negative, and thus allows more Cu^{++} to come back from solution. As long as this process can continue, the chemical action continues to maintain the electrode potential difference, and we have a useful battery. In batteries which can be charged electrically, the chemical reactions are reversed when reverse currents are forced through the battery by an external source of emf.

One factor that influences the measured emf of the battery is the *contact potential difference* between the two metals. Two dissimilar metals when placed in contact assume a characteristic difference in potential because of the preferential escape of electrons from one metal to the other. We discuss this in Sec. 7.7. This contact potential affects the net voltage measured across the electrodes. By measuring the emf between pairs of electrodes, a table of emfs can be constructed. Table

Table 7.1   Electromotive Force Series for Some Elements

(Relative to the hydrogen electrode)

Element	Ion	Potential at 25°C, volts
Li	Li^+	-2.959
Na	Na^+	-2.715
Zn	Zn^{++}	-0.762
Fe	Fe^{++}	-0.44
Cd	Cd^{++}	-0.402
Sn	Sn^{3+}	-0.336
Pb	Pb^{++}	-0.12
Pt, H_2	H^+	0.000
Cu	Cu^{++}	$+0.345$
Hg	Hg^{++}	$+0.799$
Ag	Ag^+	$+0.798$

7.1 shows such a listing, where potentials are given relative to a hydrogen electrode (a Pt electrode over which H_2 gas is bubbling). A standard ion concentration of 1 mole/liter is used for these measurements of emfs. The emf between any two kinds of electrodes is the difference between the emfs listed.

We define the emf of a battery as the potential difference between its terminals when no current is allowed to flow. There is in general a reduction in this potential difference when current flows, because the ions carrying the current must be given an extra drift velocity, and the energy for this must come ultimately from the chemical forces. This wasted energy shows up in the heating of the cell when current passes through it, and is the cause of internal resistance in the cell.

For practical purposes we may classify batteries into those which wear out by using up the material of one of the electrodes and those in which a reverse chemical reaction caused by forcing current backward through the cell renews the cell to its original state. Elementary chemistry books give examples of both types. Of particular importance in precise electrical measurements is the *standard cell,* which is constructed to give a very accurately known potential as long as no current is allowed to flow. Such cells must be used in potentiometer or other circuits that allow voltage measurement without drawing appreciable current.

7.7* Contact Potential and Thermal Electromotive Force

We next describe the difference in potential which develops between two dissimilar metals placed in contact. This phenomenon was mentioned in the last section, and is easily understood on the basis of the conduction electron energy distribution. In Fig. 7.16 is shown a plot

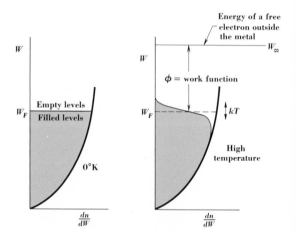

Fig. 7.16 Fermi distribution of conduction-electron energy levels in a metal. dn/dW is the number of available energy levels in a unit volume of metal per unit energy. At $0°K$ all levels are filled up to W_F, leaving corresponding vacancies among the upper levels that are filled at $0°K$.

similar to the Fermi distribution pictured in Fig. 7.5. We again show the density of occupied electron levels dn/dW versus the energy W. The plot exhibits the relatively narrow spread of partially occupied levels at the top of the distribution. We also plot a line representing the energy required to remove an electron completely from the metal. The difference between this energy and the Fermi energy is called the *work function* for the metal. This is the analogue in a metal of the *ionization potential* of a free atom, the energy required to remove an electron from a free atom.

Differences in the work functions among metals produce the contact potential between dissimilar metals. This can be shown by means of the energy diagrams of Fig. 7.17*a* and *b*, in which the energy distributions in two dissimilar metals, A and B, before (*a*) and after (*b*) they are brought into contact, are plotted. The small spread in ener-

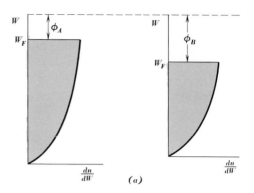

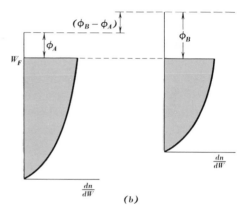

Fig. 7.17   (a) Schematic representation of potentials of two uncharged metals, A and B. Absolute values of energies are adjusted to give the same energy for electrons which have minimum energy to escape, the work function φ. (b) Potentials of the two metals when in contact. Charge redistributes to bring Fermi levels together. Contact potential difference is $\phi_B - \phi_A$.

gies at the top of the distribution is ignored for simplicity. In (a) the two energy coordinates have been adjusted to give the same energy for electrons that can just escape from the metal. The energy which must be added to electrons at the Fermi level, W_F, in order that they can just escape from a metal, is called the *work function* φ of the metal. Because of the difference of the work functions ϕ_A and ϕ_B, the Fermi energies W_F are at different levels on the energy scale. When the two metals are brought into close contact, electrons at the top of the distributions are free to move back and forth from one metal to the other. There will be a net flow of electrons from the higher to the lower Fermi level.

Two effects occur which contribute to the equalization of energies at the top of the distributions, or Fermi levels, of the two metals. One effect, of rather small importance, is the change of Fermi level due to the change in the total number of electrons in each metal, changing the number of filled states. Since the density of states is relatively high, many electrons can be transferred from one metal to the other without much change in the Fermi level with respect to a reference level within the metal. But the other consequence of charge transfer, the change in the electrostatic potential of each piece of metal because of net charge imbalance, is of major importance. We illustrate these effects of charge transfer in Fig. 7.17b.

This reasoning leads us to the approximate expression for the contact potential, $\phi_B - \phi_A$, the difference between work functions for the two metals. Work functions are in the range of one to several electron volts.

If a complete circuit is made, containing several kinds of metal, the contact potentials at the junctions cancel, and there is no net emf around the circuit. However, the contact potential varies with temperature, and so, when the two junctions are at different temperatures, there is a net emf equal to the difference between the two emfs. This is the well-known *thermal emf* used in thermocouples for temperature measurement. The effect was discovered by Seebeck in 1821. Usual values of the emf are in the range of 10^{-6} volt/°K. Thermocouples are not linear in their variation of emf with temperature, and so must be empirically calibrated for accurate measurements. The converse of the *Seebeck effect* is called the *Peltier effect*, which results in the cooling of a bimetal junction when the current passes in one direction and a heating for current in the opposite direction. In actual experiments, resistance or ohmic heating will be superposed on the heating or cooling from the Peltier effect.

The *Thomson effect* is closely related to the Peltier and Seebeck effects. It is a heating or cooling effect in a metal produced by current flow along a thermal gradient maintained in a metal. This is easy to understand in a qualitative way if we realize that the average energy of the effective electrons near the Fermi energy is slightly higher for higher temperatures. Thus, if a source of emf causes a current of electrons to flow from a cooler to a warmer end of a metal rod, the electrons will need to gain slightly in kinetic energy if they are to be in equilibrium when they get to the warmer end. They must get this energy from the thermal reservoir of the crystal lattice, which tends to cool the lattice. Charge flow in the opposite direction would produce heating rather than cooling. This effect allows one to determine the sign of the mobile carriers in a metal.

These thermally induced emfs provide a means for converting heat energy directly into electric energy. A great deal of work is now

going on to develop practical power sources using thermal emfs. However, the low efficiency of conversion has thus far prevented such
sources from being of much practical importance.

7.8*   Comments on Chapter 7

In this chapter we have shown the simple classical basis for Ohm's law.
The model treats conduction electrons as a "gas" of charged particles,
accelerated to a drift velocity by the force of an applied electric field.
The drift velocity is limited by relaxation effects to a terminal velocity
just as raindrops reach a terminal velocity as they fall through the air
under the force of gravity. In metals the relaxation effects are caused
by collisions between the electrons and imperfections or impurities in
the crystal lattice, which tend to remove the excess energy gained by
the electrons in the field. On this basis we can understand the expression for electrical conductivity in the Ohm's law equation $j = \sigma E$,

$$\sigma = \frac{ne^2\tau}{m} \quad \text{(ohm-m)}^{-1} \tag{7.5}$$

Thus the conductivity depends on n, the density of conduction electrons, the charge e on each electron, its mass m, and on a relaxation
time τ, related to the average time between collisions. The fact that the
charge has an effect proportional to e^2 results from the fact that the
accelerating force depends on eE, where E is the applied field, but in
addition the current resulting from a given drift motion of the electrons
depends on the magnitude of the charge e.

This classical expression for conductivity is satisfactory, but if we
wish to go further, to understand the drastic dependence of τ, the
relaxation time, on temperature in very pure metals and to understand why some materials are metals while others are insulators or
semiconductors, we must turn to a consideration of quantum-mechanical properties. According to quantum ideas, conduction electrons must
be treated as waves, with wavelength λ related to momentum p, as
first suggested by de Broglie:

$$\lambda = \frac{h}{p} \tag{7.7}$$

The temperature dependence of τ results from the special interaction between waves (here the conduction electrons) and the evenly
spaced, or periodic, lattice of positive ions, which allows the waves to
progress almost transparently through a *perfect* lattice. Since thermal

vibrations of the ions about their equilibrium positions distort the perfect periodicity of the lattice, thermal effects can drastically shorten the time between collisions at all but nearly zero temperatures.

A further effect of the wave-lattice interaction is to allow the crystal as a whole to interact with the electrons very strongly when they have a particular wavelength. In effect, electrons of certain wavelengths are strongly reflected within the crystal, and these reflections greatly modify the energy-momentum relationships of the electrons. In particular, certain energy states become forbidden; that is, gaps are produced in the distribution of allowed electron energy states.

These gaps separate bands of allowed energies and make understandable the fact that some materials conduct electricity and others do not. For example, if electrons completely fill one allowed band of energies while leaving all other bands empty, no conduction can occur. Here another quantum idea, the exclusion principle, is operating. This says that no two electrons can occupy the same identical state in a system. As a result, if all momentum states in a band are occupied, no external force can alter the distribution, since all possible states are occupied already.

If the forbidden gap is relatively narrow, thermal excitation can excite some electrons across the gap to populate partially the next highest band, and conduction can occur, both by changing the momentum states occupied in the upper band and by changing the distribution in the now not quite filled lower band. It also follows that in a metal there must be at least one partially filled band, so as to allow the electron-momentum distribution to change under the influence of an applied field. The same model of a crystalline solid was also used to explain the crucial importance of impurities in controlling the behavior of semiconductors.

A short discussion introduced the experimental fact of superconductors, but the state of understanding of their behavior was only touched on.

Later sections mentioned briefly the developments of electromotive force in a battery, contact potential difference, and thermal emf.

PROBLEMS

The resistivity of a metal depends on the electron relaxation time in the material. The classical model gives the correct order of magnitude.

*7.1A The resistivity ρ of copper at room temperature is 1.7×10^{-8} ohm-m. If the density of mobile electrons is $10^{27}/m^3$, find the relaxation time τ for electrons in copper.

The following questions review the concepts needed for the quantum-mechanical description of conductivity in solids.

7.2A What interaction between charge carriers and the crystal lattice is responsible for the gaps in the allowed energies of the carriers?

7.2B Discuss briefly the contrast between the so-called valence band and conduction band in a crystalline solid.

7.2C Explain why it is usually true that solids in which one electron per atom is contributed to the mobile electrons are metals.

7.2D Contrast the temperature dependence of electrical conductivity in metals and semiconductors, and explain.

7.2E What is the explanation of the difference between semiconductors and insulators?

7.2F Explain the crucial role of small amounts of certain impurities in the behavior of semiconductors.

8

the magnetic field

8.1 Introduction

Up to this point we have dealt only with charges at rest or with the static problems of steady currents. We now take up the magnetic effects of charges in motion. Electromagnetic theory provides a single framework for discussing the seemingly widely divergent phenomena of electricity and magnetism. Later we discuss the unifying ideas of the theory. First we examine the effects of moving charges, called *magnetism*.

Historically, the study of magnetism began with the observations of interactions between ferromagnetic materials; substances such as iron under appropriate conditions exhibit strong forces of attraction and repulsion, which resemble, but are quite distinct from, electrostatic forces. An early example of the knowledge of magnetism was the use of a permanent magnet in the earth's magnetic field, as a compass for navigational purposes. Much later, in 1819, Oersted first showed a connection between electricity and magnetism by demonstrating the torque on a compass needle caused by a nearby electric current. We first discuss magnetism in terms of the forces between the moving charges of current elements.

8.2   The Magnetic Force between Current Elements

We introduce the study of magnetism by inquiring about the force between two parallel wires in a vacuum, carrying currents i_1 and i_2 (Fig. 8.1). The experimental fact, as first studied by Ampère, is that

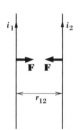

Fig. 8.1   *Two parallel wires carrying current in the same sense, showing forces of attraction.*

the two wires are attracted to each other. If we reverse one current, the force becomes one of repulsion. The forces are modified if either the current magnitudes, the shape, or the relative positions of the conductors are changed.

There is a difficulty in discussing this problem. Any current element must of necessity be a part of a complete loop or circuit. Thus a realistic formulation must be in terms of the force between two complete loops. We may, however, consider the simplified case as long as we realize that comparison with experiment involves accounting for the forces on entire circuits.

There is no possibility of confusing this force between currents with electrostatic forces. In the first place, there is in general no net charge on the conductors. The charge density of conduction electrons just compensates the positive charge on the lattice ions. Second, the force is reversed in sign by reversing the *direction* of either current. The *magnetic* force is thus associated with *moving* charges.

We quote briefly from the original paper of Ampère[1] in which he describes the conclusions to be drawn from his experiments on the forces between currents:

> I have discovered some . . . remarkable . . . [effects] . . . by arranging in parallel directions two straight parts of two conducting wires joining the ends of two voltaic piles; the one was fixed and the other, suspended on points and made very sensitive to motion by a counterweight, could approach the first or move from it while keeping parallel with it. I then observed that when I

[1] André Marie Ampère, Mutual Interactions between Two Electric Currents, *Ann. chim. et phys.*, (II) **15**:59–76 (1820).

passed a current of electricity in both of these wires at once they attracted each other when the two currents were in the same sense and repelled each other when they were in opposite senses. Now these attractions or repulsions of electric currents differ essentially from those that electricity produces in a state of repose; first, they cease, as chemical decompositions do, as soon as we break the circuit of the conducting bodies; secondly, in the ordinary electric attractions and repulsions the electricities of opposite sort attract and those of the same name repel; in the attractions and repulsions of electric currents we have precisely the contrary; . . . Thirdly, in the case of attraction, when it is sufficiently strong to bring the movable conductor into contact with the fixed conductor, they remain attached to one another like two magnets and do not separate after a while, as happens when two conducting bodies which attract each other because they are electrified, one positively and the other negatively, come to touch. Finally, and it appears that this last circumstance depends on the same cause as the preceding, two electric currents attract or repel in vacuum as in air, which is contrary to that which we observe in the mutual action of two conducting bodies charged with ordinary electricity. It is not the place here to explain these new phenomena; the attractions and repulsions which occur between two parallel currents, according as they are directed in the same sense or in opposite senses, are facts given by an experiment which it is easy to repeat.

The experimental fact is that, for a current element $i_1 \, dl_1$ (a current i_1 flowing through a length dl_1) parallel to another element $i_2 \, dl_2$ and separated from it by a distance r_{12} as shown in Fig. 8.2, the mutual

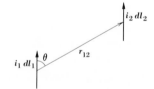

Fig. 8.2   The force between two parallel current elements $i_1 \, dl_1$ and $i_2 \, dl_2$ as given by Eq. (8.1).

force is given by

$$dF = \frac{\mu_0}{4\pi} \frac{1}{r_{12}^2} i_1 \, dl_1 \, i_2 \, dl_2 \sin \theta \qquad \text{newtons} \qquad (8.1)$$

The force between given current elements at a given distance apart is a fundamental characteristic of nature. The constant of proportionality is $\mu_0/4\pi$; the numerical value of this constant depends on the units of measurement used for current, distance, and force. In the mks system, using amperes, meters, and newtons,

$$\mu_0 = 4\pi \times 10^{-7} \qquad \text{webers/amp-m}$$

This is called the *permeability* of free space. Equation (8.1) refers to a very special case, that of parallel current elements. The expression involves no mention of a magnetic field. In both electrostatics and magnetism, fields are introduced to simplify the reasoning required. Equation (8.1) cannot be used directly since it is impossible in practice to set up isolated current elements. To be of practical use, this equation would have to be integrated over the entire current path for both i_1 and i_2.

We now reformulate the problem in terms of a field. If the mathematics seems a little more complicated than in the case of electrostatics, this is only because the physical situation is itself more complex. Our procedure is to describe the *magnetic field* (a vector quantity **B**) due to a current element and then to state the force on another current element placed in that field. This gives the general result we want, of which Eq. (8.1) is a special case.

Experiments on the force between two current circuits, when formulated in terms of the magnetic induction field, show that the experimental results can be explained if each small current element $i\,d\mathbf{l}$ gives rise to a contribution to the total magnetic field according to the equation

$$d\mathbf{B} = \frac{\mu_0}{4\pi} \frac{i\,d\mathbf{l} \times \hat{\mathbf{r}}}{r^2} \qquad \text{webers/m}^2 \tag{8.2}$$

where $\hat{\mathbf{r}}$ is again a unit vector, having a magnitude of unity and the direction of the line drawn *from* the current element *to* the point at which $d\mathbf{B}$ is being determined. This is the law of Biot and Savart. In the mks system the unit of **B** is the weber per square meter. This unit is discussed later in the chapter. We see from Eq. (8.2) that the units of permeability μ_0 are webers per ampere-meter, as given above.

Equation (8.2) involves our second use of the vector cross product (Sec. 2.3). In order to simplify the discussion we rewrite Eq. (8.2) in the alternative form

$$d\mathbf{B} = \frac{\mu_0}{4\pi} \frac{i\,d\mathbf{l} \times \mathbf{r}}{r^3} \qquad \text{webers/m}^2 \tag{8.2a}$$

This has the same meaning as Eq. (8.2), and is obtained from it by using the relationship between the unit vector $\hat{\mathbf{r}}$ and $\mathbf{r}$,

$$\hat{\mathbf{r}} = \frac{\mathbf{r}}{r}$$

Figure 8.3 shows the direction of $d\mathbf{B}$ relative to $i\,d\mathbf{l}$ and $\mathbf{r}$.

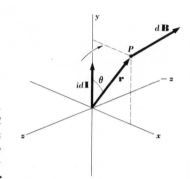

Fig. 8.3 *$d\mathbf{B}$ is the contribution to the magnetic field at P of the current element $i\,d\mathbf{l}$. $d\mathbf{B}$ is perpendicular to both $i\,d\mathbf{l}$ and $\mathbf{r}$, and is directed along the $-z$ axis.*

The resultant vector $d\mathbf{B}$, according to Eq. (8.2) or (8.2a), has a magnitude

$$dB = \frac{\mu_0}{4\pi r^3} i\,dl\,r\sin\theta = \frac{\mu_0}{4\pi r^2} i\,dl\sin\theta$$

and is pointed into the paper along the $-z$ direction. This is the value of $d\mathbf{B}$ at the point P, not at the point where the tails of the two vectors meet. This is implicit in the equation in which $\mathbf{r}$ is the vector *from* the current element *to* the point in space where we are finding $d\mathbf{B}$. As we are writing Eq. (8.2), the r^2 in the denominator is the magnitude of this distance and $\hat{\mathbf{r}}$ is the unit vector giving the direction of $\mathbf{r}$. In effect, $\hat{\mathbf{r}}$ is used only to define the value of θ. It is more usual to draw the vectors as shown in Fig. 8.4. This is completely equivalent to Fig.

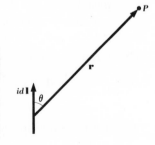

Fig. 8.4 *Vectors $i\,dl$ and r as used for obtaining field contribution dB at point P. dB at the point P is perpendicular to both $i\,dl$ and r, and is directed into the paper.*

8.3, since $i\,d\mathbf{l}$ is of infinitesimal length. $d\mathbf{B}$ at the point P is perpendicular to both $i\,d\mathbf{l}$ and $\mathbf{r}$, and is directed into the paper.

The fact that we have, as in electrostatics, an inverse-square law leads again to the usefulness of the concept of lines of field. As with electric field lines, lines of magnetic field are continuous in space and give field direction by their direction, and magnitude by their density. However, in one respect there is a very great difference between electric and magnetic field configurations. Magnetic lines have no sources, as do electric field lines, on electric charges, but are continuous and join back on themselves. An examination of Eq. (8.2) and Fig. 8.4 shows this to be true. Let the point P move around the current axis at a constant distance from the axis. From Eq. (8.2), the magnetic vector $d\mathbf{B}$ is constant along this path and at each point has a direction tangent to the path. These are just the requirements for the lines to be concentric circles around the current. Figure 8.5 shows some lines

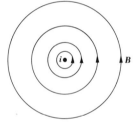

Fig. 8.5   Lines of magnetic field around a long wire carrying current upward out of the paper.

around a current element. If the right-hand thumb points in the direction of (positive) current, the lines are pointed in the direction of the fingers curled around the current element. This *right-hand rule* is an expression of the result of the cross product given in Eq. (8.2).

Before integrating Eq. (8.2) to obtain the field configuration around some extended current elements, we shall set up the other rule that must be employed to use the magnetic field $\mathbf{B}$ in calculating the force between circuit elements. The force on a current element $i\,d\mathbf{l}$, as inferred from experiments on closed current loops, is

$$d\mathbf{F} = i\,d\mathbf{l} \times \mathbf{B} \qquad \text{newtons} \tag{8.3}$$

This means $i\,dl\,B\sin\theta$, in a direction given by $d\mathbf{l} \times \mathbf{B}$ (perpendicular to the plane of $d\mathbf{l}$ and $\mathbf{B}$), again in the sense of the right-hand rule.

We apply these two equations to the two parallel current elements sketched in Fig. 8.1. The first step in calculating the force between the two current elements is to calculate the magnetic field $d\mathbf{B}$ at, say, the right-hand conductor due to the current in the left-hand conductor. This is given by Eq. (8.2) as

$$dB = \frac{\mu_0}{4\pi} \frac{|i_1 \, d\mathbf{l}_1 \times \hat{\mathbf{r}}|}{r^2} = \frac{\mu_0}{4\pi r^2} i_1 \, dl_1 \qquad \text{webers/m}^2 \tag{8.4}$$

for this special case of $i_1 \, d\mathbf{l}_1 \perp \mathbf{r}$. The direction of $d\mathbf{B}$ is perpendicular to the plane of the paper ($\perp$ to $d\mathbf{l}$ and $\mathbf{r}$), and the cross-product rule puts it *into* the paper in this case. (The vector $\mathbf{r}$ points *from* the current element causing the field.)

Next, the force equation (8.3) is applied to the right-hand conductor, giving

$$dF = |i_2 \, d\mathbf{l}_2 \times d\mathbf{B}| = i_2 \, dl_2 \, dB \qquad \text{newtons} \tag{8.5}$$

for $i_2 \, d\mathbf{l}_2 \perp d\mathbf{B}$. Combining Eqs. (8.4) and (8.5), we find exactly the expression written in Eq. (8.1), for the case of two current elements in the same plane. In this simple example it may seem that the introduction of $\mathbf{B}$ was unnecessary. Later more complicated examples will fully justify its use.

From the expressions for $\mathbf{B}$ and $\mathbf{F}$ in their vector form, it is clear that the correct general expression for the force between two current elements is given by

$$d\mathbf{F} = \frac{\mu_0}{4\pi} \frac{i_2 \, d\mathbf{l}_2 \times (i_1 \, d\mathbf{l}_1 \times \hat{\mathbf{r}}_{12})}{r_{12}{}^2} \qquad \text{newtons} \tag{8.6}$$

where $\hat{\mathbf{r}}_{12}$ is the vector pointing *from* the first *to* the second current element. The complexity of this expression, involving two cross products, is to be blamed on the complexity of nature itself. We shall not use this expression in practice, since it is easier to compute forces through the intermediate step of the magnetic field $\mathbf{B}$, via Eqs. (8.2) and (8.3).

The result of Eq. (8.6) looks as though it violates Newton's third law. Thus, suppose the two current elements are in the plane of the paper but not parallel, as shown in Fig. 8.6. $d\mathbf{B}$ at (2) will be into the

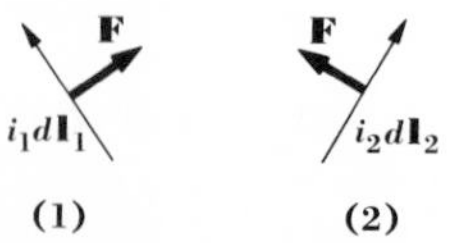

Fig. 8.6 Force between two current elements according to Eq. (8.6).

paper as before, but the force on the second element will have an upward component toward the top of the page, as will the force on the first element. Thus there is a net force upward from this pair of current elements. This difficulty is explained by the fact that, actually, Eq. (8.6) is complete only when we integrate the expression over the entire current loop of which $i_1 \, dl_1$ and $i_2 \, dl_2$ are only differential elements. It can be shown that the net force on the whole system is then always zero. From the experimental point of view, there is no difficulty, since it is impossible to set up an isolated current element. Whenever Eqs. (8.2) and (8.3) are used for determining forces between complete circuits, integration over these circuits gives no net force on the whole system. The fact that isolated current elements cannot exist means that Eqs. (8.2) and (8.3) are always used in the integral forms

$$\mathbf{B} = \frac{\mu_0}{4\pi} \int \frac{i \, d\mathbf{l} \times \hat{\mathbf{r}}}{r^2} \tag{8.2b}$$

and

$$\mathbf{F} = \int i \, d\mathbf{l} \times \mathbf{B} \tag{8.3a}$$

Another seemingly troublesome case is that of current elements resulting from isolated charges moving with a velocity v, rather than from the flow of continuous charge. Here again, as we shall see later, there is no real difficulty.

8.3   Examples
In this section we give some examples of the calculation of the magnetic field $\mathbf{B}$ for some simple arrangements of conductors.

a   *Calculation of* $\mathbf{B}$ *for points out from a long straight wire carrying a current* i. A point P is chosen at a fixed distance r from the wire (Fig. 8.7). A representative current element $i \, dx$ is at a distance l from

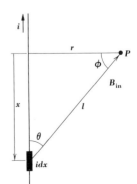

Fig. 8.7   *Magnetic field due to current in a straight wire. B is into the paper at P.*

the chosen point P. Applying Eq. (8.2), we find

$$dB_p = \frac{\mu_0}{4\pi} \frac{i \, d\mathbf{l} \times \hat{\mathbf{r}}}{r^2} = \frac{\mu_0}{4\pi} \frac{i \, dx \sin \theta}{l^2}$$

where dB_p is directed into the paper. Before integrating this, we must express the variables l and θ in terms of a single variable. It is convenient to choose ϕ as the variable and to write

$$B = \frac{\mu_0 i}{4\pi} \int_{-\pi/2}^{\pi/2} \frac{dx}{l^2} \cos \phi$$

The vector addition of the contributions to $\mathbf{B}$ from different current elements is simply arithmetical since all contributions $d\mathbf{B}$ point in the same direction. The integration covers from $-\pi/2$ to $+\pi/2$ to allow for an infinitely long wire. To replace x and dx, we use the relationships $x = r \tan \phi$, $dx = r \sec^2 \phi \, d\phi$, $l = r/\cos \phi$. Then

$$B = \frac{\mu_0 i}{4\pi r} \int_{-\pi/2}^{\pi/2} \cos \phi \, d\phi = \frac{\mu_0 i}{2\pi r} \qquad \text{webers/m}^2 \tag{8.7}$$

Thus the lines of $\mathbf{B}$ form concentric circles around the wire. Equation (8.7) shows that the field intensity falls off as $1/r$.

b *Calculation of the magnetic field* $\mathbf{B}$ *along the axis of a current loop.* We choose a point P along the axis of the loop (Fig. 8.8) and again

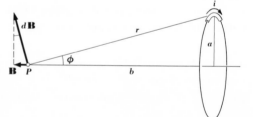

Fig. 8.8 Magnetic field along the axis of a current loop.

evaluate

$$d\mathbf{B} = \frac{\mu_0}{4\pi} \frac{i \, d\mathbf{l} \times \hat{\mathbf{r}}}{r^2} \tag{8.2}$$

Since, for all elements around the loop, $\mathbf{r} \perp i \, d\mathbf{l}$, the value of $\sin \theta$ in the cross product here is 1. However, in taking the vector sum of the vectors $d\mathbf{B}$, we must take account of the fact that each $d\mathbf{B}$ is perpendicular to $\mathbf{r}$ at the point P. Because of symmetry, all components of $\mathbf{B}$ not parallel to the axis b will cancel when the equation is integrated around the loop. Therefore the resultant field will be given by summing only the components $d\mathbf{B} \sin \theta$ along the axis. Thus B is given by

$$B = \frac{\mu_0 i}{4\pi} \frac{\sin \phi}{r^2} \int dl$$

Sin ϕ and r are constant; so they are taken outside the integral. The length dl integrated around the loop is $2\pi a$; so if $\sin \phi$ and r are expressed in terms of the constants a and b, we find

$$B = \frac{\mu_0 i}{2} \frac{a^2}{(a^2 + b^2)^{3/2}} \qquad \text{webers/m}^2 \tag{8.8}$$

At the center of the loop $b = 0$ and $B = \mu_0 i/2a$, pointing along the axis of the loop in a direction depending on the direction of current flow. If the coil has N closely packed turns, the result is multiplied by N. Although we have not accounted for the current leads to the loop, their contribution to the field can be made vanishingly small by keeping them close together. Since the lines of magnetic field are concentric circles around the wires in opposite directions for the two wires, to a good approximation they cancel when close together as in the lead wires shown in the figure.

When we choose the point P far from the loop ($b \gg a$), the equation for B may be written

$$B = \frac{\mu_0}{4\pi} \frac{2iA}{r^3} \qquad \text{webers/m}^2 \tag{8.9}$$

Here we have written $A = \pi a^2$, the area of the loop. The quantity iA is called the *magnetic dipole moment* for reasons developed later. This is an approximation like the one made for the field of the electric dipole. It is called the far-field approximation in both electric and magnetic cases. The far field $\mathbf{B}$ of the loop depends only on the area of the loop, and not on its shape.

The direction of $\mathbf{B}$ depends on the direction of the current in the loop. We can see from Fig. 8.8 that when we look at the current loop from the left, counterclockwise current gives a magnetic induction field directed toward the viewer. We adopt the sign convention that B is positive when it is directed *outward* from a current loop toward the viewer, and the current is positive when it is directed *counterclockwise* as we view it. This convention allows an unambiguous interpretation of equations like (8.9).

c   *Calculation of the field along the axis of a solenoid.*   A coil wound as

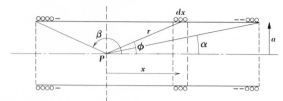

Fig. 8.9   Magnetic field inside a solenoid.

a spiral on a cylinder is called a *solenoid*.[1] In order to find the field at a point P inside a solenoid (on its axis, as shown in Fig. 8.9), we use the results of the preceding problem for the field along the axis of a loop. Since we need to know the number of turns per unit length, we take N for the total turns and L for the length of the solenoid. We then apply Eq. (8.8) to a thin section of the solenoid of width dx with a total current $i(N/L)\,dx$:

$$dB = \frac{\mu_0 N i}{2L}\frac{a^2}{(a^2 + x^2)^{3/2}}\,dx$$

This equation must now be integrated, and we choose ϕ for the variable. Making the substitutions $x = a\cot\phi$ and $dx = -a\csc^2\phi\,d\phi$, the equation becomes

$$B = -\frac{\mu_0 N i}{2L}\int_\beta^\alpha \sin\phi\,d\phi = \frac{\mu_0 N i}{2L}(\cos\alpha - \cos\beta)$$

If we have chosen the point P in the middle of a long solenoid, $\alpha \approx 0$ and $\beta \approx 180°$, and we have

$$B = \frac{\mu_0 N i}{L} \qquad \text{webers/m}^2 \tag{8.10}$$

Choosing P at one end of the solenoid, we have $\alpha \approx 90°$, $\beta \approx 180°$, and

$$B = \frac{\mu_0 N i}{2L} \qquad \text{webers/m}^2 \tag{8.11}$$

Thus the field strength at the end of a long solenoid is just one-half that at the center.

Looking again at Eq. (8.10), which gives the magnetic induction field inside a long solenoid, we shall call the quantity Ni/L the *solenoidal current density*. That is, it is the number of amperes circulating

---

[1] It was Ampère who first thought of obtaining more intense magnetic fields by passing current through a wire wound in a closely spaced helix. He thought of the cylindrical coil as a "canal" in which lines of magnetic field are confined. Hence his use of *solenoid*, from the Greek word for channel.

around the coil per meter of length of coil. The result is the same if we double the number of turns per meter and reduce the current to half the original value or if we make any other change that keeps Ni/L constant. We may thus write

$$\frac{Ni}{L} = j^s \qquad \text{amp/m, or amp-turns/m}$$

where j^s is the solenoidal current density. We may then write for Eq. (8.10)

$$B = \mu_0 j^s \qquad \text{webers/m}^2 \qquad\qquad (8.12)$$

where j^s is the solenoidal current density. This quantity is to be distinguished from the conventional current density j, which is defined in Sec. 6.2 as the current per unit cross-section area. We may again relate the direction of B to the sense of rotation of the current by use of the sign convention in which counterclockwise current is positive, and B is positive when directed outward from the current loop.

8.4   Some Properties of the Magnetic Field B

In this section we summarize what we have learned about the magnetic field and add further to our understanding of its nature. As in the case of the electric field, we can represent magnetic field strength and direction by the convention of lines of field. This we connect with the inverse-square relationship that holds for current elements. We can again describe the magnitude of the magnetic field in terms of *density of lines* and may use this point of view for a quantitative measure of field strength. In the mks system a line of induction is called a *weber*. The unit of field strength is the weber per square meter. Another unit in common use is the *gauss*, where one weber per square meter is equal to 10,000 gauss.

In principle, we are defining the units of **B** in terms of Eq. (8.2). There are, however, two difficulties with using this equation for this purpose. One is that it is a differential expression involving a length dl. The other is that we must choose units for the current i before evaluating the expression. We shall circumvent these difficulties in the following way: As will be shown, we may define the unit of current, the *ampere*, in terms of the magnetic force between two conveniently chosen current loops and then use a convenient case, where Eq. (8.2) has been integrated, for determining B in terms of the current.

We first define unit current. We have already seen [by integrating Eq. (8.2)] that the field at a distance a from a long straight wire carrying current i is

$$B = \frac{\mu_0 i}{2\pi a} \qquad \text{webers/m}^2$$

where the lines of B form closed loops around the wire. If we take two wires of length L, separated by a distance a, and form circular loops of each one, keeping the distance a small compared with the loop radius (Fig. 8.10), this same equation holds for the field at one wire due to

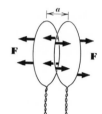

Fig. 8.10 *Force between two parallel current loops separated by a distance a.*

the current in the other. We have thus avoided the need for a very long pair of wires. We next apply Eq. (8.3) for the force on a current element. This gives $dF = i'\, dl\, B$, where dl is an element of length of the wire loop on which we shall calculate the force. Substitution of $B = \mu_0 i / 2\pi a$ and integration yields

$$F = \frac{\mu_0 i' i \int dl}{2\pi a} = \frac{\mu_0 i' i L}{2\pi a} \qquad \text{newtons} \tag{8.13}$$

where L is the circumference of each loop. If we place the two coils in series, $i = i'$, and we can use the equation to allow for an experimental determination of unit current. Thus, if we measure F in newtons and measure lengths in meters, i will be given in amperes. Once we are able to measure the current in amperes, as we could do with this pair of loops, any one of our calculations of the value of B in terms of i can be used for determining B. For example, again using a loop, we have seen that the field at its center is $B = \mu_0 i / 2r$, where r is the radius of the loop.

We have thus been able to define magnetic field strength, using the force between two current circuits. However, the lines of magnetic field are *not* in the direction of the force on a current element. The vector cross product between $d\mathbf{l}$ and $\mathbf{B}$ gives the direction.

The experimental arrangement described above not only relates **B** to the current, but also fixes the value of the unit for charge q in the mks system. This is done through the relationship given in Eq. (6.1): one ampere equals one coulomb per second. Through this relationship, the value of $\mu_0/4\pi$ is obtained, and the units in electrostatics are related to magnetic units.

We now turn to another contrasting property of the lines of magnetic field. These lines are continuous and do not arise from any source in the way that lines of electric force originate on charges. Lines of magnetic field thus form loops without a beginning or an ending. This property may be used to gain further insight into the nature of the magnetic field, and also to allow for an extremely simple way of calculating the magnetic field in certain situations of high symmetry. Going back to the expression for the field around a long wire carrying a current i, we found that at a distance r from the wire, the field is given by

$$B = \frac{\mu_0 i}{2\pi r} \qquad \text{webers/m}^2$$

and that the magnetic lines are concentric around the conductor. Let us follow a particular line at a distance r around the wires and evaluate the line integral $\oint \mathbf{B} \cdot d\mathbf{l}$ around this path, starting at any point and returning to the same point. We saw in Chap. 3 that the line integral of a vector field around a closed path is called the circulation. Thus this new integral may be identified as the circulation of the magnetic field **B**. Since the path is everywhere parallel to **B** and since $B = \mu_0 i/2\pi r$, the integration becomes

$$\oint \mathbf{B} \cdot d\mathbf{l} = \frac{\mu_0 i}{2\pi r} \oint dl = \frac{\mu_0 i}{2\pi r} 2\pi r = \mu_0 i \tag{8.14}$$

where i is the total current threading the path we choose. This is called *Ampère's circuital law*. While the integration was here performed over a circular path, Eq. (8.14) is true, whatever the nature of the closed path. This becomes apparent if any given path around the conductor is approximated by segments that either are radial in direction or are circular arcs about the conductor (Fig. 8.11). $\int \mathbf{B} \cdot d\mathbf{l}$ for a given radial segment depends only on the angle subtended at the wire by the arc, since for a given arc **B** falls off as $1/r$ while dl increases as r. The contribution of the radial segments to $\int \mathbf{B} \cdot d\mathbf{l}$ is zero, since **B** is everywhere perpendicular to the radius vector. Therefore $\oint \mathbf{B} \cdot d\mathbf{l}$ is simply

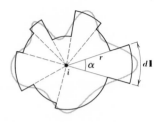

Fig. 8.11 *Approximation of an arbitrary closed path around a conductor by circular arcs and radial segments. Used for proof that* $\oint \mathbf{B} \cdot d\mathbf{l} = \mu_0 i$ *for any closed path enclosing a current* i.

the value over all the circular segments, which is the same as over a circular path. This calculation has been based on the field of a single infinitely long current, but it can be shown that, in fact, it is true for *any* current threading the area enclosed by the path chosen, whatever the current configuration. Equation (8.14) is thus completely general, though we shall not prove it for more complicated circuit shapes.

The result can be restated by saying that the circulation around any closed path equals $\mu_0 i$, where i is the total current which threads the closed path.

We may recall that in a static electric field the circulation, $\oint \mathbf{E} \cdot d\mathbf{l}$, is always zero around any closed path, and that this fact was related to the conservative nature of the electrostatic field. This property makes the concept of electric potential useful. In the case of a magnetic field, the circulation is not zero in general, so that we do not generally have a conservative field. But if we choose closed paths which are not threaded by currents, as shown, for example, in Fig. 8.12, so that

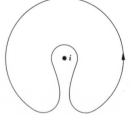

Fig. 8.12 *Path threaded by no current, for which* $\oint \mathbf{B} \cdot d\mathbf{l} = 0$.

$i = 0$, we have

$$\oint \mathbf{B} \cdot d\mathbf{l} = 0 \tag{8.15}$$

just as in the electric case. Under these conditions (only) we can define a *magnetic potential*, just as in the electric case.

Since **B** represents a force on a current element, and since there can be no isolated current element, but instead we must always deal with a complete current loop, the magnetic potential tells us about potential energy by virtue of the presence of a current loop in a magnetic field. We can expect that the orientation, as well as position of a current loop, affects the stored energy. This problem is studied in some detail in Sec. 9.7. The importance of Eq. (8.15) is that it guarantees that, within the limitation stated, the magnetic field is conservative.

8.5* The Curl of a Magnetic Field

As in Sec. 3.4 for the electric field, the zero circulation of the magnetic induction field when the path does not enclose any net current can be expressed as

$$\text{curl } \mathbf{B} = 0 \qquad (8.16)$$

In general, however, for a magnetic induction field,

$$\text{curl } \mathbf{B} = \mu_0 \mathbf{j} \qquad (8.17)$$

where $\mathbf{j}$ is the current density at the point in question. This result comes immediately from the mathematical Stokes' theorem discussed in Appendix B, which, for the magnetic induction field, may be written

$$\oint \mathbf{B} \cdot d\mathbf{l} = \mu_0 i = \int \text{curl } \mathbf{B} \cdot d\mathbf{S}$$

where $d\mathbf{S}$ is the area enclosed by the closed path. Division by $d\mathbf{S}$ gives the result of Eq. (8.17).

Use of vector-operator notation as in Appendix D gives for this basic property of a magnetic field,

$$\mathbf{\nabla} \times \mathbf{B} = \mu_0 \mathbf{j} \qquad (8.18)$$

8.6 The Flux of the Magnetic Field

We introduce at this point a quantity of considerable importance, the *magnetic flux* ϕ. This is the total number of lines of $\mathbf{B}$ through a given area. The general equation for this is

$$\phi = \int \mathbf{B} \cdot d\mathbf{S} \qquad \text{webers} \qquad (8.19)$$

Since the magnitude of $\mathbf{B}$ is the number of lines per unit area, where the area is taken perpendicular to the direction of $\mathbf{B}$, this equation follows immediately from the definition of ϕ. The quantity $d\mathbf{S}$ is an element of area (using vector notation) and is positive when directed *outward* (toward the viewer) from the area. The scalar, or dot, product takes account of the possibility that the direction of **B** may not be perpendicular to the area involved. In the special case that **B** is uniform and perpendicular to the area being considered, Eq. (8.19) reduces to $\phi = BS$, where S is the area. We had a similar expression for the flux of electric field through a given area, $\int \mathbf{E} \cdot d\mathbf{S}$, though in the electric case we did not define the electric flux by a special symbol.

In the electric field case the inverse-square law of force led to two important results relative to the flux of **E**: First, that in the absence of charge, $\int_{cs} \mathbf{E} \cdot d\mathbf{S} = 0$, or lines are continuous in empty space. The other result was that in a region where charge is present, the flux out of any volume depends only on the net charge in that volume, or $\int_{cs} \mathbf{E} \cdot d\mathbf{S} = (1/\epsilon_0)q$. This last is a statement about the sources of electric lines, or flux.[1]

What about an analogous statement regarding the magnetic field? The answer is that under *all* circumstances

$$\int_{cs} \mathbf{B} \cdot d\mathbf{S} = 0 \tag{8.20}$$

from which the microscopic form

$$\text{div } \mathbf{B} = 0 \tag{8.21}$$

follows at once.

The meaning of Eq. (8.20) is that lines of **B** are continuous, and in addition that there are no "sources" of **B** in the sense that charges act as sources of lines of **E**. This is just what we found in Sec. 8.2, where we examined in a particular case the way in which **B** lines come back on themselves. Equation (8.20) goes further, to say that this is always true, for all possible situations. The validity of Eq. (8.20) can be shown to follow formally from the law of Biot and Savart [Eq. (8.2)].[2] The result is expected, however, since the Biot and Savart law has the $1/r^2$ dependence found essential to the concept of lines in the

---

[1] The equivalent microscopic forms of these results, as shown in Chap. 2, were

$$\text{div } \mathbf{E} = \begin{cases} 0 & \text{in free space} \\ \dfrac{1}{\epsilon_0}\rho & \text{at points having charge density } \rho \end{cases}$$

[2] The proof makes the assumption that the only sources of magnetic induction are current elements, even in magnetic matter. Our model of magnetic materials (Chap. 10) is based on this idea.

electric case. Also, our example of the field lines around a straight wire carrying current showed that sourceless lines described the field in that case. The formal proof we are omitting adds only the knowledge that

$\int_{CS} \mathbf{B} \cdot d\mathbf{S} = 0$ is *always* true.

8.7 *Further Field Calculations*

We next apply the line integral as developed in Sec. 8.4 to the calculation of the field due to two highly symmetrical current configurations, both of which we have calculated earlier by integrating the fundamental equation

$$dB = \frac{\mu_0}{4\pi} \frac{i \, d\mathbf{l} \times \hat{\mathbf{r}}}{r^2} \tag{8.2}$$

a   *The magnetic field of a long straight conductor carrying a current i.* For this case we need only reverse the direction of the argument given in Sec. 8.4. We consider it here only to make the argument clear. We choose a concentric path around the conductor with a radius r. Knowing that **B** will be constant and parallel to the path around the entire loop, we can take **B** outside the integral and find

$$\oint \mathbf{B} \cdot d\mathbf{l} = B \oint dl = B 2\pi r = \mu_0 i$$

or

$$B = \frac{\mu_0 i}{2\pi r}$$

our previous result.

b   *The field inside a long solenoid.*   Here we start with a solenoid in the form of a torus as shown in Fig. 8.13. Let the average radius of the

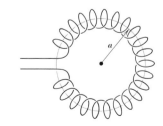

Fig. 8.13   *Toroidal solenoid.*

torus be a. Let there be N turns of wire carrying a current i. The length of the solenoid is $2\pi a$. We choose a path shown by the light line, over which we can see by symmetry that the field **B** will be uniform and also parallel to the path. The total current threading this path is Ni, since each turn carries current in the same direction through the path we have chosen. The return current on the outside of the torus is outside the closed path, and therefore need not be considered. The line integral becomes

$$\oint \mathbf{B} \cdot d\mathbf{l} = B \oint dl = B2\pi a = \mu_0 Ni$$

or

$$B = \frac{\mu_0 Ni}{2\pi a} = \frac{\mu_0 Ni}{L} = \mu_0 j^s$$

the result we found earlier for a long straight solenoid, where j^s is the solenoidal current density. If we open out the toroid to form a straight solenoid, the field at its center will not be seriously affected, although, as we have seen, the field at the ends will be reduced by a factor of 2. Although our new method is only approximate, it does give us one piece of information that the detailed calculation did not give: The field at any point well inside the solenoid is the same, whether or not it is on the axis of the coil. In other words, the field inside a long solenoid is uniform far away from its ends.

8.8 Torque on a Current Loop in a Uniform Magnetic Field, The Magnetic Dipole

Now that we have finished our discussion of the production of magnetic fields by currents, we turn again to the study of forces on conductors carrying currents. We center our attention on a very simple shape—a rectangular loop as shown in Fig. 8.14. The axis of the loop

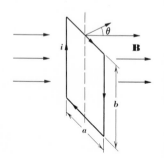

Fig. 8.14 Rectangular loop in a uniform magnetic field.

is perpendicular to the uniform magnetic field **B**, and the normal to the loop makes an angle θ with the field direction. In the uniform field **B** the net force on the loop is zero, but there is a torque acting on it. A current i flows through the loop. If the current i is clockwise as viewed from the left in Fig. 8.14, then both i and **B** are negative (in the sense of our earlier definition of the sign convention for **B** and i) when we view the loop from the left, and positive when we view from the right.

Using the force equation (8.3), applied to the top and bottom sides, we find

$$\mathbf{F} = (i\mathbf{a} \times \mathbf{B}) \quad \text{or} \quad F = iaB \sin\left(\frac{\pi}{2} - \theta\right) = iaB \cos\theta \tag{8.22}$$

When the vector cross-product rule is applied, this force is upward on the top side and downward on the bottom side. The net force on the rigid loop from these elements is thus zero, as is the torque. Applying the same equation to the vertical sides, we find

$$F = ibB \tag{8.23}$$

where the forces are again equal and opposite and outward but have components perpendicular to the plane of the coil. The torque on the coil is thus not zero. Using Fig. 8.15, which is a view looking down-

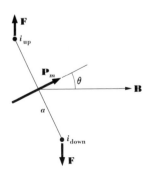

Fig. 8.15   Top view of a rectangular current loop in a uniform magnetic field. The normal to the plane of the loop makes an angle θ with the magnetic field.

ward on the loop, we find for the total torque

$$\tau = iabB \sin\theta = iBA \sin\theta \tag{8.24}$$

where A is the area ab of the loop. If there are N turns on the loop, the equation becomes

$$\tau = NiAB \sin\theta \tag{8.25}$$

If we let

$$NiA = p_m \tag{8.26}$$

as in Sec. 8.3, where p_m represents the magnetic dipole moment, the equation becomes

$$\tau = p_m B \sin \theta \tag{8.27}$$

Equation (8.25) or (8.27) shows that a current loop is subject to a torque in the presence of an external magnetic field, and that the torque is proportional to the current in the loop. This is the basis of the galvanometer, the most important current-measuring instrument. The galvanometer is discussed in some detail in Sec. 8.9.

Equation (8.27) is of exactly the same form as Eq. (2.7), which gives the torque on an electric dipole in an electric field. We may apply vector nomenclature in the magnetic dipole case just as we did in the electric case. This gives the equivalent of Eq. (8.27), which has the advantage that it gives the direction of the torque explicitly:

$$\boldsymbol{\tau} = \mathbf{p}_m \times \mathbf{B} \tag{8.27a}$$

The direction of the torque vector is along the axis of rotation and points in the direction of advance of a right-hand screw. The torque vector in Fig. 8.15 points into the page.

We have not given the proof that the dipole moment $\mathbf{p}_m$ is a true vector quantity. A proof can be based on the same arguments used in the electric dipole case.

The direction of $\mathbf{p}_m$ is perpendicular to the plane of the current loop. Equation (8.26) tells which way the vector points, if we recall our previous definitions of positive current in a loop (counterclockwise) and positive vector through a loop (toward the viewer). That is, if the current loop is viewed from a direction which gives counterclockwise current, the dipole moment vector points toward the viewer, as is shown in Fig. 8.15.

The justification for using p_m for representing NiA is that, whatever the shape of the loop, the torque depends only on NiA, and not on the shape. We can see this by taking any arbitrary shape of loop and approximating it as a sum of rectangular loops, as shown in Fig. 8.16. If the same current is sent through each rectangular loop in the same sense, the inside currents will just cancel each other, leaving only the peripheral current, which approximates the original loop as closely as we wish. The total torque is then the sum of the separate

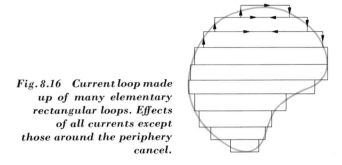

**Fig. 8.16   Current loop made
up of many elementary
rectangular loops. Effects
of all currents except
those around the periphery
cancel.**

torques on individual rectangles, and so must depend only on the current and total area of the loop.

The magnetic dipole vector tends to be aligned in the external field direction by the magnetic torque. This behavior is just like that of the electric dipole in an electric field. Figure 8.17 calls attention to

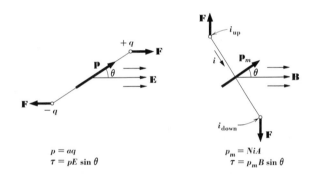

$$p = aq$$
$$\tau = pE \sin \theta$$

$$p_m = NiA$$
$$\tau = p_m B \sin \theta$$

**Fig. 8.17   Electric and magnetic dipoles in uniform
electric and magnetic fields.**

the close parallel between an electric dipole in an electric field and a current loop in a magnetic field. However, the electric dipole vector points along the line connecting the two charges, while the magnetic dipole vector is perpendicular to the plane of the current loop.

Actually, the similarity in form between these very different quantities, the electrostatic and the magnetic dipoles, goes even further. We have found the magnetic field along the axis of a magnetic loop or dipole, which we can write

$$B = \frac{\mu_0}{4\pi} \frac{2p_m}{r^3} \tag{8.9}$$

Earlier, we found for the electric field along the axis of an electric dipole

$$E = \frac{1}{4\pi\epsilon_0} \frac{2p}{r^3} \qquad (2.5)$$

Thus the expressions are very similar. Both give the far-field approximation. Not only is the comparison valid along the axis of the dipole, but the same similarity holds at all points in space around the dipole as long as we stay far enough away so that the mathematical approximations used for the electrostatic case are valid. At distances comparable with the dimensions of the dipoles, the fields are of different shapes.

For comparison, we give below the similar electric and magnetic expressions for the far field in terms of the tangential and radial components of the fields. We have not proved the equations for the magnetic case, but shall quote them anyway.

$$E_r = \frac{1}{4\pi\epsilon_0} \frac{2p}{r^3} \cos\theta \qquad B_r = \frac{\mu_0}{4\pi} \frac{2p_m}{r^3} \cos\theta$$

$$E_\theta = \frac{1}{4\pi\epsilon_0} \frac{p}{r^3} \sin\theta \qquad B_\theta = \frac{\mu_0}{4\pi} \frac{p_m}{r^3} \sin\theta$$

(8.28)

The angle θ in these equations is the angle between the dipole moment and the field direction (Fig. 8.17).

8.9*   *The Galvanometer*

We have already discussed, in Chap. 6, the use of the galvanometer in both current- and voltage-measuring instruments. Now that we have discussed the torque on a current loop in a magnetic field, we are ready to discuss galvanometer theory and design. We show in Fig. 8.18 a current loop in a fixed external field **B**, as it would be used in a

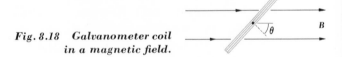

Fig. 8.18   Galvanometer coil in a magnetic field.

galvanometer. The current to be measured passes through the suspended coil, and the field **B** is obtained from a permanent magnet. A spring acts to hold the plane of the loop parallel to the magnetic field, and current in the loop causes the loop to twist toward the perpendicular to the field against the torque exerted by the spring. Motion of the loop actuates a pointer, or, in the most sensitive instruments, moves a mirror so as to cause a light beam to move over a scale.

The sensitivity of a galvanometer can be determined through the application of our earlier equation,

$$\tau = NiAB \sin \theta \tag{8.25}$$

giving the torque on a coil of N turns, area A, carrying a current i in a magnetic induction field B. Here we have used θ for the angle between the normal to the plane of the coil and the field direction. The angular deflection θ for a given current depends on the restoring torque provided by the coil suspension. We characterize this by the torque constant k, where

$$\tau = k\theta \tag{8.29}$$

When the plane of the coil is parallel to the field, $\theta = 90°$, or $\sin \theta \approx 1$, and we may equate (8.25) and (8.29) to give

$$i = \frac{k}{NAB} \theta = K'\theta \tag{8.30}$$

where K' is called the galvanometer constant. Thus the deflection angle of the galvanometer is proportional to the current through it. In practice, this equation is made applicable over a wide angle by shaping the magnetic field so that the lines of B remain nearly parallel to the coil as it turns, as shown in the sketches in Fig. 8.19. A

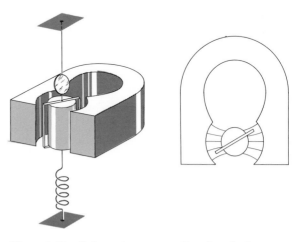

Fig. 8.19 Galvanometer coil placed between magnet poles. Soft iron core produces radial field.

soft iron cylinder is often placed at the center of the coil, which to-gether with the specially shaped poles of the permanent magnet causes the magnetic field lines to be radial.

A common practice with sensitive galvanometers is to quote sensi-tivity in terms of the current necessary to cause a 1-mm deflection of a light beam reflected by the galvanometer mirror on a scale 1 m away. Since for a mirror deflection of θ, the light beam is deflected by an angle 2θ, we have $d/L = \tan 2\theta \approx 2\theta$, where L is the distance from galvanometer to scale. Substitution in Eq. (8.30) gives

$$i = K' \frac{d}{2L} = \frac{K'}{2,000} d = Kd \tag{8.31}$$

where d is in millimeters. K is called the *figure of merit* of the galva-nometer. Currents as small as 10^{-11} amp can be measured on the most sensitive galvanometers.

8.10   Forces on Isolated Moving Charges

Our next task, to inquire about magnetic forces on individual moving charges, is comparatively easy, since we have already examined forces on current elements, and these are made up of a flow of individual charges. Our problem is to modify

$$d\mathbf{F} = i \, d\mathbf{l} \times \mathbf{B} \tag{8.3}$$

to allow it to apply to an individual charge e moving with a velocity v. In order to do this, we apply Eq. (6.5), which gives current in terms of the motion of a group of charges. Equation (6.5) gives the expres-sion for the current i in terms of n charges per unit volume moving with an average drift velocity $\mathbf{v}$ through a conductor of cross-section area A.

$$i = nevA \tag{6.5}$$

Substituting this in the equation for the force on a current element [Eq. (8.3)], we get

$$d\mathbf{F} = neA \, dl \, \mathbf{v} \times \mathbf{B}$$

This is the force on a total charge $NeA \, dl$. Dividing by $NA \, dl$, we have the force on a single charge e:

$$\mathbf{F} = e(\mathbf{v} \times \mathbf{B}) \tag{8.32}$$

This is the basic equation giving the magnetic force on any moving charge. The force is in newtons when the charge is measured in coulombs, the velocity in meters per second, and **B** in webers per square meter.

We next investigate some consequences of this force on individual charges. We could have started with this last equation as the fundamental force-field relationship and then worked backward to the force equation for a current element. Our choice was essentially arbitrary.

The first and most obvious conclusion from Eq. (8.32) is that a magnetic field acting on a moving charged particle cannot change the speed or kinetic energy of the particle. This follows from the nature of the vector cross product, which makes the resultant force always perpendicular to the direction of motion. This means that the magnetic field can do no work on a charged particle, although it can change its direction of motion.

A further result of the mutually perpendicular magnetic force and velocity vectors is that, in a uniform magnetic field, the motion of charged particles is circular or helical. Consider first a particle of positive charge e moving in a plane perpendicular to a uniform magnetic field, which in Fig. 8.20 is shown pointing into the paper. In a time Δt

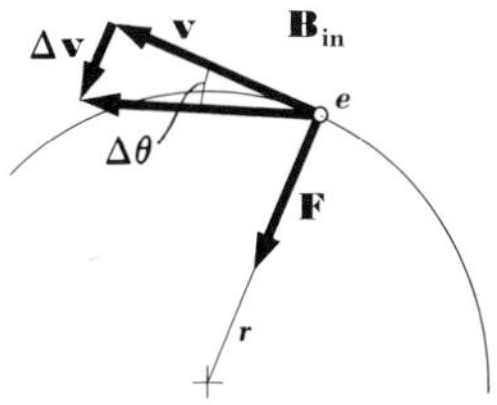

Fig. 8.20 Path of a moving charged particle in a perpendicular magnetic field.

it acquires a transverse velocity Δv, which can be obtained from $\mathbf{F} = q(\mathbf{v} \times \mathbf{B})$, using the equation $F\, dt = m\, dv$:

$$\Delta v = \frac{evB}{m} \Delta t$$

The angular change in the direction of v is given by

$$\Delta \theta = \frac{\Delta v}{v} = \frac{eB}{m} \Delta t$$

or the angular velocity

$$\omega = \frac{\Delta \theta}{\Delta t} = \frac{eB}{m} \tag{8.33}$$

Since **v** remains constant in magnitude and the velocity uniformly changes direction, the orbit must be a circle. The radius of curvature can be calculated from Newton's law, $F = ma = mv^2/r$, where the centripetal force is supplied by the magnetic field. Thus we have

$$\frac{mv^2}{r} = evB \qquad \text{or} \qquad r = \frac{mv}{eB} \tag{8.34}$$

In the more general case where the velocity is not limited to the plane perpendicular to **B**, Eq. (8.25) shows that the component of velocity in the perpendicular plane will behave as shown in Eq. (8.34), while the component parallel to **B** will be unaffected. If there is an additional velocity component parallel to **B**, the orbit is helical.

A final important consequence of the nature of the magnetic force on moving charges is that, in a uniform field, the frequency of rotation of a moving charge is constant, independent of the velocity of the charge. We have already seen this in the result of Eq. (8.33). It is also apparent from Eq. (8.34) if we substitute $r\omega = v$ and solve for ω, giving again the result of Eq. (8.33). This is often called the *cyclotron equation*, for reasons discussed later.

We now discuss briefly the difficulty mentioned earlier (Sec. 8.2), the net force due to the magnetic interaction between two moving charges. When two charges are moving along parallel lines, the forces of interaction can be shown to be equal and opposite, as we saw in the case of forces between current elements. If, however, the motion is not along parallel paths, there will appear to be a net force on the system, as suggested by our earlier discussion and shown in Fig. 8.6. This apparent breakdown of Newton's third law is resolved when we take account of an additional momentum that must be associated with the *electromagnetic* field of the moving charges. When this additional momentum is considered, the total momentum of a system of two or more moving charged particles in the absence of external fields is found to be constant, as expected.

The more general problem of the motion of charged particles in combined electric and magnetic fields is considered in Chap. 14.

8.11* *Applications*

In this section we discuss a number of important applications of the magnetic-force law on moving charged particles.

A velocity selector. In a large class of experiments in which the motion of charged ions or electrons is to be studied, it is important to have a source of particles, all having the same velocity. Since most sources of electrons or ions emit particles with a wide range of velocities, a velocity selector is often essential. It is easy to understand the behavior of such a selector (Fig. 8.21), which uses both electric and magnetic

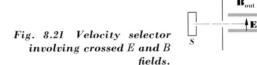

Fig. 8.21 Velocity selector involving crossed E and B fields.

forces. A capacitor-like arrangement provides a uniform electric field **E**, upward in the plane of the paper. A uniform **B** field is provided perpendicular to the paper. Collimated charged particles emerging from the slit in the source S reach the output slit only if the electric and magnetic forces acting are equal and opposite. This requires

$$Ee = evB \tag{8.35}$$

for the simple arrangement involved. Thus only charged particles with a velocity

$$v = \frac{E}{B} \tag{8.36}$$

can come out of the slit.

Determination of e/m. In building up our knowledge of atomic structure, the determination of e/m for electrons and for ions has been a basic tool. Such determination is made possible by taking ions after passage through a velocity selector through a circular path perpendicular to a uniform magnetic field. Using an appropriate detector of ions and a slit system, we can determine the radius of curvature of the electron or ion path. Knowledge of the velocity then allows evaluation of e/m. Thus, since $r = mv/eB$ [Eq. (8.34)] and $v = E/B$ [Eq. (8.36)], we find

$$\frac{e}{m} = \frac{E}{rB^2} \tag{8.37}$$

J. J. Thomson used this method for the measurement of e/m for electrons in 1897 at the Cavendish Laboratory of Cambridge University in England. As used for the study of charged ions, such an apparatus is called a *mass spectrograph*. Studies of e/m for charged ions have elucidated many of the important facts of atomic structure, including the existence of isotopes.

The cyclotron.   Probably the most familiar of all the machines for accelerating charged particles (ions) to high velocity, the cyclotron takes advantage of electric and magnetic forces on the ions. Ions starting from a central source are caused to move in circular paths by a magnetic field perpendicular to their motion. Motion takes place within two hollow electrodes between which an alternating voltage is applied. Ions that start out at the right time feel an accelerating electric field each time they pass from one electrode to the other. Such ions make larger and larger orbits as they gain kinetic energy. However, they continue to stay in step with the alternating voltage, since their angular frequency is constant [Eq. (8.33)]. A sketch of a cyclotron is shown in Fig. 8.22.

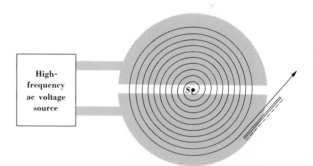

Fig. 8.22 Cyclotron. Top view of cyclotron electrodes placed in an evacuated chamber between the poles of an electromagnet. Positive ions emitted by the source S travel in circular orbits inside the hollow electrodes perpendicular to the magnetic field. Each time the ions traverse the gap between the electrodes, they are accelerated by a potential difference due to an applied alternating voltage synchronized with the ion motion. As the ions gain energy, the radius of their path increases, until they are brought out of the magnetic field region by a negatively charged deflector plate.

For energies greater than about 20 million electron volts (Mev) the ordinary cyclotron fails because of the relativistic increase in the mass of the particles being accelerated. Thus the frequency of rotation of charged particles as given by Eq. (8.33) changes at high energies, and the particles do not remain in synchronism with the alternating voltage applied. Machines have been developed that avoid this difficulty by appropriately modifying the magnetic field or the frequency of the accelerating voltage as the particles increase in energy. Machines such as the proton synchrotron produce particles with energies in the 1 to 10 billion electron volt (Bev) range.

Hall effect.   The Hall effect relates to the generation of a voltage when a current-carrying conductor is placed in a magnetic field. Useful information regarding current carriers in conductors is obtainable from this effect. Figure 8.23 shows the arrangement used in the transverse Hall

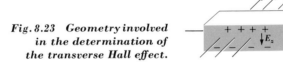

Fig. 8.23   Geometry involved in the determination of the transverse Hall effect.

effect. If placed in a field B_y, carriers of a current i_x are deflected (as shown here for electrons) until a transverse field E_z is built up by the deflected charge. This is known as the Hall field and is obtained from the equation

$$eE_z = e\mathbf{v} \times \mathbf{B} = evB \tag{8.38}$$

If we write j, the current density (current per unit cross-section area as defined in Sec. 6.2) in terms of the density of carriers n, their charge e, and their mean velocity v,

$$\mathbf{j} = ne\mathbf{v} \tag{6.4}$$

we may express the Hall constant R_H as

$$R_H = \frac{E_z}{jB} = \frac{1}{ne} \tag{8.39}$$

This constant may thus be determined experimentally by the measurement of the *Hall voltage* (from which the value of E_z can be calculated), current density, and magnetic field. The sign and magnitude of the Hall constant give the sign of the carriers of current and their density. For most metals the carriers are found to be electrons, and for many metals the density of carriers is in good agreement with the number of valence electrons in the atoms making up the metal. However, there are cases where the carriers are positive (for example, Be, Zn, Cd), and for Bi a very large value of the Hall coefficient suggests an anomalously low concentration of electrons (≈ 0.004 electron per atom). These surprising results are well understood qualitatively and are associated with the quantum nature of solids. Another important result from Hall-effect measurements on metals is that n, the charge carrier density, varies only slightly with temperature.

8.12 Comments on Chapter 8

This chapter began our discussion of the force between moving charges. This magnetic force is in addition to the electrostatic forces we have been concerned with thus far. As presented here, the entire problem of magnetism is cast in terms of the force between current elements. This is a convenient way to begin, even though current elements cannot exist in isolation, but are necessarily parts of complete circuits.

In developing magnetic theory, we turned immediately to the magnetic field **B** as the intermediary which describes the experimentally measured forces between current circuits. Thus it is asserted that all magnetic fields result from the effect of current elements which contribute to the field according to the equation

$$dB = \frac{\mu_0}{4\pi} \frac{i \, dl \times \hat{r}}{r^2} \qquad \text{webers/m}^2 \tag{8.2}$$

This is the law of Biot and Savart. The constant $\mu_0/4\pi$, which has a numerical value of 10^{-7} in the mks system, depends on the system of units used. μ_0 is called the permeability of free space.

According to the meaning of the vector cross product, this means that each current element $i \, dl$ contributes dB to the field at a distance **r** away from the element, where dB is in a direction normal to the plane of $i \, dl$ and **r**.

In any real problem, contributions dB must be added together from all current elements in a circuit. Thus, in practice, we use the equation in integral form,

$$\mathbf{B} = \frac{\mu_0}{4\pi} \int \frac{i \, dl \times \hat{r}}{r^2} \tag{8.2b}$$

The next step in the magnetic force problem is to express the force of a magnetic field on a current element. This force is given by the expression

$$d\mathbf{F} = i\,dl \times \mathbf{B} \tag{8.3}$$

which is not dignified by a name as is the field equation, but which provides the important final step in the force problem. If we are to find the net force on an entire circuit, this equation too must be integrated, and we have

$$\mathbf{F} = \int i\,dl \times \mathbf{B} \tag{8.3a}$$

In principal, these equations tell the whole story for steady magnetic fields and forces between current elements.

Just as in the electric case, there is much to be gained by developing certain general consequences of the field and force equations of magnetism. For example, the inverse-square dependence in the Biot and Savart law leads to magnetic lines, just as Coulomb's law did for electric lines. However, in the magnetic case, lines have no sources; so the expression for the flux of **B** out of any volume,

$$\int_{cs} \mathbf{B} \cdot d\mathbf{S} = 0 \tag{8.20}$$

is always true. Another expression of this result is to say that there are no magnetic "charges," or "poles," but all magnetic fields originate from current loops. The microscopic form of Eq. (8.20) is

$$\text{div } \mathbf{B} = 0 \tag{8.21}$$

Another general property of the magnetic field **B** was found to be

$$\oint \mathbf{B} \cdot dl = \mu_0 i \tag{8.14}$$

This expression shows that the circulation of **B** is not always zero, as is the circulation of a static electric field. The term $\mu_0 i$ represents the net current which threads the closed path taken in evaluating the circulation. For situations of high symmetry Eq. (8.14) provides a method for calculating the magnetic induction field produced by various simple current-carrying circuits.

In regions of space away from current circuits, no currents thread the circulation path, and so the circulation becomes zero, just as in the static electric case. Thus we write for such a situation

$$\oint \mathbf{B} \cdot dl = 0 \tag{8.15}$$

This property guarantees that the work to bring up a current loop can be discussed in terms of a potential energy.

The microscopic forms of Eqs. (8.14) and (8.15) are

$$\text{curl } \mathbf{B} = \mu_0 \mathbf{j} \tag{8.17}$$

and

$$\text{curl } \mathbf{B} = 0 \tag{8.16}$$

Curl $\mathbf{B}$ can of course be written $\nabla \times \mathbf{B}$.

A very important consequence of the field equations is that a torque is exerted by a magnetic field on a current loop. The form of this torque is given by

$$\boldsymbol{\tau} = \mathbf{p}_n \times \mathbf{B} \tag{8.27a}$$

or in scalar form,

$$\tau = p_m B \sin \theta \tag{8.27}$$

where θ is the angle between the magnetic dipole moment of a current loop and the field direction. The dipole moment p_n is given by

$$p_n = NiA \tag{8.26}$$

where N is the number of turns in the loop, i the current, and A its cross-sectional area. Use of the dipole shows the close correspondence between the electric field around an electric dipole and the magnetic field around a current loop. This is exhibited by comparing field components thus:

$$
\begin{aligned}
E_r &= \frac{1}{4\pi\epsilon_0} \frac{2p}{r^3} \cos\theta & B_r &= \frac{\mu_0}{4\pi} \frac{2p_m}{r^3} \cos\theta \\
E_\theta &= \frac{1}{4\pi\epsilon_0} \frac{p}{r^3} \sin\theta & B_\theta &= \frac{\mu_0}{4\pi} \frac{p_m}{r^3} \sin\theta
\end{aligned}
\tag{8.28}
$$

These expressions are valid for the far field of the dipoles, at distances large compared with the dipole dimensions.

A simple modification of Eq. (8.3) allowed us to determine the force on isolated moving charges in a magnetic field. The result is the equation for the Lorentz force:

$$\mathbf{F} = e(\mathbf{v} \times \mathbf{B}) \qquad \text{newtons} \tag{8.32}$$

where e = charge, coul
$\quad \mathbf{v}$ = velocity, m/sec
$\quad \mathbf{B}$ = field, webers/m²

Use of Newton's laws gave us equations which describe the orbits of moving charges in a magnetic field. Because of the cross-product nature of Eq. (8.32), it is at once clear that the component of velocity parallel to lines of **B** is unaffected by the field. In a uniform magnetic field, particle motion in planes normal to **B** is circular in the absence of electric fields which could change the energy of a charged particle. It was shown that the circular motion of a charged particle has an angular frequency

$$\omega = \frac{eB}{m} \quad \text{rad/sec} \tag{8.33}$$

where e/m is the charge to mass ratio of the particle in coulombs per kilogram. This is the cyclotron equation, which shows that the frequency of rotation perpendicular to a uniform **B** field is independent of the velocity of the particle. The path radius is affected by the velocity.

The chapter concluded with short discussions of applications. The galvanometer, the cyclotron, the Hall effect, and the measurement of the ratio e/m were described.

PROBLEMS

The force between current-carrying wires is obtained by finding the magnetic field at one wire caused by current in the other wire and then using the magnetic force equation.

★8.1A Two long parallel wires are separated by 10 cm, and each carries 10 amp in the same direction. Calculate the force between the wires per unit length.

8.1B A wire 10 cm long can slide on two parallel rods tipped at 45° to the vertical as shown in Fig. P8.1. These rods connect to a source of emf

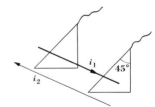

Fig. P8.1

that produces a current i_1 between the two ends of the rod. Another long conductor parallel to the movable wire carries a current i_2. The currents i_1 and i_2 are in opposite directions. If the weight of the movable rod is mg, find the equilibrium distance between the two current-carrying wires.

★8.1C   Two circular coils of N closely wound turns of radius a are coaxial and are separated by a distance b. Find the force between the two coils when a current i passes through each coil.

8.1D   In Fig. P8.2 below, a wire loop carries 5 amp around the path *abcd* in a clockwise direction. Find the magnitude and direction of the net force acting on the loop due to the magnetic field of the upward current of 10 amp in the straight wire.

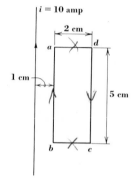

Fig. P8.2

★8.1E   Compute the tension in a circular loop of flexible wire of radius a, carrying a current I and lying in a uniform magnetic field of flux density B perpendicular to the plane of the loop.

The magnetic field of the current in a circuit or in a section of a circuit is obtained by integrating the effects of the current elements which contribute to the field at the point in question. Problem 8.2J is included to introduce the idea of magnetic flux. This is considered further in Chap. 9.

8.2A   Find the magnetic field at the center of a square wire loop of side length 10 cm, carrying 10 amp.

★8.2B   A conductor of circular cross section of radius a carries a current of uniform current density j. Find the magnetic field at all distances r from the center of the conductor.

8.2C   A long wire has a semicircular loop of radius r as shown in Fig. P8.3. A current i is flowing. Find the magnetic field at the center of curvature of the loop.

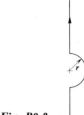

Fig. P8.3

★8.2D A long thin conductor of width b carries a current of i amp. Find the magnetic field in the plane of and outside the conductor at a distance a from its near edge.

8.2E The coaxial line shown in Fig. P8.4 carries the same current i up the inside conductor of radius a as down the outer conductor of inner radius b and outer radius c. Find the magnetic field at all distances r from the center of the conductor. (Use Ampère's circuital law.)

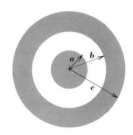

Fig. P8.4

★8.2F A solenoid 20 cm long of radius 2 cm is wound uniformly with 3,000 turns of wire. A current of 2 amp flows through the coil.
  a What is the solenoidal current density j^s?
  b What is the value of B on the axis of the solenoid, at the middle?
  c What is the value of B on the axis at an end?
  d What is the flux ϕ through the coil at the middle?
  e What is the flux ϕ through one end?

8.2G An insulating circular disk of radius a has a uniformly distributed static charge of σ coul/m². The disk rotates about its center with an angular velocity ω. Find the magnetic field at its center.

★8.2H Find the magnetic field at a distance b from the rotating disk of Prob. 8.2G, along its axis of rotation, for $b \gg a$.

8.2I A toroidal coil of inner radius 5 cm and outer radius 6 cm is uniformly wound with 1,000 turns and carries a current of 5 amp.

a Find the average magnetic field in the coil by using Ampère's circuital law.

b Find the magnetic field in the coil at a distance of 5.1 cm from the axis of the toroid.

★8.2J A current of 10 amp flows in the long wire shown in Fig. P8.2. Find the total flux through the area *abcd*.

8.2K The Helmholtz arrangement of two coils provides a large region of uniform field. Two similar coils carrying the same current are placed on the same axis, as shown in Fig. P8.5, separated by a distance equal

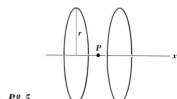

Fig. P8.5

to the coil radius. Show that at point *P* on the axis, this arrangement gives both dB/dx and d^2B/dx^2 equal to zero.

★8.2L Find the direction and magnitude of the magnetic field at the two points *a* and *b* (*a* is at the center of curvature of the semicircular loop of radius *r*, and *b* is midway between the two wires) as shown in Fig. P8.6.

Fig. P8.6

8.2M A pair of infinitely long thin wires carry equal currents *i*. They are bent as shown in Fig. P8.7. What is the magnetic field *B* at the center of the circular parts?

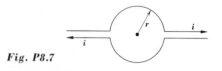

Fig. P8.7

★8.2N A large number *N* of closely spaced turns of fine wire are wound in a single layer upon the surface of a wooden sphere with the planes of the turns perpendicular to an axis of the sphere and completely covering its surface. The current in the winding is i. Find the magnetic flux density at the center of the sphere.

8.2O A flat coil is wound so that it contains a very large uniform number of turns per unit distance along its radius, as shown in Fig. P8.8.

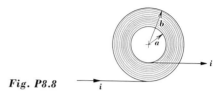

Fig. P8.8

If this number is Z, show that the magnetic field at the center of such a coil of inside radius a, outside radius b, carrying a current i, is given by

$$ B = \frac{\mu_0}{z} iZ \ln \frac{b}{a} $$

★8.2P A hydrogen atom consists of a proton and an electron separated by a distance of 0.5×10^{-10} m. Assuming that the electron moves in a circular orbit around the proton with a frequency of 10^{13} cps, find the magnetic field at the nucleus due to the moving electron.

The magnetic force equation can be modified to give the force on isolated moving charges.

8.3A Taking the radius of the earth as 6,400 m and the horizontal component of the earth's magnetic field at the equator as 0.4×10^{-4} weber/m², with what minimum momentum could a proton encircle the earth at the equator?

★8.3B An ion in vacuum starts from rest and is accelerated between two parallel plates having a potential difference of 1,000 volts, as shown in Fig. P8.9. On emerging from between the plates, the ion moves into a

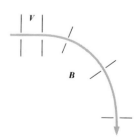

Fig. P8.9

uniform magnetic field of 0.1 weber/m², directed perpendicular to the path of the ion. If the radius of curvature of the ion path is 0.3 m, what is the mass of the ion if it is singly charged (has one electronic charge)?

8.3C Electrons are revolving in a uniform magnetic field. What is the value of the field B such that the electrons make one complete revolution in 10^{-8} sec?

★8.3D In a transverse-Hall-effect experiment, a current of 10 amp flows through a conductor of square cross section 0.5 cm on a side. The Hall voltage induced by a magnetic field of 2 webers/m² is 2.5×10^{-6} volt. Calculate the Hall constant R_H. If the carriers of current are electrons, find N, the density of carriers in the conductor, and draw a sketch showing the relative directions of the current, the magnetic field B, and the Hall field E_z.

8.3E What would be the transverse Hall field for a conductor having an equal density of positive and negative mobile charge carriers?

★8.3F The steady magnetic field of a cyclotron has a value of 0.5 weber/m². What must be the frequency of the voltage variation on the two electrodes in order that the alternation of their potentials be synchronous with the motion of hydrogen ions? What will be the energy in joules and in electron volts of the ions when the radius of their path is 1 m? How many revolutions will be required for the ions to gain this energy if the maximum potential difference between the electrodes is 20,000 volts?

A current loop in a magnetic field can be treated as a magnetic dipole.

8.4A The axis of a circular coil of radius 10 cm makes an angle θ with a uniform field B. The coil has 10 turns and carries a current of 5 amp. Find the torque on the coil.

★8.4B A current-carrying circular loop of radius r lies in a diverging magnetic induction field whose lines of B make an angle θ with the plane of the loop, as shown in Fig. P8.10. If the loop has N turns carrying a current

Fig. P8.10

I_0 in a clockwise direction as seen from above and if the external B field at the plane of the loop is B_0, find the magnitude and direction of the force on the loop.

9

induced electromotive force, emf

9.1 Introduction

We have so far investigated the electric field due to static charges and the magnetic field of moving charges. In this chapter we add a third cornerstone to the theoretical structure by considering effects due to *changing* magnetic fields. Whenever the magnetic field changes with time the result is an additional force on electric charges, best expressed as a new sort of electromotive force. This is the *Faraday induced emf*, which plays a most important role in the behavior of time-varying electromagnetism. The phenomenon of induced emf results in a new circuit element, the *inductor*, which, added to the resistor and capacitor, completes the passive elements in electric circuits.

Faraday's law leads to the factors of proportionality between current change and induced emf, the coefficients of mutual inductance between two circuits and of self-inductance in a single circuit. Finally, we discuss the storage of energy implicit in the setting up of a magnetic field in space.

9.2 *Faraday's Law of Induction*

We begin by describing a simple experimental arrangement which can demonstrate the facts of Faraday's law. As shown in Fig. 9.1, we im-

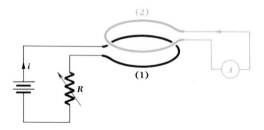

(2)

Fig. 9.1   Two circuits coupled together by the effects of Faraday induction. While the current in circuit 1 is changing, an emf is induced in circuit 2.

agine two conducting circuits, each of which contains a loop of wire. Circuit 2 is a simple wire loop, with a current meter inserted in the closed current path, so that the meter will indicate the magnitude and direction of any current which may flow. The wire loop in circuit 1, placed close to the loop of circuit 2, has a battery and adjustable resistance, so that a current will flow which can be changed by changing the value of the resistance.

Faraday discovered that whenever the current in the primary circuit 1 is caused to change, there is a current *induced* in circuit 2 while that change is occurring. This remarkable fact is not in general derivable from any of the previously discussed properties of electromagnetism. By observation we find that the induced current in the passive circuit 2 can be related to an electromotive force ε in circuit 2 and its total resistance R. Thus, at any instant, the current i_2 is given by

$$\varepsilon = i_2 R$$

The emf turns out to be proportional to the time rate of change of current, di/dt, in circuit 1.

In Faraday's early experiments, he used many turns of wire in each coil to increase the size of the effect, and made observations when the primary current was suddenly changed from zero to maximum or the reverse by closing or opening a switch in the circuit.

In the following paragraph,[1] published in 1832, Faraday described one of the numerous experiments through which he developed his ideas of induced emf:

> Two hundred and three feet of copper wire in one length were passed round a large block of wood; other two hundred and three feet of similar wire were interposed as a spiral between the turns of the first coil, and metallic contact everywhere prevented by twine. One of these helices was connected with a galvanometer, and the other with a battery of one hundred pairs of plates of four inches square, with double coppers, and well charged. When the contact was made, there was a sudden and very slight effect at the galvanometer, and there was also a similar slight effect when the contact with the battery was broken. But whilst the voltaic current was continuing to pass through the one helix, no galvanometrical appearances nor any effect like induction upon the other helix could be perceived, although the active power of the battery was proved to be great, by its heating the whole of its own helix, and by the brilliancy of the discharge when made through charcoal.

He summarizes the results of a whole group of such experiments involving both changing currents and moving magnets, in the following short paragraph,[2] which, allowing for a considerable change in nomenclature since his time, we see refers to the existence of induced emf:

> All these results show that the power of inducing electric currents is circumferentially excited by a magnetic resultant or axis of power, just as circumferential magnetism is dependent upon and is exhibited by an electric current.

Faraday developed a general description of the time-varying events which result in induced emf. He found, as we can easily show by experiment, that the emf induced in any loop depends only on the time rate of change of the flux of magnetic field surrounded by the circuit. This idea can be expressed by the equation

$$\mathcal{E} = -\frac{d\phi}{dt} \quad \text{volts} \tag{9.1}$$

where $\mathcal{E}$ is the induced emf, and ϕ the magnetic flux, $\int \mathbf{B} \cdot d\mathbf{S}$, as in Eq. (8.19), which threads the circuit. The integration is over the area surrounded by the circuit. We comment later on the negative sign used in Eq. (9.1).

To illustrate the generality of Faraday's law let us consider a

---

[1] Michael Faraday, Experimental Researches in Electricity, *Phil. Trans. Roy. Soc. London,* **122A**: 127, 155 (1832).
[2] *Ibid.*

second way to cause the magnetic flux in circuit 2 of Fig. 9.1 to change. Suppose the current in circuit 1 were held constant, but that coil 2 were moved away from coil 1, reducing the magnetic flux through circuit 2. We should again find the same kind of induced current in circuit 2, and again the emf producing the current would be according to the same general equation, Eq. (9.1). Furthermore, motion of coil 1 with coil 2 held at rest would give exactly the same effect. Only the *relative* motion of one coil with respect to the other matters. This last result is really not surprising. If it made a difference which coil was moved and which was held at rest, we should be forced to conclude that there is an *absolute* frame of reference. It is a well-known postulate of Einstein's theory of special relativity that all inertial reference systems are equivalent. This means that the laws of physics are expected to be the same for someone at "rest" as for someone traveling at some constant velocity with respect to the rest system. It is not surprising that the laws of electromagnetism are *relativistically invariant*, since the development of relativity was largely motivated by the theoretical structure of electromagnetism. The newtonian formulation of the laws of mechanics is of course not relativistically invariant.

The negative sign in Faraday's law as it is usually written refers to the sign of the emf as it relates to the sign of the rate of change of flux. It is useful here to establish a simple convention about signs: We shall consider emfs and currents positive when they are *counterclockwise* as seen from the viewer's position. Thus we show a positive current in the loop of Fig. 9.2, where $d\mathbf{S}$ is the normal to the area bounded by the current i. We must also define a sign for the flux through any circuit. We define the flux through any circuit as positive

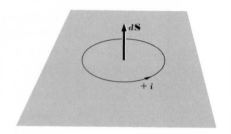

Fig. 9.2 Sign convention for current loops and direction of positive magnetic flux through a loop. Positive current is counterclockwise as viewed. The outward-drawn normal $d\mathbf{S}$ as viewed is the positive direction. Magnetic flux through the loop is positive if it points in the same sense as $d\mathbf{S}$. A positive loop current thus produces a positive flux through a loop.

when it is pointed toward the observer. Note that this definition gives the result that a positive (counterclockwise) current produces a positive (outward toward the viewer) flux within the circuit.

With these definitions of signs we may investigate the direction of induced emf according to Faraday's law. We look again at Fig. 9.1 and ask about the emf induced in circuit 2 when the current in circuit 1 is *increasing* in magnitude. Since this current is directed clockwise in the loop of circuit 1, it is a *negative* current, and since its magnitude is increasing, the sign of di_1/dt is negative. It follows that the flux in circuit 1 is pointed downward (since negative current produces a negative flux) and increasing in magnitude. We could have seen this by the direct application of

$$d\mathbf{B} = \frac{\mu_0}{4\pi} \frac{i\,d\mathbf{l} \times \hat{\mathbf{r}}}{r^2} \qquad \text{webers/m}^2 \qquad (8.2)$$

In any case we now know that the flux through circuit 2 is also downward and increasing. What is the direction of the induced emf in circuit 2? Equation (9.1) tells us that the sign of the emf $\mathcal{E}_2$ is the negative of $d\phi_2/dt$. But we have just seen that ϕ_2 is pointed away from us (downward) and increasing in magnitude; so $d\phi_2/dt$ is negative. Thus $\mathcal{E}_2$ is positive, or counterclockwise, as is the resultant current in circuit 2. This sort of reasoning can always be used to identify the sign of induced emfs. In the next section we discuss another way of determining the direction of induced emfs, based on the principle of energy conservation. This is known as Lenz's principle.

We have so far been concerned with the effect of changes in one circuit which influence the behavior of another circuit. We discuss this quantitatively later, in terms of a geometric parameter called the *mutual inductance* between the two circuits. But Faraday's law is general and applies to any situation in which the magnetic flux is changing. Current in a single isolated circuit, as in Fig. 9.2, produces magnetic flux within its own loop. If the current in the circuit is caused to change, say, by altering the value of the series resistance, the changing current produces a changing flux which sets up a counteracting emf in the circuit itself. There is thus a *self-inductance* in every circuit, as well as a mutual inductance between circuits linked by magnetic flux.

9.3 Lenz's Principle

The negative sign in Faraday's induction law gives the correct direction of induced emf when we adopt the convention that counterclockwise emf and currents are positive and that positive flux is directed outward toward the viewer. This result is a direct consequence of energy conservation. The discussion leads us to Lenz's principle, which provides an easy way of determining the direction of any induced emfs without the detailed reasoning given in the last section.

The energy argument requires that we accept for now an idea we prove later, that the presence of magnetic flux in space implies stored energy. The argument for this parallels our earlier discussion of the energy stored in an electric field.

We make the argument in terms of a single isolated circuit having, say, a battery and some resistance, so that some constant current i is flowing. As a consequence of the current, a certain amount of flux threads the circuit. Suppose we gradually decrease the resistance so that the current increases with time. Faraday's law tells that the changing flux will produce an emf; will this emf act in the same direction as the battery emf or in the opposite direction? An easy path to the correct answer is to make a choice and see whether or not the consequences are tenable. In that spirit we suppose that the induced emf is in the same direction as the battery emf, so that it tends further to increase the already increasing current. But this greater rate of current increase will lead to a still greater induced emf, producing a still more rapid rise in current, a still larger induced emf, and so on! Our guess clearly leads to a self-generating rapid buildup of current and field, once a small start is made. Since the end point of this process represents a large amount of stored energy, the whole process cannot occur, if we are to have energy conservation.

We are led by this result to the opposite and correct statement of Lenz's principle. Any change in current in a circuit results in a change in the magnetic flux through that circuit; this changing flux produces an emf which acts to oppose the flux change. In effect, Lenz's principle characterizes a magnetic "inertial" effect which acts to maintain the status quo, just as in mechanics the mass of a body exerts a reaction on any attempt to change its state of motion. The larger the mass, the larger the force, $F = ma$, necessary to give it a certain acceleration. The larger the flux through a circuit for a given current, the harder it is to produce a given rate of change of current. This effect operates both in single circuits and between coupled circuits.

9.4   *Induced Electromotive Force, a New Kind of Electric Field*

The experimental fact of Faraday induction now forces us to examine again the properties of an electric field. An induced emf implies an electric field, since it produces a force on a static charge. But this electric field, produced by a changing magnetic flux, has some properties which are quite different from those of an electrostatic field produced by fixed charges, as will now be shown. We simplify the discussion, using Fig. 9.3, by imagining a region of space in which a uniform mag-

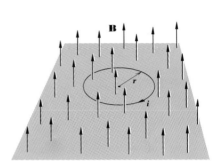

Fig. 9.3   Shown here is a region of space in which the magnetic field is uniform and pointed outward. The field intensity is increasing with time.   As a result of Faraday induction, an emf is induced in the circular conducting loop.   Both the emf and the resulting current in the loop are in a clockwise (negative) direction.

netic field (upward and toward the viewer) is increasing in magnitude at a constant rate. Let us suppose that a conducting path of radius r is situated in this field, as shown. By either of the two kinds of arguments[1] implied by Faraday's law we can determine that the induced emf and current will be clockwise. The magnitude of ε is given by

$$\varepsilon = -\frac{d\phi}{dt} \tag{9.1}$$

where ϕ is the flux inside the area of the loop.

Since the emf is the work per unit charge done in forcing a charge around the complete circuit, we may write

$$\varepsilon = iR \qquad \text{volts}$$

where i is the current, and R the resistance of the length of wire making up the loop. But the current flows because a force is exerted on the charges, and this, by definition, means there is an electric field. Where is the field, and what is its direction? For the simple geometry of a

[1] Argument 1: The flux is positive (outward) and increasing; therefore $d\phi/dt$ is positive. According to Eq. (9.1), ε or i is negative, or clockwise. Argument 2 (Lenz): The current induced must be such as to tend to cancel the change in flux. Therefore the induced current must be negative (clockwise) to produce a negative flux (into the page) to tend to cancel the increasing outward flux.

circle we can argue that, by symmetry, all points on the wire are equivalent; so the electric field must somehow be uniform all around the circular path of the wire. If we define the electric field **E** along the wire as the force per unit charge acting parallel to the wire, we can obtain it from the emf by the equation

$$\varepsilon = E \times 2\pi r \quad \text{or} \quad E = \frac{\varepsilon}{2\pi r}$$

In general, for any shape of closed path, the result of Faraday's law is

$$\oint \mathbf{E} \cdot d\mathbf{l} = \varepsilon = -\frac{d\phi}{dt} \tag{9.2}$$

It is immediately apparent that we are not dealing with an electrostatic field, even when we assume a constantly increasing **B** field, so that **E** is constant in time. This follows since, for an electrostatic field, we had always

$$\oint \mathbf{E} \cdot d\mathbf{l} = 0 \tag{3.4}$$

Equation (9.2) is the equation of most use in discussing Faraday-induced electric fields. Since this equation is true for *any* closed path, we can write it in the form

$$\oint \mathbf{E} \cdot d\mathbf{l} = -\frac{d}{dt} \int_{\text{surface}} \mathbf{B} \cdot d\mathbf{S} \tag{9.3}$$

where the integral of **B** is taken over the area bordered by the closed path.

Using the same reasoning as in Chap. 3, we can obtain the microscopic form of the Faraday law, which becomes

$$\text{curl } \mathbf{E} = -\frac{\partial \mathbf{B}}{\partial t} \tag{9.4}$$

Thus the special property of this new sort of electric field is that its curl, or its line integral around a closed path, is *not* zero. In general, the electric field at any point in space can be broken into two parts, the part we have called electrostatic, whose curl is zero, and for which electrostatic potential differences can be defined, and a part which has a nonzero curl, for which a potential function is not applicable in its usual way.

It is useful to display more clearly the extreme contrast between this new kind of electric field which results from a time rate of change of magnetic flux and the electrostatic field for which $\oint \mathbf{E} \cdot d\mathbf{l} = 0$, or curl $\mathbf{E} = 0$. We first show that the *direction* of the Faraday-induced electric field is indeterminate. Figure 9.4 shows a wire loop of radius r

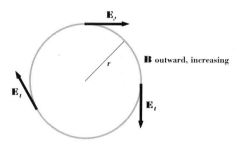

Fig. 9.4 A wire loop of radius r in a region of uniform magnetic field. The field is outward (positive) and is increasing at a rate dB/dt. The resulting induction electric field is in the negative (clockwise) direction, tangent to the path.

B outward, increasing

placed in a region of uniform magnetic field which is varying at a rate dB/dt. Faraday's law tells us that the emf $\mathcal{E}$, which can be expressed as the line integral of the Faraday field $\mathbf{E}$ around the closed path, is given by

$$\mathcal{E} = \oint \mathbf{E} \cdot d\mathbf{l} = -\pi r^2 \frac{dB}{dt} = -\frac{d\phi}{dt}$$

Because of the circular symmetry of the problem, we can obtain a definite value for the tangential component of $\mathbf{E}$ at each point on the loop. Thus, using

$$\oint \mathbf{E} \cdot d\mathbf{l} = E_t \oint dl = E_t 2\pi r$$

we find

$$E_t = -\frac{1}{2\pi r} \frac{d\phi}{dt} \qquad \text{volts/m}$$

We now know the size and direction of the effective Faraday electric field at each point on the path. But suppose, as in Fig. 9.5, we have a loop of irregular shape enclosing the identical amount of area or flux as does the circular loop. The induced emf can be written as before, equal to $-d\phi/dt$, but in this case the direction and the magnitude of E_t at points around the loop vary quite differently. Faraday's law does not allow us to find anything more than the average magnitude of E_t, and its direction depends on the path chosen. It is the essence of the law of induction that, in general, it can tell us only about the average value of E_t around a closed path and that the direction and magnitudes depend on the path chosen.

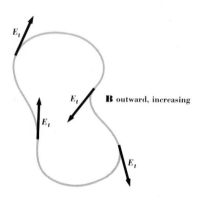

Fig. 9.5 A loop in a region of changing magnetic flux, in which the time rate of change of flux enclosed is the same as in Fig. 9.4. By Faraday's law the total induced emf is the same, but the magnitude and direction of E_t vary quite differently around the circuit.

A further point is that the induced emf around a closed path has meaning whether or not a conductor lies on the path chosen. This fact is well exemplified in a kind of electron accelerator called the *betatron*. In this machine, electrons in a vacuum travel in circular paths in a magnetic field. The strength of the magnetic field changes with time, and as a result of the changing magnetic flux in the area enclosed by the electron orbit, an emf is induced that accelerates the electrons.

Finally, we emphasize that the Faraday electric field at a given point is not related directly to the value of B at points on the path taken, but depends, as stated, only on $d\phi/dt$ within the area included by the loop. This situation is strikingly shown by the arrangement in Fig. 9.6, a closely wound toroidal solenoid, which, as we have seen,

Fig. 9.6 A tightly wound toroidal solenoid, producing a magnetic field only within the body of the solenoid. The loop surrounding the solenoid is thus at all points in a region of zero magnetic field. Nevertheless, an emf is induced around the loop when a changing solenoid current produces a changing flux within the solenoid.

produces a field inside the solenoid but *none* outside. Also shown is a loop which surrounds a cross section of the solenoid. Each point on the loop is thus in a region of zero magnetic field. Nevertheless, when the current in the solenoid is changed, there is an induced emf in the loop which produces a current in the loop. This arrangement simply reinforces the meaning of Eq. (9.1), that only the value of $d\phi/dt$ within the loop is involved in Faraday induction. At a more advanced level, problems involving Faraday induction are usually discussed in terms of a quantity called the vector potential, but we shall not pursue this treatment further here.

9.5 *Motional Electromotive Force*

Although Faraday's law is a new experimental fact, to be added to the laws of electrostatic forces and of magnetic forces between moving charges, there is one aspect of Faraday's induction that we could have predicted on the basis of our earlier discussions. This is the case of a fixed loop which is moved in space from a region of one magnetic field intensity to another of differing intensity. This motion then must result in an induced emf, since there is a time rate of change of flux threading the circuit. In this kind of situation we can immediately calculate the induced emf without invoking Faraday's law. This special case is often labeled *motional emf*.

We simplify the description of this problem by taking a plane rectangular circuit as shown in Fig. 9.7, which we move with a con-

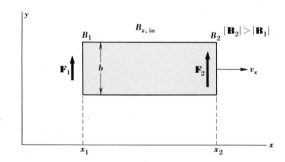

Fig. 9.7 *Motional emf. Motion in a magnetic field produces current in a conduction loop.*

stant velocity v_x in a plane perpendicular to the magnetic induction field B_z, which is pointed inward and which increases with increasing values of x, but does not vary with y. Thus the magnitude of the (negative) flux through the circuit is increasing with time. The vertical dimension of the circuit is b.

Now that we have set up the problem in terms of a magnetic field that is fixed in space and involves the motion of charges (those within the conductor), we are back on familiar ground, and can calculate the net force on these charges through the equation for the magnetic force on a moving charge e.

$$\mathbf{F} = e(\mathbf{v} \times \mathbf{B}) \tag{8.32}$$

We shall find a net force around the loop which corresponds exactly to the Faraday emf. The forces on charges in the wire on each side of the loop are calculated as follows: We assume that all charges are at rest within the loop; so the velocity of all charges is v, the velocity of the loop itself. We first see that the forces evB on charges on the top and bottom wires of the loop are directed perpendicular to the wires, and therefore do not contribute to the force urging charges around the loop. The forces on charges in the vertical end sections of the loop are directed according to $\mathbf{v} \times \mathbf{B}$, as shown in the figure. But since the field at the end B_2 is greater in magnitude than the field B_1, the force on the right-hand side exceeds that on the left. A net force thus acts in the positive (counterclockwise) direction.

The size of the net magnetic force on charges on the two ends of the moving loop is

$$F_2 = |eB_2v_x| \quad \text{and} \quad F_1 = -|eB_1v_x| \tag{9.5}$$

We have called F_1 and F_2 negative and positive in order to relate them to the sense in which they urge positive current around the loop. They are both upward forces, as shown in the drawing. To calculate the effective emf around the loop, we must find the net work per unit charge. Since the net force acts only over the distance b, the net work done per unit charge taken around the loop is

$$\frac{W}{e} = \frac{1}{e} \oint \mathbf{F} \cdot d\mathbf{l} = |B_2 - B_1|v_x b \quad \text{joules/coul} \tag{9.6}$$

But the last term can be rewritten in terms of the net time rate of change of flux within the loop. Thus the rate at which new flux is being introduced at the right is given by B_2bv_x, and the rate it is leaving at the left is B_1bv_x. Thus the net rate of change is

$$B_2bv_x - B_1bv_x = |B_2 - B_1|v_x b = -\frac{d\phi}{dt} \tag{9.7}$$

The negative sign in Eq. (9.7) results from the negative direction of the flux through the circuit, which is increasing in magnitude as the circuit moves. Thus we find that the net emf resulting from the motion is given by

$$\varepsilon = -\frac{d\phi}{dt} \quad \text{volts}$$

in exact agreement with Faraday's law.

We expect agreement between these two ways of considering this problem. However, no such calculation can be made for situations where changing flux results from changing currents. Faraday's law is a new principle of behavior which overlaps and is consistent with the law of magnetic force on a moving charge.

9.6 Examples, Electrical Generators

Faraday induction lies behind the operation of both mechanical generators of electric power and of the converse, electric motors, which convert electric to mechanical energy. Here we show by calculations of Faraday induced emfs how two very simple generators behave. The discussion of motors is delayed until Sec. 9.8.

a *An elementary generator.* The simple device sketched in Fig. 9.8, although not a practical apparatus for generating electric power, never-

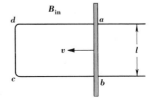

Fig. 9.8 Sliding wire on a stationary loop in a field B.

theless conveniently exhibits the principle of operation of a mechanical generator. A metal rod can be slid along a rigid wire frame which is in a uniform magnetic field **B**, as shown. While the rod of length l is being moved with velocity v, the area within the loop decreases at a rate vl. If the field intensity in the region is B, the time rate of change of flux within the loop is $d\phi/dt = vlB$. In this example it is assumed that ϕ is negative (away from the reader). Once the time variation of ϕ inside the loop is found, the Faraday law can be used to find the induced emf.

$$\mathcal{E} = -\frac{d\phi}{dt} = |vlB| \qquad \text{volts} \tag{9.8}$$

Since ϕ itself is negative (away from the viewer) and decreasing with time, $d\phi/dt$ is positive; so the emf is negative, or clockwise. This calculation could equally well have been made by means of the motional emf discussed in the preceding section.

It is instructive to calculate the rate of electric energy dissipation into heat compared with the mechanical work rate. This is easy to do if we first determine the current which results from the emf around the circuit. The current is given by

$$i = \frac{\mathcal{E}}{R} = \frac{vlB}{R} \qquad \text{amp} \tag{9.9}$$

where R is the resistance around the loop.

Electric energy is being dissipated in the resistance at a rate

$$P = \mathcal{E}i = \frac{v^2l^2B^2}{R} \qquad \text{watts} \tag{9.10}$$

The source of this energy is the mechanical work being done in moving the rod. The force on the rod carrying a current i in a field B is $F = Bil$, so that the rate at which mechanical work is being done is

$$\frac{dW}{dt} = Fv = vlBi = \frac{v^2l^2B^2}{R} \qquad \text{watts} \tag{9.11}$$

Comparison of the work rate and power dissipation in the resistance of the loop gives the identity expected on the basis of energy conservation. Would it be very easy or very hard to pull the rod at a given speed if the rod and loop were superconducting? Would the answer be the same if the rod were being pulled in the opposite direction?

b *Calculation of emf of a generator.* A more practical generator for converting mechanical work into electric energy than the one discussed in Example 9.6a is shown in Fig. 9.9. A coil of N turns and area A is rotated in a uniform magnetic field B, at an angular velocity ω_0 rad/sec. We calculate the emf generated, using the Faraday induction law. The flux linkage threading the coil at an angle θ between the plane of the

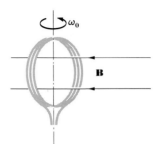

*Fig. 9.9 A simple genera-
tor: a rotating coil in an
external magnetic field.*

coil and the direction of B is given by

$$N\phi = NAB \sin \theta = NAB \sin \omega_0 t$$

where $\omega_0 t$ is the value of θ for a particular time t. Then

$$\mathcal{E} = -N \frac{d\phi}{dt} = -\omega_0 NAB \cos \omega_0 t \qquad (9.12)$$

Thus this generator gives a sinusoidal emf of amplitude $\omega_0 NAB$. The source of this emf is the mechanical work done in rotating the coil. This is zero (in a frictionless system) if no current flows and increases linearly with increasing current, as found in Example 9.5a above. Further discussion of several practical types of generators is given in Sec. 11.13.

9.7 Stored Energy of a Current Loop in a Magnetic Field

We saw in Chap. 8 that a current loop in a magnetic field is subject to torques. We now show that, as a result, a current loop in a field involves stored energy. Our interest in this problem is twofold. In the first place we have here a case where we can consider a magnetic potential energy, as was discussed briefly in Sec. 8.4. In the second place, we find that the stored energy involved in the presence of a current loop in an external field depends only on the net external flux through the loop. This is an important result which will be useful in our later work on inductance (Sec. 9.9).

We now set about the calculation of the work to move a current-carrying loop into a region of static magnetic field. In order to do this we need the result that the work to bring the loop up to a given position in the field is independent of the path taken. But we found in Sec. 8.4 that as long as paths taken do not enclose a current, the field may be considered conservative. This idea is contained in the statement $\oint \mathbf{B} \cdot d\mathbf{l} = 0$, or equivalently, that the circulation of the field is zero, or that the curl of the field is zero. We therefore bring the current loop into the field along a path which does not take the loop around the coil which produces the field. For example, as in Fig. 9.10,

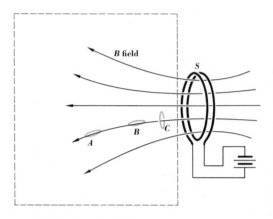

Fig. 9.10 ***Work to bring a current loop into a field. A constant-current loop carrying a current i in N turns, brought up from far away into a region of magnetic field produced by another current coil S. The work to bring the coil into a position C, in which it surrounds a flux, can be calculated by moving the coil through successive positions like A and B while keeping its orientation such that it surrounds no flux. This takes no work since there is no net magnetic force. All the work done can be concentrated in the process of rotation of the coil at its final location into its flux-linking orientation C. Since in this conservative system the work done is independent of the path, the result that the work depends only on the final flux through the loop, W = −Niϕ, is true for any method of bringing the loop to its final position.***

we could set up a field by means of a current coil. The field within the dotted line, or for that matter everywhere in space except through the coil circuit, is conservative. We have indicated a current loop carrying a constant current i which is energized by the battery. The current loop is shown in three successive positions. It has been brought up from far away through the positions A and B with orientation such that no lines of B thread the loop. In its final position, C, it has been turned with its plane at right angles to B, so that a maximum flux threads it.

We can show that as long as the loop is oriented so that no external magnetic flux threads it, no mechanical work is done in moving it quasi-statically into a uniform-field region. This follows from the direction of the forces on the elements of the loop. If we take a rectangular loop for simplicity, application of the force equation $F = i\,d\mathbf{l} \times \mathbf{B}$, as in Sec. 8.8, shows that the only forces on the sides of the loop will be in directions perpendicular to the motion into the field along lines of B. This means that all the work done in bringing the current loop into the field can be localized in the work which must be done against the torque in order to change the external flux through the loop from zero to its final value. In Fig. 9.11 we draw again the

B field   **B** field $\mathbf{p}_m$

$\mathbf{p}_m$

B C

Fig. 9.11   Another view of the same loop of Fig. 9.10, showing the rotation of the loop into its final position and orientation, C. Also shown is the magnetic dipole vector of the loop, p_m.

current loop, in position B of Fig. 9.10, with no external flux through the loop, and in position C, with maximum external flux through the loop. The direction of current is shown, as well as the orientation of the magnetic dipole vector, as in Sec. 8.8.

The work required is calculated by integrating the torque over the angle θ from 90 to 180°. Thus we write

$$W = -\int_{90°}^{180°} \tau\,d\theta = -\int_{90°}^{180°} \mathbf{p}_m \times \mathbf{B}\,d\theta \tag{9.13}$$

We have used Eq. (8.27a) for the torque. We write the cross product in terms of $\sin\theta$ to get

$$-\int_{90°}^{180°} p_m B \sin\theta\,d\theta = [p_m B \cos\theta]_{90°}^{180°} = -p_m B = -NiAB$$
$$= -Ni\phi \tag{9.14}$$

where N is the number of turns in the loop, and A its area, and ϕ is the external magnetic flux through the loop. Equation (9.14) gives the external mechanical work necessary to bring a constant current loop into a region where an externally produced flux ϕ threads it. Since in the case chosen we end up with the loop oriented so that the external flux through the loop and the current have opposite sign, Eq. (9.14) tells that it takes positive work to arrange the loop as shown in position C. If we had oriented the loop oppositely ($\theta = 0$), the dipole moment would be aligned parallel rather than antiparallel to the field, and the external work would be negative, since the signs of i and ϕ would be the same.

The calculation above is confined to the *mechanical* work done in moving a current loop in a magnetic field. There is of necessity some electric work done also. The source of emf producing the current i in the coil must do extra work beyond the i^2R term in order to compensate for the induced emf in the loop caused by the changing flux in the loop. In addition, the motion of the current loop produces a changing flux in the external circuit acting as the source of external magnetic field and requires work by this source to compensate for the induced emf in the external circuit. This electric work need not concern us at present.

9.8   Examples, Electric Motors

We now consider the behavior of electric motors, which convert electric to mechanical energy. The mechanical force produced by a motor comes from the magnetic force on current-carrying conductors, as we show in Example 9.8a below. In addition, we examine the role of Faraday induction in the energy balance between electric and mechanical power.

a   *An elementary motor.*   We choose first the equivalent of the elementary generator discussed in Example 9.6a. In order to operate this device as a motor, a source of emf $\mathcal{E}_0$ is connected as shown in Fig. 9.12. The chemical cell of emf $\mathcal{E}_0$ causes a current i to flow through the loop whose total resistance is R. The magnetic force on the movable rod is

$$F = ibB \tag{9.15}$$

The rate at which work is done by this force is easily calculated by supposing that the rod is displaced a distance dx in a time dt. Multi-

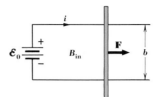

Fig. 9.12 *An elementary motor.*

plying Eq. (9.15) by dx/dt then gives the expression for the mechanical power, dW/dt.

$$F\frac{dx}{dt} = Fv = ibB\frac{dx}{dt} = i\frac{d\phi}{dt} \qquad (9.16)$$

The right-hand term expresses the motion of the rod in terms of the resulting changing flux within the loop. The negative sign usual in the work-force relationship is omitted here because dW is the mechanical work done *by* the magnetic force rather than against it. Equation (9.16) provides a useful method of calculating the rate at which electric energy is being converted to mechanical energy.

A fully equivalent calculation involves the stored energy when a current loop is threaded by an external magnetic field. We found in the last section that if a current loop is threaded by a flux ϕ, the stored energy involved is

$$U = -Ni\phi \qquad (9.14)$$

This relation was developed by calculating the mechanical work required to bring a current loop to a position in which it is threaded by the flux. In our present example the number of turns N is one. According to this energy analysis, the mechanical work done in displacing the rod is done at the expense of stored energy due to flux threading the loop; so we may write

$$dW = -dU = i\,d\phi$$

or

$$\frac{dW}{dt} = Fv = i\frac{d\phi}{dt}$$

as found above. The direction of F can be obtained by using the standard sign convention for the loop current i and flux ϕ.

According to the result we have now found in two different ways, a time rate of change of flux accompanies the conversion of electric to mechanical energy in a motor. As a consequence Faraday induction causes an additional induced emf which opposes the applied emf $\mathcal{E}_0$ and reduces the current in the loop. (In Example 9.8b below we give an argument which shows that the induced emf always acts to reduce the current in a motor.) With the addition of the induced emf, the circuit equation becomes

$$\mathcal{E}_0 - \frac{d\phi}{dt} = iR \tag{9.17}$$

If this equation is multiplied by i, we get

$$\mathcal{E}_0 i = i\frac{d\phi}{dt} + i^2R = Fv + i^2R \tag{9.18}$$

Thus the battery supplies energy at a rate $\mathcal{E}_0 i$, producing mechanical work at the rate Fv and dissipating energy in the resistance of the circuit at the rate i^2R.

These last two equations show an important property of a motor. If the force against which the motor is acting is small, the velocity will tend to increase. Then, according to Eq. (9.17), $d\phi/dt$ will increase, and the current will be relatively small. According to Eq. (9.18), the power delivered by the battery will be small. When the mechanical force increases, the motion decelerates, the Faraday induction decreases, and the current and power drain on the battery increase. Thus the greater the mechanical load, the more power is taken from the battery. The Faraday emf induced in a motor is usually called the *back emf*, since it opposes the battery or other source of emf.

b   *Back emf in a motor.*   A more practical motor than the one discussed in Example 9.8a is sketched in Fig. 9.13. Here the torque acting on a current-carrying loop in a magnetic field is used to cause rotation of the coil. A *commutator* is used to reverse the current connections at the appropriate phase of rotation, so that the torque always acts in the same direction. Let us suppose that the angular velocity of the coil is ω_0, with some particular external mechanical load. As in the previous example, the changing external flux through the rotating windings produces a Faraday induction back emf. The magnitude of this induced emf is proportional to the speed of the motor. The induced emf always acts to *reduce* the current in the motor coils, as stated in Example 9.8a.

The direction of the induced emf may be found as follows: The motor coils exert torque by virtue of the fact that the coils are always

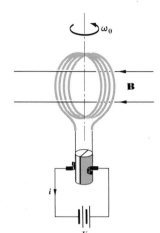

*Fig. 9.13 A simple motor:
a current-carrying coil
with commutator, in ex-
ternal magnetic field.*

turning toward the low-energy orientation in the external field. According to Eq. (9.14), with its negative sign, minimum stored energy occurs when i and ϕ have the same sign. This means that in the low-energy coil position the external flux threading the coil is in the same direction as the flux caused by the current in the coil. Thus the driven motion of the motor coil is always such as to increase the (positive) flux through the coil. Hence the induced emf must always oppose this increase. That is, the induced emf must always act to decrease the motor current.

The induced back emf is given by

$$\varepsilon = -N\frac{d\phi}{dt} \tag{9.19}$$

where N is the number of turns in the coil. If the magnetic field strength is B_0 and the coil area is A,

$$N\phi = NAB_0 \sin \omega_0 t$$

and

$$-N\frac{d\phi}{dt} = -NAB_0\omega_0 \cos \omega_0 t$$

The commutator changes the $d\phi/dt$ curve from $\cos \omega_0 t$ to one like that in Fig. 9.14. The back emf thus varies in a similar fashion, according to Eq. (9.19). If we call this back emf which varies periodically $\varepsilon(t)$, the current in the coil is given by the expression

$$V - \varepsilon(t) = iR$$

and we see that i will also vary with time, in a way indicated in Fig.

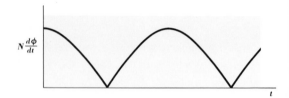

$N\frac{d\phi}{dt}$

*Fig. 9.14   Back emf of the motor as seen
through the commutator.*

9.15. In the figure, i_0 is the current that would flow if the loop were held stationary. Here we have neglected the further modifications that would occur if the self-inductance of the coil were important at the frequency ω_0. The average current is given by

$$V - \overline{\mathcal{E}(t)} = iR$$

where $\overline{\mathcal{E}(t)}$ is the average value of the induced emf.

In practice, rather than using a single coil, the rotating unit of a motor, called an *armature*, is made up of a number of coils which are oriented at different angles around the axis of rotation. The commutator connects the external source of power to each coil consecutively in such a way that maximum torque is obtained from each coil in turn.

The back emf plays an important role in the operation of a motor. Let us explain this by considering a motor armature in which the coils have very little resistance. If a power source is connected to the coils,

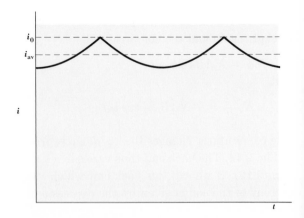

*Fig. 9.15   Variation of current in the motor due
to back emf.*

a large current flows while the coils are at rest, limited only by the resistance of the coils. However, as soon as the coils begin to turn in the static magnetic field produced by stationary coils in the motor, a back emf is induced that opposes the externally applied voltage causing the current in the rotating coils. If the motor is running without a mechanical load, the back emf reduces the current to a small value, just large enough to supply the energy used up by friction and electric-resistance losses. A heavy mechanical load tends to slow down the motor, causing a reduction in the back emf that allows enough electric power to be used to account for the greater mechanical load. On this basis, one can understand the large electric-power drain when starting a motor.

9.9   Mutual Inductance

If magnetic flux from one circuit threads the current path of another circuit, changing current in the first circuit influences the current in the second circuit, as we have seen in Sec. 9.2. The quantitative aspects of this mutual interaction are best discussed in terms of a purely geometric quantity called the *mutual inductance*. The mutual inductance M gives the magnitude of the emf induced in one circuit per unit time rate of change of current in the other, as expressed by the equation

$$\mathcal{E}_2 = -M_{21}\frac{di_1}{dt} \tag{9.20}$$

As in Fig. 9.16, the subscripts 1 and 2 indicate the two circuits in-

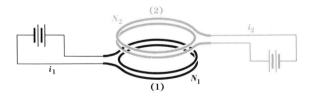

Fig. 9.16   Mutual inductance between two circuits.

volved. Equation (9.20) gives the effect of changes in circuit 1 on circuit 2. The opposite effect would be described by

$$\mathcal{E}_1 = -M_{12}\frac{di_2}{dt} \tag{9.21}$$

We shall show that the two effects are complementary, that is, that

$$M_{12} = M_{21} \tag{9.22}$$

so that the subscripts on the parameter are in fact unnecessary. The negative signs are written in the same sense as in Faraday's law.

The unit of mutual inductance in both the mks and the practical system of units is the *henry*, named in honor of the American scientist Joseph Henry, who developed the idea of inductance almost simultaneously with Faraday. The mutual inductance is unity if a change of 1 amp/sec in one coil induces an emf of 1 volt in the other coil. Thus one henry is one volt per ampere per second. We give an example of a simple calculation of the effect of mutual inductance in Sec. 9.11.

The mutual inductance M is the geometric parameter which describes the inductive effect of one circuit on another. The procedure will be to apply Faraday's law to circuit 2, as shown in Fig. 9.16. The emf $\mathcal{E}_2$ induced in this circuit can be expressed in terms of the number of turns N_2 and of the flux ϕ_{21} in circuit 2 caused by the current in circuit 1. This last quantity is the geometry-dependent one in the equation. The emf can be written

$$\mathcal{E}_2 = -\frac{N_2 \, d\phi_{21}}{dt} \tag{9.23}$$

Our present interest is in only that part of the flux in circuit 2 caused by circuit 1, since this measures the influence of one circuit on the other.

We now have two statements of the emf induced in circuit 2 by changes in circuit 1, Eqs. (9.20) and (9.23). If we solve these two for the mutual inductance, we find

$$M_{21} = \frac{N_2(d\phi_{21}/dt)}{di_1/dt} \tag{9.24}$$

But with fixed geometry, ϕ_{21} is proportional only to i_1; so we can integrate this last equation to get

$$M_{21} = \frac{N_2 \phi_{21}}{i_1} \tag{9.25}$$

Because of the proportionality of the flux ϕ_{21} threading circuit 2 to the current i_1 in circuit 1, we see that indeed the mutual inductance M_{21} is a quantity that depends only on the geometry of the two circuits. If we call $N_2\phi_{21}$ the *flux linkage* in coil 2 due to current in coil 1, we see that the mutual inductance is simply the flux linkage in one circuit due to unit current in the other circuit. We can also write

$$M_{12} = \frac{N_1\phi_{12}}{i_2} \tag{9.26}$$

for the complementary mutual inductance, which always has the same numerical value as M_{21}, as is now shown by an energy argument.

The argument rests on the equation developed earlier for the energy stored in a constant-current loop in an external field. We found for this energy storage

$$U = -Ni\phi \tag{9.27}$$

This shows that the stored energy is proportional to the total external magnetic flux through the current loop. Let us now imagine that we hold constant the current and position of circuit 2 and the current in circuit 1, and that we move circuit 1 up to circuit 2 from far away. The amount of work done is given by

$$W = N_1 i_1 \phi_{12} \tag{9.28}$$

where ϕ_{12} is the final flux from circuit 1 through circuit 2. On the other hand, we could have held circuit 1 fixed, and brought circuit 2 up from far away. The work required would be given by

$$W = N_2 i_2 \phi_{21} \tag{9.29}$$

But since the same final situation results from either method of bringing the two circuits together, the work done must be identical. So, equating Eqs. (9.28) and (9.29), we find

$$N_1 i_1 \phi_{12} = N_2 i_2 \phi_{21}$$

or

$$\frac{N_1\phi_{12}}{i_2} = \frac{N_2\phi_{21}}{i_1} \tag{9.30}$$

But by comparison with Eqs. (9.25) and (9.26) we see that we have demonstrated that

$$M_{12} = M_{21} \tag{9.22}$$

as we set out to do. The energy-conservation argument here is clearly a powerful tool.

9.10   Self-inductance

The effects of Faraday induction can be of importance even when
only a single circuit is involved. This can be seen by examining the
effect in a single coil such as that shown in Fig. 9.17. If the current is

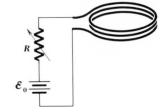

**Fig. 9.17   Self-inductance
in a coil.**

changed (say, by varying the resistance R), the flux threading the coil
changes, and there is a consequent emf induced in it. By analogy with
the definition of mutual inductance, the self-inductance L may be
defined as

$$L = \frac{N_1 \phi_{11}}{i_1} \quad \text{henrys} \tag{9.31}$$

Here ϕ_{11} is the flux in the coil due to its own current; so the self-
inductance is *the flux linkage in a circuit per unit current in that circuit.*
As above, we find for the emf induced by a changing current,

$$\mathcal{E}_1 = -\frac{N_1 \, d\phi_{11}}{dt}$$

From Eq. (9.18) we have

$$\phi_{11} = \frac{L_1 i_1}{N_1}$$

so

$$d\phi_{11} = \frac{L_1}{N_1} \, di_1$$

Substitution in the equation for $\mathcal{E}_1$ then gives

$$\mathcal{E}_1 = -L \frac{di_1}{dt} \quad \text{volts} \tag{9.32}$$

Any closed circuit must have a self-inductance, even if no coil is included, since a complete circuit involves at least one loop that contains some flux when current flows. However, if the area of the loop is

small, the flux linkage also is small, and the self-inductance is much reduced. The unit of self-inductance is also the henry.

The effect of inductance in a circuit is like inertia in a mechanical system. Thus any change in a steady current is accompanied by an induced emf that tends to counteract this change. This is analogous to the force exerted by a moving mass when we try to modify its velocity.

9.11 *Examples*

a *Effect of mutual inductance in coupled circuits.* We examine the quantitative behavior of two circuits coupled by mutual inductance. As shown in Fig. 9.18, the current in circuit 2 can be changed by

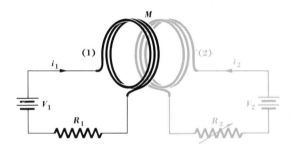

Fig. 9.18 *Two circuits coupled by mutual inductance M.*

varying R_2. We calculate the effect on the current in circuit 1 of a given value of di_2/dt in circuit 2. Using Eq. (9.21), we write directly for the induced emf in circuit 1 due to the mutual inductance

$$\mathcal{E}_1 = -M\frac{di_2}{dt} \qquad \text{volts}$$

The negative sign tells us that if the current in the two circuits is going around the coils in the same sense, $\mathcal{E}_1$ will be opposed to the source V_1 when di_2/dt is positive. When the direction of V_1 is reversed or when one of the coils is rotated 180°, $\mathcal{E}_1$ and V_1 act in the same direction if di_2/dt is positive.

One additional effect to be considered is that of L_1, the self-inductance in circuit 1. This produces another emf in circuit 1, according to Eq. (9.32),

$$\mathcal{E}_1' = -L \frac{di_1}{dt} \qquad \text{volts}$$

which acts in opposition to di_1/dt. The equation for circuit 1 becomes

$$V_1 \pm M \frac{di_2}{dt} - L_1 \frac{di_1}{dt} = i_1 R_1$$

This is a differential equation which contains information about the transient effect on i_1 when i_2 is caused to change at a rate di_2/dt. If di_2/dt is held constant, a steady current i_1 is approached, and the term in di_1/dt becomes zero. The steady-state equation then becomes

$$V_1 \pm M \frac{di_2}{dt} = i_1 R_1$$

which can be solved for i_1 directly.

The problem of transient effects on i_1 is similar to the transient problems discussed later, in Sec. 11.9.

b *Calculation of self-inductance.* In a few cases it is easy to calculate the self-inductance of particular geometric arrangements. We make an illustrative calculation for the case of a uniform long coil, neglecting end effects that in practice would reduce the inductance somewhat, because of the lower flux at the ends of the coil. We expect the number of turns N to enter as N^2, once as the N in $N\phi$ and once again, since ϕ itself is proportional to N. We have already calculated the field B inside a solenoid of length l and N turns. We found $B = \mu_0 N i/l$. Substitution in Eq. (9.31) gives for the self-inductance

$$L = \frac{\mu_0 N^2 A}{l} \qquad \text{henrys} \tag{9.33}$$

If this is a toroidal solenoid, no flux leaks out, and the result is accurate.

The longer a coil is compared with its diameter, the more closely its self-inductance approaches the value given in Eq. (9.33).

9.12 *Calculation of Mutual Inductance*

There is one situation in which it is easy to calculate the mutual inductance between two circuits in terms of the self-inductance of each circuit alone. This is the case of maximum flux linkage, when all the flux through one circuit links the other. One physical arrangement that would achieve this would be to place two coils of equal area (but not necessarily of equal numbers of turns) next to each other. Another arrangement giving maximum flux linkage would be two coils wound one on top of the other on a toroidal solenoid. Calling the coils 1 and 2, we can write for the mutual inductance

$$M = \frac{N_1\phi_{12}}{i_2} = \frac{N_2\phi_{21}}{i_1}$$

Similarly, the self-inductance of the coils is given by

$$L_1 = \frac{N_1\phi_1}{i_1} \quad \text{and} \quad L_2 = \frac{N_2\phi_2}{i_2}$$

Since all the flux of coil 2 links coil 1,

$$\frac{\phi_{12}}{i_2} = \frac{\phi_2}{i_2}$$

that is, the flux ϕ_{12} in coil 1 due to the current i_2 is the same as the flux ϕ_2 in coil 2 due to the same current i_2. Similarly,

$$\frac{\phi_{21}}{i_1} = \frac{\phi_1}{i_1}$$

If we replace ϕ_{12}/i_2 and ϕ_{21}/i_1 in the equations for M above and multiply M_{21} by M_{12}, we get

$$M_{12}M_{21} = M^2 = \frac{N_1N_2\phi_1\phi_2}{i_1i_2} = L_1L_2$$

or

$$M_{\max} = \sqrt{L_1L_2}$$

This represents the maximum possible value of M in terms of L_1 and L_2. In general, the mutual inductance is given by

$$M = k\sqrt{L_1L_2} \tag{9.34}$$

where k is a number between 0 and 1 which depends on the shape of the coils and their relative positions.

9.13   *Combinations of Inductances*

Several inductances in series, if so arranged that there are no inter-actions through mutual inductance, are easily shown to behave as a single inductance equal to their sum. Thus the induced voltage across

*Fig. 9.19   Three self-induct-
ances in series; no interactions between them.
Equivalent value,*
$L = L_1 + L_2 + L_3.$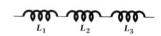

*Fig. 9.19   Three self-induct-
ances in series; no interactions between them.
Equivalent value,*
$L = L_1 + L_2 + L_3.$

the three isolated inductances shown in Fig. 9.19 will be

$$-L_1 \frac{di}{dt} - L_2 \frac{di}{dt} - L_3 \frac{di}{dt} = -L \frac{di}{dt}$$

where

$$L = L_1 + L_2 + L_3 \tag{9.35}$$

However, the situation is modified when the flux from one inductance links another, giving rise to mutual-inductance terms. Figure 9.20

*Fig. 9.20   Interacting self-
inductances in series.
Equivalent value,*
$L = L_1 + L_2 \pm 2M.$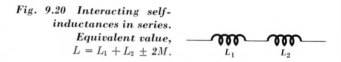

shows two coils that interact in this fashion. The voltage across this pair of coils is given by

$$\varepsilon = -L_1 \frac{di}{dt} - L_2 \frac{di}{dt} \pm 2M \frac{di}{dt}$$

The mutual inductance occurs twice, once for the voltage induced in the second coil by current changes in the first, and once for the converse. The $\pm$ allows for the possibility that the mutual interaction adds to the total flux or that it gives flux in the opposite direction from that due to the self-induction. The sign of M and its magnitude depend on the geometric arrangement of the coils. This is illustrated in Fig. 9.21. In the top drawing, two coils A and B are connected to-

*Fig. 9.21   Pairs of coils in
series linked by mutual inductance. A and B are
wound in the same sense,
so that the mutual in-
ductance adds to the total
inductance of the pair. C
and D are wound oppo-
sitely, so that the mutual
inductance subtracts from
the total inductance.*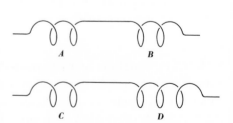

gether and wound in the same sense. Thus the flux in B due to current in A is in the same direction as the flux due to current in B. In this case the mutual inductance adds to the total inductance of the two coils; so the self-inductance of the combination is

$$L = L_A + L_B + 2M$$

In the lower drawing the two coils C and D are wound in the opposite sense; so the flux from these two coils has opposite directions. In this case the combination has an inductance given by

$$L = L_C + L_D - 2M$$

In general, the inductance of a series pair of coils is given by

$$L = L_1 + L_2 \pm 2M \qquad (9.36)$$

For the case of noninteracting inductances in parallel, as shown in Fig. 9.22, we may write

$$\varepsilon_1 = -L_1 \frac{di_1}{dt}$$

$$\varepsilon_2 = -L_2 \frac{di_2}{dt}$$

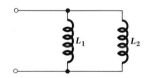

Fig. 9.22   Two inductances in parallel.

But in the parallel arrangement, $\varepsilon_1 = \varepsilon_2$, and also

$$\frac{di}{dt} = \frac{di_1}{dt} + \frac{di_2}{dt} = -\left(\frac{1}{L_1} + \frac{1}{L_2}\right)\varepsilon$$

The equivalent inductance L is given by $\varepsilon = -L\, di/dt$; so we have

$$\frac{1}{L} = \frac{1}{L_1} + \frac{1}{L_2} \quad \text{or} \quad L = \frac{L_1 L_2}{L_1 + L_2} \qquad (9.37)$$

These rules for combining noninteracting inductances prove to be of the same form as the rules for series and parallel combinations of resistances.

9.14   Stored Magnetic Energy

The induced emf in a circuit resulting from changing magnetic flux can be shown to lead to the expenditure of energy in order to set up a magnetic field in a region of space. Since this expended energy can be recovered and used, for instance, to generate heat in a resistance, we are led naturally to the idea of energy stored in a magnetic field. The situation is analogous to the storage of energy in an electric field, as discussed in Chap. 4. We begin the discussion by asking how much energy must be expended to build up a current i in an inductance L_1,

Fig. 9.23   Buildup of current in an inductance.

as shown in Fig. 9.23. The induced emf across the inductance is

$$\mathcal{E} = -L\frac{di}{dt} \qquad \text{volts}$$

The amount of work required to move a charge dq against this emf is

$$dW = -\mathcal{E}\,dq = L\frac{di}{dt}\,dq = L\frac{dq}{dt}\,di = Li\,di \qquad (9.38)$$

Here we have changed variables and used $i = dq/dt$. The total work to build up the current from 0 to i is obtained by integrating Eq. (9.38):

$$U = \int dW = L\int_0^i i\,di = \tfrac{1}{2}Li^2 \qquad \text{joules}$$

We have written this as the stored energy U, since, as we shall show, the energy expended can be recovered.

If two interacting circuits are involved as in Fig. 9.24, the energy required to build up the currents i_1 and i_2 in the two circuits is ob-

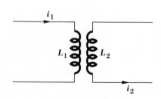

Fig. 9.24   Energy stored in two interacting circuits.

tained similarly. Thus

$$dW = -\mathcal{E}_1\, dq_1 - \mathcal{E}_2\, dq_2$$

$$= \left(L_1\frac{di_1}{dt} \pm M\frac{di_2}{dt}\right) dq_1 + \left(L_2\frac{di_2}{dt} \pm M\frac{di_1}{dt}\right) dq_2$$

$$= L_1 i_1\, di_1 \pm M i_1\, di_2 + L_2 i_2\, di_2 \pm M i_2\, di_1$$

Since $M i_1\, di_2 + M i_2\, di_1$ is a perfect differential, these two terms can be written $d(M i_1 i_2)$. Integration of the entire expression then yields

$$U = \tfrac{1}{2}L_1 i_1{}^2 + \tfrac{1}{2}L_2 i_2{}^2 \pm M i_1 i_2 \qquad \text{joules}$$

We can show that this energy is stored rather than dissipated by arranging that the stored energy be used to heat up the resistance. Suppose, then, that while the current i is flowing steadily, we instantaneously remove from the circuit the battery producing the current. The circuit becomes that shown in Fig. 9.25. This change can be made

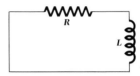

Fig. 9.25 Dissipation of energy stored in the magnetic
field of an inductance.

essentially instantaneously by simply shorting out the battery. In the absence of the inductance, the current in the circuit would fall to zero immediately the battery was removed by shorting. However, with the inductance present, the circuit equation becomes

$$-L\frac{di}{dt} = iR \qquad \text{volts}$$

The inductance acts so as to try to maintain the current constant. Since in its absence the current would decrease, di/dt is negative, and we see that the induced emf acts in the same direction as did the battery. The inductance thus supplies the energy to force the current through the resistance. The instantaneous rate of energy dissipation will be

$$-Li\frac{di}{dt} = i^2R \qquad \text{watts}$$

obtained from the equation above by multiplying by the instantaneous current i. Since in this situation i and di/dt have opposite signs, the left-hand term is positive. The total energy supplied to the resistance is the integral of this expression over the time while both i

and di/dt are not zero. We have already found this to be $\frac{1}{2}Li^2$. This is equal to $\int i^2 R\, dt$, the total energy dissipated in the resistance after the battery is removed from the circuit.

We have now demonstrated that an amount of energy $\frac{1}{2}Li^2$ is necessary to build up a current i in an inductance and that this energy is stored. This energy is associated with the existence of current in the inductance. A more useful point of view, however, is that the energy is stored in the magnetic field existing in space because of the current. This is closely analogous to the situation in the case of energy stored in an electrostatic field, where we found $U/\text{vol} = \frac{1}{2}\epsilon_0 E^2$ in a vacuum. A rather similar calculation gives the energy storage in a magnetic field. We choose a toroidal solenoid because the field exists only inside the toroid and also is essentially uniform within it, making the calculation easy.

We calculate the work done against the emf of Faraday induction in building up the field within the toroidal solenoid from zero to a final value B_0. In order to express the work done per unit volume of space containing the field, we find the induced emf generated per unit length of the coil, which has a length L, N turns, and a cross-section area A. Then the Faraday law gives

$$\frac{\mathcal{E}}{L} = -\frac{N}{L}\frac{d\phi}{dt} = -\frac{NA}{L}\frac{dB}{dt}$$

Multiplication of both sides of this equation by i/A transforms it into

$$\frac{\mathcal{E}i}{AL} = -\frac{Ni}{L}\frac{dB}{dt}$$

This is the rate of doing work against the induced emf per unit volume of magnetic field when the current is increasing at a rate to cause a changing field dB/dt and when the instantaneous current is i.

We now express the current in the right-hand side of the equation in terms of the field it produces within the solenoid, according to

$$B = \mu_0 j^s = \mu_0 \frac{Ni}{L} \qquad \text{webers/m}^2 \qquad (8.12)$$

to find

$$\frac{\mathcal{E}i}{AL} = -\frac{1}{\mu_0} B \frac{dB}{dt}$$

or

$$\frac{\mathcal{E}i}{AL}\, dt = -\frac{1}{\mu_0} B\, dB$$

This gives the work per unit volume of field to increase the field from B to $B + dB$. This equation must be integrated from $B = 0$ to B_0 to find the total work to bring the field to its final value. The result may be expressed as the stored energy in a field in vacuum per unit volume.

$$\frac{U}{\text{vol}} = \frac{1}{2}\frac{B_0{}^2}{\mu_0} \quad \text{joules/m}^3 \tag{9.39}$$

9.15*   Applications of Inductance
Here we give three practical situations where induced emf plays an important role.

The ballistic galvanometer.   Perhaps the most popular method for measuring the strength of a constant magnetic field is that using a *flip coil*. A small coil of known geometry is placed in the unknown field so as to be threaded by the maximum flux. Then the coil is suddenly removed from the field, or rotated so as to reduce the flux through it to zero. If the rate of change of flux that occurs could be integrated from beginning to end, the flux, and hence B, could be obtained. Thus

$$\int \frac{d\phi}{dt}\, dt = \phi = BA \qquad \text{webers}$$

where ϕ is the value of the original flux through the coil. We now show that, under suitable conditions, this change in flux can be related to a galvanometer deflection caused by the induced emf in the flip coil, $\mathcal{E} = -N\, d\phi/dt$, where N is the number of turns on the coil.

The method involves the use of the *ballistic galvanometer*, a galvanometer built with its natural period of mechanical oscillation reasonably long. The galvanometer is connected across the coil as shown in Fig. 9.26. When the magnetic flux in the coil is suddenly changed,

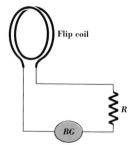

**Fig. 9.26   Flip coil used with
a ballistic galvanometer
to measure B.**

the galvanometer coil is given an angular impulse, the magnitude of which is proportional to the total change in flux. If the galvanometer characteristics are known, the absolute magnitude of the field can be determined.

The principle involved is as follows: The magnetic torque τ on a galvanometer coil, when its plane is parallel to the magnetic field, as we have found, is

$$\tau = NiAB \qquad \text{newton-m} \tag{8.25}$$

where the quantities $NiAB$ refer to the galvanometer coil, not the flip coil. When, instead of a steady current i, we supply a short pulse of current such as shown in Fig. 9.27, the angular impulse given to

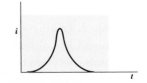

Fig. 9.27 Typical current pulse through a ballistic galvanometer. Pulse must be finished before appreciable motion occurs in the galvanometer.

the galvanometer coil is $\int \tau \, dt$, where the integration is over an interval covering the entire time during which current flows. Using Eq. (8.25), we integrate this to get

$$\int \tau \, dt = NBA \int i \, dt = NBAQ$$

We have used the fact that $\int i \, dt$ is the charge flow through the galvanometer. This is the special feature of the ballistic galvanometer. It receives an angular impulse that depends only on the total charge pulse flowing through it, and not on the way the charge flow varies with time. However, since in Eq. (8.25) the more general expression is $\tau = NiAB \sin \theta$, where θ is the angle between the coil and field direction, the pulse must be completed before the coil has time to move from its initial position, where $\sin \theta = 1$. The pulse must therefore be short compared with the natural period of the galvanometer coil. From mechanics we know that this angular impulse gives the coil an angular momentum $I\omega_0$, where I is its moment of inertia and ω_0 is the angular velocity just after the pulse has passed. Thus we have

$$\int \tau \, dt = I\omega_0 = NBAQ \tag{9.40}$$

The initial angular momentum $I\omega_0$ corresponds to an initial kinetic energy $\frac{1}{2}I\omega_0^2$. As the coil turns against the restoring torque of the galvanometer coil suspension, this kinetic energy is converted into potential energy. At the maximum deflection θ_{max}, conversion is complete, and we may write

$$KE = \tfrac{1}{2}I\omega_0{}^2 \to PE = \tfrac{1}{2}k\theta^2{}_{max} \qquad \text{joules} \tag{9.41}$$

where k is the torque constant of the suspension. Solving for ω_0 in Eq. (9.40) and substituting in Eq. (9.41), we find

$$Q = \frac{\sqrt{Ik}}{NBA}\,\theta_{max} \qquad \text{coul} \tag{9.42}$$

This equation can be put in a more useful form by substituting the expression for the period of oscillation T of a torsional pendulum, $T = 2\pi(I/k)^{1/2}$, in Eq. (9.42):

$$Q = \frac{kT}{2\pi NAB}\,\theta_{max} = \frac{K'T}{2\pi}\,\theta_{max} \qquad \text{coul}$$

K' is the galvanometer constant (Sec. 8.9). In terms of the figure of merit of the galvanometer [Eq. (8.31)], this becomes

$$Q = \frac{KT}{2\pi}\,d_{max} \qquad \text{coul} \tag{9.43}$$

where d_{max} is the initial deflection of the galvanometer in millimeters on a scale 1 m away. If the galvanometer is appreciably damped, correction must be made for the effect of damping on the initial deflection.

Knowledge of the galvanometer constant, or figure of merit, and of the period of oscillation of the galvanometer coil allows us to measure the total charge passing through the galvanometer in a time short compared with its period. This property of the ballistic galvanometer is used to measure the value of B. The current flowing in the flip coil connected across the galvanometer is given by

$$i = \frac{\text{emf}}{R} = -\frac{1}{R}\left(N'\frac{d\phi}{dt} + L\frac{di}{dt}\right) \qquad \text{amp} \tag{9.44}$$

Here L represents the self-inductance in the circuit, and N' is the number of turns in the flip coil. Upon integration, we find the total flow of charge to be

$$Q = \int_0^\infty i\,dt = -\frac{N'}{R}(\phi_2 - \phi_1) - \frac{1}{R}\int_0^0 L\,di = \frac{N'}{R}(\phi_2 - \phi_1) \tag{9.45}$$

where $(\phi_2 - \phi_1)$ is the change of the flux involved. If we pull the coil entirely out of the field, ϕ_2 becomes zero, and we have

$$Q = -\frac{N'}{R}\phi_1 = \frac{N'}{R}BA' \quad \text{or} \quad B = \frac{QR}{N'A'} \quad \text{webers/m}^2 \quad (9.46)$$

where A' is the area of the flip coil. Here it is assumed that the coil was originally oriented with its plane perpendicular to the magnetic field.

Eddy currents and skin depth. One very important practical effect which results from Faraday induction is the generation of eddy currents. These occur whenever alternating currents flow through conductors. Consider, for example, what happens when an alternating current flows through a wire of circular cross section, as in Fig. 9.28,

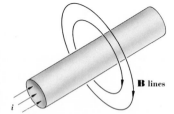

Fig. 9.28 Some magnetic field lines surrounding a uniform current in a wire. Some of the field is inside the conductor.

which shows the conductor at an instant when the current is directed away from the viewer. We have also shown some of the lines of **B** which would result. Some of the **B** lines, in fact, are inside the conductor. In Fig. 9.29 we have plotted the magnitude of **B** against the

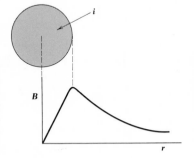

Fig. 9.29   A plot of the magnetic field intensity produced by a uniform current in a conductor. The direction of the field reverses when the current reverses.

distance out from the center of the conductor on the assumption that the current density is uniform.

When the current alters in direction there are emfs set up because of the resulting $d\phi/dt$, and within the conductor the emfs will induce *eddy currents*. These eddy currents, by Lenz's principle, act to decrease the magnitude of $d\phi/dt$. But $d\phi/dt$ will be reduced if ϕ within the metal is reduced, and the concentration of current at the wire surface, as in Fig. 9.30, accomplishes this. It is easy to show that the

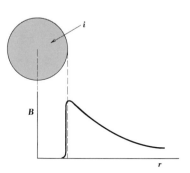

Fig. 9.30 If the current is limited to the outer skin of the conductor, the magnetic field within the body of the conductor is zero. In the ac case, eddy currents within the conductor tend to limit the current to the skin region, since this minimizes $d\phi/dt$ within the conductor.

field outside the conductor is not affected by this change in current distribution.

Thus with ac currents there is a tendency to limit currents to a skin at the surface of the metal. Since the emfs which produce this effect are proportional to $d\phi/dt$, the degree of current concentration at the surface increases with the ac frequency.

The detailed account of the eddy-current effect and the calculation of skin depths in conducting media is best given in a discussion of electromagnetic waves (Appendix L).

Measurement of electron relaxation times by eddy-current damping. An important application of Faraday induction enables the measurement of conduction electron relaxation times in metals. We saw in Chap. 7 that the conductivity of metals is proportional to electron mean free paths, or relaxation times. In the study of metals it is often of interest to measure relaxation times directly. This can be done by using the arrangement shown in Fig. 9.31, which measures the decay rate of an induced current in a metal specimen. The decay rate can be related to electron relaxation time. The specimen of material to be tested is placed in the magnetic field of an external coil. Another coil is placed closely around the specimen, which connects to a cathode-ray oscilloscope. The measurement is made by suddenly reducing the externally applied field by turning off the current in the external coil. As a result of the consequent sudden change in the field within the specimen,

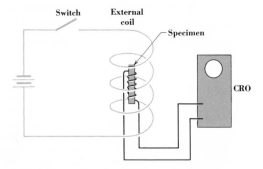

Fig. 9.31   Measurement of resistivity, or electron relaxation times, by eddy-current damping. When the magnetic field is suddenly reduced to zero by opening the switch, eddy currents in a metal specimen produce an emf which is picked up by the coil surrounding the specimen. The decay rate of this induced emf depends on the conductivity of the specimen, which is affected by the electron relaxation time.

Faraday induction produces eddy currents within it. The eddy currents, as they die out, induce an additional signal in the surrounding coil which is examined as a function of time by means of the oscilloscope. The rate at which the current dies down can be determined, and from this the relaxation time can be found. An advantage of this method is that no electrical connections are made to the specimen. This avoids possible trouble with contacts and possible damage to delicate single crystals of metals.

9.16   Comments on Chapter 9

The material in this chapter adds an important new principle to the previously discussed static electric and magnetic fields. For the first time we investigate what happens when a field changes with time. Here the quantity which changes in time is the magnetic field **B**. Later we examine the other case, that of a changing electric field.

The important effects of a changing magnetic field can all be described by the one idea, that of the Faraday law of induced emf, which we wrote as

$$\mathcal{E} = -\frac{d\phi}{dt} \qquad \text{volts} \tag{9.1}$$

Here it is to be understood that the emf ε is the work per unit charge done by an induced field in taking a charge completely around an arbitrary path. The effective electric field $\mathbf{E}$ that exerts the force on the charge is then given formally by

$$\oint \mathbf{E} \cdot d\mathbf{l} = \varepsilon \qquad \text{volts} \tag{9.2}$$

The magnitude of this induced emf depends only on the time rate of change of magnetic flux ϕ within the area surrounded by the path chosen. The flux through the area is defined as

$$\phi = \int \mathbf{B} \cdot d\mathbf{S} \qquad \text{webers} \tag{8.19}$$

In the special case that the path chosen is in a plane perpendicular to a uniform field $\mathbf{B}$, the flux within the area S of the path would be given by the expression

$$\phi = BS \qquad \text{webers}$$

Equation (9.2) immediately shows the great difference between the Faraday electric field and any static field resulting from fixed electric charges, since, as we have seen, the static field is conservative; so

$$\oint \mathbf{E} \cdot d\mathbf{l} = 0 \tag{3.4}$$

The sign of the induced emf is given by Eq. (9.1) if it is understood that the usual convention of positive direction, meaning counterclockwise motion around a closed path, is chosen, and similarly, we call positive field or flux direction outward from the closed path, toward the viewer.

Another way to find the direction of an induced emf is to use Lenz's principle, a result of energy conservation. This principle states that an induced emf is always in a direction that opposes the change which produces it.

In another section it is shown that for the special case that the change in flux through a loop results from motion of the loop through a fixed magnetic field, Faraday's law is exactly equivalent to the emf which would be calculated by applying the Lorentz force

$$\mathbf{F} = e(\mathbf{v} \times \mathbf{B})$$

to charges in all elements of the moving circuit, where $\mathbf{v}$ is the velocity of the circuit. The term motional emf is often given to this special case. For other kinds of situations, where no motion is involved but the change in flux results from a change with time of the magnitude of $\mathbf{B}$, only the Faraday induction law can be used for calculating the induced emf.

A static magnetic field in space involves stored energy. It was shown that the energy density in space is given by

$$\frac{U}{\text{vol}} = \frac{1}{2}\frac{B^2}{\mu_0} \qquad \text{joules/m}^3 \tag{9.39}$$

Another useful energy result relates to the work to bring a current-carrying coil into a region of externally produced magnetic field. If a coil has N turns, carries a current i, and is threaded by a flux ϕ from an external field, the work done, or the energy stored, is

$$W = -Ni\Phi \qquad \text{joules} \tag{9.14}$$

Here again, signs of current and flux are to be taken according to the standard convention. Another method of determining whether the work is positive or negative is to consider the direction of the magnetic dipole moment vector produced by the current in the coil. If this vector is in the same direction as the field, this is the low-energy orientation, and the external work is negative. If the dipole moment is pointed in the opposite direction, positive work must be done to bring the coil to its final position. This energy expression is often useful in calculations of magnetic forces on circuits.

Another new set of concepts is developed which will be of great practical importance when we deal with ac circuits. These are the mutual- and self-inductance parameters, which depend entirely on the shape and position of current-carrying conductors.

The basic idea of the inductance parameter is that it measures the Faraday induced emf in one circuit which results from variation in the current in another circuit. The coupling between the circuits is through the flux threading one circuit by virtue of the current in another circuit.

Thus the mutual inductance M is defined by equations like

$$\mathcal{E}_2 = -M\frac{di_1}{dt} \qquad \text{volts} \tag{9.20}$$

where $\mathcal{E}_2$ is the emf induced in circuit 2 by a change in the current in circuit 1. The opposite case of the emf induced in circuit 1 by changing currents in circuit 2 is written

$$\mathcal{E}_1 = -M\frac{di_2}{dt} \qquad \text{volts} \tag{9.21}$$

We showed from energy consideration that the value of M is exactly the same in both cases given above.

Since the current in a single circuit produces a magnetic flux through that circuit itself, inductive effects occur even when only one circuit is involved. Such effects are described by the self-inductance L of the circuit. The emf induced in a circuit is thus given by

$$\varepsilon = -L\frac{di}{dt} \qquad \text{volts} \tag{9.32}$$

The mutual- and self-inductance parameters are measured in henrys. The inductance in henrys gives the number of volts induced emf for a time rate of change of one ampere per second.

An equivalent definition of inductance is the flux linkage per unit current. Thus we may write

$$M = \frac{N_1\phi_{12}}{i_2} = \frac{N_2\phi_{21}}{i_1} \tag{9.26}$$

and

$$L = \frac{N\phi}{i} \tag{9.31}$$

where N is the number of turns in the circuit in which the emf is to be calculated.

In the practical application of inductances, where a given inductance is required in a single circuit or between circuits, inductance elements are built by winding appropriate coils to give the required flux linkage. We found that noninteracting self-inductances, when combined, add in series and add reciprocally in parallel combinations, just as do resistances. That is, in series,

$$\sum_i L_i = L \tag{9.35}$$

and in parallel,

$$\sum_i \frac{1}{L_i} = \frac{1}{L} \tag{9.37}$$

If there is any flux linkage between one inductance element and another, the effect of this is accounted for by the mutual inductance between them; thus

$$L = L_1 + L_2 \pm 2M \tag{9.36}$$

where the sign of the mutual inductance term depends on the sign of
the flux linkage.

PROBLEMS

A Faraday induced emf is generated around any closed path whenever there
is a time rate of change in the magnetic flux linking that path.

    9.1A   A rectangular wire loop, as shown in Fig. P9.1, encloses an area ab m².
It is in a uniform B field which is decreasing in magnitude with time

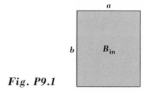

Fig. P9.1

at the rate $dB/dt = K$ webers/(m²)(sec). Calculate the induced emf
around the loop, and give the direction of the emf. What is the average
value of the component parallel to the path of the induced field E along
the wire?

  ★9.1B   A coil of n turns and area A rotates with a frequency ω about a diameter that is perpendicular to a uniform magnetic induction field B.
Calculate the peak emf (amplitude) induced in the coil.

    9.1C   A stiff wire bent into a semicircle of radius R is rotated at a frequency f
in a uniform magnetic field B, as shown in Fig. P9.2. What are the

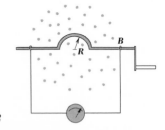

Fig. P9.2

amplitude and frequency of the induced voltage and of the induced
current when the internal resistance of the meter is 1,000 ohms and the
remainder of the circuit has negligible resistance?

9.1D   A solenoid is moving toward a conducting loop as shown in Fig. P9.3. As viewed from the solenoid, what will be the direction of the induced current in the loop?

Fig. P9.3

9.1E   A uniform field of induction B is changing in magnitude at a constant rate dB/dt. Given a mass m of copper to be drawn into a wire of radius r and formed into a circular loop of radius R, show that the induced current in the loop does not depend on the size of the wire or the loop and is given by

$$i = \frac{m}{4\pi\rho\delta}\frac{dB}{dt}$$

where ρ is the resistivity and δ is the density of copper.

When an induced emf results from translational motion of a conductor or conducting loop in a static magnetic field, the emf can be calculated either on the basis of the Faraday law or by means of the motional emf.

*9.2A   A metal rod of length L moves with a velocity v in a direction perpendicular to its axis and to a constant magnetic induction field B, as shown in Fig. P9.4.

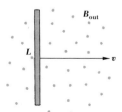

Fig. P9.4

a   Write the expression for the force on charges in the rod by virtue of the motion of the rod.

b   What will be the magnitude and direction of the electric field set up by the separation of charges due to this motion?

c   What will be the potential difference between the ends of the rod?

d   If the rod moves on a stationary conducting loop as shown in Fig. P9.5, what current will flow in the loop if the resistance of the loop and rod is R?

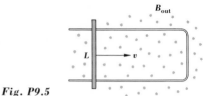

Fig. P9.5

e Calculate the emf induced by the motion by means of Faraday's law of induction and compare the result with (c).

9.2B A conducting rod of length L rotates with an angular velocity ω about one end in a plane perpendicular to a uniform magnetic induction field B. Find the emf induced in the rod, first in terms of the motional emf and then by means of the Faraday induction law.

★9.2C A horizontal magnetic field of strength B is produced across a narrow gap between square iron pole pieces as shown in Fig. P9.6. A closed

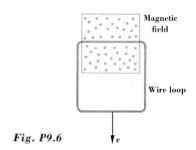

Fig. P9.6

square wire loop l m on a side is allowed to fall with the top of the loop in the field. The loop has a resistance R and a weight mg. Find the terminal velocity of the loop while it is between the poles of the magnet. How would this velocity be modified if the cross section of the wire of the loop were doubled?

The inductance of a coil relates the induced emf to the time rate of change of current in the coil. The inductance also gives the total magnetic flux produced by a given current in the coil.

9.3A How can 50 volts be generated across the terminals on a 2-henry inductor of negligible resistance?

★9.3B The inductance of a close-packed coil is 10 mh. The coil has 100 turns. Find the total magnetic flux through the coil when the current is 0.5 ma.

9.3C The self-inductance of a coil can be computed by equating the stored energy in the magnetic induction field of the coil to the work necessary to build up the current in the coil from zero. Do this for the simple case of a toroidal solenoid of length l, cross section A, having N turns.

The mutual inductance measures the flux linkage between two coils.

★9.4A Two identical coils are connected in series and spaced in such a way that one-half the flux from one coil threads the second coil. If the self-inductance of one coil is L henrys, find the self-inductance of the pair of coils connected in series, assuming the coils are connected in such a way that the fluxes add (rather than subtract).

9.4B A small loop of wire of radius a is coaxial with a large loop of wire of radius b. The two loops are separated by the distance l. Under the assumption that $b \gg a$, compute the mutual induction between the loops. (*Note:* The problem is easy or hard depending on which loop you let produce the magnetic field.)

★9.4C The rectangle shown in Fig. P9.7 is moving with a uniform velocity V away from the long wire carrying current i. The wire and rectangle

Fig. P9.7

remain coplanar. Calculate the electromotive force induced in the rectangle. What is the mutual inductance between the two circuits as a function of time if the nearer wire of the rectangle is distance l from the long wire at time $t = 0$?

9.4D A current loop is made by connecting the ends of two long parallel wires of radius a separated by a distance d between centers. Neglecting end effects and the magnetic flux within the wires, show that the self-inductance of a length l of the parallel wires is

$$L = \frac{\mu_0 l}{\pi} \ln \frac{d - a}{a}$$

Current in an inductance produces magnetic flux. The work done in setting up the flux is stored in the magnetic field.

★9.5A A large electromagnet has an inductance of 5 henrys. If a current of 10 amp flows through its coils, what is the energy stored in the inductance? When the current is interrupted, it drops to 1 amp in 1/20 sec. Approximately what voltage is induced in the coil? How might this voltage have a detrimental effect on the coil windings?

9.5B   A current of 10 amp produces a total flux of 10 webers in a closely wound coil of 200 turns. Find the energy stored in the magnetic field.

★9.5C   Find the magnetic energy stored *inside* a 1-m length of wire carrying 10 amp. The wire is 1 mm in radius, and the current density is uniform.

This problem involves the calculation of requirements for the shape of the magnetic field in a betatron, a kind of particle accelerator.

9.6A   The accelerating action in a betatron depends on the induced emf produced by a changing magnetic field. Electrons in a vacuum travel in circular paths in a magnetic field that increases with time. The radius of curvature of the electron orbit depends on the field B_R, *at the* orbit and perpendicular to its plane. The accelerating force depends on $d\Phi/dt$ over the area enclosed by the orbit.

a   Show that, for the radius of the orbit to stay constant as electrons are accelerated, the average field $\bar{B}$ within the orbit must be $2B_R$.

b   Express the energy gained per cycle in terms of dB_R/dt.

10

magnetism in matter

10.1 Introduction

This chapter considers the magnetic properties of matter. The experimental basis for this study is that the presence of matter modifies the magnetic field produced by currents. The sources of this effect are the circulating currents which produce atomic magnetic dipole moments within matter. All magnetic effects of matter may be understood on the basis of current loops or their magnetic dipoles.

The shape of magnetic specimens has an important effect on the field inside and outside the specimen, except in a few very special cases. This situation is mathematically similar to the effect of shape on the electric polarization in dielectric bodies. The contributions of atoms to magnetism account for the three most important kinds of magnetic behavior, *paramagnetism*, *diamagnetism*, and *ferromagnetism*. We further consider stored magnetic energy in matter and some properties of permanent magnets. Finally, we consider the analysis of the *magnetic circuit* of particular importance in the design of electromagnets.

10.2   *Magnetic Contributions of Matter*

Before investigating the effect of matter on magnetic forces we recall the nature of magnetic forces in free space. The force between current elements is described by means of a field **B**, produced by one current element acting on the current in the other element. The effect of the presence of matter is to modify the magnetic field both outside and inside magnetic specimens. Outside a specimen the field can be investigated by experiments which measure the force on moving charges or current elements. Inside matter this is not generally possible; so we use methods involving Faraday induction. Thus a test coil wound around a specimen will have induced in it an emf whenever there is a changing flux within the specimen. Using a ballistic galvanometer, as described in Sec. 9.15, the flux ϕ threading the coil can be determined. A comparison of the flux with and without the specimen present leads to a knowledge of the effect of the specimen on the field within it.

Basically, the magnetic properties of matter are the result of microscopic atomic currents which produce magnetic moments in matter. The discussion is limited at first to those materials in which an external field induces magnetic moments and in which the magnetic contribution of the matter is proportional to the external field applied. If the specimen material is isotropic, as is most often the case, and as we shall assume, the effect of an external field is to induce magnetic dipoles which, on the average, are aligned with their moments along the direction of the applied field.

There are two classes of materials in which the effect of induced magnetic moments is proportional to the applied field. In *paramagnetic* materials there are permanent magnetic moments associated with the intrinsic angular momentum (spin) of single electrons. In the absence of an external applied field these magnetic moments are randomly oriented. An applied field tends to orient these moments along the field direction. In *diamagnetic* materials, all intrinsic electron moments are canceled out by the pairing of electrons of oppositely oriented moments, a quantum-mechanical phenomenon. The remaining magnetic effect comes from the orbital motion of atomic electrons. Faraday induction produced by the applied field causes a perturbation of the orbital motion which results in effective magnetic dipoles oriented in a direction opposed to the applied field. Thus paramagnetic materials enhance the applied field while diamagnetic materials decrease the field. Both effects are proportional to the strength of the applied field. Paramagnetic effects are generally much larger than diamagnetic effects.

Actually, the diamagnetic effect occurs in all materials, but if the paramagnetic effect is also present, it overshadows the negative diamagnetism, and the material has a net (positive) paramagnetism. We discuss both effects in more detail later.

We now investigate the qualitative aspect of shape and orientation of specimens in an applied field. We can give a description of specimen shape and orientation effects, using Fig. 10.1, and calling the direction

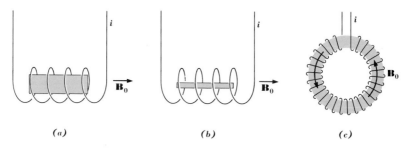

(a)   *(b)*   *(c)*

Fig. 10.1   The demagnetizing effect of a magnetized specimen occurs
whenever the direction of magnetization has a component normal
to a surface of the specimen. The effect thus depends on the shape
of the specimen. It is largest in a, less in b, and zero in the
toroidal specimen c.

of the induced magnetic dipoles the *direction of magnetization*. Whenever the magnetization direction has a component normal to the specimen surface, there are *demagnetizing* effects at the surface which diminish the magnetic contribution of the specimen. We see later that this effect is very similar to the effect of polarization surface charges in dielectrics.

In specimen *a* in the figure, with large end areas compared with the specimen length, the demagnetizing effect of the end surfaces perpendicular to the magnetization is large. In specimen *b*, the end area is smaller relative to the length, and the effect is less. Finally, in specimen *c*, in which a toroidal solenoid winding produces a magnetization which is everywhere parallel to the surface, there is *no* demagnetizing effect. To begin with, our discussion is limited to toroidal specimens magnetized as in *c*, since this avoids demagnetizing effects entirely.

In Fig. 10.2 is shown an experimental arrangement using a toroidal specimen and coil for measuring magnetic effects of matter, uninfluenced by end effects. An extra secondary winding is employed which connects to a ballistic galvanometer.

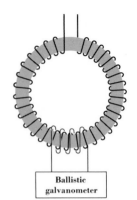

*Fig. 10.2 Toroidal solenoid
with secondary winding
for flux measurement.*

In order to measure the magnetic effect of matter, a fixed current is passed through the toroidal coil. The magnetic flux in the empty coil is then compared with the flux when the coil is filled with matter. The difference in these two measurements gives the magnetic contribution of the specimen. The flux ϕ in the coil is determined by measuring the deflection of the ballistic galvanometer when the current is suddenly turned off.

In a vacuum the magnetic induction in the solenoid is given by

$$B = \mu_0 \frac{Ni}{L} = \mu_0 j^s \qquad \text{webers/m}^2 \tag{8.12}$$

where j^s is the solenoidal current density as defined in Sec. 8.3. This value of **B** was obtained by integrating

$$d\mathbf{B} = \frac{\mu_0}{4\pi} \frac{i\, d\mathbf{l} \times \hat{\mathbf{r}}}{r^2} \tag{8.2}$$

for the geometry of the solenoid, or alternatively, by using Ampère's circuital law,

$$\oint \mathbf{B} \cdot d\mathbf{l} = \mu_0 i \tag{8.14}$$

around the path inside a toroidal solenoid.

The total flux ϕ measured by the ballistic galvanometer in the empty coil thus depends on the solenoidal current density j^s and on the cross-section area A of the coil.

$$\phi = BA = \mu_0 \frac{NiA}{L} = \mu_0 j^s A$$

When the experiment is repeated with a specimen filling the toroid, the field **B** is modified by the matter. With paramagnetic specimens,

B is increased, and with diamagnetic specimens, **B** is decreased. To account for the presence of matter, Eq. (8.12) is rewritten

$$B = \mu_0(j^s_{\text{free}} + j^s_{\text{mag}}) \tag{10.1}$$

where $j^s_{\text{free}} = Ni/L$ is the solenoidal current density in the coil, and j^s_{mag} is an *effective* solenoidal current density that describes the magnetic effect of the matter.

This important modification of the vacuum equation implies that the magnetic effects of the material of the specimen may be completely accounted for by an equivalent solenoidal current surrounding the specimen, just as the real solenoid surrounds it. This current is often called the *amperian surface current*. It is shown below that as long as we are willing to settle for an average value of the contributions of the whole population of dipoles to the field, this surface current is equivalent to the effect of the dipoles.

We now present another parameter which equally well describes the average effect of oriented magnetic dipoles. This is the vector **M**, the *magnetic moment per unit volume*. Suppose there were n dipole moments per unit volume of material, each dipole having a moment $\mathbf{p}_m$, making an average angle θ with the field direction. Then, since the magnetic moment is a vector quantity, the effective total magnetic moment per unit volume would be

$$\mathbf{M} = n\mathbf{p}_m\langle\cos\theta\rangle \tag{10.2}$$

where $\langle\cos\theta\rangle$ is the average value of $\cos\theta$. Since the usual measurements of **M** do not measure the number or size or directions of individual dipoles, we do not learn about the number or strength of the individual dipoles, but only about the product $np_m\langle\cos\theta\rangle$. In the usual paramagnetic situation, the increase in **M**, proportional to the applied field, reflects the increasingly perfect alignment of the dipoles as the field increases. *Saturation* occurs at very high fields, in which all dipoles align with the field and $\langle\cos\theta\rangle = 1$. In isotropic materials the magnetization points along the direction of the field that causes the magnetization, even though individual dipoles are not perfectly aligned. A schematic representation of this situation in a weak and a strong field is shown in Fig. 10.3.

There is a simple relationship between these two magnetization parameters j^s_{mag} and **M**. We first show the detailed argument that the effects of individual dipoles can be replaced by a fictitious surface current, and then relate this to the magnetization vector **M**. We note that

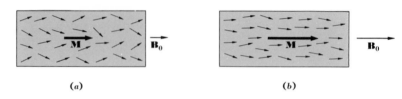

Fig. 10.3   (a) Dipoles partially aligned in a moderate field; (b) dipoles almost completely aligned in a strong field.

whatever the nature of the magnetic dipoles in matter, their far fields can be represented by current loops having dipole moments $p_m = iA$. Since we are not attempting to describe the field *close* to any dipole, the far-field approximation is valid. Thus we can describe an array of oriented dipoles in matter as an array of current loops in a volume of magnetized matter. We show this in Figs. 10.4 and 10.5*a* and *b*. In

Fig. 10.4   (a) Atomic dipole p_m represented by dipole moment vector; (b) current loop which produces a dipole moment.

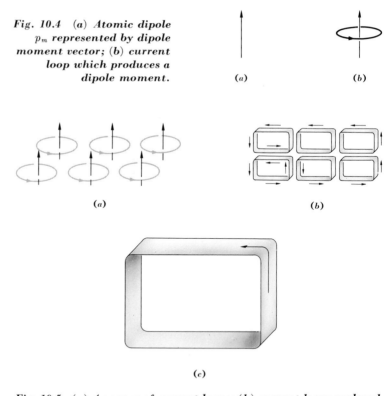

Fig. 10.5   (a) An array of current loops; (b) current loops replaced by a grid of loops; (c) grid of loops replaced by a ribbonlike single loop that has the same average effect as the grid.

Fig. 10.5c we replace these current loops by a ribbon of current surrounding the volume of matter. This current sheet reproduces the magnetic effects of the actual dipoles in the volume. The argument for this equivalence is that, within the grid of loops, all adjacent currents are equal and opposite, leaving only the peripheral current sheet. Thus the magnetic effect of any uniformly magnetized piece of matter can be represented by a peripheral current sheet conforming to the specimen as shown.

We now give the simple reasoning which leads to a quantitative relation between the magnetization **M** of a magnetized specimen and the effective peripheral current. The dipole moment p_m of the specimen which can duplicate its far field is

$$p_m = i_{mag}A \tag{10.3}$$

as seen in Fig. 10.6, where A is the area of the loop. We may also express the magnetization **M**, or magnetic moment per unit volume in

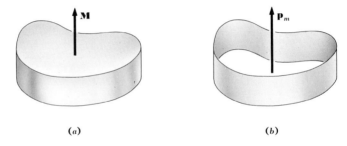

(a)   (b)

Fig. 10.6   (a) Uniformly magnetized specimen; (b) equivalent current sheet which gives same B field.

the specimen:

$$M = \frac{i_{mag}A}{xA} = \frac{i_{mag}}{x} = j^s_{mag} \qquad amp/m \tag{10.4}$$

where j^s_{mag} is the equivalent solenoidal current density circulating around the body and giving the same magnetic moment as the sum of the individual atomic magnetic dipoles.

This same reasoning may be applied to the special shape of the toroidal cylinder specimen. Again, as shown in Fig. 10.7, the atomic current loops may be replaced by the equivalent amperian surface currents, and the simplicity of the shape leads to a uniform solenoidal current density.

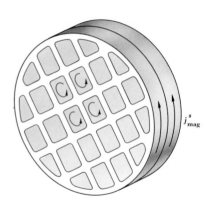

Fig. 10.7 *Section of a magnetized toroidal specimen
showing how individual
current loops can be re-
placed by an equivalent
amperian surface current
density. The size of the
current loops, which are
on an atomic scale, is ex-
aggerated in this schematic
drawing.*

An additional complication is that if the magnetization of matter
is not uniform, the individual current loops do not cancel completely,
and we must add to the effective surface current density a term involving a volume distribution of effective currents. The fact that magnetized matter can be replaced by magnetically equivalent amperian
currents shows that lines of **B** continue to be sourceless in the presence
of matter, and that they therefore form closed loops in the presence of
matter, as in free space. Thus the equations

$$\int_{CS} \mathbf{B} \cdot d\mathbf{S} = 0 \quad \text{or} \quad \text{div } \mathbf{B} = 0 \tag{10.5}$$

remain true under all conditions.

The ability to characterize the state of magnetization of matter by
M or j^s_{mag} remains, no matter what the shape of a magnetic specimen.
But the calculation of the field **B** within and outside a specimen is more
difficult when we must account for the effects of the ends of a specimen,
as shown in Sec. 10.5.

10.3   Magnetic Field **H**

Equation 10.1 gives **B** in terms of the free currents and the amperian
currents used to describe the magnetization of specimens of matter. In
many situations it is mathematically difficult to obtain the amperian-
current distributions which describe the magnetic effects of bodies. We
now introduce a useful new field quantity, **H**, usually called the magnetic field intensity. We simply call it the field **H**.

We first show that Eq. (10.4), $M = j^s_{\text{mag}}$, can be converted to an
expression for the circulation of **M**. The simple argument will be based

on a uniformly magnetized toroidal specimen, though the result is completely general. In Fig. 10.8 we see a section of a toroidal solenoid

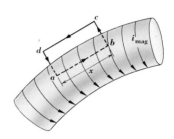

Fig. 10.8   Section of a uniformly magnetized toroidal specimen, used in showing how the line integral of **M** *leads to* $\oint \mathbf{H} \cdot d\mathbf{l} = i_{\text{free}}$.

sample on which the amperian surface current has been indicated. This current replaces the effects of the oriented magnetic dipoles of the sample. The magnetization is produced by real current in a solenoidal coil surrounding the sample and not shown in the figure. We evaluate the line integral $\oint \mathbf{M} \cdot d\mathbf{l}$ around the closed path *abcd*. Along *ab*, *M* is parallel to the path and equal to j^s_{mag}. If we let the distance *ab* be *x*, the integral from *a* to *b* becomes $j^s_{\text{mag}}x$. The line integral is zero over the rest of the path, since *M* is perpendicular to the paths *bc* and *da* and is zero over the path *cd*. Since $j^s_{\text{mag}}x$ is the total amperian current i_{mag} enclosed by the path, we have

$$\oint \mathbf{M} \cdot d\mathbf{l} = i_{\text{mag}} \tag{10.4a}$$

This, then, is the circulation of the magnetization vector **M**.

Earlier we found an expression for the circulation of **B** in free space:

$$\oint \mathbf{B} \cdot d\mathbf{l} = \mu_0 i \tag{8.14}$$

where *i* is the current threading the closed path of integration. Now that matter is being considered, it is appropriate to generalize this to

$$\oint \mathbf{B} \cdot d\mathbf{l} = \mu_0(i_{\text{free}} + i_{\text{mag}}) = \mu_0 i_{\text{total}} \tag{10.6}$$

where i_{free} is the real current, and i_{mag} is the amperian current that describes the magnetic behavior of matter.

Combining Eqs. (10.4a) and (10.6) gives

$$\oint \left(\frac{1}{\mu_0} \mathbf{B} - \mathbf{M}\right) \cdot d\mathbf{l} = i_{\text{free}} \qquad \text{amp} \tag{10.7}$$

This equation allows us to define a new vector field quantity, $(1/\mu_0)$ **B** − **M**, which has the property that its circulation depends only on the free macroscopic current. This is the quantity we call **H**, or

$$\mathbf{H} = \frac{1}{\mu_0} \mathbf{B} - \mathbf{M} \qquad (10.8)$$

Different treatments deal differently with the constant μ_0, but our choice is a popular one. With this definition we may write this first statement of a property of this new field vector, its circulation,

$$\oint \mathbf{H} \cdot d\mathbf{l} = i_{\text{free}} \qquad \text{amp} \qquad (10.9)$$

The nonzero circulation shows that the vector **H** describes a nonconservative field, depending for its circulation on only the free current threading the integration path. The microscopic form of this would be

$$\text{curl } \mathbf{H} = j_{\text{free}} \qquad \text{amp/m}^2 \qquad (10.10)$$

Since $\mathbf{M} = 0$ in free space, Eq. (10.8) tells us that in free space **H** and **B** are the same, except for the constant μ_0. Thus we write

$$\mathbf{B} = \mu_0 \mathbf{H} \qquad (10.11)$$

for free space.

In any region of space where there are no current-carrying conductors (and no moving charges), i_{free} is zero, and Eq. (10.9) becomes

$$\oint \mathbf{H} \cdot d\mathbf{l} = 0 \qquad (10.12)$$

or in microscopic form,

$$\text{curl } \mathbf{H} = 0 \qquad (10.13)$$

Equation (10.9) can be used in the special case of the toroidal specimen and coil to get an explicit expression for **H**. Thus, since the field **B** or **H** outside the coil is zero, a path like the one shown in Fig. 10.9 allows evaluation of **H** inside the solenoid, with or without a speci-

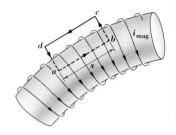

Fig. 10.9. Section of a toroidal solenoid showing magnetizing windings. Since H depends only on real currents, the value of H within the toroid is independent of the presence of matter. Calculation gives $H = Ni/L = i_{\text{free}}^s$.

men present. Thus, if the solenoid carries a current of i amp in a coil of N/L turns per unit length, giving a solenoidal current density $j^s_{\text{free}} = Ni/L$, the circulation around the path is given by

$$\oint \mathbf{H} \cdot d\mathbf{l} = \mathbf{H} \cdot \mathbf{x} = j^s_{\text{free}} x = \frac{Ni}{L} x$$

or

$$H = j^s_{\text{free}} = \frac{Ni}{L} \qquad \text{amp/m} \tag{10.14}$$

When we go to other shapes than this special toroidal one, we shall find that there is another contribution to **H** from the ends of magnetic matter.

Next is the question of Gauss' flux theorem and its possible application to the new vector field **H**.

Since, in a vacuum, $\mathbf{B} = \mu_0 \mathbf{H}$, Gauss' flux theorem for **B** can be written for $\mu_0 \mathbf{H}$, and the constant μ_0 can be removed from the integration, to give Gauss' flux theorem applied to **H** in free space.

$$\int_{CS} \mathbf{H} \cdot d\mathbf{S} = 0 \qquad \text{in free space} \tag{10.15}$$

We next enquire about a region entirely filled with isotropic matter in which **M** is proportional to the field. Such linear dependence of the magnetization on the field is often found, as it was in the experiment described in Sec. 10.2. Equation (10.8) shows that if **M** is proportional to **B** (or **H**), **B** and **H** are proportional. Therefore we may conclude again that

$$\int_{CS} \mathbf{H} \cdot d\mathbf{S} = 0 \qquad \text{entirely within uniform linear matter} \tag{10.16}$$

In contrast to these two results, things are different when we choose a gaussian surface which includes a boundary between free space and matter, or between specimens having different susceptibilities. We discuss the behavior of **H** at boundaries in Sec. 10.5.

The microscopic form of the equations above is

$$\text{div } \mathbf{H} = 0 \tag{10.17}$$

We have shown that at least in regions away from boundaries of matter, lines of **H** are continuous and form continuous loops without sources, just as with lines of **B**.

10.4   Magnetic Parameters in Matter

Before turning to the problem of specimen end effects we pause to discuss some useful parameters describing the magnetization of bodies by an external field.

It is common practice to describe the magnetic characteristics of matter in terms of its *magnetic susceptibility* χ_m, or its *magnetic permeability* μ. We define these terms, using Eq. (10.8), written in the form

$$\mathbf{B} = \mu_0(\mathbf{H} + \mathbf{M}) \tag{10.8}$$

In the case of a toroid we have seen that $\mathbf{H}$ is just j^s_{free}, the real solenoidal current density. As stated in the last section, for other specimen shapes there are other contributions to $\mathbf{H}$, which we consider later. With this proviso, Eq. (10.8) is always true.

It was mentioned in the last section that in a large class of *linear* materials, the magnetization is proportional to the applied field, although we later discuss the ferromagnetic materials in which this may not be true. For the time being the discussion is restricted to linear and isotropic materials, in which the magnetization depends linearly on the applied field and is parallel to it. In such cases the vectors $\mathbf{B}$, $\mathbf{H}$, and $\mathbf{M}$ are parallel in matter. Because of the linear behavior, we may write $\mathbf{M}$ in terms of a magnetic susceptibility χ_m, defined by[1]

$$\mathbf{M} = \chi_m\mathbf{H} \tag{10.18}$$

As defined here, χ_m is a pure number, since $\mathbf{M}$ and $\mathbf{H}$ have the same units. It then follows from Eq. (10.8) that

$$\mathbf{B} = \mu_0(1 + \chi_m)\mathbf{H} \tag{10.19}$$

If we write

$$\mu = \mu_0(1 + \chi_m) \tag{10.20}$$

where μ is the magnetic permeability, we have

$$\mathbf{B} = \mu\mathbf{H} \tag{10.21}$$

---

[1] Since the field $\mathbf{B}$ expresses the total magnetic force on a current element (or on an atomic magnetic moment), it would be more logical to look for the dependence of $\mathbf{M}$ on $\mathbf{B}$ rather than on $\mathbf{H}$. But since the field vectors are all parallel to each other, the only consequence of a redefinition of the susceptibility would be to alter its numerical value for a given material. The important thing is the slope of the linear relationship between $\mathbf{B}$ and $\mathbf{H}$, which is fixed by experiment and not by the definition of susceptibility. We follow the universal practice, as in Eq. (10.18).

In free space this reduces to the vacuum equation

$$\mathbf{B} = \mu_0\mathbf{H} \tag{10.11}$$

since X_m is zero in a vacuum.

It is useful to define a *relative permeability* μ/μ_0. The relative permeability in the mks system has the same numerical value as μ, the permeability, in cgs magnetic units (emu).

We can classify magnetic matter in terms of the susceptibility X_m. In paramagnetic materials, X_m is positive and much less than 1. In diamagnetic materials, X_m is negative and also small compared with 1. The characteristic of ferromagnetic materials is that X_m is positive and very large. However, in ferromagnetic materials $\mathbf{M}$ is not accurately proportional to $\mathbf{H}$; so X_m is not a constant, except over small ranges of $\mathbf{H}$. We discuss these three cases in detail later.

We may also classify magnetic materials in terms of the magnetic permeability μ. From its definition, we may characterize magnetic matter.

Diamagnetic: $\mu < \mu_0$
Paramagnetic: $\mu > \mu_0$
Ferromagnetic: $\mu \gg \mu_0$

10.5 Boundary Sources of H

In the discussion of **H** in Sec. 10.3 we considered primarily a toroidal specimen of matter. The special property of this shape is that a toroidal specimen of material uniformly magnetized along its length produces no field outside the material. This follows from the same property of a current coil wound in toroidal form, which also produces no field outside. We now remove this special limitation and discuss magnetized specimens of more general shape. Figure 10.10 shows a

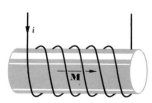

Fig. 10.10 Cylindrical mag-netic cylinder in an ap-plied field.

cylindrical specimen with ends. It is assumed to be made of isotropic matter having a constant susceptibility. In this kind of situation the presence of the specimen affects the field both inside and *outside* itself. This was not the case for the toroidal shape, for which **H** depends only on the real currents providing the magnetizing field. The equation **B** = μ_0(**H** + **M**) is still valid, but now **H** is modified by specimen end effects.

Under all conditions Gauss' flux theorem gives

$$\int_{cs} \mathbf{B} \cdot d\mathbf{S} = 0 \tag{10.5}$$

and we use this to find the consequence of the definition of **H** in Eq. (10.8). If we substitute **B** from Eq. (10.8) in Gauss' flux theorem [Eq. (10.5)], we find

$$\mu_0 \int_{cs} \mathbf{H} \cdot d\mathbf{S} + \mu_0 \int_{cs} \mathbf{M} \cdot d\mathbf{S} = 0$$

or

$$\int_{cs} \mathbf{H} \cdot d\mathbf{S} = - \int_{cs} \mathbf{M} \cdot d\mathbf{S} \tag{10.22}$$

The equivalent microscopic form of this equation is

$$\operatorname{div} \mathbf{H} = -\operatorname{div} \mathbf{M} \tag{10.22a}$$

This formal statement of the behavior of **H** in the presence of matter is to be compared with Eq. (10.16), $\int_{cs} \mathbf{H} \cdot d\mathbf{S} = 0$, in all regions of free space or in regions completely occupied by uniform matter. Equation (10.22) in fact reduces to $\int_{cs} \mathbf{H} \cdot d\mathbf{S} = 0$ in any region of free space, where **M** = 0, and also in any region entirely filled with uniform matter, since **M** and **B** would be proportional. Thus $\int_{cs} \mathbf{M} \cdot d\mathbf{S}$ would equal zero, following the universal rule, $\int_{cs} \mathbf{B} \cdot d\mathbf{S} = 0$.

Equation (10.22) thus narrows down to one possibility, the region of a boundary, where there may be sources or sinks of lines of **H**. Going back to the dielectric case where $\int_{cs} \mathbf{P} \cdot d\mathbf{S}$ was considered, we see that **M** and **P** are mathematically very similar. The discontinuity in **P** at a boundary was found to be related to the polarization surface charge which acts as source or sink of lines of **E**. The discontinuity in **M** at a boundary similarly gives rise to sources and sinks of lines of **H**. In the magnetic case, however, there are no real "magnetic charges" as there are electric charges. Nevertheless, a surface region where $\int_{cs} \mathbf{M} \cdot d\mathbf{S}$ is not zero is a true source of lines of **H**, and the presence of such sources adds to the total value of **H**.

For the simple case of a surface normal to the magnetization vector **M**, the integral is easy to evaluate. Thus, taking a gaussian pillbox enclosing the right-hand end of the bar in Fig. 10.11, which has an area

Fig. 10.11   Lines of M which end within a gaussian pillbox placed at the end of a magnetized specimen. Lines of M thus terminating act as sources of lines of H.

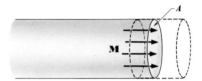

A equal to the cross section of the bar, we find

$$\int_{cs} \mathbf{M} \cdot d\mathbf{S} = -MA \tag{10.23}$$

This follows from the fact that the total number of lines of **M** entering the left-hand side of the pillbox is MA, while the number of lines leaving the pillbox surface outside the sample is zero, since M is zero outside the sample. The negative sign results from the fact that the lines of M are directed *inward* at the gaussian surface. If this result is substituted in Eq. (10.22), we get

$$\int_{cs} \mathbf{H} \cdot d\mathbf{S} = MA \tag{10.24}$$

This is Gauss' flux theorem for **H**. It tells us that, in addition to the closed lines of **H** originating from real currents, there is a net flux of **H** out from any region in which there is a component of **M** perpendicular to a surface. Lines of **H** emerge from the surface (or in the case of the left-hand end of the sample in Fig. 10.10, where **M** is directed *out* of the gaussian pillbox in the sample, the net flux of **H** lines is *into* the surface). These extra lines originating or ending at surfaces modify the field both inside and outside the sample.

In view of the mathematical similarity of these sources of **H** to electric charges as sources of **E**, we argue that the lines of **H** originating at boundaries behave according to Gauss' flux theorem, so that end effects of matter can be computed according to the usual inverse-square dependence of the field (here **H**) on the distance from each small element of source. This property is particularly helpful since it reduces problems of field calculation to the already known ones of electric fields.

Because of this close correspondence of sources of $\mathbf{H}$ at boundaries to electric charges, it is often convenient, especially in the case of permanent magnets, to think in terms of a fictitious magnetic charge q_m, given by

$$- \int_{CS} \mathbf{M} \cdot d\mathbf{S} = q_m \tag{10.25}$$

where we call q_m the *magnetic charge*, or *pole*. Gauss' flux theorem for these sources of $\mathbf{H}$ then becomes

$$\int_{CS} \mathbf{H} \cdot d\mathbf{S} = q_m \qquad \text{amp-m} \tag{10.26}$$

Since $\int_{CS} \mathbf{M} \cdot d\mathbf{S}$ is zero at surfaces where $\mathbf{M}$ is parallel to the surface, no sources of $\mathbf{H}$ are found at the side surface of uniformly magnetized specimens where $\mathbf{M}$ is parallel to the surface. This is approximately the case in a bar such as shown in Fig. 10.10. It is now easy to see why the special solenoidal shape was chosen to introduce the treatment of magnetic matter. For that case no sources of $\mathbf{H}$ exist, and as a result the only causes of $\mathbf{H}$ were the real currents. We have now verified that in general there are two ways in which $\mathbf{H}$ can arise, from the macroscopic real currents and from discontinuities in $\mathbf{M}$ at boundaries.[1]

The existence of sources of $\mathbf{H}$ lines does not imply the reality of magnetic charges or poles. The behavior of lines of $\mathbf{H}$ is a consequence of their definition, and is consistent with the point of view that all magnetic properties of matter result from microscopic current loops. The important physical result is that there are no sources of lines of $\mathbf{B}$.

Although we have now an additional source of $\mathbf{H}$, from end effects of a magnetized specimen, it is important to note that Eq. (10.9) for the circulation of $\mathbf{H}$ is not modified. This follows from an argument identical with that for $\oint \mathbf{E} \cdot d\mathbf{l} = 0$ in the electrostatic case. Thus, under all conditions of steady state, the circulation of $\mathbf{H}$ is given by

$$\oint \mathbf{H} \cdot d\mathbf{l} = i_{\text{free}} \tag{10.9}$$

In a paramagnetic or ferromagnetic material, $\mathbf{M}$ is in the direction of $\mathbf{H}$. As a result, the extra contribution to $\mathbf{H}$ from the ends is opposed

---

[1] When magnetic material is nonuniform, so that the susceptibility is not the same throughout a sample, there can be discontinuities in M within the volume of the sample. Such discontinuities produce an additional term in Eq. (10.24), giving in effect additional sources of lines of $\mathbf{H}$ within the volume. We shall not discuss this complication further.

to the **H** in the sample and decreases the net value of **H** inside. Outside the ends of the sample the lines of **H** originating at the sample ends augment the **H** due to currents causing the magnetization, and thus enhance **B** $= \mu_0$**H** outside the sample. In the case of ellipsoidal samples, the effects of the ends can be discussed in terms of a *demagnetizing* field, just as we treated the depolarizing field in dielectrics.

Figure 10.12 shows an ellipsoidal magnetized specimen, and the lines of **H** which originate at the ends. Not shown is the external

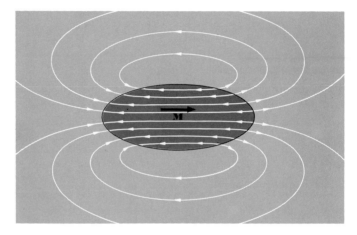

Fig. 10.12   Ellipsoidal magnetized specimen, showing lines of H, originating at ends. The uniform external field producing the magnetization is not shown.

magnetic field responsible for the magnetization of the specimen. Inside the specimen the field is weakened by the demagnetizing field of the ends, while outside near the ends the field is enhanced. Although we may discuss other than ellipsoidal specimens in terms of a demagnetizing factor, results will be only approximate, as in the case of dielectric materials.

10.6   Boundary Conditions for **B** and **H**

The next step in utilizing the two field quantities **B** and **H** is to show how they behave at boundaries between different materials. The procedure will recall the similar development of the conditions on **E** and **D** at a dielectric boundary, since the mathematics is identical.

In the case of **B**, we proceed by imagining a cylindrical gaussian surface as shown in Fig. 10.13, drawn so as to have one surface in

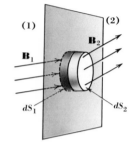

Fig. 10.13 Gaussian surface for obtaining boundary condition on B between two different magnetic media.

region 1 and the other in region 2. The two regions have different magnetic properties; for example, region 1 may be a vacuum, while region 2 could be a magnetic material. We make the thickness of the cylinder vanishingly small, so that the lines of **B** that come out of the sides of the cylinder may be neglected. Then we can use the zero net flux of **B** out of any volume, or zero divergence, to write

$$\int_{S_1} \mathbf{B}_1 \cdot d\mathbf{S}_1 = - \int_{S_2} \mathbf{B}_2 \cdot d\mathbf{S}_2 \qquad (10.27)$$

This means that the normal components of $\mathbf{B}_1$ and $\mathbf{B}_2$ are equal, or

$$B_{n1} = B_{n2} \qquad (10.28)$$

We next study the behavior of **H** at this boundary by taking the line integral as shown in Fig. 10.14. If no real currents flow along the

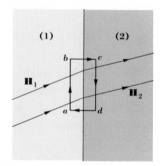

Fig. 10.14 Line integral for obtaining boundary condition on H between two different magnetic media.

boundary, the resulting zero circulation of **H**, according to Eq. (10.9), leads to

$$\int_a^b \mathbf{H}_1 \cdot d\mathbf{l}_1 = - \int_c^d \mathbf{H}_2 \cdot d\mathbf{l}_2 \qquad (10.27a)$$

This means that the tangential components of **H** are equal on the two sides of the boundary, or

$$H_{t1} = H_{t2} \tag{10.29}$$

In this discussion of boundary conditions we have so far made no assumption as to how **H** and **B** are related. When we are dealing with materials in which $\mathbf{B} = \mu\mathbf{H}$, we can determine the behavior of **B** and **H** at a boundary, using the rules just derived for B_n and H_t. Since these conditions are identical with those for D_n and E_t found for dielectric boundaries, we may take over the earlier results directly, to write

$$\frac{\tan \phi_1}{\tan \phi_2} = \frac{\mu_1}{\mu_2} \tag{10.30}$$

for the directions of **B** and **H** on the two sides of a boundary (see Sec. 5.10 for the electrostatic case).

10.7   Stored Energy in Magnetic Matter

We have already found, in Sec. 9.14, that the energy density in a vacuum containing a magnetic field **B** is

$$\frac{U}{\text{vol}} = \frac{1}{2}\frac{B^2}{\mu_0} \quad \text{joules/m}^3 \tag{9.39}$$

The argument is now modified to allow for the presence of magnetic matter. A toroidal solenoid is again chosen for convenience, since, with a uniform specimen filling the toroid, **B** and **H** are uniform and limited to the region inside the solenoid.

The field H is given by

$$H = j^s_{\text{free}} = \frac{Ni}{L} \tag{10.14}$$

according to our usual terminology. If, to begin with, both B and H are zero, the work to build up a certain field can be calculated in terms of the work done against the emf of Faraday induction. This is a back emf resulting from the flux linkage of the coil. For a given rate of change of B, dB/dt, the emf is given by

$$\varepsilon = N\frac{d\phi}{dt} = NA\frac{dB}{dt}$$

Here A is the cross-section area of the coil and specimen, and N the turns in the coil. The emf per meter of coil length is

$$\mathcal{E} = \frac{N}{L}\frac{d\phi}{dt} = \frac{N}{L}A\frac{dB}{dt}$$

While the current and field are increasing, the power required against the induced emf, per unit length of coil, is

$$P = \mathcal{E}i = \frac{N}{L}iA\frac{dB}{dt} = HA\frac{dB}{dt}$$

Thus the power per unit volume of field is

$$\frac{P}{\text{vol}} = H\frac{dB}{dt}$$

More generally, this would be written as $\mathbf{H} \cdot d\mathbf{B}/dt$, but in the special geometry chosen, $\mathbf{H}$ and $\mathbf{B}$ are parallel. The work per unit volume to produce a final field $\mathbf{B}_f$ in matter is

$$\frac{W}{\text{vol}} = \int_0^{B_f} \mathbf{H} \cdot d\mathbf{B} \qquad \text{joules/m}^3 \tag{10.31}$$

If the material has constant susceptibility, so that $\mathbf{B} = \mu\mathbf{H}$, with μ constant, the work done in producing the field goes into stored energy, and we can evaluate the integral

$$\frac{U}{\text{vol}} = \mu\int_0^H \mathbf{H} \cdot d\mathbf{H} = \frac{1}{2}\mu H^2 = \frac{1}{2}\frac{B^2}{\mu} = \frac{1}{2}BH \tag{10.32}$$

This discussion has been based on toroidal solenoid geometry, but the result is true in general. Equation (10.31) is always true, and Eq. (10.32) is true whenever materials with linear response to a field are involved.

10.8   Examples, Field Calculations

We now review and summarize the ideas which have been developed for calculating fields in a vacuum and in the presence of matter, and give some specific examples. For free space with only real currents causing the magnetic field, as symbolized in Fig. 10.15, the field $\mathbf{B}$ may be calculated by using

$$\mathbf{B} = \frac{1}{4\pi\mu_0}\int\frac{i\,d\mathbf{l} \times \hat{\mathbf{r}}}{r^2} \tag{8.2}$$

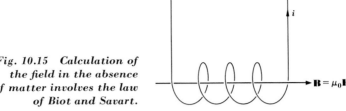

*Fig. 10.15 Calculation of
the field in the absence
of matter involves the law
of Biot and Savart.*

the law of Biot and Savart. In special cases of high symmetry, a consequence of the Biot and Savart law,

$$\oint \mathbf{B} \cdot d\mathbf{l} = \mu_0 i \tag{8.14}$$

provides a simple method for evaluation of **B**.

It would be possible, though to no particular advantage, to first calculate the value of **H**, using

$$\mathbf{H} = \frac{1}{4\pi} \int \frac{i\, d\mathbf{l} \times \hat{\mathbf{r}}}{r^2} \tag{10.33}$$

or

$$\oint \mathbf{H} \cdot d\mathbf{l} = i_{\text{free}} \tag{10.9}$$

and then find **B** through $\mathbf{B} = \mu_0 \mathbf{H}$. There is no advantage in using **H** in a problem limited to currents in free space.

In Fig. 10.16 a symbolic sketch is shown of the class of problems involving both real currents and matter. It is assumed that the matter

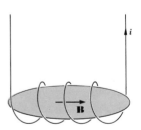

*Fig. 10.16 With matter
present, the field calculation involves both the effects of real currents and
of magnetized matter.*

is isotropic and linear in its response to an applied field, that is, $\mathbf{M} = \chi_m \mathbf{H}$.

It is apparent that the field at any point outside or inside matter is the vector sum of two contributions, one a term $\mathbf{B}_i$, caused by real currents, and the other $\mathbf{B}_m$, caused by the magnetic specimen. This could be written

$$\mathbf{B} = \mathbf{B}_i + \mathbf{B}_m$$

The calculation of the contribution $\mathbf{B}_i$ would follow the same methods outlined above for the free-space problem, using Eq. (8.2) or (8.14).

The contribution $\mathbf{B}_m$ could be found in principle by replacing the magnetized matter by surface currents and then integrating the contributions from all these currents, just as for real currents. The specimen is simply replaced by its equivalent surface currents.

Another way of dividing up the contributions to the field is as follows:

Outside the specimen:　$\mathbf{B} = \mu_0(\mathbf{H}_0 + \mathbf{H}_m)$

where $\mathbf{H}_0$ is the $\mathbf{H}$ field from the real currents, and $\mathbf{H}_m$ is the contribution from the boundary sources of $\mathbf{H}$ contributed by the discontinuities in $\mathbf{M}$ at the ends of the specimen.

Inside the specimen:　$\mathbf{B} = \mu_0(\mathbf{H}_0 + \mathbf{H}_m + \mathbf{M})$　(10.34)

where $\mathbf{H}_0$ and $\mathbf{H}_m$ are from real currents and boundary sources as above, and $\mathbf{M}$ is the contribution from the magnetization at points inside the specimen.

These last two equations are actually just examples of the use of the general equation

$$\mathbf{B} = \mu_0(\mathbf{H} + \mathbf{M})$$　(10.8)

Problems of this kind are generally very difficult to solve. But for the ellipsoidal specimen shape the problem is somewhat simplified by the fact that the field $\mathbf{H}_m$ will be uniform within the specimen if the external field was originally uniform. The contribution $\mathbf{H}_m$ in this simple shape is opposed to the original field and is therefore often called the demagnetizing field. This is the mathematical analogue of the depolarizing field discussed under dielectrics (Chap. 5). The demagnetizing factor depends entirely on specimen shape and has exactly the same shape dependence as does the depolarizing factor.

Since the fields inside and outside the specimen depend both on the applied field and on the field contribution of the magnetization of the specimen, determination of the magnetization requires a self-consistent solution. That is, the magnetization must be consistent with the resultant field within the specimen.

The two methods, one of which replaces the magnetized specimen by surface currents and the other which attributes the changed field inside and outside the specimen to boundary sources of **H**, give identical results for the field **B** both inside and at points outside the specimen. The most important use of **H** comes when we deal with permanently magnetized matter.

We now discuss some particular cases to clarify these rather complicated matters. In all examples it is assumed that the matter is isotropic and linear, with a constant susceptibility χ_m, or permeability μ, and that the external applied field caused by real currents[1] was uniform in the region of the specimen prior to placing it in the field.

a   *A long thin rod placed parallel to the original field* **B**$_0$ *(Fig. 10.17).* Our first method neglects the end effects of the rod, since the ends are

Fig. 10.17   A long thin rod of magnetic material, with its axis parallel to the original uniform field **B**. *End effects are negligible.*

small and far away, and replaces the rod by equivalent solenoidal currents. If we stay away from the ends, the magnetization **M** is related to the amperian current density j^s_{mag} by $M = j^s_{\text{mag}} = \chi_m H$.

In general, the field **B** inside the rod is given by

$$\mathbf{B} = \mu_0(\mathbf{H}_0 + \mathbf{H}_m + \mathbf{M})$$

but if the ends are neglected, **H**$_m$ is zero. Thus **B** inside the rod is

$$\mathbf{B} = \mu_0(\mathbf{H}_0 + \mathbf{M}) = \mu_0(\mathbf{H}_0 + \chi_m \mathbf{H}_0) = \mu \mathbf{H}_0$$

This is the same as the result in a toroidal specimen, as is to be expected, since here the effects of the ends are negligible.

The same result is available using the approximation we found for the electrostatic case, namely, that for this shape, the depolarizing or

---

[1] We discuss later the fields produced by permanent magnets in which there are no real currents. An external field might be produced in this way. However, it is not significant whether the original external field is produced by real currents or by the boundary sources of **H** in permanent magnets. Since either produces a field **B**$_0$ where we want it, it is of only formal interest to decide whether the field is produced by real currents or boundary sources of **H**.

demagnetizing factor is zero. Thus **H** in the rod is given by

$$\mathbf{H} = \mathbf{H}_0 - L\mathbf{M}$$

but

$$L = 0$$

so

$$\mathbf{H} = \mathbf{H}_0 \qquad \text{and} \qquad \mathbf{B} = \mu\mathbf{H}_0$$

A final approach to this problem is to use the known boundary conditions for **H**. We argue that the ends of the rods, being small and far away from the middle section of the rod, leave the original **H**₀ unmodified outside the rod. But since **H** outside the rod is tangent to the rod surface away from the ends, and $H_{t1} = H_{t2}$ across the boundary, **H**₀ is the value of **H** both outside and inside; so inside the rod

$$\mathbf{B} = \mu\mathbf{H}_0$$

These several statements of the problem are equivalent in meaning, though couched in somewhat different terms.

b *A thin flat plate with its plane normal to* **B**₀ (*Fig.* 10.18). We can apply the general equation

$$\mathbf{B} = \mu_0(\mathbf{H}_0 + \mathbf{H}_m + \mathbf{M}) \tag{10.34}$$

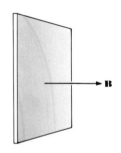

Fig. 10.18 A thin flat plate of magnetic material with its surface perpendicular to the original uniform field. Demagnetizing effects are a maximum with this geometry.

The term **H**ₘ represents lines of **H** which originate and end at surface discontinuities of **M** within the specimen. These lines emerge uniform and perpendicular to the surface in both directions, just as lines of **E** from a uniform plane distribution of charge. Since the lines of **H** are parallel, **H** is uniform inside the plate. We can obtain its value inside the plate from

$$\int_{cs} \mathbf{H} \cdot d\mathbf{S} = - \int_{cs} \mathbf{M} \cdot d\mathbf{S} \tag{10.22}$$

Outside the plate, contributions to **H** from the surface discontinuity in **M** at each surface will just cancel. Thus $\mathbf{H}_m$ contributes nothing, and the magnetized plate does not affect **H** outside.

Inside the plate, Gauss' flux theorem shows that the contribution to **H** is $-\mathbf{M}$, as given in Eq. (10.22). Thus, inside the plate, the contribution from $\mathbf{H}_m$ is $-\mathbf{M}$; so Eq. (10.34) becomes

$$\mathbf{B} = \mu_0[(\mathbf{H}_0 - \mathbf{M}) + \mathbf{M}] = \mu_0\mathbf{H}_0$$

The problem may equally well be considered in terms of the demagnetizing field $-L\mathbf{M}$. From this point of view the term $\mathbf{H}_0 - \mathbf{M}$ is the original field less the demagnetizing field $-\mathbf{M}$, since the demagnetizing factor for this geometry is 1.

The boundary condition for **B**, $B_{n1} = B_{n2}$, is satisfied, since **B** is perpendicular to the surface and has the same value inside and outside the plate.

c   *A uniform magnetic sphere placed in a uniform field* $\mathbf{B}_0$.   The resulting **B** field, inside and outside the sphere, is plotted in Fig. 10.19.

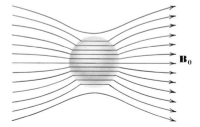

Fig. 10.19   Field perturbation due to magnetized sphere in a uniform field.

We are assuming that inside the sphere $\mu > \mu_0$. The field **B** inside the sphere is increased over its original value and is uniform. This uniformity is to be expected because the sphere is a special case of the general ellipsoid, for which the internal demagnetizing field is uniform.

Because of the similarity between the dielectric and magnetic equations, we have argued that the demagnetization factor for the sphere is the same as the depolarization factor for a dielectric sphere, which is determined in Appendix F. If we use the result found there, $L = \frac{1}{3}$, the field H inside the sphere is

$$H = H_0 - \tfrac{1}{3}M$$

where H_0 is the original value in the absence of the sphere. Then we obtain B from

$$B = \mu_0(H + M) = \mu_0[(H_0 - \tfrac{1}{3}M) + M] = \mu_0(H_0 + \tfrac{2}{3}M)$$

To express this result in terms of the susceptibility, we use $\mathbf{M} = \chi_m\mathbf{H}$ to write

$$H = H_0 - \tfrac{1}{3}\chi_m H$$

or

$$H = \frac{1}{1 + \tfrac{1}{3}\chi_m} H_0 \qquad\qquad (10.35)$$

for the internal H in the sphere. For the general case, this is

$$H = \frac{1}{1 + L\chi_m} H_0 \qquad\qquad (10.36)$$

Just as in the dielectric case, the perturbation on the *external* field due to the uniformly magnetized sphere will be exactly the field of a dipole. This applies only outside the sphere, since the field inside the sphere is uniform. Although we have chosen here to think in terms of the end effects caused by the discontinuity in M at the body surface, it would be equally satisfactory to replace the magnetized body by the effective magnetic solenoidal surface currents. We show in Example 10.14d, that if the magnetized sphere is replaced by an effective solenoidal current density $j^s_{\mathrm{mag}} = M$ at its surface, the contribution to $\mathbf{B}$ inside the sphere is $\tfrac{2}{3}\mu_0\mathbf{M}$. This agrees with the result obtained above, where we considered the effect of the surface discontinuity in $\mathbf{M}$ (magnetic poles). The two points of view always give identical results. The choice of which point of view to take is purely a matter of convenience.

10.9* Paramagnetism

In this section we begin the discussion of the physical causes of magnetism in matter with a description of the nature of paramagnetism. The essential feature of a paramagnetic material is that it has a positive but small magnetic susceptibility ($\chi_m \ll 1$), which results from the existence of permanent magnetic dipoles that are free to be oriented under the influence of an external field. The dipoles exert very small forces on each other; therefore, at ordinary temperatures, thermal vibrations of the solid ensure random orientation of the dipoles, giving an average magnetization of zero. The greater the applied magnetic field, the more nearly the dipoles tend to be aligned, and the greater is the net magnetic moment per unit volume, or magnetization **M**.

Let us consider the magnetic susceptibility of a paramagnetic substance, having N atoms in a unit volume and each having a magnetic dipole p_m, which can be aligned in an applied field. Let us assume, as is often the case, that in an applied field there are only two possibilities: either the dipoles are aligned parallel to the field or they are aligned antiparallel.[1] The magnetization at a given temperature and applied field depends on the excess number of magnetic moments aligned parallel to the field over those aligned antiparallel. The excess fraction of moments aligned parallel to the field is given by

$$f = \frac{p_m B}{3kT} \tag{10.37}$$

where k is the Boltzmann constant, and T the absolute temperature. We shall not derive this result, but we note that the numerator relates to the energy of orientation of dipoles in the external field, and the denominator relates to the thermal energy of the substance. Thus the higher the temperature, the more seriously thermal vibrations interfere with alignment, and the smaller is the excess fraction of aligned moments.

The susceptibility is obtained from the last equation as follows: The magnetization is given by[2]

$$M = N p_m f = \frac{N p_m^2 \mu_0 H}{3kT}$$

Then

$$\chi = \frac{M}{H} = \frac{N \mu_0 p_m^2}{3kT} \tag{10.38}$$

This dependence of the susceptibility of paramagnetic materials on T^{-1} is known as the Curie law.

---

[1] It is a result of quantum mechanics that magnetic dipoles in a field are subject to the condition that they may take up only certain specified average positions with respect to the field direction (Sec. 7.4). If all orientations are allowed, the same result is obtained within a numerical constant.

[2] The magnetic field B has been replaced here by $\mu_0 H$. This amounts to neglecting the effect of M in the equation $B = \mu_0(H + M)$, as justified by the small value of M in paramagnetic materials.

Figure 10.20a shows a plot of the magnetization M against the magnetizing field H. The slope of this curve is the susceptibility χ.

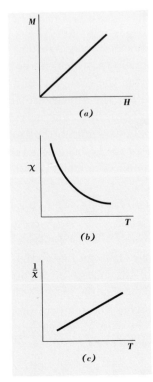

Fig. 10.20　Paramagnetic susceptibility. (a) Slope of magnetization M versus applied field H curve gives the susceptibility $\chi = M/H$; (b) susceptibility χ as a function of temperature; (c) $1/\chi$ versus T plot is a straight line.

A plot of the susceptibility χ against T, in Fig. 10.20b, shows the way the susceptibility falls off with temperature, according to Eq. (10.38). It is common practice to plot the reciprocal $1/\chi$ against temperature, in which case a straight-line plot is obtained as shown in Fig. 10.20c.

We now want to investigate the nature of p_m, the atomic dipole moment. Beginning with a discussion of free atoms or ions, we avoid the use of quantum mechanics by accepting certain simple facts about atomic structure that result from their quantum-mechanical nature. Classical considerations will then answer our questions. Thus we start with an atomic model in which electrons revolve in orbits about the much heavier nucleus. These electrons in motion act as small current loops and therefore contribute magnetic moments $p_m = Ai$, where A is the area of the orbit. We begin by calculating p_m for a simple orbit, such as that of a single electron around a nucleus in a free atom.

The area of a circular orbit is $A = \pi r^2$, and the current due to an electron of charge e is e times the number of times the electron passes any point in the orbit per second, or $i = ef = ev/2\pi r$, where f is the frequency of rotation and v the electron velocity. We determine v classically in terms of the orbit radius by equating the coulomb force between the electron and the nucleus of charge Ze to the centripetal force holding the electron in orbit. Thus we write

$$ma = \frac{mv^2}{r} = \frac{1}{4\pi\epsilon_0}\frac{Ze^2}{r^2} \tag{10.39}$$

to give

$$v = e\left(\frac{Z}{4\pi\epsilon_0 mr}\right)^{\frac{1}{2}}$$

Substitution gives, for the moment,

$$p_m = Ai = \frac{e^2}{2}\left(\frac{Zr}{4\pi\epsilon_0 m}\right)^{\frac{1}{2}} \tag{10.40}$$

For an atomic radius of 10^{-10} m this gives $p_m \approx 10^{-23}$ amp-m². Most of the electrons circulating about the nucleus need not be considered as contributors to the permanent magnetic moment. This results from the tendency in atoms for the electrons to pair off in such a way that they produce equal and opposite moments that cancel out. Classically, this would result from two electrons going around in opposite directions in the same orbit. However, in many atoms and ions there is one electron (or more) whose moment is not canceled by that of another.

Another source of magnetic moment, in addition to the contributions from orbital motion described above, is the spin of the electron. That is, the electron behaves as though it were spinning on its own axis. This again produces an effective current loop, with a consequent magnetic moment. In atoms and ions it is again usually true that electrons have a strong tendency to pair up in arrangements having opposite spins, with a consequent cancellation of the magnetic moments. However, all atoms or ions having an odd number of electrons, as well as some other cases of incomplete cancellation, exhibit spin magnetism. The magnetic moment due to electron spin is of the same order of magnitude as that due to orbital motion.

In solids, the magnetic moment due to electron spin is usually the principal contributor to the magnetic properties. This results from the effect of the local electric fields that exist in solids on the orbital motion of electrons. These fields tend to cause the plane of the orbit to precess rapidly so that the average value of the magnetic moment in any given direction is zero. Thus the magnetic moment of the free atom or ion is usually not the correct value in solids or liquids.

An additional, though much smaller, contribution to the magnetization in matter comes from the fact that some nuclei have magnetic moments. This can be thought of as due to the motion of charge within the nucleus. The magnitude of nuclear moments is about 10^{-3} that of electronic moments.

Substituting real values of moments in Eq. (10.38), we find that paramagnetic materials at room temperature have at most a susceptibility of order 10^{-3}. Thus magnetic effects in these materials are quite weak, and the value of μ differs from μ_0 by less than 1 percent. Even so, it is possible to measure these effects with considerable accuracy. One method is to use the arrangement shown in Fig. 10.2, though a more accurate result can be obtained by measuring the force on a paramagnetic sample in a nonuniform magnetic field.

10.10* Diamagnetism

Diamagnetism results from the negative magnetic moments induced in all matter upon the application of an external magnetic field. It is characterized by a *negative* susceptibility, and is independent of temperature. Since it is small compared with paramagnetic (and ferromagnetic) magnetization, it can be observed directly only in materials that are otherwise nonmagnetic. This negative susceptibility can be understood on the basis of Faraday induction acting on the orbital motions of electrons in atoms or ions.

We can understand this effect and its negative sign by thinking of an electron in a circular orbit, around a nucleus such as shown in Fig. 10.21, and asking what happens if a field **B** is introduced perpendicular to the plane of the orbit. According to the Faraday law, there is an emf

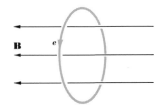

Fig. 10.21 Effect of external field on electronic orbit.

acting on the electron given by

$$\mathcal{E} = -\frac{d\phi}{dt} = -A\frac{dB}{dt} \tag{9.1}$$

during the time the field is changing, where A is the area of the orbit. This emf has the effect of changing the nature of the circulating motion of electrons in atomic orbits. We show below that, for magnetic induction fields that make reasonably small changes in the circular motion, the size of the orbit is not altered. We therefore make a calculation based on constant orbital radius. The emf produced by the changing **B** field results in an electric field E_t, which acts tangentially to the direction of the electronic motion. The magnitude of this field is

$$E_t = \frac{\mathcal{E}}{2\pi r}$$

As a result of this field, the electron will be accelerated according to Newton's law, giving

$$m\frac{dv}{dt} = eE_t = \frac{e\mathcal{E}}{2\pi r} = -\frac{e}{2\pi r}\frac{d\phi}{dt} \tag{10.41}$$

To find the total change in velocity during the time the magnetic flux is being increased, we integrate both sides of Eq. (10.41) to get

$$\Delta v = -\frac{e}{2\pi rm}\phi$$

where ϕ is the final magnetic flux through the loop, and Δv is the total *change* in velocity due to the force from the Faraday induction. When we express this as a change in angular velocity through the relationship $\Delta v = r\omega_L$, we have

$$\omega_L = -\frac{e}{2\pi r^2 m}\phi = -\frac{e}{2\pi r^2 m}AB = -\frac{e}{2m}B \tag{10.42}$$

This change in angular velocity ω_L is called the *Larmor frequency*. The negative sign means that ω_L is negative (clockwise) when **B** is positive (outward), in conformity with Lenz's principle.

This additional velocity accounts for an induced magnetic moment that always acts antiparallel to the field, to give a negative susceptibility. Before showing this we establish the fact that the radius of the orbital motion remains unchanged. We begin by showing that, in the absence of a magnetic field, the electrostatic force between nucleus and electron provides the centripetal force that holds the electron in circular motion. Thus we write

$$F = ma = \frac{mv^2}{r} = mr\omega_0{}^2 \tag{10.43}$$

where F is the electrostatic force, and ω_0 is the angular velocity of the electron.

When a magnetic field B is turned on, the velocity ω_0 changes to $\omega_0 + \omega_L$, as we saw above (ω_L may be either positive or negative, depending on the direction of B with respect to the original motion). Also, a new term $e(\mathbf{v} \times \mathbf{B})$ is added to the centripetal force. For the geometry we have taken, this term is evB. We wish to show that this new magnetic force due to the applied B accounts for the change in the centripetal force necessary to balance the new rotational velocity $\omega_0 + \omega_L$. We do this by writing the equation for the balance of forces similar to Eq. (10.43) under the new conditions of an applied $\mathbf{B}$. This is

$$F = mr(\omega_0 + \omega_L)^2 + evB \tag{10.44}$$

When this is multiplied out, using $v = r(\omega_0 + \omega_L)$, we find

$$F = mr\omega_0{}^2 + 2mr\omega_0\omega_L + mr\omega_L{}^2 + er\omega_0 B + er\omega_L B \tag{10.45}$$

When B is expressed in terms of ω_L according to Eq. (10.42), the second and fourth terms exactly cancel, leaving $F = mr\omega_0{}^2$ plus terms in $\omega_L{}^2$, which can be neglected as long as $\omega_L \ll \omega_0$.[1] This is the case we wish to consider. This important result tells us that after the magnetic field is applied there is a cancellation of terms which shows that the original electrostatic force for an orbit of the original radius r is still the required value for equilibrium. The applied field $\mathbf{B}$, which causes a change in velocity as it is turned on, also provides just the necessary additional (magnetic) force to keep the orbit in equilibrium. Thus the radius remains constant.

We next calculate the contribution to the magnetic moment of the orbit due to the *additional* angular frequency ω_L. The magnetic moment of a circular current is $p_m = iA$, where i is the current and A the area of the current loop. Since $\omega_L = 2\pi f_L$ and the additional current $i = ef_L$, where f_L is the frequency of rotation due to the magnetic field, we have

$$p_m = iA = ef_L A = \frac{e\omega_L}{2\pi} A \tag{10.46}$$

---

[1] The fifth term involves $\omega_L{}^2$, since from Eq. (10.42), $B \propto \omega_L$.

Lenz's rule gives the result that the direction of the induced dipole moment is always such as to minimize the change in flux threading the loop. This means that p_m always acts in opposition to the applied **B** change, resulting in the negative magnetic susceptibility of diamagnetism.

An example that brings out the nature of the diamagnetic effect is the case of two electrons traveling in opposite directions in the same orbit. In the absence of an external field, the magnetic effects of the orbital motion of these electrons will vanish. When a magnetic field is applied, however, the velocity of one electron is increased and that of the other is decreased by the Larmor frequency; so both orbital motions will contribute to a negatively oriented induced magnetic dipole.

We have examined only the case where the applied magnetic field is perpendicular to the orbit. Although we shall not show it here, the induced diamagnetic moment is the same for any orientation of the orbit with respect to the field. In the nonperpendicular case, however, ω_L is not parallel to ω_0. That is, the motion in the applied field is circular motion in an orbit that itself precesses in the magnetic field with a precessional frequency ω_L.

Since the diamagnetic effect involves induced magnetic moments that are independent of the orientation of atoms, thermal vibrations do not affect diamagnetic susceptibilities. A plot of diamagnetic susceptibility against temperature is thus as shown in Fig. 10.22. We are

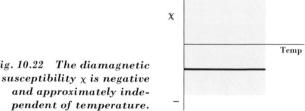

Fig. 10.22 The diamagnetic susceptibility χ is negative and approximately independent of temperature.

neglecting certain other effects, such as the changing of lattice constants with temperature, which may make the diamagnetic susceptibility vary slightly with temperature.

Since paramagnetic susceptibilities decrease with temperature,

Table 10.1   Magnetic Susceptibilities, $\chi_m = M/H$, of Various Substances†

(At approximately room temperature)

Substance	$\chi_m \times 10^{-6}$, mks units
Paramagnetic	
Aluminum	+0.82
Iron ammonium alum	+38.2
Calcium	+1.4
Chromium	+4.5
Cuprous oxide	+1.5
Ferric oxide	+26.0
Magnesium	+0.69
Manganese	+1.
O_2 liquid ($-219°C$)	+390
Platinum	+1.65
Tantalum	+1.1
Diamagnetic	
Bismuth	−1.7
Cadmium	−0.23
Copper	−0.11
Germanium	−0.15
Helium	−0.59
Gold	−0.19
Lead	−0.18
Zinc	−0.20

† Paramagnetic materials have positive susceptibilities; diamagnetic materials have negative susceptibilities. These values are given in mks units and are 4π times values quoted for cgs units. This factor results from the cgs definition of magnetization, $B = H + 4\pi M$.

while the diamagnetic term stays essentially constant, it follows that all materials become diamagnetic at high enough temperatures.

Table 10.1 gives a listing of the net susceptibility of a number of paramagnetic and diamagnetic materials. Ferromagnetic materials will be discussed in Sec. 10.11.

Some metals are diamagnetic, while others are paramagnetic. In the case of metals, the net susceptibility is made up of contributions from the ion cores and the conduction electrons. There is a diamagnetic term contributed by the conduction electrons. This has to do with a quantum-mechanical effect in the presence of a magnetic field. There is also a paramagnetic contribution from the conduction electron spins, which more than cancels the diamagnetic term. Only a small fraction of the electron spins contribute to the paramagnetism, since most of the conduction electrons are arranged in pairs with opposite spin orientation. Since the net susceptibility of a metal is made up of a number of terms, it is often difficult to predict whether a given metal will be diamagnetic or paramagnetic.

10.11* *Ferromagnetism*

We now come to the most easily observed of all magnetic effects, and indeed to the historic beginning of the study of magnetism, ferromagnetism, so called because of its occurrence in metallic iron and in a number of iron compounds. The experimental facts about ferromagnetic materials include the following: Although the magnetization is not usually proportional to **H**, as in the previously studied materials, in certain situations a susceptibility of several thousand can be measured, and very large magnetizations can be obtained. The value of the magnetization depends not only on the applied field, but also on the previous history of the sample. In some cases, for example, a sample may retain its magnetization even in the absence of an external applied field. This is the source of the permanent magnets with which we are all familiar. However, it is notable that the very same material that can show such a large permanent magnetization can also exist in a state showing little or no permanent magnetization. These phenomena alone require considerable explanation, and even so we have left out some of the more esoteric experimental facts. It is of historic interest to note that the magnetism of permanent magnets has been known for at least 2,500 years, although the connection of magnetism with moving charges was discovered less than 150 years ago by Oersted, in 1820.

We begin by showing how the very large magnetic effects of ferromagnetism can occur. The ultimate source of magnetic moments in ferromagnetic materials turns out to be (as is primarily the case in paramagnetic materials) the magnetic moments of electron spin. The big difference, however, is that in ferromagnetics there are large interactions *between* spins that cause them to align parallel with each other. Even at room temperatures the torques of interaction are so strong that thermal vibrations cannot destroy the alignment. Thus the very large maximum magnetization is of the same order as would occur in a paramagnetic material if all the dipoles were perfectly aligned along one direction. The source of the interaction between dipoles in ferromagnetics is of quantum-mechanical nature. As a result of the quantum-mechanical torque, the energy of two neighboring dipoles (of two neighboring atoms) is very much less when they are aligned parallel than for any other arrangement. They therefore are highly constrained to take a parallel orientation. Only when a ferromagnetic material is heated to a high temperature are the thermal motions sufficient to destroy this alignment, thus causing the material to change its behavior to that of a paramagnetic material.

A question that arises immediately is how a ferromagnetic material can ever exist in a nonmagnetized state, in view of the large forces tending to align the dipoles. The solution to this puzzle was suggested long before there was any direct experimental evidence on the subject. The answer given, which has indeed been shown experimentally to be correct, is that there is a strong tendency for the material to break up into many magnetic *domains* (regions in which all dipoles are aligned), each with a different direction of magnetization, so that the macroscopic effect is to give zero magnetization.

We are still faced, however, with the problem of why the material chooses to break up into domains, since at their boundaries (the *domain walls*) there will be dipoles that are not parallel. We must account for the forces that pull the dipoles at the boundaries away from the low energy parallel arrangement. This phenomenon can be accounted for if we examine the situation from the point of view of stored energy. Figure 10.23 shows schematically a number of alternative domain con-

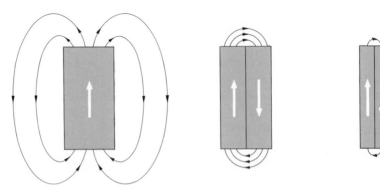

Fig. 10.23   *Effect of domains in diminishing the external field.*

figurations in a piece of material, starting with all the material in a single domain and proceeding to a larger and larger number of domains, which have been chosen in a rather idealized way, to illustrate the idea involved. The orientation of all the dipoles in each domain has been indicated by an arrow. The field outside the material is also indicated in a qualitative manner. A magnetic field outside the material involves stored energy

$$\frac{1}{2}\frac{B^2}{\mu_0} \quad \text{joules/m}^3 \tag{9.38}$$

As the number of domains is increased, the external field produced is smaller and smaller, so that the energy stored in the field is greatly decreased. This decrease must be balanced against the energy stored in making the domain walls, and the equilibrium state is that for which the total energy stored is a minimum. Calculations based on the known work required to disorient adjacent moments indicate that the stable configuration occurs with domains of dimensions of the order of 10^{-5} cm. This agrees with the measured size of domains in a number of ferromagnetics.

We are now in a position to understand the nature of the magnetization curves of ferromagnetic materials. Figure 10.24 shows a

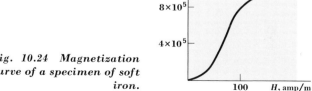

Fig. 10.24 Magnetization curve of a specimen of soft iron.

typical curve of **M** versus **H**. As the magnetizing field is applied, domain walls move so as to favor the growth of domains that happen to have their direction of magnetization more or less along the external field direction. As the field is further increased, forces are great enough to cause the gradual rotation of magnetization direction into exact alignment with the field. There are certain directions of orientation of the dipoles in a domain with respect to the crystal axes that are of lower energy than others, and these directions are taken until the external field forces overcome the internal orienting forces.

Finally, when all the dipoles are aligned, **M** has reached a constant value, or is *saturated*. It is often more convenient to plot **B** than **M**, but the difference is often rather small, except for the factor μ_0, since **B** = μ_0(**H** + **M**), and **M** is usually much greater than the magnetizing force **H**.

If the field is removed after a ferromagnetic specimen is magnetized, the material tends to return to its unmagnetized state. But the motion of domain walls is partially inhibited by crystal boundaries and other crystal imperfections. This produces a kind of friction which causes the walls to lag behind the position they would take if they moved easily within the specimen.

A typical experimental curve of **B** versus **H** is plotted in Fig. 10.25, showing the effect of past history on the magnetization of a

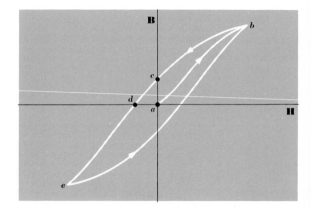

Fig. 10.25   Hysteresis loop characteristic of a ferromagnetic specimen. The specimen being studied is originally unmagnetized at (a). The applied field **H** *is increased to bring the field in the specimen to its value at (b), after which* **H** *is reduced. At (c) the applied* **H** *is back to zero. The remaining field* **B** *in the specimen at zero applied field is called the remanence. At (d) the negative applied field, called the coercive force field, has reduced the net field in the specimen to zero. A complete hysteresis loop has been traced when the specimen has been carried in a cycle through (e) and back to (b).*

ferromagnetic sample. We start with the material unmagnetized at a and apply an increasing H (via a current winding around the sample) until the point *b* is reached. When we decrease **H**, the magnetization **M** or **B** decreases, but along a different path. When **H** has been decreased to zero, we find magnetization remaining (point *c*). The value of **B** at *c* is called the *remanence*, which gives the state of permanent magnetization of the sample. Point *d* gives the *coercive force*, the reverse field necessary to demagnetize the sample. If we continue to point *e* and reverse the direction of change of **H**, we eventually can trace out a closed loop, called the *hysteresis loop*.

This behavior is the result of the difficulty of shifting the domain walls. As a result of this frictional effect the state of magnetization of a ferromagnetic specimen lags behind the applied field, and thus depends not only on the field applied but also on the past history of magnetization. It is this hysteresis, which is very great in some materials, that allows highly magnetized permanent magnets to exist, a fact of tremendous practical importance. Ferromagnetic materials with large hysteresis are called *hard*, while those having small hysteresis are called *soft*.

Knowledge of the nature of magnetic materials has been greatly increased in recent years by the use of neutrons in the investigation of permanently magnetized materials. The method depends on the fact that neutrons themselves have magnetic moments[1] and that, as a result, the passage of neutrons through matter is affected by the orientation of the atomic magnetic moments in the matter. Thus neutron diffraction experiments can give information on the relative orientation of the magnetic dipoles of neighboring atoms. Such experiments show the parallel orientation of neighboring dipoles in ferromagnetic materials and the antiparallel orientation of neighbors in *antiferromagnetic* materials. In the latter class of materials, the magnetic moments may be divided into two interpenetrating sublattices in which all moments associated with one lattice are parallel to each other but are antiparallel to the moments on the other sublattice. Such materials do not give rise to external magnetic fields, since the effects of the two sublattices cancel.

Another class of materials, called *ferrimagnetic*, consists of two sublattices, with the moments on one lattice contributing larger fields

---

[1] It may seem surprising that a neutron, which has a net electric charge of zero, has a magnetic moment. This is explained by the idea that the neutron is a compound structure made up of equal amounts of positive and negative circulating charge, whose contributions to the magnetic moment do not cancel, although their electric fields do.

than those on the other, resulting in a net ferromagnetic effect. One group of such materials is called *ferrite*, which, because it happens to be a nonconductor, is widely used as a magnetic material in high-frequency microwave work. The absence of conduction electrons prevents the serious eddy-current losses that would otherwise occur in high-frequency applications.

10.12*   *Hysteresis Losses in Magnetic Materials*

In many practical systems, as, for example, in transformer cores, ferromagnetic materials are placed in an alternating field. As a result the magnetization alternates from one direction to another, and the material is taken through a hysteresis loop once each cycle. Each time a specimen is taken through a magnetizing cycle, the magnetizing field does work on the material in moving the domain walls back and forth. This process converts energy from the field into heat. We next show that the work done in each cycle is proportional to the area of the $\mathbf{B} - \mathbf{H}$ hysteresis loop.

It has been shown earlier that in order to build up a magnetic field $\mathbf{B}_f$ within a specimen, the amount of work which must be done against Faraday induction emfs per unit volume is

$$\frac{W}{\text{vol}} = \int_0^{B_f} \mathbf{H} \cdot d\mathbf{B} \qquad \text{joules/m}^3 \tag{10.31}$$

When $\mathbf{B}$ and $\mathbf{H}$ are linearly related, we found this integral became

$$\frac{W}{\text{vol}} = \frac{1}{2} \mathbf{B}_f \mathbf{H}_f \qquad \text{joules/m}^3 \tag{10.32}$$

where $\mathbf{B}_f$ and $\mathbf{H}_f$ are the final values of the two field quantities.

Suppose, however, that the **B-H** relation were nonlinear, and dependent on specimen history, as shown in Fig. 10.26 for a typical ferromagnetic material. Then the integral in Eq. (10.31) must be obtained by using the **B-H** relation shown in the figure. Usually, this is done graphically. We now show that when there is a hysteresis curve for the magnetization, there is a loss of energy each time a specimen is taken through one cycle. The work done to take the system from (a) to (b) in Fig. 10.26 is given by Eq. (10.31), $\int \mathbf{H} \cdot d\mathbf{B}$, and is numerically equal to the area of horizontal shading in the figure. Since **H** and $d\mathbf{B}$ are both positive, this is positive work which must be supplied by the emf which produces the magnetizing current. In going

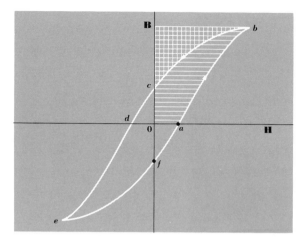

Fig. 10.26   Calculation of the work done in carrying a magnetic material through a hysteresis loop.

from (*b*) to (*c*) in the diagram, the work is negative, since **H** is positive but *d***B** is negative. The amount of negative work is given by the vertically shaded area in the figure.

Similarly, the work in carrying the system from (*c*) to (*d*) is positive, since both **H** and *d***B** are negative. The magnitude of the work is the triangular area *ocd*. Continuation of this graphical integration back to the starting position at (*a*) shows that there is a net work done per unit volume of material which is just equal to the area within the hysteresis loop traversed. This work to carry a system through a magnetization cycle goes into heat. It is obvious that for ac applications it is highly desirable to choose materials which have hysteresis loops enclosing the smallest possible area. The energy dissipation can be regarded as due to frictional losses during the process of altering the domain structure of the material.

10.13*   *Permanent Magnets*

Up to this point we have attributed the magnetization **M** to the existence of external fields that cause alignment of the elementary magnetic dipoles in matter. In the case of permanent magnets we must consider that the alignment of dipoles results from internal forces within the matter. We then inquire as to the resulting **B** and **H** fields that this self-magnetization produces, both inside and outside the matter.

As in our earlier work on other magnetic materials, we have the choice of accounting for fields outside and inside a permanent bar magnet in terms of the **M** discontinuities at the ends acting as sources of **H** or in terms of the equivalent solenoidal currents. We here take the former view.

If we are dealing with a permanent magnet in the absence of other fields, the only **H** field is that from sources and sinks at the ends of the magnet. Thus a property of **H** in permanent magnets is

$$\oint \mathbf{H} \cdot d\mathbf{l} = 0 \tag{10.9}$$

In order to relate the field inside the magnetized material to the magnetization **M** of the material, we again use the equation $\mathbf{B} = \mu_0(\mathbf{H} + \mathbf{M})$. But since $\mathbf{H}_0$, the applied field, is zero, **H** arises only from end effects from the permanent magnetization **M**, as given by the equation $\int_{cs} \mathbf{H} \cdot d\mathbf{S} = -\int_{cs} \mathbf{M} \cdot d\mathbf{S}$. In the simple case of ellipsoidal shapes, as we have seen, $H = H_0 - LM$, but since H_0 is zero, this becomes $H = -LM$ inside the sample. Thus **H** inside the sample is opposed to **M** (and to **B**), and in fact is just the demagnetizing field we considered in the last section. Only for ellipsoidal samples in which **M** is uniform will **H** be uniform. Outside the sample **H** is not uniform, but it can be calculated on the basis of effective poles, as discussed below.

For nonellipsoidal shapes, the field will not be uniform inside or outside the magnet. However, we can calculate the values of **B** and **H** by using Coulomb's law for the effective poles. Consider the case of a bar magnet as shown in Fig. 10.27, in which we assume that **M** is

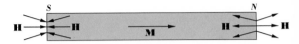

Fig. 10.27 Permanent bar magnet showing sources and sinks of lines of **H** *at ends of the magnet.*

uniform. We have shown the lines of **H** originating and ending at the discontinuities in **M** at the ends of the magnet. The strength of these poles, we have seen, is given by

$$q_m = - \int_{cs} \mathbf{M} \cdot d\mathbf{S} = MA \tag{10.25}$$

where A is the cross section of the magnet. The end of the magnet from which lines of $\mathbf{H}$ emerge is called the north pole, and the end on which lines of $\mathbf{H}$ converge is called the south pole. When we examine the field at a point far away from the end of the magnet so that the size of the end region is small compared with the distance from the region to the point in question, the pole can be taken as a point. Applying Gauss' law for $\mathbf{H}$, $\int_{cs} \mathbf{H} \cdot d\mathbf{S} = q_m$, over a gaussian sphere of radius r, gives us

$$H = \frac{1}{4\pi} \frac{q_m}{r^2} \quad \text{or} \quad B = \frac{\mu_0}{4\pi} \frac{q_m}{r^2} \tag{10.47}$$

This gives $\mathbf{B}$ anywhere outside the rod due to the pole q_m. Since there are always both a north and a south pole associated with a magnetized body, the net field at any point is the vector sum of contributions from both poles. This is exactly the same situation we had in electrostatics when we calculated the electric field from an electric dipole. Since lines of $\mathbf{H}$ emerge from a north pole, q_m is positive for a north pole and negative for a south pole. If the point at which we are examining the field is far away from the magnet relative to its length L, the equations for $\mathbf{B}$ or $\mathbf{H}$ reduce to the usual dipole equation (8.28), where the magnetic dipole is $p_m = q_m L$.

The torque on a permanent bar magnet placed in a uniform field, using the magnetic dipole equation, is

$$\tau = p_m B \sin \theta \tag{8.27}$$

Furthermore, we can obtain the expression for the force on a magnetic pole. We modify the torque equation by replacing p_m by $q_m L$, to obtain

$$\tau = q_m L B \sin \theta \tag{10.48}$$

This is exactly analogous to the case of an electric dipole in an electric field, where the force is $F = qE$. By analogy, the force on a magnetic pole must be

$$F = q_m B \tag{10.49}$$

For a north pole $(+)$, the force is parallel to $\mathbf{B}$; for a south pole $(-)$, the force is antiparallel to $\mathbf{B}$.

We have now developed the field and force equations for permanent bar magnets. We can calculate the field anywhere in space due to an assembly of permanent magnets through Eq. (10.47) and can calculate the force on each pole in a given field through Eq. (10.49). This treatment is possible only if the magnetization of the magnets is constant and not affected by external fields. For many situations this is a good approximation. In principle, all the results we have obtained by using the concept of magnetic poles could have been obtained by replacing each magnet by an equivalent solenoidal surface current.

A word must be said about the nomenclature of north and south magnetic poles and the connection between this and the magnetic field of the earth. A more correct name for the north pole of a magnet as we have defined it would be the *north-seeking* pole. The south pole of a magnet is more correctly the *south-seeking* pole. Since opposite poles attract, this means that the magnetic pole near the north of the earth is a south magnetic pole. The magnetic field of the earth is approximately described in terms of a magnetic dipole whose axis is roughly parallel to the axis of rotation of the earth. The horizontal component of the earth's field points generally in the south-north direction. The principal source of the earth's field is probably the convection currents of molten conducting matter in the central volume of the earth. This motion gives rise to an electric current within the earth and a consequent magnetic field. It is unlikely that ferromagnetic materials play a dominant role in the earth's magnetism, since it is expected that they lose their very large susceptibility and become paramagnetic at the high temperatures in the interior of the earth.

10.14*   *Examples*

a   *The field in and around a permanently magnetized rod.*   In Sec. 10.8 we found that the demagnetization factor L for this shape is about zero. Therefore, inside the rod, $H = H_0 - LM$ is approximately zero, since the externally applied field is zero. Whatever H does exist in the rod is opposed to M. Outside the rod, the field can be calculated by the use of Eq. (10.47), $B = \dfrac{\mu_0}{4\pi} \dfrac{q_m}{r^2}$, applied to both ends, where $q_m = MA$. The resulting field is shown in Fig. 10.28.

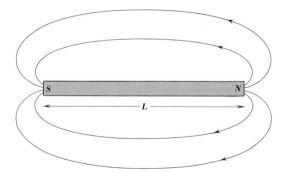

Fig. 10.28   *Bar magnet. External field can be*
described by poles of strength q_m separated
by a distance L.

b *The field in and around a thin plate permanently magnetized perpen-*
dicular to its plane.   For this magnetization, we found in Sec. 10.8 that
the demagnetization factor is 1. The equation for **B** inside the plate was

$$\mathbf{B} = \mu_0[(\mathbf{H}_0 - \mathbf{M}) + \mathbf{M}] = \mu_0\mathbf{H}_0 \qquad (10.34)$$

so in this case, where the applied field $\mathbf{H}_0 = 0$, $\mathbf{B} = 0$ inside the plate
and $\mathbf{H} = -\mathbf{M}$. Thus **H** inside the plate is opposed to **M** and equal to it
in magnitude. Outside the plate, since $B_{n1} = B_{n2}$, **B** is also zero, as is
H. We neglect the perturbing effects of the edges of the plate.

c *The field in and around a uniformly magnetized sphere.*   We found
in Sec. 10.8 that the field inside a sphere of magnetization **M** in an
external field is

$$\mathbf{B} = \mu_0(\mathbf{H}_0 + \tfrac{2}{3}\mathbf{M})$$

In the absence of an external field, then, $\mathbf{B} = \tfrac{2}{3}\mu_0\mathbf{M}$. This result
followed from the fact that the demagnetizing factor for a sphere, as
shown in Appendix F for the dielectric case, is $L = \tfrac{1}{3}$. The field inside
the sphere is then $\mathbf{H} = -\tfrac{1}{3}\mathbf{M}$. **H** is uniform and opposed to the
permanent magnetization **M**. Outside the sphere we have argued that
the shape of the field is that of a dipole. We can determine the magnitude of the dipole moment by matching boundary conditions at the
surface of the sphere at the point on the sphere along its axis of magnetization. This is the point P in Fig. 10.29. At this point, **B** is normal
to the surface; so **B** inside and just outside the surface must have the
same value (since $B_{n1} = B_{n2}$). The value of **B** inside the surface at P is

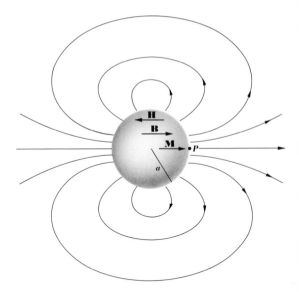

Fig. 10.29 Magnetic field in region around a uniformly magnetized sphere; M, B, and H are uniform inside the sphere. Note that H is opposite to B inside the sphere.

$\frac{2}{3}\mu_0\mathbf{M}$. Using the dipole formula outside the sphere and setting $\cos \theta = 1$, we have from Eq. (8.28)

$$B_r = \frac{\mu_0}{4\pi} \frac{2p_m}{a^3} \qquad (10.50)$$

where a is the radius of the sphere. Comparing these two expressions, we can solve for p_m to obtain

$$p_m = \tfrac{4}{3}\pi a^3 M \qquad (10.51)$$

The value of **B** anywhere outside the sphere may now be obtained by taking the vector sum of the two perpendicular components of **B**, B_r, and B_θ, obtained by substitution of this value of p_m in the dipole equations (8.28). The dipole moment of the sphere is just its magnetization times its volume.

d *Calculation of the field inside a permanently magnetized sphere by means of the effective solenoidal surface current.* We show this calculation as an illustration of the fact that the effect of magnetized bodies can be simulated by an effective solenoidal current density at the

surface of the body. We found in Sec. 10.2 that the magnetic effects of
a uniformly magnetized body can be simulated by the amperian surface
current density j^s_{mag}, where

$$j^s_{mag} = M \tag{10.4}$$

Figure 10.30 shows a few of the turns of wire wound around the sphere
in which a current i produces the field equivalent to that of the ampe-

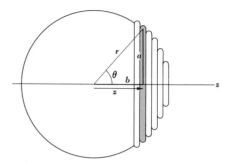

**Fig. 10.30   Uniform solenoi-
dal current winding on
surface of a sphere.**

rian surface current. The turns are wound uniformly along the z axis in
order to give a uniform solenoidal current density. We now calculate
the field due to this current, at the center of the sphere. We calculate
the contribution from one turn and then integrate over all the turns on
the sphere.

The contribution from the one turn we have chosen is given by

$$dB = \frac{\mu_0 i}{2} \frac{a^2}{(a^2 + b^2)^{3/2}} = \frac{\mu_0 i}{2} \frac{a^2}{r^3} \tag{8.8}$$

If z is the distance along the z axis from the center of the sphere to a
given turn, $z = r \cos \theta$ and $dz = -r \sin \theta \, d\theta$. If dz is the thickness of
one turn, then $i = j^s \, dz$. Also, the radius of the turn is $a = r \sin \theta$.
Substitution of these quantities into Eq. (8.8) gives

$$dB = - \frac{\mu_0 j^s}{2} \frac{r^3 \sin^3 \theta \, d\theta}{r^3}$$

or

$$B = - \frac{\mu_0 j^s}{2} \int_\pi^0 \sin^3 \theta \, d\theta = \frac{\mu_0 j}{2} \left[\frac{1}{3} \cos \theta \, (\sin^2 \theta + 2) \right]_\pi^0$$
$$= \tfrac{2}{3} \mu_0 j^s$$

Since the current density j^s is to simulate j^s_{mag}, we set it equal to M.

Then we have

$$B = \tfrac{2}{3}\mu_0 M \qquad (10.52)$$

which is the value found in the last problem, using the method of magnetic poles. This proof applies only for the point at the center of the sphere. We could show, however, that B is indeed uniform throughout the sphere.

10.15* Magnetic Circuits

The general problem of magnetic bodies in external fields is extremely difficult. We are involved in the simultaneous solution of

$$\oint \mathbf{H} \cdot d\mathbf{l} = i_{\text{free}} \qquad (10.9)$$

$$\int_{CS} \mathbf{B} \cdot d\mathbf{S} = 0 \qquad (10.5)$$

$$\mathbf{B} = \mu \mathbf{H} \qquad (10.21)$$

and the boundary conditions on $\mathbf{B}$ and $\mathbf{H}$ [Eqs. (10.28) and (10.29)]. However, there is one kind of situation involving ferromagnetic materials that is both important practically and easy to solve approximately. An example is shown in Fig. 10.31. This is an electromagnet. The prob-

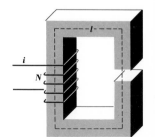

Fig. 10.31 Electromagnet, illustrating a magnetic circuit.

lem is to determine the value of $\mathbf{B}$ anywhere in the path through the magnetic circuit shown. In particular, we might wish to know the value of $\mathbf{B}$ in the air gap. We assume we know the magnetizing current i through the N turns of the coil, the cross-section area A of all sections, and the value of μ for all parts. We must further assume that the lines of $\mathbf{B}$ are parallel to and confined to the circuit of matter. This is approximately true if the material used has a large μ (as is the case for ferromagnetic materials).

We first use Eq. (10.9) and take the line integral around the circuit.

$$\oint \mathbf{H} \cdot d\mathbf{l} = H_1 l_1 + H_2 l_2 + H_3 l_3 + \cdots = Ni \tag{10.53}$$

We have here divided the line integral into sections, each taken over a length having a constant value of μ and a constant cross-section area. The $\cos \theta$ term of the scalar product goes to 1 because $\mathbf{H}$ is everywhere parallel to the path taken. Equation (10.5) tells that the lines of $\mathbf{B}$ are continuous around the circuit. Therefore the flux ϕ passing through any cross section of the circuit is the same. We can relate the value of H in any section to the flux, using Eq. (10.21) to give

$$\phi = BA = \mu H A \tag{10.54}$$

where the μ and A must be taken for that section. We thus find

$$H_1 = \frac{\phi}{\mu_1 A_1} \qquad H_2 = \frac{\phi}{\mu_2 A_2} \cdots$$

Substitution in Eq. (10.53) then gives

$$Ni = \phi \left(\frac{l_1}{\mu_1 A_1} + \frac{l_2}{\mu_2 A_2} + \cdots \right) \tag{10.55}$$

This equation can be solved for ϕ, after which $B = \phi/A$ can be found for any section required, in particular for the air gap in our example of an electromagnet (for the air gap we use $\mu = \mu_0$). We may think of Eq. (10.55) as a circuit in analogy to a series electric circuit, $V = i(R_1 + R_2 + \cdots)$. Just as current is continuous, in the magnetic case the flux ϕ is continuous. The terms $l/\mu A$ are of the same form as resistance and combine in series and parallel in the same way. They are often called the *magnetic reluctance* $\mathcal{R}$. The driving force for the magnetism is Ni, called the *magnetomotive force* (mmf). The equation can be written

$$\phi = \frac{\text{mmf}}{\mathcal{R}} \tag{10.56}$$

It is easy to see from the foregoing ideas why the magnetic field of an electromagnet can be increased by tapering the poles of the magnet. The total reluctance of the magnetic circuit is almost unchanged by tapering the poles; so the flux is almost unaltered. However, the effective cross-section area of the air gap is greatly reduced, so that $B = \phi/A$ will be much increased. If the tapering is too sharp, the lines of B are not pulled in, and improvement is only slight.

10.16 Comments on Chapter 10

This chapter, being concerned with the magnetic behavior of matter, takes us rather far afield from the basic theory of electromagnetism. Such an excursion is justified by the fact that we are often, in physics, involved with magnetism because of its effects on matter. We have undertaken to develop in some detail the concepts and terminology used for describing magnetism in matter. These ideas are particularly important as background for many aspects of the rapidly growing fields of solid-state physics.

The first step in developing a description of magnetic properties is to see that all magnetic effects of matter may be explained on the basis of magnetic dipoles induced or oriented by external fields. We except ferromagnetic materials, which may have a net magnetization in the absence of an external applied field. The true source of magnetic dipoles in matter is the effective motion of charge, producing current loops, with their consequent magnetic fields. These currents dissipate no energy and consist of effective current loops within nuclei and within electrons (nuclear and electron spin effects) and of circulating currents within atoms and molecules.

The extent of the response of matter to magnetic fields is described by the magnetic moment per unit volume, $\mathbf{M}$, the magnetization.

We next make the crucial argument that shows that the effects of magnetization can be simulated by a solenoidal current density j^s_{mag}. This current, called the amperian surface current, is the resultant of the circulating currents referred to above. It characterizes the magnetic behavior of a magnetized specimen, and is simply related to the magnetization $\mathbf{M}$ of a specimen by the relation

$$j^s_{\mathrm{mag}} = M \tag{10.4}$$

On the basis of this equivalence of magnetization and a solenoidal current, the important argument can be made that not only in a vacuum, but also in the presence of matter, it is always true that

$$\int_{cs} \mathbf{B} \cdot d\mathbf{S} = 0 \quad \text{or} \quad \operatorname{div} \mathbf{B} = 0 \tag{10.5}$$

In other words, lines of $\mathbf{B}$ are always continuous and have no sources.

In the case of a toroidal specimen uniformly magnetized, with the magnetization vector everywhere parallel to the surface of the specimen, the contribution of the specimen to the field is limited to the inside of the specimen, and the region outside is unaffected. This property makes the toroidal shape a convenient one for the initial discussion of magnetization.

In order to handle problems involving more complicated specimen shapes, a new kind of magnetic vector field is defined. This new field quantity, called **H**, is so defined that it has two special properties. The first is that its line integral around a closed path, the circulation, is dependent only on the real currents, i_{free}, threading the path, or

$$\oint \mathbf{H} \cdot d\mathbf{l} = i_{\text{free}} \qquad \text{amp} \tag{10.9}$$

or in microscopic form,

$$\text{curl } \mathbf{H} = \mathbf{j}_{\text{free}} \qquad \text{amp/m}^2 \tag{10.10}$$

The equivalent expression for **B** depends on both real and fictitious currents.

$$\oint \mathbf{B} \cdot d\mathbf{l} = \mu_0(i_{\text{free}} + i_{\text{mag}}) \tag{10.6}$$

The second property of **H** is that there are effective sources of lines of **H** wherever there is a discontinuity in **M** at a boundary, where **M** is not parallel to the boundary. This situation arises at the ends of magnetized specimens. The effective sources of **H** behave mathematically just like charges which are sources of **E** lines. This idea is expressed formally by the relation

$$\int_{CS} \mathbf{H} \cdot d\mathbf{S} = - \int_{CS} \mathbf{M} \cdot d\mathbf{S} \tag{10.22}$$

The microscopic form of this source equation is

$$\text{div } \mathbf{H} = - \text{ div } \mathbf{M} \tag{10.22a}$$

Since the effective sources of **H** at boundaries behave just as charges do in the electric case, we can define an effective magnetic charge, or pole, q_m, according to the relation

$$- \int_{CS} \mathbf{M} \cdot d\mathbf{S} = q_m \tag{10.25}$$

These effective sources of **H** do not alter Eq. (10.9) for the circulation of **H**, since that part of **H** which arises from effective boundary sources has zero circulation; that is,

$$\oint \mathbf{H} \cdot d\mathbf{l} = 0$$

In general, the connection between **B**, **M**, and **H** is defined by the relation

$$\mathbf{B} = \mu_0(\mathbf{H} + \mathbf{M}) \tag{10.8}$$

where **H** is caused by real currents and also by the effective sources at the boundaries of magnetized matter. The field external to the specimen is modified only by the presence of the boundary sources.

For linear materials, in which the state of magnetization is proportional to the external field, the ease with which the material is magnetized is described by its magnetic susceptibility, χ_m, defined as

$$\chi_m = \frac{\mathbf{M}}{\mathbf{H}} \tag{10.18}$$

Another equivalent parameter is the magnetic permeability μ, defined by

$$\mu = \mu_0(1 + \chi_m) \tag{10.20}$$

With this definition we found

$$\mathbf{B} = \mu\mathbf{H} \tag{10.21}$$

in matter, in contrast to $\mathbf{B} = \mu_0\mathbf{H}$ in free space. The relative permeability is the ratio μ/μ_0.

These parameters are often used in describing ferromagnetic materials approximately, even though the quantities are not constant.

The stated properties of **B** and **H**, $\int_{cs} \mathbf{B} \cdot d\mathbf{S} = 0$ and $\oint \mathbf{H} \cdot d\mathbf{l} = i_{\text{free}}$, allow us to determine general conditions which must apply at all boundaries between materials of different susceptibilities or between a magnetic specimen and free space. The normal component of B is the same on the two sides of any boundary:

$$B_{n1} = B_{n2} \tag{10.28}$$

and the tangential components of H behave similarly:

$$H_{t1} = H_{t2} \tag{10.29}$$

These results are essential for solving boundary-value problems involving the magnetic field.

The work required to build up a magnetic field in the presence of matter was shown to be

$$\frac{W}{\text{vol}} = \int_0^B \mathbf{H} \cdot d\mathbf{B} \tag{10.31}$$

In a material with fixed susceptibility μ, this results in a stored energy

$$\frac{U}{\text{vol}} = \tfrac{1}{2}\mu H^2 = \frac{\tfrac{1}{2}B^2}{\mu} = \tfrac{1}{2}BH \tag{10.32}$$

The sources of magnetism in matter were discussed, including the important case of ferromagnetism. Permanent ferromagnetic magnets, in which atomic magnetic dipoles can be held in an oriented state in the absence of an external applied field, are of great practical importance.

In situations where the magnetic flux of an electromagnet is approximately confined to a definite region as a result of the shape of its ferromagnetic core, it is possible to derive a simple relationship between the driving current in the coil which activates the magnet and the magnetic flux in the magnet. This gives the equation of the "magnetic circuit,"

$$\phi = \frac{\text{mmf}}{\Re} \tag{10.56}$$

where mmf is the magnetomotive force, which amounts to the total ampere-turns activating the magnet, and $\Re$ is the reluctance, where

$$\Re = \sum_i \frac{l_i}{\mu_i A_i}$$

This quantity refers to the flux path, where l_i and A_i are the length and area of path sectors in which the major part of the magnetic flux is concentrated. μ is the magnetic susceptibility of the material in each sector of the flux path.

PROBLEMS

The following problems review the important magnetic parameters which describe magnetic material.

*10.1A   A toroidal sample of magnetic material of susceptibility $\chi_m = 2 \times 10^{-2}$ is wound with 1,000 turns of wire carrying a current of 2 amp. The toroid is 15 cm long.

   a   Find the solenoidal current density j^s_{free}.

   b   Determine the magnetic field intensity H produced by the current.

   c   Calculate μ, the magnetic permeability of the material.

   d   Calculate the induced magnetization M in the material.

   e   Calculate the magnetic field B resulting from the current and the magnetization of the material.

10.1B   An iron ring of radius 5 cm has a cross section of 2 cm². Its permeability is 1,000 μ_0 (assumed constant). It is wound with 1,500 turns carrying 5 amp. Calculate

a The self-inductance of the coil
b The magnetic field intensity
c The solenoidal current density of the coil
d The magnetization of the iron
e The induced amperian surface current density
f The stored magnetic field energy

★10.1C Metallic iron contains approximately 10^{29} atoms per cubic meter. The magnetic moment of each iron atom is 1.8×10^{-23} amp-m². If there were no internal ferromagnetic forces tending to align the dipoles (that is, if iron were paramagnetic), what would be the susceptibility of iron at 300°K? What would be the dipole moment of an iron bar (if it were paramagnetic) of dimensions 10 cm long and 1 cm² cross section in a field of 1,000 gauss (0.1 weber/m²)? If all the dipoles were aligned in one domain as a result of ferromagnetic interactions, what would be the magnetization M in the bar? What would be the magnetic moment of the bar? What would be the torque on this ferromagnetic bar in a field of 100 gauss perpendicular to the axis of the bar? What would be the magnetic pole strength of the ferromagnetic bar?

Uniformly magnetized ferromagnetic rods, as in the next two problems, can be described either by their pole strength or by their magnetic moments.

10.2A Two uniformly magnetized rods have length L and cross-section areas A. They have a magnetization M amp/m. Find their pole strengths q_m. One magnet is suspended above the other by the repulsion of like poles. The mass of each magnet is m kg. Find the equation whose solution will give equilibrium spacing x between the rods.

★10.2B Two similar permanent magnets A and B, having magnetic moments p_m, are arranged as shown in Fig. P10.1. They are separated by a dis-

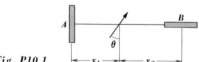

Fig. P10.1

tance large compared with their lengths. A compass needle is placed a distance x_1 from one magnet and x_2 from the other. The compass needle takes up a position θ, as shown in the figure. Find the ratio x_1/x_2.

The principle of virtual displacement can be used to determine the force on a paramagnetic rod in a nonuniform field.

10.3A A rod of paramagnetic material of uniform cross section A is placed in a nonuniform magnetic field between the poles of a magnet, as shown in Fig. P10.2. Calculate the vertical force on the rod as a result

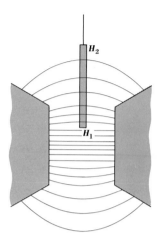

Fig. P10.2

of the nonuniform field. Proceed by calculating the effect on the stored magnetic energy of a small displacement dx of the rod in the direction of its axis. To simplify the problem, consider that, instead of moving the entire rod, a thin slice of thickness dx is removed from the bottom of the rod and added to the top. If the field at the bottom of the rod is H_1 and at the top is H_2, show that the *change* of magnetic energy is given by (Sec. 10.7)

$$dW = \tfrac{1}{2}A(\mu - \mu_0)(H_1{}^2 - H_2{}^2)\,dx$$

Using this result, show that the force on the rod is

$$F = \tfrac{1}{2}A\mu_0\chi(H_1{}^2 - H_2{}^2) \qquad \text{newtons}$$

This is a method often used for measuring the static susceptibility of paramagnetic substances. Note that the force is in the opposite direction if the material is diamagnetic.

Power losses caused by hysteresis in a ferromagnetic specimen are determined by the hysteresis-loop area.

*10.4A An inductance is formed of 100 turns of wire wrapped around a closed iron loop 20 cm in length and of 1×1 cm cross section, as shown in Fig. P10.3. A 60-cps alternating current is passed through the coil. The iron goes through the hysteresis loop once each cycle. Find the approximate power loss due to hysteresis. Use the expression for $\oint \mathbf{H} \cdot d\mathbf{l}$ to

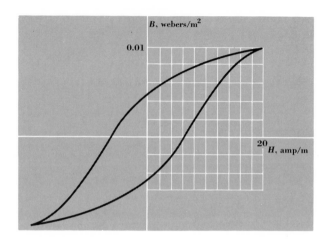

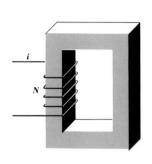

Fig. P10.3

obtain the peak current in the coil from information given on the hysteresis plot. What is the self-inductance of the inductor under the conditions of the problem? If twice the current were passed through the coil, how would this affect the inductance (qualitative)?

The magnetic circuit equation gives approximate solutions to problems involving the flux generated by a magnetizing coil in an electromagnet.

10.5A The electromagnet shown in Fig. P10.4 is made of iron with a magnetic permeability $\mu = 800\ \mu_0$. The cross section of the iron is 10 ×

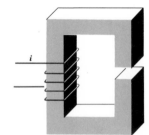

Fig. P10.4

10 cm, and the length of the path around the iron and across the 2-cm gap is 200 cm. How many ampere-turns will be required in the windings to give a 5,000-gauss (0.5 weber/m²) field in the gap, assuming no bulging of magnetic field lines out of the gap? What is B inside the iron? What is H in the gap? What is H in the iron? What is the magnetization M in the iron?

*10.5B   A variable inductance is made by winding a coil on an iron core 30 cm long, which has an adjustable air gap. With no air gap, the self-inductance is 2 henrys. For what air gap is the inductance reduced to 1 henry? The permeability of the iron is 1,000 μ_0.

The following problem shows a possible way of observing the magnetic properties of matter.

10.6A   Four fixed coils are connected in pairs as shown in Fig. P10.5. An ac current through the primary coils gives no signal at the CRO because

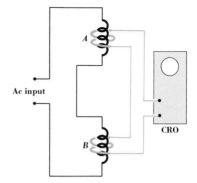

Fig. P10.5

the two secondary coils are oppositely connected. Thus the emfs induced in them just cancel. What happens when a rod of paramagnetic material is inserted in pair A? Could this effect be distinguished from that of a rod of diamagnetic material? Why is it advantageous to use two sets of coils rather than one?

11

alternating-current circuits

11.1 Introduction

We turn next to a consideration of ac circuits. This involves no new electric or magnetic principles, but depends on the characteristics of the three passive circuit elements R, C, and L, which have already been investigated. The ac circuit is of major importance in applied electricity, though here we limit the discussion to elementary circuits and the study of some simple methods for their analysis. Our objective is to be able to describe currents and voltages in a circuit such as shown in Fig. 11.1 when it is connected to a sinusoidal source of voltage. We develop the ideas of phase and amplitude of sinusoidal functions, which are used to describe the behavior of the circuit and its individual compo-

Fig. 11.1 Series ac circuit.
The three elements shown,
resistance, inductance,
and capacitance, are linear
in their response; that is,
the ac current through
each one is proportional
to the ac voltage across it.

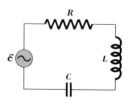

nents. The analysis of ac circuits involves the setting up and solving of certain differential equations. In order to gain insight into the behavior of such circuits, we examine the problem from several points of view.

In addition to developing the ideas necessary for discussing current-voltage relationships in ac circuits, we examine the transient behavior of circuits and the dissipation of power in ac circuits. We also list a few instruments used for measuring ac current, voltage, and power. We conclude this chapter with short discussions of the transformer, generators of electric power, and motors for converting electric energy into mechanical energy.

11.2 Sinusoidal Time Variation

Many systems that vary periodically with time are describable by a *sinusoidal* time variation. Thus the vibrations of springs, strings, sound in organ pipes, and small-amplitude oscillations of a pendulum can all be described accurately or approximately as simple harmonic oscillations with sinusoidal variations of displacement with time. The choice of whether the description is by means of sines or of cosines is unimportant, since changing the zero-time position transforms the one to the other. Electric circuits as well as mechanical systems tend to develop sinusoidally varying currents and voltages, or have particularly simple responses to sinusoidal signals. A case in point is the sinusoidal emf induced in a coil rotating uniformly in a uniform field. Another example is that of Fig. 11.2. If the capacitor C is charged and the switch is then

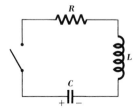

Fig. 11.2 Series LCR circuit. If the switch is closed after the capacitor has been charged, current in the circuit will oscillate sinusoidally if $R \ll \sqrt{4L/C}$. For larger values of R the sinusoidal amplitude will decrease exponentially with time. If $R > \sqrt{4L/C}$, sinusoidal oscillations do not occur, and the current in the circuit decreases exponentially with time. The detailed behavior of this circuit is analyzed in Appendix I.

closed, the current in the circuit, and the voltage across each element, oscillate sinusoidally. The charge oscillates back and forth much as a pendulum swings back and forth. If the resistance R is much smaller than $\sqrt{4L/C}$, the amplitude of the oscillations decreases only very slowly with time, so that the oscillations are accurately sinusoidal. With larger resistance values the signal attenuates with time, so that the oscillations are not strictly sinusoidal, but are described by a sinusoidal oscillation multiplied by a term giving an exponential amplitude decrease with time. If $R > \sqrt{4L/C}$ the sinusoidal oscillations no longer occur, and the current decays exponentially with time. We discuss the details of this case in Appendix I.

Figure 11.3 shows a sinusoidal voltage with negligible attenuation with time. The *amplitude* of the signal is h. If time is arbitrarily chosen

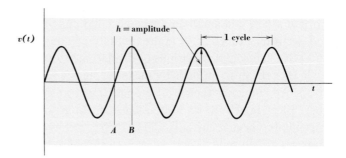

Fig. 11.3 *A sinusoidal voltage, with amplitude* h*. If A is chosen as zero time,* $v(t) = h \sin \omega t$*. If B is chosen as zero time,* $v(t) = h \cos \omega t$*.*

as zero at a point like A in the diagram, the instantaneous voltage $v(t)$ at any time t is given by

$$v(t) = h \sin \omega t = h \sin (2\pi f)t \tag{11.1a}$$

where ω is the *angular frequency*, or f is the *frequency*, of the oscillations.

If a point on the time axis, like B, is chosen for zero time, then the appropriate description is

$$v(t) = h \cos \omega t = h \cos (2\pi f)t \tag{11.1b}$$

Another reason for the importance of sinusoidal time variations is that, for *any* sort of periodic phenomena, the most useful analysis is in terms of a *series* of sine and cosine terms. In Fig. 11.4 are shown three

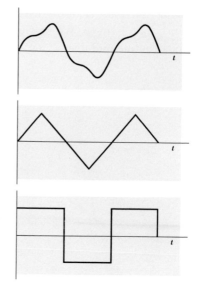

*Fig. 11.4   More complicated
periodic functions. Each
of these can be represented
by the sum of sine and cosine functions.*

examples of more complicated periodic variations. Electronic circuits
can be devised to provide voltages which vary in these ways. According
to the basic mathematics of *Fourier analysis*, all such periodic functions
can be synthesized by adding together the displacements of a series of
sine and cosine functions of appropriate amplitudes and frequencies.
In addition, what happens to any such nonsinusoidal electric signal,
passed through a device such as an amplifier, can best be understood by
asking how each of the sinusoidal signals into which the signal can be
decomposed will behave. Thus, if we have an understanding of the
response of electronic circuits to sinusoidal signals, we can predict the
circuit's behavior toward more complicated signals.

Our immediate goal is to learn how to describe and understand the
response of circuits like Fig. 11.1 when a sinusoidal emf, such as from a
rotating coil, is the source of voltage. But because of the extreme
importance of the sinusoidal functions, we develop the necessary ideas
along several parallel lines. We first develop a graphical treatment
which leads to a convenient vectorial representation, and also show
how the powerful methods of complex numbers minimize the com-
putational problems.

11.3   The Nature of Sinusoidal Functions
Before discussing the behavior of circuit elements under sinusoidal
excitation, we review briefly some important characteristics of sinus-

oidal functions. The discussion is confined to sinusoidal functions of time, like $A \sin \omega t$. We first present a very simple graphical method of constructing and displaying such functions, as in Fig. 11.5. This shows

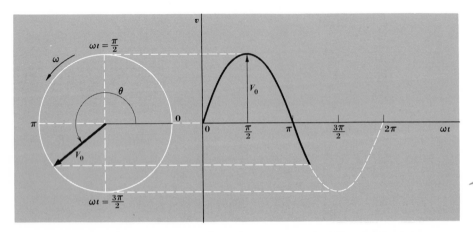

Fig. 11.5 *Projection of rotating generating vector* $\mathbf{V}_0$ *plotted against time gives a sinusoidal function.* $\mathbf{V}_0$ *is the amplitude,* θ *is the phase angle, and* $\omega = d\theta/dt$ *is the angular frequency in radians per second.* $\omega = 2\pi f$, *where* f *is the frequency in cycles per second, or the rate of rotation of the generating vector in revolutions per second.*

how the projection of a component (here the y component) of a uniformly rotating generating vector $\mathbf{V}_0$, when plotted against time, generates a sinusoidal function. In this example, starting at $t = 0$, with the vector in a position giving a zero component in the y direction and rotating the vector in a counterclockwise direction, a sine function is generated. The *amplitude* V_0 of the function is just the length of the rotating vector. The *phase* of the signal at any instant is given by the angular position of the generating vector with respect to its initial position. The *angular frequency* ω is the rate of rotation of the vector in radians per second. The *frequency* is the rotational rate in revolutions per second, or cycles per second.

In electric circuits we are often interested in the result of adding two sinusoidal quantities which have different amplitudes and phases, but which have the same frequency. Such addition is easy to do formally, using the properties of sines and cosines. But it is revealing to make such additions using the rotating generating vectors. We show an example in Fig. 11.6, in which two sine functions of amplitudes A

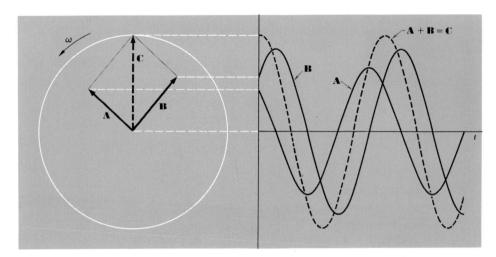

Fig. 11.6   Two sinusoidal waves are generated by the rotating amplitude vectors A and B. Their sum may be obtained by point-to-point addition or by finding the new generating vector C, which is the vector sum of A and B. The sum could be obtained analytically. The sum of sinusoidal waves of the same frequency is always another sinusoidal wave.

and B, of the same frequency and with a phase difference θ, are to be added, as shown in the time plot. If the displacements add at each instant of time, the sum of the two signals is readily seen to be obtained by constructing a new generating vector C by adding A and B vectorially. This graphical argument shows at once that the sum of any two sinusoidal signals having the same frequency is another sinusoidal signal of the same frequency, having a definite phase relation to the phases of the two original signals.

The importance of this result is that it illustrates and develops the reasons why, in dealing with sinusoidal functions of time, each function can be treated as a simple vector. Thus addition and subtraction of sinusoidal signals are easily expressed in terms of simple vector diagrams. Once the resultant vector is obtained, the sinusoidal signal it represents can be generated by rotating the vector at an angular frequency ω. This graphical method of treating problems of combinations of sines and cosines depends on the properties of the functions concerned, but results are much easier to visualize graphically than by means of formal analysis.

A still more concise way of handling these rotating vectors is to use the method of complex variables. We give a brief review of the needed elementary properties of complex numbers in Appendix H, and carry along the complex treatment in parallel with the simple vector treatment.

A final property of sinusoidal functions which accounts in large part for the simplicity of ac circuit analysis is that derivatives and integrals of sinusoidal functions are also sinusoidal, having the same frequency as the original function. It will become apparent in the next section how important this simple property is.

11.4 AC Voltage Applied to Resistors, Inductors, and Capacitors

We now use these ideas about sinusoidal functions to develop the relationships between the ac current through the individual elements R, L, and C and the ac voltages across them. It will then be possible to combine the results in order to understand the behavior of circuits like that of Fig. 11.1, which combines two or more circuit elements.

Resistors.   Figure 11.7 shows a resistor connected to a source of sinusoidal voltage, with ac meters for measuring current and voltage. We

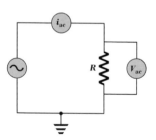

Fig. 11.7   Resistor connected to an ac source. Current and voltage meters are shown. It is assumed that the current meter has zero resistance and that the voltmeter passes no current.

assume that the meters are ideal, that is, that the current meter has negligible resistance and that the voltmeter passes negligible current. We also assume that the meters can tell the instantaneous phases of current and voltage.

In order to determine what happens in this simple case we turn back to the circuit equations developed in Chap 6. The current conservation equation, $\Sigma i = 0$, is easy to apply in this circuit. It simply means that at all points in the circuit the same current flows.

We could indicate that the current is a time-varying quantity by writing the equation

$$\Sigma i(t) = 0 \tag{6.23}$$

Similarly, the second circuit equation can be written

$$\Sigma \mathcal{E}(t) = \Sigma i(t)R \tag{6.24}$$

Since R is a constant, the time variation of i must be proportional at every instant to the time variation of the source $\mathcal{E}$. Thus, if $\mathcal{E}(t)$ is written

$$\mathcal{E}(t) = V_0 \cos \omega t$$

where V_0 is the sinusoidal voltage amplitude of the generator, we find

$$i(t)R = V_0 \cos \omega t$$

or

$$i(t) = \frac{V_0}{R} \cos \omega t$$

The only way this equation can be satisfied is to set

$$i(t) = I_0 \cos \omega t$$

where I_0 is the sinusoidal amplitude of the current. This gives

$$I_0 \cos \omega t = \frac{V_0}{R} \cos \omega t \tag{11.2}$$

From this result it follows that the amplitude of the ac current is given by

$$I_0 = \frac{V_0}{R} \tag{11.3}$$

The result is just Ohm's law which for resistances works equally well for both ac and steady voltages. The nomenclature for R can be generalized for alternating current by calling it the ac *resistive impedance*.

In terms of the vector model, $\mathbf{V}_0$ is the generating vector for the voltage and $\mathbf{I}_0$ is the generating vector for the current, whose amplitude is given by V_0/R. $\mathbf{I}_0$ is in phase with $\mathbf{V}_0$; so the result can be symbolized by Fig. 11.8. The vectors have been placed on a circulating background to make clear that the actual values of v and i across and through the resistor, respectively, are obtained by rotating the vectors with an angular velocity ω and taking the projections of these vectors, as was done in Fig. 11.5.

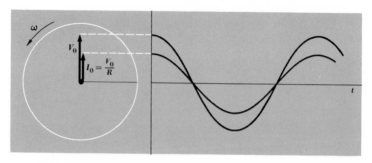

Fig. 11.8 *Generating* **I** *and* **V** *vectors shown for a pure resistance. The vectors are plotted in the same phase on a rotating
diagram. Their projections plotted against a time base give
rise to a sinusoidal current and voltage as shown.*

Inductance.   Figure 11.9 shows a simple inductance connected to a
source of sinusoidal emf. We assume that the coil gives a pure inductive
effect, that is, that there are negligible resistive or capacitative effects

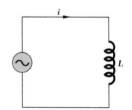

**Fig. 11.9   *A pure inductance
connected to an ac source.
Meters have been omitted
for simplicity.***

from the coil. (Later, in treating real circuits, we include stray resistance terms along with the resistance of the whole circuit.) According to
the circuit equation,

$$\mathcal{E} + \mathcal{E}_L = 0$$

where $\mathcal{E}_L$ is the self-induced Faraday emf in the coil. It was found in
Chap. 9 that this induced emf is given by

$$\mathcal{E}_L(t) = -L\frac{di}{dt} \qquad \text{volts} \tag{9.32}$$

where L is the self-inductance of the inductor. The negative sign here
means that the effect of $\mathcal{E}_L$ in the circuit is to decrease the magnitude of
di/dt.

Combining the last two equations and substituting

$$\mathcal{E} = v(t) = V_0 \cos \omega t \tag{11.4}$$

gives

$$\frac{di}{dt} = \frac{V_0}{L} \cos \omega t \tag{11.5}$$

This says that the equation for $i(t)$, the current as a function of time, must be such that its *slope*, di/dt, is a sinusoidally varying quantity, with the same phase as the generating voltage and an amplitude given by V_0/L. An expression must be found which has a time derivative of this kind. This can be done by integrating the cosine,

$$i(t) = \frac{V_0}{\omega L} \int \cos \omega t \, \omega \, dt = \frac{V_0}{\omega L} \sin \omega t = I_0 \sin \omega t \tag{11.6}$$

where I_0 is the amplitude of the sinusoidal current. We show in Fig. 11.10 the plot of $v(t)$ and $i(t)$ as given in Eqs. (11.4) and (11.6). The

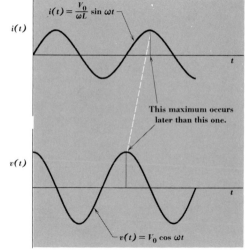

Fig. 11.10   Voltage and current across a pure inductance. The slope di/dt is in phase with V_0. This puts the phase of the current $\pi/2$ rad, or 90°, behind the voltage. (The maximum i comes at a later time than the maximum v.)

current curve has a slope di/dt, which matches the phase of v in the lower curve. This simple relation between a sinusoidal curve and its derivative has given a remarkably simple result: The current through a pure inductance which is connected to a sinusoidal voltage is also sinusoidal, and of the same frequency, but is $\pi/2$, or 90°, behind the voltage in phase. In addition, the amplitude of the current, being given by

$$I_0 = \frac{V_0}{\omega L} \tag{11.7}$$

depends not only on L but also on the frequency. The higher the ac frequency, the smaller the ac current.

The 90° phase lag of the current becomes obvious if we use the well-known trigonometric transformation

$$i(t) = \frac{V_0}{\omega L}\sin\omega t = \frac{V_0}{\omega L}\cos\left(\omega t - \frac{\pi}{2}\right) \qquad (11.8)$$

Equation (11.7) shows that ωL plays the same role as does R in the resistive case, Eq. (11.3). ωL is called the *inductive reactance* X_L.

We conclude the discussion of the inductance in ac circuits by drawing the vector diagram consistent with the foregoing analysis, as in Fig. 11.11. This drawing shows the 90° phase lag of the current.

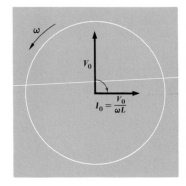

Fig. 11.11   Relative phase of I_0 and V_0 across a pure inductance. The current lags the voltage by 90°, or $\pi/2$ rad. Rotation of this diagram generates the $i(t)$ and $v(t)$ curves of Fig. 11.10.

Capacitance.   The instantaneous voltage v across the capacitor shown in Fig. 11.12 is

$$v(t) = \frac{q(t)}{C} \qquad (4.8)$$

Fig. 11.12   Circuit consisting of a capacitor connected to an ac source. The voltage at A due to the source of emf must always equal the voltage at B resulting from the charge on the capacitor plates. The bottom part of the circuit is grounded to indicate that voltages are measured relative to the lower conductor.

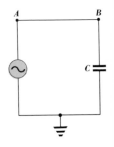

The circuit equation for this case has to be modified to accommodate the voltage across the capacitor, caused by the charge q on it at any instant. Choosing zero time when the voltage at A caused by the generator is positive and, say, increasing, the charge on the capacitor, starting from an instant when its charge was zero, is

$$q(t) = \int_0^t i \, dt \tag{11.9}$$

The situation at time t is described by the circuit equation, written

$$\mathcal{E}(t) = v(t) = \frac{q(t)}{C} \tag{11.10}$$

that is, the potential at A due to the source $\mathcal{E}$ always equals the potential at B caused by the instantaneous charge on the capacitor plates. Using, again, $\mathcal{E} = v(t) = V_0 \cos \omega t$, we find

$$V_0 \cos \omega t = \frac{1}{C} q(t) \tag{11.11}$$

In order to express this result in terms of $i(t)$, since $i = dq/dt$, we differentiate Eq. (11.11) to find

$$-\omega C V_0 \sin \omega t \, dt = dq$$

or

$$-\omega C V_0 \sin \omega t = \frac{dq}{dt} = i(t) \tag{11.12}$$

We can now write the current as $I_0 \sin \omega t$.

$$I_0 \sin \omega t = -\omega C V_0 \sin \omega t$$

Figure 11.13 is a plot of the source potential, $v(t)$, and the resulting current through the capacitor, $i(t)$, showing that the current *leads* the sinusoidal voltage by 90°. The current amplitude I_0 is given by

$$I_0 = \omega C V_0 \tag{11.13}$$

Comparison with Eq. (11.3) shows that the term $1/\omega C$ plays the role of R in the resistance case. $1/\omega C$ is called the *capacitative reactance* X_C.

Figure 11.14 shows the vector diagram for a capacitor, with the phase of the current leading the applied voltage by 90°.

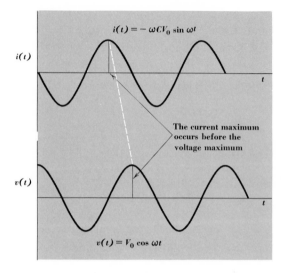

Fig. 11.13 *Voltage and current across a capacitor. The current vector* I_0 *leads the voltage vector* V_0 *by 90°.*

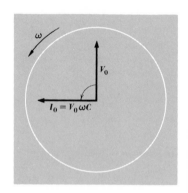

Fig. 11.14 *Relative phase of* I_0 *and* V_0 *across a capacitor. The current leads the voltage by 90°. Rotation of this diagram generates the* $i(t)$ *and* $v(t)$ *curves of Fig. 11.13.*

11.5* Use of Complex Numbers

Before turning to practical circuits involving more than one kind of circuit element, we discuss the current-voltage relations in R, L, and C elements by the method of complex numbers. The application of complex numbers is so natural in this application that even in this initial discussion of ac circuit elements it greatly simplifies the analysis. In Appendix H it is shown that numbers in the complex plane can be characterized by the vector sum of two directed numbers, as shown in Fig. 11.15, one the *real* number A and the other the *imaginary* num-

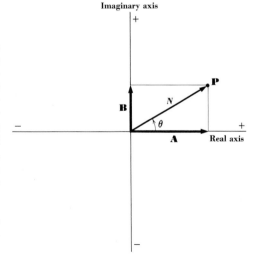

*Fig. 11.15   A point **P** in the complex plane represents a complex number. It describes a vector which is the sum of the real vector A and the imaginary vector B. An imaginary number is a real number multiplied by $j \equiv \sqrt{-1}$. **P** can also be described by the complex number*

$$\mathbf{P} = Ne^{j\theta} = N(\cos\theta + j\sin\theta)$$

where N and θ give the magnitude and direction of the vector.

ber jB. Imaginary numbers are real numbers multiplied by $j \equiv \sqrt{-1}$. The complex number **P** can be written

$$\mathbf{P} = A + jB \tag{11.14}$$

Another way to characterize the complex number **P** is to write it

$$\mathbf{P} = Ne^{j\theta} \tag{11.15}$$

where N is a real number, called the *modulus*, and θ is an angle, in radians. Together, N and θ describe the magnitude and direction of a vector in the complex plane, as shown in Fig. 11.15. e is the base of natural logarithms. This result depends on the identity shown in Appendix H:

$$e^{j\theta} = \cos\theta + j\sin\theta \tag{11.16}$$

The particular advantage of complex numbers in ac circuits is that they provide a two-dimensional framework which is particularly appropriate for describing the ac generating vectors. In particular, if we let the angle θ be a function of time, using $\theta = \omega t$, Eq. (11.16) becomes

$$e^{j\omega t} = \cos\omega t + j\sin\omega t \tag{11.17}$$

$e^{j\omega t}$ now represents a unit vector rotating with constant angular velocity ω, and is thus suited for representing any rotating vector in an ac circuit. The two terms $\cos\omega t$ and $j\sin\omega t$ give the real and imaginary components of the rotating vector. Either one can be used to represent a sinusoidal function of time. The following discussion now parallels that in the preceding section.

Resistor. We replace the sinusoidal voltage $\mathcal{E}(t) = V_0 \cos \omega t$ by the expression

$$\mathcal{E}(t) = V_0 e^{j\omega t} \tag{11.18}$$

This gives a vector amplitude V_0 rotating at an angular frequency ω, according to Eq. (11.17), from which we can get either the cosine or sine function of time variation of voltage. The circuit equation now gives

$$i(t)R = V_0 e^{j\omega t}[= V_0(\cos \omega t + j \sin \omega t)]$$

So

$$i(t) = \frac{V_0}{R} e^{j\omega t} \left[= \frac{V_0}{R} (\cos \omega t + j \sin \omega t) \right] \tag{11.19}$$

As before, we find the current to be in phase with the driving voltage, regardless of whether we carry through the real or imaginary components. The ac resistive impedance of the resistor is the real number R.

Inductor. We take over from Eq. (11.5) by writing the generator voltage in complex notation, giving

$$\frac{di}{dt} = \frac{V_0}{L} e^{j\omega t} \tag{11.20}$$

This may be written in integrable form:

$$di = \frac{V_0}{j\omega L} e^{j\omega t} j\omega \, dt$$

which immediately integrates to

$$i(t) = \frac{V_0}{j\omega L} e^{j\omega t} \tag{11.21}$$

One of the charms of the exponential form is the ease with which it can be integrated or differentiated. By comparison with the resistive case, we see that the complex form of the inductive reactance is

$$X_L = j\omega L \tag{11.22}$$

If the term $V_0/j\omega L$ were real, the current would have the same phase as the voltage across the inductor. Since this term is a real number,

$V_0/\omega L$, multiplied by

$$\frac{1}{j} = \frac{j}{jj} = \frac{j}{-1} = -j \tag{11.23}$$

it is a pure imaginary number. As shown in Fig. 11.16, multiplying a real number $V_0/\omega L$ by $-j$ has the effect of rotating the vector $-90°$

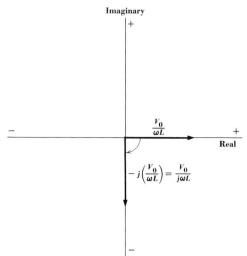

Fig. 11.16   The real number $V_0/\omega L$, when multiplied by $-j$ or by $1/j$, is rotated $-90°$. This gives the $90°$ lag of the current behind the voltage in a pure inductance.

into the pure imaginary axis. In other words, the current lags the voltage by $90°$. Thus, in complex notation, phase information is automatically contained in the expression for the reactance vector.

Capacitor.   Starting with Eq. (11.10), the circuit equation for a capacitor connected to an ac voltage source, we write

$$q(t) = CV_0 e^{j\omega t} \tag{11.24}$$

Differentiation with respect to time gives

$$i(t) = \frac{dq}{dt} = j\omega C V_0 e^{j\omega t} \tag{11.25}$$

Thus $1/j\omega C$ is the complex form of the capacitative reactance,

$$X_C = \frac{1}{j\omega C} = -\frac{j}{\omega C} \tag{11.26}$$

In this case the ac current vector, according to Eq. (11.25), is the

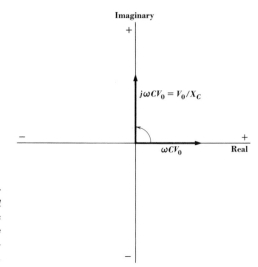

Fig. 11.17 *The real number*
ωCV₀, when multiplied
by j, is rotated +90°. This
gives the 90° lead of the
current ahead of the volt-
age in a capacitor.

real number ωCV_0 multiplied by j. As shown in Fig. 11.17, this rotates the current vector 90° ahead of the voltage, to lead it by 90°.

To summarize, the current amplitude in each kind of element, R, L, and C, can be written in terms of the ac *impedance* Z, using the equation

$$I_0 = \frac{V_0}{Z} \tag{11.27}$$

where $Z_R = R$ resistive impedance I_0 in phase with V_0

$\quad\quad Z_L = \omega L = X_L$ inductive reactance I_0 lags V_0 by 90°   (11.28a)

$\quad\quad Z_C = \dfrac{1}{\omega C} = X_C$ capacitive reactance I_0 leads V_0 by 90°

All three terms contribute to the total ac impedance in a circuit, as illustrated in the following sections.

Using complex notation, the phase information is self-contained:

$$Z_R = R$$
$$Z_L = j\omega L = X_L \tag{11.28b}$$
$$Z_C = \frac{1}{j\omega C} = X_C$$

11.6 *Series LCR Circuit*

So far we have dealt with the ac current-voltage relations in individual R, L, and C elements. We have found that, with a sinusoidal voltage applied across these elements, there is a sinusoidal current through each one which is either in phase (R), 90° behind the voltage (L), or 90° ahead (C). We now show the application of the idea of rotating amplitude vectors to the problem of a simple LCR series circuit like that shown in Fig. 11.1.

In a series circuit with no branches, the current-continuity equation, $\Sigma i = 0$, leads to the result that everywhere in the circuit the current is the same. Thus, for example, at point (a) in Fig. 11.18, the

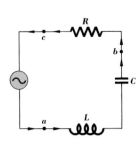

Fig. 11.18   A series LCR circuit connected to an ac source. Here the currents in the three elements have the same amplitude and phase, since at each point, such as a, b, and c, in the circuit the current in one side equals the current out the other side, according to the rule $\Sigma i = 0$.

current coming in from the left equals that going on to the right. This principle applies to all points in the circuit, such as (b) and (c).

The ac current everywhere in the circuit thus has the same amplitude and phase. It can therefore be written in the form

$$i = I_0 \cos \omega t \qquad (11.29a)$$

or

$$i = I_0 e^{j\omega t} \qquad (11.29b)$$

But if the currents are everywhere the same, and if the phase and amplitude relations we have just developed for the individual elements are to be obeyed, it follows that the ac voltage vectors for each element must have different amplitudes and phases. In addition, the instantaneous values of the voltages across each element must always add to equal the voltage of the generator. This satisfies the second circuit equation, as modified by the inclusion of the voltage across any capacitor,

$$\sum \varepsilon = \sum iR + \sum \frac{q}{C} \qquad (11.30)$$

The effect of the inductance is contained in the left-hand term. That is, $\Sigma\varepsilon$ contains not only the generator emf but also the term $-L\dfrac{di}{dt}$.

Since the voltage across each element is sinusoidal and has the same frequency, each voltage can be represented by a rotating amplitude vector moving at the same frequency. Thus, if the relative phase and amplitude of each voltage vector can be found, and if the vector sum is made equal to and in phase with the voltage source, the circuit equation will be satisfied at all times.

Figure 11.19 reviews the current-voltage relations for each circuit element at the same time, t. The relative phase of V_R, V_L, and V_C can

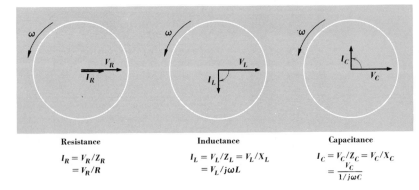

Resistance	Inductance	Capacitance
$I_R = V_R/Z_R$	$I_L = V_L/Z_L = V_L/X_L$	$I_C = V_C/Z_C = V_C/X_C$
$= V_R/R$	$= V_L/j\omega L$	$= \dfrac{V_C}{1/j\omega C}$

Fig. 11.19 *Relative orientation of current and voltage amplitude vectors in R, L, and C elements at a time t. The complex expressions are not used; the arguments of Sec. 11.4 are necessary to determine the relative phases of the amplitude vectors.*

be found by rotating these figures until the current-generating vectors are all in phase. The resulting directions of the voltage vectors are

Fig. 11.20 *Rotating vector diagram showing relative phase of voltage vectors across each element in a series LCR circuit. This result is obtained by requiring the current in each element to be the same.*

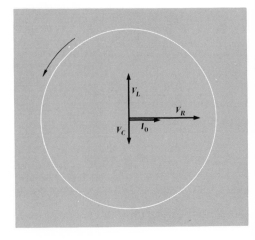

shown in Fig. 11.20, along with the current vector I_0. The vector sum of V_R, V_L, and V_C is the voltage between points (a) and (c) in Fig. 11.18. This sum can be obtained by redrawing the voltage vectors as in Fig. 11.21a or b. In either case the vector sum is given by the

Fig. 11.21 Two ways of showing the vector sum of the voltage amplitude vectors across each element in a series LCR circuit. The vector V_{ac} is the voltage across all three elements, points (a) and (c) in Fig. 11.18. In (b) above, the angle θ is the phase difference between the current vector and the resultant voltage across all three elements.

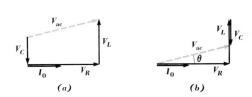

(a) (b)

dotted vector labeled V_{ac}. The angle θ is the resultant phase difference between the current in any of the elements and the voltage across the combination, V_{ac}.

According to the circuit equation this voltage V_{ac} must be just equal in phase and amplitude to the driving emf ε. Therefore we may write

$$\varepsilon = \mathbf{V}_{ac} = \mathbf{V}_R + \mathbf{V}_L + \mathbf{V}_C \tag{11.31}$$

The magnitudes of these separate voltages are given by

$$V_R = RI_R$$
$$V_L = \omega L I_L \tag{11.32}$$
$$V_C = \frac{1}{\omega C} I_C$$

But since

$$I_R = I_L = I_C = I_0$$

Eq. (11.31) can be written

$$\varepsilon = I_0 \left(\mathbf{R} + \boldsymbol{\omega}\mathbf{L} + \frac{1}{\boldsymbol{\omega}\mathbf{C}} \right) = I_0 \mathbf{Z} \tag{11.33}$$

The impedance terms have been written as vectors to allow for the different phases of the vectors. The meaning of this vector equation is

Fig. 11.22 *Rotating vector diagram for a series LCR circuit. Since the applied emf ε is given by ε = I₀Z, as in Eq. (11.33), this diagram shows that the impedance is given by*

$$Z = \sqrt{R^2 + \left(\omega L - \frac{1}{\omega C}\right)^2}$$

and the phase angle θ by which the current lags the driving voltage by

$$\tan \theta = \frac{\omega L - 1/\omega C}{R}$$

The circle is shown as a reminder that the phases of all these vectors change with time.

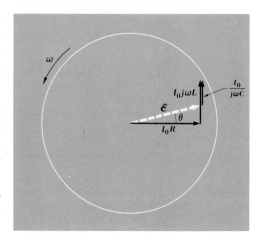

shown in Fig. 11.22. Complex notation has been used. The diagram is identical with Fig. 11.21b except that each voltage vector is expressed as the current times the appropriate impedance term. It is apparent from the figure that the magnitude of **Z** in Eq. (11.33) is given by

$$Z = \sqrt{R^2 + \left(\omega L - \frac{1}{\omega C}\right)^2} \tag{11.34a}$$

This is the ac impedance of the three elements in series. The phase angle θ between the driving voltage and the current in the circuit is given by

$$\tan \theta = \frac{\omega L - 1/\omega C}{R} \tag{11.35a}$$

As defined here, θ is the angle by which the ac current lags the driving voltage ε.

If the common factor I_0 is removed in the vector diagram of Fig. 11.22, it becomes the *impedance diagram* Fig. 11.23.

In the usual terms for inductive and capacitative reactance, the impedance may be written

$$Z = \sqrt{R^2 + X^2} = \sqrt{R^2 + (X_L - X_C)^2} \tag{11.34b}$$

**Fig. 11.23 Impedance dia-
gram for a series *LCR* circuit gives the relative
phase and amplitude of
the impedance terms of
each element. It is ob-
tained from the voltage
diagram of Fig. 11.22 by
dividing through by I_0.
Complex notation is used
here; so the relative directions are implicit in each
impedance term.**

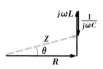

and

$$\tan \theta = \frac{X_L - X_C}{R} \tag{11.35b}$$

The instantaneous current is given by

$$i(t) = \frac{V_0 \cos (\omega t - \theta)}{Z} \tag{11.36a}$$

Using complex notation, the impedance becomes

$$Z = R + j \left(\omega L - \frac{1}{\omega C} \right) \tag{11.37}$$

which has the same meaning as Eq. (11.34a). This notation gives for
the current in an *LCR series circuit*

$$i(t) = \frac{V_0 e^{j\omega t}}{R + j(\omega L - 1/\omega C)} \tag{11.36b}$$

11.7   Parallel LCR Circuit

The parallel *LCR* circuit shown in Fig. 11.24 provides an interesting
contrast to the series circuit we have just examined. In this case it is

**Fig. 11.24   A parallel *LCR*
circuit connected to an ac
source. In this circuit the
voltage across each ele-
ment is the same. As a result the currents in each
element have different amplitude and phase.**

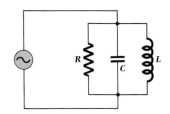

the voltage, rather than the current, which is the same on each element. As a result, the currents in the three branches have different amplitudes and phase. If the amplitude of the ac voltage applied to the circuit is V_0, the current amplitudes will be

$$I_R = \frac{V_0}{R}$$

$$I_C = \frac{V_0}{X_C} = \frac{V_0}{1/C\omega}$$ (11.38)

$$I_L = \frac{V_0}{X_L} = \frac{V_0}{L\omega}$$

The requirement on the three currents at any instant is that they add to give the total current passing through the source of emf. This requirement is satisfied if the generating vectors of the three ac currents add vectorially to equal the total current vector.

As in the last section, the relative phases of the vectors can be obtained by rotating the current-voltage diagrams of Fig. 11.19 until the circuit requirements are met. In this case the requirement is that the phases of the voltage vectors of the three elements are the same. Figure 11.25 shows the resulting current phase diagram, which is more

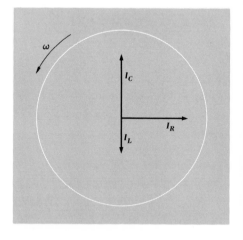

Fig. 11.25   Relative phase of currents in a parallel LCR circuit, obtained from Fig. 11.19 by setting the voltage amplitude and phase the same across each element. The rotating circle on which the vectors are plotted is again a reminder of the continually changing phase of all vectors.

convenient to use in the form of Fig. 11.26. This diagram gives the basis for calculation of the total current in the circuit as follows: Using I_0 for the amplitude of the total current, we write

$$I_0 = I_R + I_C + I_L = V_0\left(\frac{1}{R} + \frac{1}{X_C} + \frac{1}{X_L}\right) = V_0\frac{1}{Z}$$ (11.39)

*Fig. 11.26   Relative phase of
currents in parallel LCR
elements, in convenient
form to obtain the vector
sum* I_0 *of the three parallel
currents. This diagram
shows that*

$$\frac{1}{Z} = \left[\frac{1}{R^2} + \left(\omega C - \frac{1}{\omega L} \right)^2 \right]^{\frac{1}{2}}$$

and

$$\tan \theta = \frac{\omega C - 1/\omega L}{R}$$

*where θ is the angle by
which the current leads
the applied voltage. When*
V_0 *is divided out, this diagram becomes the recipro-
cal impedance diagram.
Complex notation has been
used for the impedance
terms.*

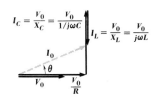

The impedance terms are written as vectors to allow the phase information of Fig. 11.26 to be included. Using this diagram, the reciprocal
impedance can be evaluated as

$$\frac{1}{Z} = \left[\frac{1}{R^2} + \left(\frac{1}{X_C} - \frac{1}{X_L} \right)^2 \right]^{\frac{1}{2}} = \left[\frac{1}{R^2} + \left(\omega C - \frac{1}{\omega L} \right)^2 \right]^{\frac{1}{2}} \tag{11.40}$$

Note that the signs of X_C and X_L are reversed in comparison with their
use in the series circuit. The full expression for the current becomes

$$i = \left[\frac{1}{R^2} + \left(\frac{1}{X_C} - \frac{1}{X_L} \right)^2 \right]^{\frac{1}{2}} V_0 \cos (\omega t + \theta) \tag{11.41}$$

where

$$\tan \theta = \frac{1/X_C - 1/X_L}{1/R} = \frac{\omega C - 1/\omega L}{1/R} \tag{11.42}$$

Here θ is the phase angle by which the current *leads* the voltage, as can
be seen from Fig. 11.26.

The same problem can be handled in complex notation by using
the complex form for the impedance terms.

$$Z_R = R$$
$$Z_L = j\omega L = X_L \tag{11.43}$$
$$Z_C = \frac{1}{j\omega C} = X_C$$

Substitution of these in Eq. (11.40) gives

$$I_0 = \frac{V_0}{Z} = V_0 \left(\frac{1}{R} + \frac{1}{j\omega L} + \frac{1}{1/j\omega C} \right) \tag{11.44}$$

or

$$i(t) = \left(\frac{1}{R} + \frac{1}{j\omega L} + \frac{1}{1/j\omega C} \right) V_0 e^{j\omega t} \tag{11.45}$$

The reciprocal of the impedance can be written

$$\frac{1}{Z} = \frac{1}{R} + j \left(\omega C - \frac{1}{\omega L} \right) \tag{11.46}$$

Evaluation of this complex number gives the result of Eq. (11.40) directly.

11.8 Resonance

There is one other aspect of the series circuit of Fig. 11.18, which we now examine. If we look again at the equation for the current in the series circuit,

$$i = \frac{V_0 \cos (\omega t - \theta)}{\sqrt{R^2 + (\omega L - 1/\omega C)^2}} \tag{11.36a}$$

we find that, for a given set of values of R, L, C, and V_0, the impedance $Z = [R^2 + (\omega L - 1/\omega C)^2]^{1/2}$ varies, and hence i varies in both amplitude and phase as the frequency varies. The maximum current occurs for the frequency such that

$$\omega L - \frac{1}{\omega C} = 0$$

If we call this frequency for which a maximum current flows in the series circuit the *resonance* frequency ω_0, we have

$$\omega_0 = \left(\frac{1}{LC} \right)^{1/2}$$

For this frequency the inductive and capacitative reactance terms in the impedance are just equal and opposite, and therefore drop out of Eq. (11.36a). i and v are in phase, and the equation reduces to Ohm's law, involving only the resistive term. This is also shown by reference to Fig. 11.22. The voltages across L and C are just equal and opposite at the resonance frequency; so the phase angle is zero. If the resistance term is very small, the current becomes very large at the resonance frequency. Also, the lower the resistance, the more rapidly does the current vary with frequency at frequencies near resonance.

A plot of the amplitude of the ac current through the circuit for a fixed-amplitude input voltage is plotted against frequency in Fig. 11.27. The maximum current occurs at the resonance frequency ω_0.

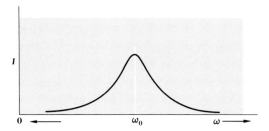

Fig. 11.27 Current in a series *LCR* circuit plotted as a function of the generator frequency. Resonance peak occurs when $X_C = X_L$. The generator voltage amplitude is assumed fixed.

The importance of this resonance behavior is very great, since exactly similar effects are found in many fields of physics. One simple example is that of a pendulum, in which there is some damping (giving a term equivalent to the resistance term).

The parallel circuit of Fig. 11.24 also shows resonant behavior. In this case the resonance is given by $1/X_C = 1/X_L$, leading again to $\omega_0 = (1/LC)^{1/2}$. On resonance Z is a maximum, giving a minimum current. One way of looking at the situation at resonance is to note that I_0 is just equal to the current through the resistance, while there are large circulating currents through L and C which are of equal magnitudes and in opposite directions and which therefore cancel out to give no contribution to the external current I_0.

11.9* Transients

In any circuit in which energy can be stored, as in a charged capacitor or in an inductance while it is carrying current, the sudden application or removal of an applied voltage causes a momentary changing response in the circuit while it adjusts to the new conditions. These temporary effects on current and voltage are called *transients*. We discuss a few cases.

The first example is that of an inductance and resistance in series to which we connect a voltage by closing a switch as shown in Fig. 11.28. The resistance here might be simply the minimum unavoidable

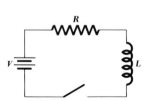

Fig. 11.28   Circuit for show-
ing transient behavior of
series RL circuit. The in-
stant the circuit is closed,
i is zero; so the equation
V = Ri + L di/dt becomes
V = L di/dt at t = 0. Later
the current reaches a
steady state; so di/dt be-
comes zero, and the equa-
tion becomes V = Ri, or
the steady current
$I_0 = V/R$.

resistance in the circuit, or it might be a resistor put in on purpose. As soon as the switch is closed, the situation is described by

$$V = Ri + L\frac{di}{dt} \tag{11.47}$$

This differential equation is easy to solve when we put in the required initial and final boundary conditions. But before solving it formally we may see by inspection the kind of time variation of current to expect. The instant the switch is closed, since the current is zero, the entire voltage drop in the circuit must be across the inductance. Thus the initial value of di/dt is V/L. After a long time the current will become steady; so the inductive voltage term goes to zero. The steady-state value of the current, I_0, will thus be

$$I_0 = \frac{V}{R}$$

The initial rate of increase of the current has now been established, as well as its final steady value, as displayed in Fig. 11.29. All that is needed is to establish the details of the transition region, as shown by the dotted part of the curve.

We now show formally that the current, after starting from zero, approaches its final value exponentially, that is, according to the equation

$$i(t) = I_0(1 - e^{-t/\tau}) \tag{11.48}$$

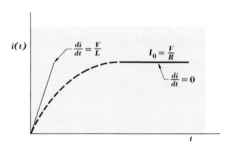

Fig. 11.29 Transient current in a series RL circuit, showing initial and final values of current and of slope di/dt. Only the dotted region is in doubt until solution is obtained.

where τ is the *relaxation time* of the circuit. We begin by separating the variables i and t in Eq. (11.47), putting it in the form

$$\frac{-R\,di}{V - Ri} = -\frac{R}{L}\,dt$$

where we have multiplied both sides by $-R$ to make the left-hand side a perfect differential. Integration gives

$$\ln\,(V - Ri) = \frac{-R}{L}\,t + C$$

where we evaluate the constant of integration C from the initial condition that, at $t = 0$, when the switch is closed, $i = 0$. This gives $C = \ln V$. We put this in and convert the equation to the exponential form

$$V - Ri = Ve^{-(R/L)t} \tag{11.49}$$

The current is given by

$$i = \frac{V}{R}\,(1 - e^{-(R/L)t}) = I_0(1 - e^{-(R/L)t}) \tag{11.50}$$

A plot of this solution is given in Fig. 11.30. The behavior of the circuit is completely determined by the value of R/L, or by its reciprocal $L/R = \tau$, the relaxation time of the circuit. With the use of τ as defined,

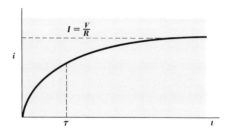

Fig. 11.30 Time variation of current in an RL circuit. The relaxation time τ is the time required for the current to build up to $1 - 1/e$ of its steady-state value. In a series RL circuit, $\tau = L/R$.

the equation becomes

$$i = I_0(1 - e^{-t/\tau})$$ (11.51)

τ is the time for the current to build up to $(1 - 1/e)$, or 0.632 of its final value. We see this by letting $t = \tau = L/R$, giving

$$i = I_0\left(1 - \frac{1}{e}\right) = I_0(1 - 0.368) = 0.632I$$ (11.52)

There are many physical situations which lead to equations like Eq. (11.47), and hence to solutions of the form of Eq. (11.50). With experience these can be identified as giving rise to an exponential approach of the variable to a final value. When this identification can be made it is possible to omit the formal steps to the solution to the differential equation, write a solution which has the correct exponential form, and evaluate the required constants. We illustrate this procedure now. Using Fig. 11.29 we start with

$$i(t) = I_0(1 - e^{-t/\tau})$$ (11.48)

which we have designed after a little thought to give $i = 0$ at $t = 0$ and $i = I_0$ for $t \gg \tau$, and to give exponential approach to I_0. But the values of I_0 and τ must be found which satisfy the differential equation, if any do. We have already given the argument showing that the steady-state current value is $I_0 = V/R$. In order to evaluate the constant τ, we differentiate Eq. (11.48) to get

$$\frac{di}{dt} = \frac{I_0}{\tau} e^{-t/\tau}$$ (11.53)

But for $t = 0$, $e^{-t/\tau} = 1$; so $(di/dt)_0 = I_0/\tau$. We have already argued that the initial slope of the current curve is V/L; so we have

$$\left(\frac{di}{dt}\right)_0 = \frac{I_0}{\tau} = \frac{V}{L} = \frac{V}{R\tau}$$ (11.54)

This gives for the relaxation time

$$\tau = \frac{L}{R}$$ (11.55)

in agreement with the earlier result, Eq. (11.50). We have not depended on the method of separation of variables here, but have simply assumed an exponential approach to the final steady state, and have matched the initial and final boundary conditions of the problem.

For the next problem we take the same circuit elements, but this time suddenly change the applied voltage from V to zero by switching from A to B in Fig. 11.31. This removes the battery from the circuit

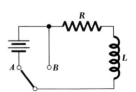

Fig. 11.31 RL circuit arranged to produce transient by sudden removal of voltage source. When the switch is suddenly moved from A to B, the battery is removed from the circuit. The circuit continues to pass current until the current decays exponentially to zero.

while allowing the current to continue flowing until it decays exponentially to zero. Letting $t = 0$ at the moment the switch is changed, the equation describing the circuit becomes

$$0 = Ri + L\frac{di}{dt} \tag{11.56}$$

This problem could be solved by separation of variables, but instead we go directly to the solution by applying the boundary conditions of the problem to an assumed exponential solution. In this case, at $t = 0$, $i = V/R = I_0$, since there is no voltage drop across the inductance when the current is steady. Also, after a long time, the current will go to zero. So the obvious solution to Eq. (11.56) is of the form

$$i(t) = I_0 e^{-t/\tau} = \frac{V}{R} e^{-t/\tau} \tag{11.57}$$

It is easy to verify that τ has the same value, L/R, as in the last example by substituting in the differential equation being solved. A plot of the current against time is shown in Fig. 11.32. Here τ is the

Fig. 11.32 Decay of current in RL circuit after voltage source is removed. The relaxation time τ is the time for the current to decay to the fraction $1/e$ of its steady-state value.

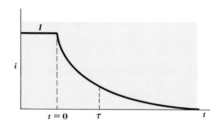

time for the current to fall to the fraction $1/e$ of its original steady-state value.

We next develop the equations for the decay and rise of current in a series RC circuit, as shown in Fig. 11.33.

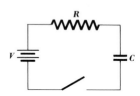

Fig. 11.33 Series RC circuit for applying a voltage V suddenly. When the switch is closed, a current carries charge to the capacitor plates. The current decays exponentially and becomes zero when the voltage across the capacitor reaches V, the battery voltage.

The equation that applies when the switch is closed is

$$V_0 = R\frac{dq}{dt} + \frac{q}{C} \tag{11.58}$$

using dq/dt for the current so as to limit the variables to q and t, where q is the charge on the capacitor.

At $t = 0$, $q = 0$, and after a long time, when the flow of charge to the capacitor has ceased,

$$q_{t=\infty} = CV_0 = Q_0 \tag{11.59}$$

We therefore guess the solution to Eq. (11.58) to be of the form

$$q(t) = Q_0(1 - e^{-t/\tau}) \tag{11.60}$$

since this gives a function which has the correct value for q at $t = 0$ and at $t = \infty$. The form of this function is shown as the dotted curve in Fig. 11.34. Substitution of Eq. (11.60) and its time derivative, dq/dt, in the circuit equation (11.58) gives

$$V_0 = \frac{R}{\tau}Q_0 e^{-t/\tau} + \frac{Q_0}{C}(1 - e^{-t/\tau}) \tag{11.61}$$

At $t = 0$ this becomes

$$V_0 = \frac{RQ_0}{\tau}$$

which, with the use of Eq. (11.59), leads to

$$\tau = RC \tag{11.62}$$

With this evaluation of the constant τ, Eq. (11.58) or (11.61) is satisfied for all times, showing that Eq. (11.60) is indeed the solution needed. The same result could have been obtained by separation of variables in Eq. (11.58) and direct integration.

The expression for the current as a function of time is obtained by differentiating Eq. (11.60).

$$\frac{dq}{dt} = i = \frac{Q_0}{RC} e^{-t/\tau} = \frac{V}{R} e^{-t/\tau} \tag{11.63}$$

The current decay curve is shown as the solid curve in Fig. 11.34.

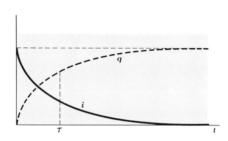

Fig. 11.34 Transient response of a series RC circuit. The dotted curve shows the rate at which the charge q on the capacitor plates reaches its final value CV_0. The solid curve shows the decay of the initial current to zero. The relaxation time τ has the value RC.

Finally, we study the case of the discharge of a capacitor as shown in Fig. 11.35. We start with the capacitor charged to a potential $V_0 =$

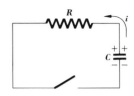

Fig. 11.35 Discharge of a capacitor through a resistance. The capacitor is initially charged by connecting a battery across it prior to closing the switch. After the capacitor is charged, the battery is removed.

Q_0/C. When the switch is closed, the situation is described by

$$\frac{q}{C} + R\frac{dq}{dt} = 0 \tag{11.64}$$

The signs in this equation can be verified as follows: Assume, as in the diagram, positive charge initially on the upper plate, and take clockwise for the positive-current direction. Then, since positive current depletes the positive charge on the upper plate,

$$i = -\frac{dq}{dt} \tag{11.65}$$

Treating the charged capacitor as a source of voltage, we write

$$V(t) = \frac{q}{C} = iR \tag{11.66}$$

or

$$\frac{q}{C} - iR = 0$$

which with Eq. (11.65) leads to Eq. (11.64).

This is the same as Eq. (11.58), except that the battery voltage is zero. Also, the starting condition is different since there is an initial charge on the capacitor, which starts to leak off when the switch is closed at $t = 0$. These boundary conditions are easily shown to be satisfied by

$$q = Q_0 e^{-t/RC} \tag{11.67}$$

which is also seen by substitution to be a solution of the differential equation.

The equation for current is

$$i = -\frac{dq}{dt} = \frac{Q_0}{RC} e^{-t/RC} = \frac{V_0}{R} e^{-t/\tau} \tag{11.68}$$

This result is identical with that of Eq. (11.57). However, the current is flowing in a direction to discharge the capacitor in the latter case, whereas in the former case the current was in the direction to charge the capacitor.

It is possible to make capacitance-resistance circuits having time constants ranging from very short times up to many seconds. There are many practical uses of such circuits for timing, or time-delay circuits. For example, the most common method of measuring very high resistance resistors is to measure the rate at which the charge on a capacitor decreases when the resistor is connected across it. Resistances as high as 10^{12} ohms can be measured in this way. The method involves the determination of τ, from which R can be determined via $RC = \tau$, if the capacitance is known.

In each of the above cases, the method of separation of variables can be used to obtain the solutions. But once the exponential nature of the time variation is apparent, the trial solution method is simpler.

In Appendix I we discuss transients in the series LCR circuit.

11.10 Filter Circuits

There are many situations that require the use of a *filter* network to modify a time-varying voltage or current. Filters are used to eliminate all time variations of a voltage, to select only a narrow band of sinusoidal frequencies from a time-varying voltage, or to select all frequencies above or below some given value. A simple case is that of obtaining a steady voltage from a rectified ac voltage. In Chap. 16 the rectifying action of a vacuum tube or semiconductor diode is described. Rectifying action converts a sinusoidal signal that has a time-average value of zero into a signal that is time-varying but has a non-zero average value. A filter circuit is used with a rectifier to smooth out the time variations of voltage to whatever extent is required in the application. For example, radio receivers or amplifiers are usually powered by 60 cycle ac: The dc power voltage required is obtained by rectifying and filtering the ac supply voltage. After filtering, the amplitude of any remaining 60-cycle variation in the rectified supply voltage must be very small compared with the audiofrequency signal being amplified. Otherwise the audio signal will contain a noticeable ac signal at 60 cycles.

One of the simplest filter circuits for producing a nearly constant dc voltage from a rectified ac voltage is shown in Fig. 11.36. This cir-

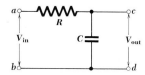

Fig. 11.36 A simple low-pass filter circuit.

cuit is similar to the RC circuit studied in Sec. 11.9. The electric signal is brought in at terminals a and b and is taken off at c and d.

The output is the voltage across the capacitor. The impedance across the resistance is R and across the capacitor is $1/\omega C$. The impedance of the C and R in series is

$$\left[R^2 + \left(\frac{1}{\omega C} \right)^2 \right]^{\frac{1}{2}}$$

For a constant input voltage amplitude, we obtain the output voltage as a function of frequency by taking the ratio

$$V_{\text{out}} = V_{\text{in}} \frac{1/\omega C}{[R^2 + (1/\omega C)^2]^{1/2}} \tag{11.69}$$

This result is plotted in Fig. 11.37. When $1/\omega C = R$ or $\omega = 1/RC$, the output is $(1/\sqrt{2})V_{\text{in}}$. In our simple derivation of Eq. (11.69) we

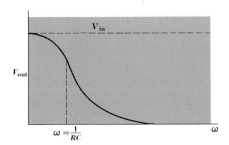

Fig. 11.37   *Output of a low-pass filter.*

have ignored the possible effects of the impedance across the output. In many applications this will be a resistance or impedance much higher than R or $1/\omega C$ in the frequency range of interest, so its effects can be ignored.

The effect of this *low-pass* filter on the rectified 60-cycle signal can be understood qualitatively by reference to Fig. 11.37. Suppose R and C are chosen so that $1/RC$ is say 20 cps. This means that the 60-cycle signal will be highly attenuated, as will be all other higher frequency components of the rectified signal. What remains will be largely a zero frequency or dc signal.

The more complete removal of ac components from the filtered signal is usually accomplished by putting two or more sections like that shown in Fig. 11.36 in series. It is also usual to replace the resistance shown in our simple example by an inductance.

In another common filter application, a *high-pass* filter, of which a single section is shown in Fig. 11.38, passes signals of higher fre-

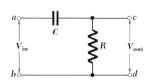

Fig. 11.38   *A simple high-pass filter circuit.*

quencies while attenuating the low-frequency components. The output voltage as a function of frequency is obtained as above, and is given by

$$V_{\text{out}} = V_{\text{in}} \frac{R}{[R^2 + (1/\omega C)^2]^{1/2}} \tag{11.70}$$

using the same reasoning as above. The attenuation curve is shown in Fig. 11.39.

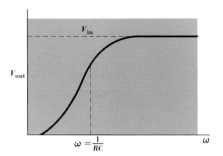

Fig. 11.39 Output of a high-pass filter.

Other filters, called *bandpass* filters, allow only a narrow range of frequencies to pass. A *band-stop* filter attenuates a narrow band of frequencies and allows lower and higher frequencies to pass. Such circuits are in common use in the design of audio amplifiers and have other applications in a wide range of electronic devices.

11.11 Power in AC Circuits

We now turn to a discussion of power dissipation in ac circuits. Resistive elements absorb net electric energy in ac circuits. Capacitors store electric field energy while they are charged, but feed the energy back to the circuit when they discharge, and inductances store magnetic energy while current flows, but also return the energy to the circuit when the current goes to zero. Thus, in steady-state ac operation, capacitors and inductances alternately store and release energy but do not give rise to dissipation of energy.

The central problem in this section is to show how to calculate the power transferred from an ac source to any kind of ac circuit. A knowledge of the ac current from the source and the ac voltage at the input to the circuit, along with the relative phase of the current and voltage, is all that is required to measure the average power provided by the source. The energy transferred to the circuit is generally dissipated in the total resistance of the circuit. At high frequencies, some energy may be radiated by electromagnetic waves generated by ac currents and voltage oscillations in inductances and capacitances. Electromagnetic waves are discussed in Chap. 12. Another sink for the energy transferred to an ac circuit would be mechanical work done, as by a motor.

Before turning to the problem of power transfer to an ac circuit, we consider the nomenclature used in ac power considerations. Consider a resistance which is carrying ac current as a result of an ac voltage applied across it. What is the average power dissipation in the resistor for a given amplitude of ac current? It will be less than I_0^2R, the dc power for a constant current I_0, since I_0 here is the peak of the ac current, and during most of the cycle the current is less. It is common practice to characterize ac currents and voltages for power considerations by using the *effective* values I_{eff} and V_{eff}. These are the dc currents and voltages which would give the same heating in a resistance as the average heating from the ac currents. When the ac voltage in household circuits is called 110 volts, what is meant is that this is the effective value of the voltage. The ac amplitude, or peak value, is actually $110 \times \sqrt{2} = 155$ volts.

The effective value of an ac current can be found as follows: Let the ac current through a resistance R be written $i = I_0 \sin \omega t$. The average power dissipation in the resistance will then be

$$\text{AC:} \quad \overline{P} = \overline{i^2 R} = I_0^2 R \overline{\sin^2 \omega t} \tag{11.71}$$

where $\overline{\sin^2 \omega t}$ means the average value of $\sin^2 \omega t$. The power dissipation in the case of a steady current I is

$$\text{DC:} \quad P = I^2 R \tag{11.72}$$

If the average power in the ac case is made equal to the dc power, the current I will be the effective value of the ac current, I_{eff}. Thus

$$I_{eff}^2 R = I_0^2 R \overline{\sin^2 \omega t} = I_0^2 R \frac{\int_0^t \sin^2 \omega t \, dt}{t} \tag{11.73}$$

Here the average value of $\sin^2 \omega t$ is to be obtained by integrating it over the time of one cycle, or over many cycles, and dividing by the elapsed time. It is easy to show analytically that the average value is $\frac{1}{2}$. Or this can be seen from Fig. 11.40, which gives a time plot of $\sin \omega t$ along

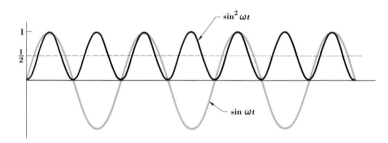

Fig. 11.40   Plot of sin ωt and sin² ωt showing that the average value of sin² ωt is ½.

with a plot of $\sin^2 \omega t$. With this result, we find

$$I_{\text{eff}}^2 = \frac{I_0{}^2}{2} \quad \text{or} \quad I_{\text{eff}} = \frac{1}{\sqrt{2}} I_0 = 0.707 I_0 \tag{11.74a}$$

The same kind of argument gives

$$V_{\text{eff}} = \frac{1}{\sqrt{2}} V_0 = 0.707 V_0 \tag{11.74b}$$

The effective values of current and voltage are usually called the *root-mean-square* (rms) values, and these are generally used when ac power is involved.

The argument is now repeated using complex notation. We wish to evaluate the average value of $i^2 R$. To this end we obtain the real part of i

$$i = \text{Re } I_0 e^{j\omega t}$$
$$= -\tfrac{1}{2}(e^{j\omega t} + e^{-j\omega t})$$

This procedure follows the usual rule that one-half the sum of a complex quantity and its complex conjugate is the real part of the complex quantity. Then

$$i^2 R = \tfrac{1}{4} I_0{}^2 R (e^{j\omega t} + e^{-j\omega t})^2$$
$$= \tfrac{1}{4} I_0{}^2 R (e^{2j\omega t} + 2 + e^{-2j\omega t}) \tag{11.75}$$

Since the average value of each exponential term is zero, the average value of $i^2 R$ is thus

$$\overline{i^2 R} = \tfrac{1}{2} I_0{}^2 R$$

as we found before.

We now turn to the problem of relating the power transfer to any circuit to the ac current through it and the ac voltage across it. Suppose we have any sort of circuit with two terminals connected to an electric power source. We can measure the ac voltage across the terminals of the circuit and the current through the circuit. In general, unless the circuit is purely resistive, the current and voltage amplitude vectors at the terminals do not have the same phase. We want to see what effect this has on the power transferred to the circuit.

During a time interval dt, when the voltage across the terminals is v, a charge $i\,dt$ flows. The work done against the voltage v in the time interval is

$$dW = v\,i\,dt$$

or the rate of doing work is

$$\frac{dW}{dt} = vi$$

To find the average value of the work or the average power, dW/dt is averaged over one or more complete cycles. Thus

$$P = \left(\frac{dW}{dt}\right)_{\mathrm{Av}} = \frac{1}{t}\int_0^t i\,v\,dt \qquad (11.76)$$

If sinusoidal currents and voltages are involved, and if i and v are in phase, we may write $i = I_0 \sin \omega t$ and $v = V_0 \sin \omega t$. Then Eq. (11.76) gives

$$P = I_0 V_0 \left[\frac{1}{t}\int \sin^2 \omega t\,dt\right]$$
$$= I_0 V_0 \sin^2 \omega t = \tfrac{1}{2}I_0 V_0 = I_{\mathrm{eff}} V_{\mathrm{eff}} \qquad (11.77)$$

On the other hand, if a phase angle θ exists between current and voltage, so that

$$i = I_0 \sin \omega t$$
$$v = V_0 \sin (\omega t + \theta)$$

then the power is given by

$$P = iv = I_0 V_0 \left[\frac{1}{t}\int_0^t \sin \omega t \sin (\omega t + \theta)\,dt\right] \qquad (11.78)$$

We must again evaluate the quantity in brackets, which gives the average value of the quantity inside the integral. Using a familiar trigonometric equation, we rewrite Eq. (11.78)

$$P = I_0 V_0 \left[\frac{1}{t} \int_0^t \sin \omega t \ (\sin \omega t \cos \theta + \cos \omega t \sin \theta) \ dt \right]$$

$$= I_0 V_0 \left[\frac{1}{t} \int_0^t (\sin^2 \omega t \cos \theta + \sin \omega t \cos \omega t \sin \theta) \ dt \right] \qquad (11.79)$$

The second term has an average value of zero since $\sin \omega t \cos \omega t$ is symmetrical about zero and multiplies a constant, $\sin \theta$. Thus we find

$$P = \tfrac{1}{2} I_0 V_0 \cos \theta = I_{\text{eff}} V_{\text{eff}} \cos \theta \qquad (11.80)$$

Here again, complex notation could have been used to obtain the same result. The quantity $\cos \theta$ is called the *power factor*. The average value of the power is obtained by multiplying one rotating vector, say, V_0, by the projection on it of the other vector, $I_0 \cos \theta$, as shown in Fig.

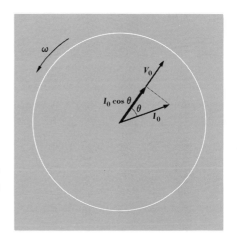

Fig. 11.41 Power dissipation in a circuit or element is given by $P = \tfrac{1}{2} I_0 V_0 \cos \theta = I_{\text{eff}} V_{\text{eff}} \cos \theta$. Note that $I_0 V_0 \cos \theta$ is simply the vector $\mathbf{V}_0$ multiplied by the projection of $\mathbf{I}_0$ along $\mathbf{V}_0$.

11.41. The factor $\tfrac{1}{2}$ in Eq. (11.80) comes as before from the average value of $\sin^2 \omega t$.

The average power dissipation in a pure inductance or capacitance is zero. Equation (11.77) shows this immediately since θ has the magnitude $\pi/2$ in both cases, which gives $\cos \theta = 0$ for the power factor.

As long as θ is not zero, there are times during an ac cycle when the power fed to the circuit is negative. This occurs whenever i and v have opposite signs. During such times, stored electric or magnetic energy in the circuit is being fed back to the source.

11.12* AC Instruments

Because of the mechanical inertia of the coil of an ordinary galvanometer, it does not respond to ac currents. In this section we examine the principles of a number of ac measuring instruments that solve this difficulty by various methods.

Hot-wire ammeter. This instrument solves the problem that the torque on a current-carrying coil in a fixed magnetic field reverses each time the ac current reverses by avoiding it completely. It depends instead on the heating of a wire by the current. The heated wire is under slight spring tension, so that it elongates when heated, and a pointer is connected so as to measure the extension. This device is not useful for very small ac currents. Since the heating is proportional to i^2, if calibrated in terms of i, it will give nonlinear response. It can be used to measure dc current, but since galvanometers are generally much more convenient, this is not normally done. If it is calibrated using direct current, it will measure effective, or rms, current.

Dynamometer. This is a galvanometer-type device in which the fixed magnetic field of the usual permanent magnet is replaced by a field produced by current in an auxiliary coil. Both coils are placed in series or parallel, so that the current variation is the same in both. Since the magnetic field now reverses its direction in step with the current in the suspended coil, the torque on the coil keeps the same sign, and the deflection is proportional to the average torque. Since the torque is proportional in the first place to the current in the suspended coil, and in the second place to the magnetic field, which also depends on the current, the torque depends on i^2. The dynamometer can be used to measure either voltage or current, just as can a galvanometer. It is calibrated to read rms values.

When the two coils are connected separately, one to measure the current to a system and the other to measure the voltage across the system, the dynamometer measures power directly. A schematic diagram is shown in Fig. 11.42. Even if V and I are out of phase, this meter still gives the correct power since the torque is $iv = I_0 V_0 \sin \omega t \sin (\omega t + \theta)$, and, as we have seen, the average value of this is $I_0(V_0/2) \cos \theta$. This type of wattmeter can be used with direct current. Sensitivities of dynamometer devices tend to be low because of the relatively small magnetic fields obtained from available currents compared with the fields of the fixed magnets used in galvanometer movements.

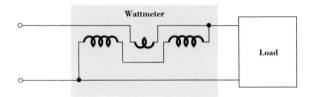

Fig. 11.42 Schematic diagram of a dynamometer connected as a wattmeter.

Rectifier galvanometer. A rectifying device, usually a semiconductor crystal, is sometimes used to provide direct current, which is then measured by a conventional galvanometer. We discuss rectifiers later. It is sufficient here to remark that the dc voltage obtained in this way is proportional to the amplitude of the ac voltage; so the galvanometers give readings proportional to voltage (or current) amplitude. It is calibrated to read rms values of voltage or current.

Cathode-ray oscilloscope (CRO). Although this device comes in a rather different category than the other instruments mentioned, it is in constant use in laboratories for the measurement of ac, and sometimes dc, voltages. In this day of universal familiarity with the CRO in the form of television display tubes, it is probably unnecessary to go into great detail, and in any case this is not the place. The heart of the CRO is the electron beam, obtained from a hot cathode and focused after electrostatic acceleration on fluorescent material inside the face of the tube. The position of the beam is controlled by either an electrostatic field or a magnetic field produced by a coil. The special advantage of the device is the extremely rapid response of the beam to the voltage applied to the signal electrode. It is common practice to look at signals up to the megacycle frequency range. In addition, the use of an appropriate electronic ac or dc amplifier makes possible the easy observation of signals in the range of 10^{-3} volt or less. Although the CRO is not an absolute device, it can be easily calibrated so that its signals can be measured directly in volts. Another great advantage of the CRO is that it has a high impedance, so that it draws very little current and does not upset the circuit it is being used to measure.

11.13* The Transformer

A transformer is a device that allows a voltage change to be made in an ac supply voltage with small loss of power. Thus a 6-volt lamp may be lit by a 110-volt ac supply by connecting it through an appropriate tranformer, or we can obtain 10,000 volts for an x-ray generator by using an appropriate transformer on the same 110-volt line. If some of the magnetic flux due to current in one coil links another coil so that there is a mutual inductance between the two coils, the pair of coils can be used as a tranformer. Usually, however, efforts are made to ensure that, as nearly as possible, all the flux of one coil links the other. A very common design is to wind both coils on the same closed ferromagnetic core (Fig. 11.43). As mentioned earlier, the flux tends to be confined

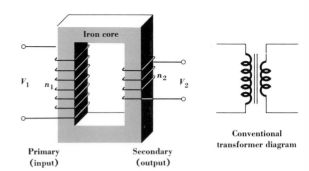

Fig. 11.43   The transformer.

within the ferromagnetic path, so that the mutual inductance between the two coils is a maximum.

The ratio of primary to secondary voltage is just the turns ratio of the primary to secondary windings. Suppose the ac supply voltage to the primary (power input) coil is V_1. If the resistance of the coil is negligible compared with its inductive reactance, an ac current i_1 will flow in the coil, causing a varying magnetic flux that is just enough to give an emf equal and opposite to V_1; so we have

$$V_1 = -n_1 \frac{d\phi}{dt} \qquad\qquad (11.80a)$$

where n_1 is the number of turns in the primary. Now since all the flux links the secondary coil, we have at once, for the output voltage,

$$V_2 = -n_2 \frac{d\phi}{dt} \qquad\qquad (11.81)$$

where $d\phi/dt$ has the same value as in Eq. (11.80a).

Combining these equations, we have

$$\frac{V_1}{V_2} = \frac{n_1}{n_2} \quad \text{or} \quad \frac{V_1}{n_1} = \frac{V_2}{n_2} \tag{11.82}$$

The voltage per turn is the same in each coil because the flux through each coil is the same.

We may determine the magnitude and phase of the current in the primary for no load on the secondary by relating the flux ϕ to the mmf. As we saw earlier,

$$\phi = \frac{\text{mmf}}{\mathcal{R}}$$

where $\mathcal{R}$ is the reluctance of the magnetic circuit. When we apply this to the primary winding and assume a sinusoidal primary current, we get

$$\phi = \frac{n_1 i_1}{\mathcal{R}} = \frac{n_1 I_0 \sin \omega t}{\mathcal{R}} \tag{11.83}$$

Thus the flux varies sinusoidally with time and has the same phase as i_1. When we now differentiate to get $d\phi/dt$ and substitute in Eq. (11.80a), we get

$$V_1 = \frac{-\omega n_1{}^2 I_0 \cos \omega t}{\mathcal{R}} \tag{11.84}$$

This shows that i_1 and V_1 are out of phase by 90°, as was to be expected from our general result for a pure inductance. According to our earlier argument, since the power factor is zero, there is no power dissipation. Also, if the reluctance of the magnetic circuit is small, the current amplitude I_0 is small. Actually, in practical cases there is some power loss because the power factor is not exactly zero. This is the result of the finite resistance of the winding and of the eddy-current and hysteresis losses in the iron core. Power losses are usually unimportant in applications in which the total power transferred through the transformer is small, but in high power applications involving kilowatts of power or more, the losses can be of much significance. Modern high-power transformer design involves great care in minimizing both eddy current and hysteresis losses.

We now examine the change in the situation when a load is connected to the secondary winding, allowing a secondary current i_2 to flow. For simplicity we assume a pure resistive load, so that V_2 and i_2 have the same phase. As a result of the current i_2, an additional magnetic flux is produced in the iron. By Lenz's rule, this flux opposes the original flux due to i_1; so the flux is now given by

$$\phi = \frac{n_1 i_1}{\mathcal{R}} - \frac{n_2 i_2}{\mathcal{R}} \tag{11.85}$$

But the magnitude of the sinusoidally varying flux must remain fixed if we are to continue to satisfy Eq. (11.80) for the voltage across the primary. This argument uses the fact that ϕ and $d\phi/dt$ are proportional when the frequency is held constant. Thus, as a consequence of introducing i_2, i_1 must increase, and we may write

$$\phi = \frac{n_1(i_1 + i_1') - n_2 i_2}{\mathcal{R}} \tag{11.86}$$

where i_1' is the increase in i_1 produced by allowing i_2 in the secondary circuit. Comparison of Eq. (11.86) with Eq. (11.83) gives

$$n_1 i_1' = n_2 i_2 \tag{11.87}$$

If we neglect the primary current for no load, i_1' becomes the total primary current, and we get the relationship that

$$\frac{i_2}{i_1} = \frac{n_1}{n_2} \tag{11.88}$$

that is, the primary and secondary currents are inversely proportional to the primary and secondary turns. Equations (11.82) and (11.88) lead to

$$V_1 i_1 = V_2 i_2 \tag{11.89}$$

showing that the power input to the transformer is equal to the power output. We are here neglecting the losses, which may amount to a few percent in ordinary transformers. We shall not make a quantitative study of the losses in transformers, but shall make a few remarks about the reduction of eddy-current losses in the ferromagnetic cores of transformers. Since the losses increase with frequency, the problem is most serious at high frequencies. For ordinary 60-cps applications, it is usually sufficient to construct the iron core of laminations which are insulated from each other, so as to prevent large-scale eddy currents. For higher-frequency applications, losses are kept sufficiently low by using finely divided iron particles immersed in an insulating matrix. Finally, for very high frequency application, ferrites, which are insulating magnetic materials, are used (Sec. 10.11).

Other losses in transformers are the i^2R losses in the primary and secondary windings, and hysteresis losses in the ferromagnetic core.

11.14* Generators

We have already discussed, in Examples 9.6a and 9.6b, the connection between Faraday's induction law and the operation of an electric generator. Here we add a few of the details of construction of practical electric generators. We saw in Example 9.6b how a rotating coil in a magnetic field gives ac power. For dc operation, two kinds of modification are usual. The first involves the use of a *commutator* to reverse the connections to the coil at the proper time to keep the emf always in one direction, as discussed in connection with the rotating coil used as a motor in Example 9.8b. This gives the equivalent of a dc output with a ripple superimposed. This is carried further, as was discussed in connection with motors, by constructing an armature composed of many separate coils, each of which is connected to the output by the commutator for only that part of the cycle for which its output is nearly maximum. The resulting output has a very much reduced ripple, which can be even further reduced, if necessary, by external filter circuits. The second important modification is to supply the current to the fixed coils, which provide the static magnetic field, from the output of the armature itself. This is the *self-excited* generator. Figure 11.44 shows two circuits used for applying voltage to the field coils.

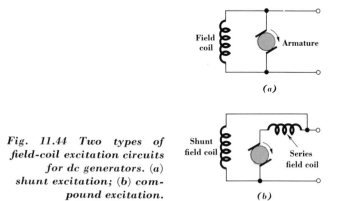

Fig. 11.44 Two types of field-coil excitation circuits for dc generators. (a) shunt excitation; (b) compound excitation.

The rate at which mechanical energy is converted to electric energy is $\mathcal{E}i_a$, where $\mathcal{E}$ is the emf generated in the armature coils and i_a

is the current through them. This neglects the power dissipation in the resistance of the field coils that maintain the magnetic flux in the generator. In a well-designed generator this loss is a small fraction of the power converted into electric energy.

The usual ac generator is constructed somewhat differently. The armature coils are placed in fixed positions outside a set of rotating magnetic poles. The poles are made of iron and are kept polarized by a dc current fed through slip rings to the rotor.

In many power applications there are three sets of armature coils, connected so that there is an ac voltage between each of three terminals coming from the coils. The phase of the alternating current between each pair of terminals is different, so that the three lines from the generator deliver what is called *three-phase* power. Figure 11.45 shows a

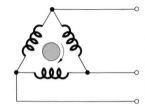

Fig. 11.45 Schematic drawing of a three-phase ac generator. Rotating magnetic field produces ac voltages across each pair of terminals, with phase separations of 120°.

schematic diagram of this arrangement. The phase angle between each pair of terminals is 120°, as can be inferred from the arrangement. This three-phase power is used for specially designed three-phase motors, which we discuss in the next section.

In all mechanical generators the internal resistance comes from the actual resistance in the coils in which the emf is induced. In the compound-wound dc generator, an increase in the current to the load results in an increase in the magnetizing current in the series field coil (Fig. 11.44*b*). The resulting increase in static field can compensate for the otherwise lower voltage output under heavy loads, to give a very low effective internal resistance over a wide range of currents.

11.15* Motors

In Example 9.8*a* we saw how magnetic forces on a current-carrying conductor can be used to convert electric to mechanical energy. In Example 9.8*b* we discussed the back emf in a motor, resulting from the flux change when the moving coil rotates. These ideas cover the fundamentals of motor operation. Here we add a few more remarks regarding the operation of several common types of motors.

The usual dc motor consists of a rotating armature containing a number of separate coils connected to the current source by means of a commutator. In miniature motors the magnetic field is provided by permanent magnets, but for most motors the field is produced by electromagnets consisting of iron cores wound with field coils and energized by the external current source.

In the shunt-excited motor, the field coils are connected in parallel with the armature. The current in the armature is given by

$$V_s - \mathcal{E} = i_a R_a$$

where V_s = source voltage

$\mathcal{E}$ = average back emf due to motion of armature coils in the field

i_a and R_a = current and resistance in armature coils

The back emf $\mathcal{E}$ is proportional to ϕf, where ϕ is the magnetic flux cut by the coils in one revolution and f is the frequency of rotation. The rate at which electric energy is converted into mechanical energy is given by $\mathcal{E} i_a$. This neglects the power dissipated in the resistance of the field coils that maintain the magnetic flux, which is usually small compared with the mechanical work rate. The expression for power conversion is the same as that for conversion from mechanical to electric power in a generator. The rate at which mechanical work is done by the motor is $P = \tau \omega$, where τ is the torque and ω is the angular velocity of the motor. When we equate the electric power going into mechanical work to the mechanical-power output, we find

$$\mathcal{E} i_a = \tau \omega \propto \phi f i_a = \frac{\phi \omega}{2\pi} i_a$$

or

$$\tau \propto \frac{\phi}{2\pi} i_a$$

Thus the torque is proportional to the current through the armature windings in a shunt-excited motor.

In a series-excited motor, the field coils and armature windings are in series; so the circuit equation is

$$V_s - \mathcal{E} = (R_a + R_f) i_a$$

where R_f is the field-coil resistance. The magnetic flux ϕ is roughly proportional to i_a, and since the torque is proportional to ϕi_a, it is therefore proportional to $i_a{}^2$. This contrast between the torque in shunt- and series-excited dc motors shows that the series motor has a higher starting torque since current requirements increase only with $\tau^{1/2}$ rather than with τ.

AC motors can be constructed on the same principles as dc motors, since the torque depends on ϕi_a, and both ϕ and i_a change sign at the frequency of the ac voltage, giving a torque always in the same direction. In a shunt-excited motor, however, there is the difficulty that the phases of the current in the field windings and armature are not the same, since the inductances of the two windings are different. This problem does not exist in series-excited motors, where the currents are necessarily in phase. However, the large inductance of the motor windings limits the current to small values, and this seriously limits the torque available, using ordinary voltage supplies. The iron cores of the field coils must be laminated in order to avoid excessive eddy-current losses. That is, the iron core is divided into thin sheets which are electrically insulated from each other. This reduces the power loss from induced eddy currents (Sec. 11.13).

The most common ac motor is the induction motor, in which a rotating magnetic field induces currents in a set of copper loops in the rotor. Magnetic forces on these current loops exert a torque on the rotor and cause it to rotate. The rotating field can be produced by feeding three-phase power from a three-phase generator, as described in the preceding section. The motor windings are similar to the windings on the generator. When they are connected to the three out-of-phase lines from the generator, a rotating field is produced in the motor. Another method of producing a rotating field uses a single-phase power supply, but a phase shift in part of the field-coil windings is produced by connecting a capacitance to part of the windings. The intensity of the rotating field is increased by including a laminated iron core in the rotor, thus decreasing the reluctance of the magnetic circuit. This type of motor is not synchronous with the rotating field, since, if the rotor moves at the same speed as the field, no currents are induced and there is no torque. A simple induction motor has a low starting torque, since the large induced ac currents on the stationary rotor induce a large back emf on the field coils, reducing the field-coil current and the magnetic flux. The starting torque can be increased by bringing connections from the rotor loops through slip rings, to an external resistance that is connected in series while starting.

A synchronous motor can be built by combining regular armature windings that are fed current from the external supply with some short-circuited loops, as in an induction motor. With no load, the rotor comes into synchronism with the rotating field, just as a permanent magnet would rotate with the field. When mechanical torque is applied, the rotor falls back in phase and ac currents are induced in the induction loops. The extra force on the induced-current loops keeps the rotor in synchronism with the rotating field, though behind it in phase. The induction torque increases to a maximum when the phase lag becomes 90°. If the mechanical torque applied produces a lag greater than this, the motor falls out of synchronism.

11.16   Comments on Chapter 11

The principal purpose of this chapter has been to develop a framework for discussing ac circuits involving R, L, and C elements. Three important properties of sinusoidal functions play a major role in ac circuit behavior:

1.   The sum of sinusoidal functions having the same frequency and arbitrary phase relations is also a sinusoidal function of the same frequency.
2.   The derivative of any sinusoidal function is also a sinusoidal function of the same frequency.
3.   The integral of any sinusoidal function is also a sinusoidal function of the same frequency.

Because of these properties, ac current-voltage relations in resistances, inductances, and capacitances are remarkably simple. Using I_0 and V_0 for the rotating generating vectors which describe ac currents and voltages, and using Z for the ac impedance of an element or circuit, according to

$$I_0 = \frac{V_0}{Z} \tag{11.27}$$

it was shown that

$$Z_R = R \qquad \text{resistive impedance} \qquad I_0 \text{ in phase with } V_0$$
$$Z_L = \omega L = X_L \qquad \text{inductive reactance} \qquad I_0 \text{ lags } V \text{ by } 90°$$
$$Z_C = \frac{1}{\omega C} = X_C \qquad \text{capacitative reactance} \qquad I_0 \text{ leads } V_0 \text{ by } 90°$$

Two special consequences of the ac impedance of the circuit elements exhibited here are that the current is not generally in phase with the voltage in ac circuits and that the impedance is, except for a pure resistance, a function of frequency.

If complex notation is used, as discussed in Appendix H, the impedance considered as a complex number contains the phase information explicitly:

$$Z_R = R$$
$$Z_L = j\omega L = X_L$$
$$Z_C = \frac{1}{j\omega C} = X_C$$

It is a simple matter to describe the current-voltage relations in any series or parallel combination of L, C, and R elements, using the impedance terms for the individual elements.

In a series LCR circuit, in which currents are in phase, it was shown that the sinusoidal current is given by

$$i(t) = \frac{V_0 \cos (\omega t - \theta)}{Z}$$

where

$$Z = \sqrt{R^2 + \left(\omega L - \frac{1}{\omega C}\right)^2}$$

and θ, the angle by which the current *lags* the voltage, is given by

$$\tan \theta = \frac{\omega L - 1/\omega C}{R}$$

The same result in complex notation is

$$i(t) = \frac{V_0 e^{j\omega t}}{R + j\omega L + 1/j\omega C}$$

In a parallel LCR circuit, in which the voltage is the same across each element, the current is given by

$$i(t) = \frac{1}{Z} V_0 \cos (\omega t + \theta)$$

where

$$\frac{1}{Z} = \left[\frac{1}{R^2} + \left(\omega C - \frac{1}{\omega L}\right)^2\right]^{1/2}$$

and θ, the angle by which the current *leads* the voltage, is given by

$$\tan \theta = \frac{\omega C - 1/\omega L}{1/R}$$

In complex notation this is

$$i(t) = \left(\frac{1}{R} + \frac{1}{j\omega L} + \frac{1}{1/j\omega C} \right) V_0 e^{j\omega t}$$

Since the impedance of ac circuits is a function of frequency, the current through an LCR circuit varies with frequency. In a series LCR circuit a *maximum* current occurs when the two reactance terms are of equal size, given by the condition

$$\omega_0 = \sqrt{\frac{1}{LC}}$$

ω_0 is called the resonance frequency of the circuit. The smaller the resistive term R compared with either of the reactive terms at resonance, the more rapidly the current varies with frequency around the resonance value, or the "sharper" is the resonance peak.

In a parallel LCR circuit, the same condition for resonance leads to a *minimum* total current through the circuit. In both circuits the total current is in phase with the voltage applied at the frequency ω_0.

The transient behavior of ac circuits when a dc voltage is suddenly applied was investigated in several cases. Appendix I discusses the case of transient response of a series LCR circuit to an applied voltage. Complex notation is used to show the conditions for damped oscillations or for exponential current attenuation, depending on the relative values of R, L, and C.

The short discussion of filter circuits gave a simple analysis of low-pass and high-pass filters as used for modifying the signal obtained from rectifiers and amplifier circuits. Bandpass and band-stop filters are also of great importance in many applications. The design of filter circuits for particular purposes is an important part of electronic circuit analysis.

The discussion of power dissipation in ac circuits shows that a dc voltage V_{eff} or current I_{eff} dissipates the same power in a resistance as would be dissipated by an ac peak voltage V_0 if

$$V_{eff} = \frac{1}{\sqrt{2}} V_0$$

V_{eff} is usually called the rms voltage.

The power dissipated in an ac circuit by passing an ac current of amplitude I_0 and having across it an ac voltage amplitude V_0 depends on the phase difference between current and voltage, according to

$$P = \tfrac{1}{2}I_0V_0 \cos\theta = I_{\text{eff}}V_{\text{eff}} \cos\theta$$

$\cos\theta$ is called the power factor of the circuit.

The transformer is considered as a device for converting a power source from, say, a high-voltage, low-current supply to a lower-voltage, higher-current source without appreciable loss of power. To a good approximation, the voltage rate between input and output of the transformer is given by the ratio of turns in the input and output winding.

$$\frac{V_1}{V_2} = \frac{n_1}{n_2}$$

The chapter concludes with a short discussion of some practical generators and motors.

Even though this chapter discusses only the simplest ac circuit problems, it should make apparent the great simplicity of the complex number formulation of ac problems. Once the basic ideas of ac circuit behavior are understood on the basis of rotating generating vectors, the polar form of complex nomenclature is simple to apply.

PROBLEMS

The first group of problems is included as a review of the nomenclature and concepts used in simple ac circuits.

11.1A An inductance of L henrys and a resistance of R ohms are connected in series across a source of ac voltage given by $V = V_0 \sin \omega t$.

a Find the current i in the circuit and the phase angle between the voltage source and the current. Explain the meaning of phase angle.

b What is the phase angle between the current in the inductance and the current in the resistance?

c What is the phase angle between the voltage across the inductance and the voltage across the resistance?

d Find the amplitude of the voltage V_R across the resistance, and the amplitude V_L of the voltage across the inductance.

e Explain why $|V_R| + |V_L| \neq V_0$. Prove that the *vector* sum $\mathbf{V}_R + \mathbf{V}_L = \mathbf{V}_0$.

★11.1B In Prob. 11.1A, replace the inductance L by a capacitance C farads and answer the same questions.

11.1C   *a*   Compute the inductive reactance of a 2-henry inductor at 60 cps.

         b   Compute the capacitative reactance of a 50-μf capacitor at 60 cps.

         c   At what frequency would the reactances of these two elements be equal in magnitude?

         d   Plot a qualitative curve of the reactance of each as a function of frequency.

★11.1D   A tightly wound circular coil of area A has N turns of wire and rotates about its diameter, which is perpendicular to a uniform magnetic field B. It has a frequency of rotation $\omega = 2\pi f$. The coil has a self-inductance L, and is connected to an external resistance R. Assume that the field in the coil due to the current in the coil is negligible compared with the external field.

         a   Write the expression for the magnetic flux linkage through the coil as a function of the angle $\theta = \omega t$ between the plane of the coil and the direction of B.

         b   Write the expression for the emf induced in the coil.

         c   What is the amplitude of this emf?

         d   Find the current in the coil.

         e   Find the phase angle between the induced emf and the current, and explain what this means.

         f   What is the phase angle between the voltage across the external resistance and the current through it?

         g   What is the phase angle between the voltage across the coil and the current through it?

11.1E   A 60-cps voltage is placed across a 400-ohm resistance in series with a capacitor of unknown capacitance. An ac voltmeter across the source reads 80 volts, and an ac ammeter (of negligible resistance) in the circuit reads 0.1 amp. Calculate

         a   The impedance of the circuit

         b   The power dissipation in the circuit

         c   The value of the capacitance

Peak, average, and rms values of ac electrical quantities must be understood when dealing with ac problems.

11.2A   A 60-cps voltage of amplitude 120 volts is placed across a pure resistance of 20 ohms. What is the rms value of the applied voltage? Find the peak current, average current, rms current, and power dissipation.

11.2B   A pure inductance of 0.2 henry is placed across a 400-cps voltage source of amplitude 120 volts. Find the peak current, average current, rms current, and power dissipation.

11.2C   Show that the average value of a sinusoidal alternating current during the positive half-cycle is $2I_0/\pi$, where I_0 is the current amplitude.

11.2D   Calculate the rms value of a voltage given by
$V = 50 \sin \omega t + 20 \sin 2\omega t$

Series and parallel *LCR* circuits exhibit resonant behavior.

*11.3A   A series circuit as shown in Fig. P11.1 has resistance R_1, R_2 ohms, capacitance C farads, and inductance L henrys. An ac voltage of amplitude V_0 volts is placed across the circuit.

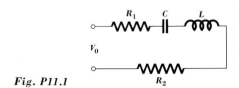

Fig. P11.1

a   For what frequency will the current in the circuit be a maximum?
b   What will be the value of the maximum current?
c   For what frequencies will the current be one-half its maximum value?
d   For what frequencies will the current be a minimum?

11.3B   A parallel *LCR* circuit as shown in Fig. P11.2 has an ac voltage of amplitude V_0 applied.

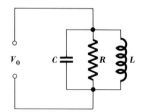

Fig. P11.2

a   For what frequency is the current in the capacitance C the same magnitude as the current in the inductance L? ´
b   For what frequency is the current through the ac source a maximum? A minimum?
c   For what frequencies is the current through the ac source twice the minimum value?

The transient behavior of circuits containing inductance or capacitance can be determined by solving the appropriate differential equations.

*11.4A   The switch in the circuit shown in Fig. P11.3 is closed at $t = 0$.

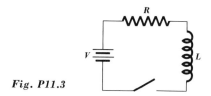

Fig. P11.3

a   Make a qualitative plot of the potential V_R across the resistance
R as a function of time. On the same time scale plot V_L, the
potential across the inductance L. Add the two curves to get the
sum $V_R + V_L$.

b   At what time does $V_R = V_L$?

c   What is the characteristic time of this circuit?

11.4B   Suppose that after the switch in the circuit shown in Fig. P11.3 has
been closed for a time long compared with the characteristic time of
the circuit, the switch is almost instantaneously opened. Make a
qualitative plot of the voltages V_R and V_L versus time. Can you see
any limitation on the speed with which the current can be reduced to
zero?

*11.4C   a   In the circuit shown in Fig. P11.4, find the time after the switch
is closed when the voltage $V_R = V_C$.

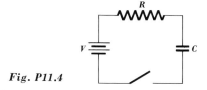

Fig. P11.4

b   What is the maximum current that can flow in the circuit, and
when does this maximum occur?

c   What is the maximum charge on the capacitance and when does
this occur?

d   Show that the current in the circuit drops down to half its original
value at the same time as the charge on the capacitor reaches half
its final value. What is the time after closing the switch that these
two events occur?

11.4D   An induction coil of inductance 10 henrys and resistance 100 ohms
is connected to a 20-volt battery. What resistance must be con-

nected in parallel with the coil in order to prevent the voltage across the coil from rising above 100 volts when the battery circuit is suddenly opened? What is the initial rate of decrease of current in the inductance?

This problem tests your understanding of transformer action, using a strange design for the ferromagnetic core.

★11.5A   A transformer, as shown in Fig. P11.5, has n_1 primary turns and n_2 secondary turns. Sixty percent of the magnetic induction flux due to current in the primary goes through the shorting branch A. Find the ratio of primary to secondary voltage with no load on the secondary.

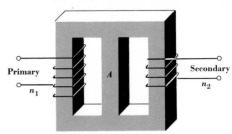

Fig. P11.5

12

Maxwell's equations and electromagnetic waves

12.1 Introduction

The fundamental experimental facts about electricity and magnetism studies so far include all but one of the basic ideas of the modern theory of this subject. In this chapter we indicate the revolutionary work of Maxwell, published in 1865, which took the individual and seemingly unconnected phenomena of electricity and magnetism and brought them together into a coherent and unified theory. Maxwell's theoretical work showed up a missing principle and led to his postulation of energy transmission by *electromagnetic waves*. Maxwell's discovery that electromagnetic waves should travel with a velocity extremely close to that known experimentally for the velocity of light led him to conclude that light itself is an electromagnetic wave, as had been suggested earlier by Faraday.

12.2 The General Theory of Electromagnetism

We begin by rewriting the experimentally determined equations discussed earlier in a more generalized form equivalent to the formulation by Maxwell. For simplicity we consider the case of a vacuum in which there may be a charge density σ coul/m² and a current density **j** amp/m². The modifications necessary in the presence of dielectric and magnetic materials are discussed later.

The first Maxwell equation to be written is simply a statement of Faraday's law of induction. We call this the Maxwell equation for induced electric fields. It gives the circulation, or curl, of **E** resulting from a changing magnetic flux. Faraday's law for the induced emf is

$$\mathcal{E} = -\frac{\partial \phi}{\partial t} \tag{9.1}$$

where $\partial \phi/\partial t$ is the rate of change of flux within the area enclosed by the path. Using

$$\oint \mathbf{E} \cdot d\mathbf{l} = \mathcal{E} \tag{9.2}$$

to express the emf in terms of the circulation of the electric field **E**, and

$$\phi = \int \mathbf{B} \cdot d\mathbf{S} \tag{8.19}$$

to relate magnetic flux ϕ to the field **B**, Faraday's law may be written

$$\oint \mathbf{E} \cdot d\mathbf{l} = -\int \frac{\partial \mathbf{B}}{\partial t} \cdot d\mathbf{S} \tag{12.1}$$

This is the integral form of the Maxwell equation for induced **E** field, relating the line integral of the field **E** over any closed path to the time rate of change of **B**, integrated over the area enclosed by the path. This same idea can be expressed in differential form, using the results of Appendix B. The result is

$$\text{curl } \mathbf{E} = -\frac{\partial \mathbf{B}}{\partial t} \tag{12.1a}$$

Qualitatively, either form of this Maxwell equation tells us that in a region where the magnetic field changes with time, an electric field is set up.

Since, in a vacuum, $\mathbf{B} = \mu_0 \mathbf{H}$, the expressions for the time rate of change of field can be written $\mu_0(\partial \mathbf{H}/\partial t)$. Nothing new has been added to the previous statement of Faraday's law, but the present formulation emphasizes the fact that this is a property of space and does not depend on the presence of a conducting loop of wire.

The next two Maxwell equations are a consequence of the inverse-square law of force, applied to the electric and magnetic fields. We give them in both the integral and differential forms. The first of these we call the Maxwell electric flux equation.

$$\int_{CS} \mathbf{E} \cdot d\mathbf{S} = \frac{1}{\epsilon_0} \int_V \rho \, dV \tag{2.9}$$

or

$$\text{div } \mathbf{E} = \frac{1}{\epsilon_0} \rho \tag{2.10}$$

If the charge density ρ is zero in the region considered, the right-hand terms become zero.

The analogous equation for the magnetic field, which we call the Maxwell magnetic flux equation, is

$$\int_{CS} \mathbf{B} \cdot d\mathbf{S} = 0 \tag{8.20}$$

or

$$\text{div } \mathbf{B} = 0 \tag{8.21}$$

We have now written three of the four fundamental relationships of Maxwell. In the next section we see the way in which Maxwell was led to the fourth and final relation, involving the new concept of *displacement current*.

12.3 Displacement Current

In the process of unifying electromagnetic theory, Maxwell discovered the final relationship that leads to the possibility of electromagnetic waves. This relationship is the converse of Faraday's law, as given in Eq. (12.1). Maxwell showed that, just as a varying magnetic field gives rise to an electric field, a varying electric field gives rise to a magnetic field. The argument given here is similar to the one given by Maxwell.

We begin by examining the generalized form of Ampère's law for the production of a magnetic field by a current:

$$\oint \mathbf{B} \cdot d\mathbf{l} = \mu_0 i \tag{8.14}$$

An equivalent form is

$$\oint \mathbf{B} \cdot d\mathbf{l} = \mu_0 \int \mathbf{j} \cdot d\mathbf{S} \tag{12.2}$$

Here the line integral is taken around any closed path, and the surface integral is taken over *any* surface bounded by the path of the line integral. The surface integral of the current density $\mathbf{j}$ is the total current threading the path of the line integral. When we choose the path so that **B** is constant and parallel to the path, **B** can be evaluated, as we have seen earlier. Figure 12.1 illustrates the idea that *any* surface

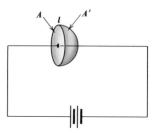

Fig. 12.1 Two areas A and A' bounded by the same closed line l. The integral $\mu_0 \int \mathbf{j} \cdot d\mathbf{S}$ has the same value over any surface bounded by the same line.

bounded by the path of the line integral gives the same result. In the case of a wire carrying the current, we know this is true since the surface integral is always equal to i as long as the wire threads the path. The figure shows one plane surface A and one hemispherical surface A', both bounded by the same line l.

We now examine the situation when the battery is replaced by an ac source and a capacitor is included in the circuit, as shown in Fig. 12.2. An ac current passes through a capacitor, as we have seen earlier,

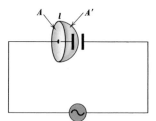

Fig. 12.2 The battery of Fig. 12.1 has been replaced by an ac source and a capacitor included in the circuit. The integral $\oint \mathbf{B} \cdot d\mathbf{l}$ over the area A is i; it is zero over A' unless displacement current is taken into account.

though no actual charge is transferred between the plates. Maxwell's reasoning involved taking the two areas A and A', bounded by the same path l. He pointed out that, according to Eq. (12.2), when the surface integral is taken over A, the integral $\oint \mathbf{B} \cdot d\mathbf{l} = \mu_0 i$, but if it is taken over A', the integral equals 0. This contradictory situation can be remedied only if we postulate, with Maxwell, an additional term in Eq. (12.2) in which the changing electric field occurring in the capacitor takes the place of the real current as a producer of the magnetic field.

This step is more than just a formalism. Maxwell's reasoning indicated that in any region of space in which the electric field is changing with time, a magnetic field is produced. This postulation not only removes the double meaning of the mathematics of Eq. (12.2) in the ac case, but in the process also suggests a completely new source of magnetic field.

A simple parallel-plate capacitor can be used to arrive at a formal expression for the effect. Since the current is the rate at which charge accumulates on the capacitor plates (because charge is conserved), we can write

$$i = \int \mathbf{j} \cdot d\mathbf{S}$$

But $i = dq/dt = A \, d\sigma/dt$, or $j = d\sigma/dt$. We have already seen that, between the plates of a parallel-plate capacitor, $E = (1/\epsilon_0)\sigma$; so $d\sigma/dt$ can be replaced by $\epsilon_0 \, dE/dt$. We have thus developed a new term to be added to Eq. (12.2) whenever there is a changing electric field. The term to be added involves $\epsilon_0 \, \partial E/\partial t$, which plays the same role as the current density $\mathbf{j}$, and is called the *displacement current density*. The complete equation then becomes

$$\oint \mathbf{B} \cdot d\mathbf{l} = \mu_0 \epsilon_0 \int \frac{\partial \mathbf{E}}{\partial t} \cdot d\mathbf{S} + \mu_0 \int \mathbf{j} \cdot d\mathbf{S} \tag{12.3}$$

We call this the Maxwell equation for induced magnetic field.

It is often useful to express this result in terms of $\mathbf{D}$ and $\mathbf{H}$ as developed in Chaps. 5 and 10. In a vacuum it is easy to show that Eq. (12.3) becomes

$$\oint \mathbf{H} \cdot d\mathbf{l} = \int \frac{\partial D}{\partial t} \cdot d\mathbf{S} + \int \mathbf{j} \cdot d\mathbf{S} \tag{12.4}$$

The integral containing $\mathbf{D}$ gives the displacement current. The differential form of these equations is

$$\text{curl } \mathbf{B} = \mu_0 \epsilon_0 \frac{\partial \mathbf{E}}{\partial t} + \mu_0 \mathbf{j} \tag{12.3a}$$

or

$$\text{curl } \mathbf{H} = \frac{\partial \mathbf{D}}{\partial t} + \mathbf{j} \tag{12.4a}$$

For most situations involving conducting bodies, the new term involving the displacement current is trivial compared with the current term at low frequencies. In the absence of currents, however, it is the only term.

Since we show below that this new concept of magnetic field generation by displacement current is necessary to account for electromagnetic waves, we may consider the proved existence of such waves as the final proof of the validity of Maxwell's reasoning.

The development of the idea that light is an electromagnetic radiation is one of the most dramatic in the history of physics. We quote below from the introduction to the paper[1] in which Maxwell announced the electromagnetic theory of light. In the introduction, Maxwell summarizes the results of his mathematical investigations, describing eight relationships, which he calls the general equations of the electromagnetic field. These are essentially equivalent to the four relationships now called Maxwell's equations. Maxwell then goes on to discuss some of the implications of his results in the following paragraphs:

> The general equations are next applied to the case of a magnetic disturbance propagated through a nonconducting field, and it is shown that the only disturbances which can be so propagated are those which are transverse to the direction of propagation, and that the velocity of propagation is the velocity v, found from experiments such as those of Weber, which expresses the number of electrostatic units of electricity which are contained in one electromagnetic unit.
>
> This velocity is so nearly that of light, that it seems we have strong reason to conclude that light itself (including radiant heat, and other radiations if any) is an electromagnetic disturbance in the form of waves propagated through the electromagnetic field according to electromagnetic laws. If so, the agreement between the elasticity of the medium as calculated from the rapid alternations of luminous vibrations, and as found by the slow processes of electrical experiments, shows how perfect and regular the elastic properties of the medium must be when not encumbered with any matter denser than air. If the same character of the elasticity is retained in dense transparent bodies, it appears that the square of the index of refraction is equal to the product of the specific dielectric capacity and the specific magnetic capacity. Conducting media are shown to absorb such radiations rapidly, and therefore to be generally opaque.
>
> The conception of the propagation of transverse magnetic disturbances to the exclusion of normal ones is distinctly set forth by Professor Faraday in his "Thoughts on Ray Vibrations." The electromagnetic theory of light, as proposed by him, is the same in substance as that which I have begun to develop in this paper, except that in 1846 there were no data to calculate the velocity of propagation.

[1] James Clerk Maxwell, A Dynamical Theory of the Electromagnetic Field, *Phil. Trans. Roy. Soc. London,* **155:**459 (1865).

12.4   The Physics and Mathematics of Waves

Our next task is to see how Maxwell's general formulation of electromagnetism leads to self-propagating waves. Before doing this, however,
it is useful to review the simple theory of traveling waves. We discuss
the simple situation of wave propagation on a stretched string.

Figure 12.3 shows a section of a long string tied tightly at both

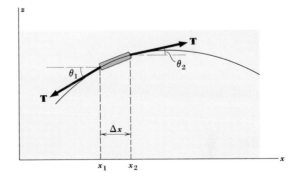

**Fig. 12.3   Element on a stretched string, used
for developing traveling-wave equation. *T* is
the tension in the string.**

ends, under a tension T. A section of the string has been pulled transversely in the direction z and then released. As a result, a wave of displacement travels down the string in the x direction. We concentrate
our attention on a small segment Δx of the string, in order to work out
the way in which the wave moves along the string. The motion of the
segment is obtained by applying Newton's second law; so we first work
out the external forces acting on it as a result of the tension in the string.

The diagram shows that the components of force along the x
direction cancel out for small displacement. Let ΔF_x be the net force in
the x direction. Then we find

$$\Delta F_x = T \cos \theta_2 - T \cos \theta_1 \approx 0$$

since for small displacements $\cos \theta_2 \approx \cos \theta_1$. As a result of this, the
motion of the segment is only along the z direction. The net force along
the z direction is given by

$$\Delta F_z = T \sin \theta_2 - T \sin \theta_1 \qquad\qquad (12.5)$$

For small displacements,

$$\sin \theta_1 \approx \tan \theta_1 = s_1$$
$$\sin \theta_2 \approx \tan \theta_2 = s_2$$

where s_1 and s_2 are the slopes of the line at x_1 and x_2. That is,

$$s = \frac{dz}{dx} \tag{12.6}$$

For small Δx, we may write

$$s_2 = s_1 + \frac{ds}{dx} \Delta x \qquad \text{or} \qquad s_2 - s_1 = \frac{ds}{dx} \Delta x \tag{12.7}$$

Here it is assumed that the rate of change of slope is linear with x over the small distance Δx. With this approximation, we may rewrite Eq. (12.5) as

$$\Delta F_z = T \frac{ds}{dx} \Delta x \tag{12.8}$$

We now apply Newton's law to the segment, noting that its mass can be written $\Delta m = \rho(x_2 - x_1) = \rho \, \Delta x$, where ρ is the mass density of the string:

$$\Delta F_z = \Delta m \frac{dv_z}{dt} \qquad \text{or} \qquad T \frac{ds}{dx} \Delta x = \rho \, \Delta x \frac{dv_z}{dt}$$

When Δx is canceled in the last equation, we find

$$\rho \frac{\partial v_z}{\partial t} = T \frac{\partial s}{\partial x} \tag{12.9}$$

an equation that relates acceleration to the rate of change of slope along x. We take the derivative of Eq. (12.9) with respect to time to get

$$\rho \frac{\partial^2 v_z}{\partial t^2} = T \frac{\partial^2 s}{\partial x \, \partial t} \tag{12.10}$$

Finally, we simplify this by using the following relationships:

$$v_z = \frac{\partial z}{\partial t} \rightarrow \frac{\partial v_z}{\partial x} = \frac{\partial^2 z}{\partial x \, \partial t}$$

$$s = \frac{\partial z}{\partial x} \rightarrow \frac{\partial s}{\partial t} = \frac{\partial^2 z}{\partial x \, \partial t}$$

Therefore $\quad \dfrac{\partial s}{\partial t} = \dfrac{\partial v_z}{\partial x}$ \hfill (12.11)

When we differentiate Eq. (12.11) with respect to x, we find

$$\frac{\partial^2 s}{\partial t\, \partial x} = \frac{\partial^2 v_z}{\partial x^2} \qquad (12.12)$$

Substitution in Eq. (12.10) then gives

$$\rho\, \frac{\partial^2 v_z}{\partial t^2} = T\, \frac{\partial^2 v_z}{\partial x^2} \qquad (12.13)$$

This final equation is the differential equation for a transverse traveling wave on a string. It is essentially the equivalent of $F = ma$, giving the transverse acceleration in terms of the effective force, $T\, \partial^2 v_z/\partial x^2$.

Whenever an equation of the form of Eq. (12.13) appears, showing a constant proportionality between the second space and time derivatives of some quantity, we can be sure that a traveling wave can exist.

In the case of the equation for a string, we can verify at once that the differential equation implies wave motion along the string. It is necessary only to show that the differential equation is satisfied by an equation for a transverse traveling wave. We take

$$v_z = v_0 \cos \frac{2\pi}{\lambda}\, (x - ut) \qquad (12.14)$$

which is a transverse-velocity sinusoidal wave of wavelength λ traveling with a velocity u along the positive x direction. Substitution of the appropriate derivatives of this equation in (12.13) shows that the velocity of travel is given by

$$u = \sqrt{\frac{T}{\rho}}$$

On this basis Eq. (12.13) can be written in the form

$$\frac{\partial^2 v_z}{\partial x^2} = \frac{1}{u^2}\, \frac{\partial^2 v_z}{\partial t^2} \qquad (12.13a)$$

In this case the transverse velocity v_z is the quantity involved, but equally well it could have been written in terms of the transverse displacement z.

$$\frac{\partial^2 z}{\partial x^2} = \frac{1}{u^2}\, \frac{\partial^2 z}{\partial t^2} \qquad (12.13b)$$

The important point is that whenever *any* parameter z obeys an equation of this form, involving a constant relationship between a second space derivative and second time derivative of the parameter, a traveling wave is indicated, whose velocity is u as given.

It is now demonstrated explicitly that Eq. (12.14) represents a wave traveling along the x direction, in this case in the positive direction, with a velocity u and a wavelength λ. The wavelength is determined by holding t constant and noting that if we move from some position x_0 to a new position $x_0 + \lambda$, the argument of the cosine goes from $2\pi(x_0 - ut)/\lambda$ to $2\pi(x_0 + \lambda - ut)/\lambda = 2\pi(x_0 - ut)/\lambda + 2\pi$. Since the cosine is repetitive with a period 2π, it has the same phase at these two positions; so v_z at these positions has the same phase. This result holds for all positions $x_0 + n\lambda$, where n is an integer; so λ is the wavelength of the disturbance. The velocity of the wave is determined by choosing a point x along the wave at a time t and requiring that this point move along x with a velocity such that $(x - ut) = $ constant. Under this condition the cosine remains constant and the point moves with the velocity of the disturbance. If the time is increased by dt, the position x must increase by dx so that

$$x + dx - u(t + dt) = x - ut$$

This requires that $dx - u\,dt = 0$, or $dx/dt = u$. We have thus shown that u is the wave velocity. For a wave traveling in the negative x direction, Eq. (12.14) is written

$$v_z = v_0 \cos \frac{2\pi}{\lambda}(x + ut) \tag{12.14a}$$

We may also use Eq. (12.14) to deduce the relationship between frequency f, wavelength λ, and u, the velocity of wave propagation. For this purpose we stay at one position along the x axis (at $x = 0$ for convenience). The argument of the cosine then becomes $2\pi ut/\lambda$. The disturbance that propagates along x then results in a periodic variation in v_z at the point $x = 0$ we have chosen. If we now let time advance from t to $t + \lambda/u$, the argument of the cosine becomes $2\pi ut/\lambda + 2\pi$, which gives the same value to v_z as for t. Thus λ/u is the *period* or u/λ the *frequency* f of the disturbance, and we have

$$\lambda f = u \tag{12.15}$$

We could equally well have made this discussion in terms of an equation for the *displacement* of the string z, from its equilibrium position,

$$z = z_0 \sin \frac{2\pi}{\lambda}(x - ut) \tag{12.16}$$

It is common practice to modify the modulus of the sine or cosine, $(2\pi/\lambda)(x + ut)$, by introducing the *wave vector*

$$k = \frac{2\pi}{\lambda} \tag{12.17}$$

and the *angular frequency*

$$\omega = 2\pi f \tag{12.18}$$

With this change, Eq. (12.15) becomes

$$k = \frac{\omega}{u} \tag{12.19}$$

and the modulus of the sine or cosine becomes

$$(\omega t \pm kx) \tag{12.20}$$

An alternative form often used is

$$\omega\left(t \pm \frac{x}{u}\right) \tag{12.21}$$

Using Eq. (12.20), the general equation for a traveling wave becomes

$$z = z_0 \sin(\omega t \pm kx) \tag{12.22}$$

or in complex exponential notation,

$$z = z_0 e^{j(\omega t \pm kx)} \tag{12.23}$$

This last form includes both the sine and cosine form of the wave. The sign of the term $(\omega t \pm kx)$ does not affect the direction of travel of the wave. The direction of the wave is positive if ωt and kx have opposite signs and negative if they have the same sign.

Although for simplicity we limit discussion of waves to sinusoidal waves, it is possible to show with very little more trouble that *any* reasonable function of $(\omega t \pm kx)$ satisfies the differential equation for a traveling wave.

Appendix J discusses the more complicated kinds of wave motion which result when the velocity of the wave varies with its frequency. The discussion develops the ideas of *phase* and *group* velocities, which are essential to the understanding of waves traveling through a *dispersive* medium, that is, one in which the velocity of a wave depends on its frequency.

12.5   *Electromagnetic Waves*

Maxwell's equations provide the framework for the discussion of the many situations in which electromagnetic energy propagates, in a vacuum, in a dielectric medium, or in a conducting medium. Here we consider only the simplest case, that of a wave propagating in a vacuum. For convenience we rewrite Maxwell's equations in integral form as they would apply in free space with zero charge density ($\sigma = 0$) and with no currents ($\mathbf{j} = 0$).

$$\oint \mathbf{E} \cdot d\mathbf{l} = - \int \frac{\partial \mathbf{B}}{\partial t} \cdot d\mathbf{S} \tag{12.1}$$

$$\oint \mathbf{B} \cdot d\mathbf{l} = \mu_0 \epsilon_0 \int \frac{\partial \mathbf{E}}{\partial t} \cdot d\mathbf{S} \tag{12.24}$$

$$\int_{cs} \mathbf{E} \cdot d\mathbf{S} = 0 \tag{12.25}$$

$$\int_{cs} \mathbf{B} \cdot d\mathbf{S} = 0 \tag{8.20}$$

For reference, we also write these equations in differential form, again assuming $\sigma = 0$ and $\mathbf{j} = 0$.

$$\text{curl } \mathbf{E} = - \frac{\partial \mathbf{B}}{\partial t} \tag{12.1a}$$

$$\text{curl } \mathbf{B} = \mu_0 \epsilon_0 \frac{\partial \mathbf{E}}{\partial t} \tag{12.3a}$$

$$\text{div } \mathbf{E} = 0 \tag{2.10}$$

$$\text{div } \mathbf{B} = 0 \tag{8.21}$$

We consider a plane wave propagating along the x axis. In Sec. 12.7 we show that for a plane wave, the electric and magnetic fields involved in the wave are directed transverse to the direction of travel (in the yz plane). In the meantime we assume this, and further specialize our model by assuming a *polarized* wave, one in which the electric field is along only the y direction. This field E_y depends only on x and t. We shall see below that $\mathbf{B}$ is similarly limited and is in the z direction, perpendicular to $\mathbf{E}$. Figure 12.4 is a sketch of the $\mathbf{E}$ vectors (*not* lines of force) that would exist. Only the variation with x is shown. The variation with time could be shown by making a number of sketches in which the position of the wave along the x axis is different for each time chosen. A sinusoidal variation is drawn here, but this is not required. The vectors are shown only along the x axis of our coordinate system. In this plane wave the same $\mathbf{E}$ fields exist for *all* positions in

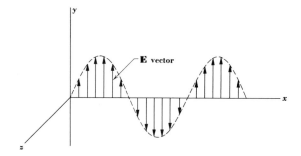

Fig. 12.4 **E** *vectors in xy plane, showing variation of* **E** *with x in the case of a polarized wave.*

the yz plane having a given value of x. Our demonstration involves the use of the first two Maxwell equations to show that such a postulated time and space variation of **E** gives rise to a similar time and space variation of **B** (but at right angles to **E**) and that this **B** variation acts back to cause the postulated variation in **E**. Thus, once such a wave is initiated, it is self-propagating.

Figure 12.5 is used to show the application of Eq. (12.1) to the

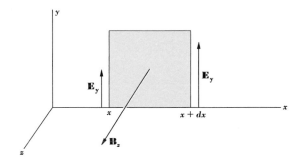

Fig. 12.5 *Generation of B$_z$ by a varying E$_y$, showing application of Maxwell's induction equation to the* **E** *component of the plane wave.*

plane **E** wave, postulated to be moving along the x direction. A convenient closed path is drawn in the xy plane, around which we shall take the line integral of **E**. This is equated through (12.1) to the time rate of change of flux of **B** through the plane bounded by the path of the line integral. Only the vertical parts of the line integral contribute since **E** is in the y direction, so that $\mathbf{E} \cdot d\mathbf{x} = 0$. If we go around in a counterclockwise direction, the line integral around the path chosen becomes

$$\oint \mathbf{E} \cdot d\mathbf{l} = (E_y)_{x+dx} \, dy - (E_y)_x \, dy = [(E_y)_{x+dx} - (E_y)_x] \, dy$$

where we are to take the values of E_y at $x + dx$ and x, respectively. The difference between these two values of E_y at the two positions is $(\partial E_y/\partial x) \, dx$; so we can write the line integral of Eq. (12.1) as

$$\frac{\partial E_y}{\partial x} \, dx \, dy = - \frac{\partial B_z}{\partial t} \, dx \, dy$$

Since this relationship is true for *any* area $dx \, dy$, we may write

$$\frac{\partial E_y}{\partial x} = - \frac{\partial B_z}{\partial t} \tag{12.26}$$

The next step is to make the converse calculation of the **B** resulting from a varying **E**, through Eq. (12.24). Using Fig. 12.6, we find, by a

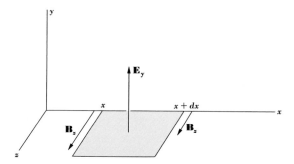

Fig. 12.6   *Generation of E_y by a varying B_z, showing application of Maxwell's induction equation to the **B** component of the plane wave.*

similar calculation,

$$\oint \mathbf{B} \cdot d\mathbf{l} = [(B_z)_x - (B_z)_{x+dx}] \, dz$$

$$= - \frac{\partial B_z}{\partial x} \, dx \, dz = \mu_0 \epsilon_0 \frac{\partial E_y}{\partial t} \, dx \, dz$$

or

$$\frac{\partial B_z}{\partial x} = - \mu_0 \epsilon_0 \frac{\partial E_y}{\partial t} \tag{12.27}$$

Equations (12.26) and (12.27) relate the space variation of one field to the time variation of the other, and vice versa. When we differentiate the first with respect to x and the second with respect to t, we can combine the information into one equation as follows:

$$\frac{\partial^2 E_y}{\partial x^2} = -\frac{\partial^2 B_z}{\partial x\, \partial t}$$

$$\frac{\partial^2 B_z}{\partial x\, \partial t} = -\mu_0 \epsilon_0 \frac{\partial^2 E_y}{\partial t^2}$$

Therefore

$$\frac{\partial^2 E_y}{\partial x^2} = \epsilon_0 \mu_0 \frac{\partial^2 E_y}{\partial t^2} \tag{12.28}$$

When we differentiate in the opposite order, we find that the same equation holds for B_z:

$$\frac{\partial^2 B_z}{\partial x^2} = \epsilon_0 \mu_0 \frac{\partial^2 B_z}{\partial t^2} \tag{12.29}$$

These last two equations give the results we have been working toward. Comparison with Eq. (12.13) for a tranverse wave on a string shows immediately that we have found a differential equation that implies wave propagation. The velocity of propagation along the x direction is given by

$$c = \frac{1}{\sqrt{\epsilon_0 \mu_0}} \tag{12.30}$$

The two fields are perpendicular to each other and travel together in the x direction. The agreement between the experimentally observed velocity of light ($\approx 3 \times 10^8$ m/sec) and the calculated value based on laboratory measurements of ϵ_0 and μ_0 gave the first quantitative proof of the electromagnetic nature of light.

Using the results of Sec. 12.4, we write the equation for the electric field component of the electromagnetic wave,

$$E_y = E_0 \sin (\omega t - kx) \tag{12.31}$$

The equivalent complex exponential form is

$$E_y = E_0 e^{j(\omega t - kx)} \tag{12.31a}$$

The argument $(wt - kx)$ in the last two equations could have been written $(2\pi/\lambda)(x - ct)$, but the form used is often simpler to work with and is more commonly used. Either of the last two equations is a solution of Eq. (12.28). The corresponding equation for the magnetic field is the solution to Eq. (12.29), and is

$$B_z = B_0 \sin (\omega t - kx) \tag{12.32}$$

or

$$B_z = B_0 e^{j(\omega t - kx)} \tag{12.32a}$$

The program of showing how Maxwell's equations lead to electromagnetic waves is now completed. We can use Fig. 12.7 to visualize a plane wave. The wave advances along the x axis at a velocity c.

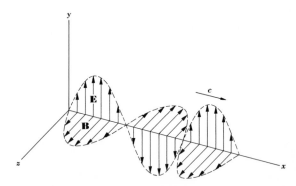

Fig. 12.7   Schematic representation of a plane electromagnetic wave as the wave advances along the x axis at velocity c.

To find the relationship between the magnitudes of the electric and magnetic vectors in the wave, we proceed by differentiating Eq. (12.31) for a sinusoidal wave, with respect to t. This gives

$$\frac{\partial E_y}{\partial t} = E_0 \omega \cos (\omega t - kx)$$

Substitution in Eq. (12.27) gives

$$\frac{\partial B_z}{\partial x} = -\mu_0 \epsilon_0 E_0 \omega \cos (\omega t - kx)$$

which can be integrated with respect to x to give

$$B_z = \mu_0 \epsilon_0 E_0 \omega . \frac{1}{k} \sin (\omega t - kx)$$

For electromagnetic waves in free space, $\omega/k = c$, as shown in Eq. (12.19). Thus this result can be written

$$B_z = \sqrt{\mu_0 \epsilon_0} \, E_0 \sin (\omega t - kx)$$

The same result could have been obtained using the exponential forms for a traveling wave. By comparison with Eq. (12.31), it is apparent that B_z and E_y are in phase, as drawn in Fig. 12.7. The amplitudes of B_z and E_y are related by

$$B_z = \sqrt{\mu_0 \epsilon_0} \, E_y \qquad \text{or} \qquad E_y = c B_z \qquad\qquad (12.33)$$

Unpolarized plane waves are made up of a superposition of polarized plane waves in which the directions of **E** and **B** are randomly distributed in the yz plane. The **E** and **B** of each component of these plane waves are perpendicular to each other.

In Appendix K we show a derivation of the differential wave equation, using the differential forms of Maxwell's equations. Once the meanings of curl and divergence are clearly understood, this alternative treatment is very useful. It involves the same physical ideas as does our more explicit demonstration.

12.6   Electromagnetic Waves in Matter

In the presence of matter the electromagnetic-wave problem can become much more complicated. In general, it is necessary to find solutions to boundary-value problems. In Sec. 12.12 the reflection and refraction of electromagnetic waves at a dielectric boundary are discussed, and in Sec. 12.11 we consider the effect of a boundary of high conductivity. The case of an infinite isotropic medium in which the electromagnetic energy losses are negligible is less complicated. The equations for a plane wave in free space can easily be modified to find the wave velocity and the relationship between the magnitudes of **E** and **B**. We need only replace the free-space constants ϵ_0 and μ_0 by the values ϵ and μ appropriate to the medium.

Thus the velocity of the wave becomes

$$V = \frac{1}{\sqrt{\mu \epsilon}} \qquad\qquad (12.34)$$

and

$$B_z = \sqrt{\mu \epsilon} \, E_y \qquad\qquad (12.35)$$

Materials transparent to electromagnetic waves are those in which the losses are negligible. Since conductivity produces $i^2 R$ losses, conducting materials are generally opaque to electromagnetic waves. Most transparent materials are nonmagnetic. That is, they have magnetic permeabilities μ which are very close to μ_0, the value for free space.

As a result the velocity of a plane wave in a transparent medium is principally determined by the value of the dielectric permittivity ϵ. The ratio of the free-space velocity c to the velocity u in a transparent medium is called the *index of refraction* n of the medium. It can be calculated as follows:

$$n = \frac{c}{u} = \frac{\sqrt{\epsilon\mu}}{\sqrt{\epsilon_0\mu_0}} \approx \frac{\sqrt{\epsilon\mu_0}}{\sqrt{\epsilon_0\mu_0}} = \sqrt{\frac{\epsilon}{\epsilon_0}} = \sqrt{K} \tag{12.36}$$

where K is the dielectric constant of the medium as defined in Eq. (5.15).

Situations in which losses are important are more complicated. Appendix L presents a discussion of the attenuation of an electromagnetic wave incident on a conducting boundary.

12.7   The Transverse Nature of Plane Waves

We now show that for a plane wave traveling in, say, the x direction in free space, the directions of **E** and **B** are limited to the transverse direction (in the yz plane). We do this by taking an elementary cube of dimensions dx, dy, and dz as shown in Fig. 12.8. We apply Eq.

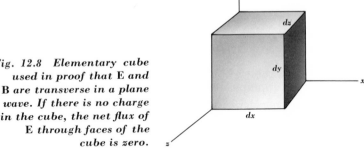

Fig. 12.8   Elementary cube
used in proof that **E** and
B are transverse in a plane
wave. If there is no charge
in the cube, the net flux of
E through faces of the
cube is zero.

(12.25) at some instant to the surface of this cube. This assures that the net flux of **E** through the faces of the cube is zero. Furthermore, since we are dealing with a plane wave, **E** does not vary with y or z; so the net flux through the faces $dx\,dy$ and $dx\,dz$ is zero. This leads us to the conclusion that the net flux through the faces $dy\,dz$ is also zero, since the total flux is zero. Now the flux through the left-hand face $dy\,dz$ is $-E_x\,dy\,dz$ (the negative sign results from the negative sign of the outward normal of this face). The flux through the right-hand $dy\, dz$ is $E_x\, dy\, dz$. It follows that E_x must have the same value at both faces for all times, and therefore it cannot vary with x. Only the space-varying field enters into the traveling wave; so the wave has no field component in the direction of travel. Any E_x which exists is not involved in the wave. A similar proof regarding B_x is obtained through application of Eq. (8.20). We now have shown that both the **E** and **B** components of the wave are limited to the yz plane and are therefore transverse to the direction of propagation.

12.8 Propagation of Energy, the Poynting Vector

The propagation of electric and magnetic fields through space implies the transmission of energy, since **E** and **B** fields involve stored energy. In this section we define and evaluate the energy propagation vector **S**, called the *Poynting vector*. This is the rate of energy flow across a unit area placed perpendicular to the flow direction. In optics this is often called the *intensity*. Its meaning may be understood by considering a volume surrounded by a closed surface and writing an expression for the rate of change of energy within the volume. Let the electromagnetic energy within the volume be U; then the rate of change of this energy is

$$\frac{\partial U}{\partial t} = -\int_{cs} \mathbf{S} \cdot d\mathbf{A} \tag{12.37}$$

Thus the rate of change of energy within the volume is the surface integral of **S** taken over the surface surrounding the volume. Here the usual symbol for an element of surface area, $d\mathbf{S}$, has been replaced by $d\mathbf{A}$ to avoid confusion with the Poynting vector **S**. The negative sign is used to allow for the fact that the integral on the right-hand side of the equation is negative when energy is entering the volume.

Our problem is to evaluate **S** for an electromagnetic wave. We proceed by considering a volume $dx\, dy\, dz$ (Fig. 12.9) through which a

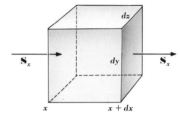

Fig. 12.9 Energy flow of a plane wave through an elementary cube.

plane wave is passing in the x direction. We express the energy within the volume in terms of the electric and magnetic field energies, but will gain some simplicity in the expressions by using the field $\mathbf{H}$ instead of $\mathbf{B}$. But since in free space this merely replaces $\mathbf{B}$ by $\mu_0\mathbf{H}$, or in a medium, by $\mu\mathbf{H}$, it is not a substantial change. The rate of change of the electromagnetic energy is then to be related to the flux of $\mathbf{S}$ across the surface surrounding the volume. From our previous results, the energy in the volume is

$$U = \left(\frac{\epsilon_0 E_y{}^2}{2} + \frac{\mu_0 H_z{}^2}{2}\right) dx\, dy\, dz \tag{12.38}$$

and by differentiating with respect to time, we get

$$\frac{\partial U}{\partial t} = \left(\epsilon_0 E_y \frac{\partial E_y}{\partial t} + \mu_0 H_z \frac{\partial H_z}{\partial t}\right) dx\, dy\, dz$$

We have chosen, as before, a plane wave with $\mathbf{E}$ and $\mathbf{H}$ in the y and z directions, respectively. We now replace the time derivatives of E_y and H_z by space derivatives, using Eqs. (12.26) and (12.27). Hence

$$\frac{\partial U}{\partial t} = -\left(E_y \frac{\partial H_z}{\partial x} + H_z \frac{\partial E_y}{\partial x}\right) dx\, dy\, dz$$

$$= -\frac{\partial}{\partial x}(E_y H_z)\, dx\, dy\, dz \tag{12.39}$$

We next put $\int_{CS} \mathbf{S} \cdot d\mathbf{A}$ in the same form as Eq. (12.39) so that $\mathbf{S}$ may be evaluated in terms of E_y and H_z. For a plane wave traveling in the x direction, energy flow must be in the x direction only (since E_y and H_z depend only on x and t); so the flow of energy into and out of the volume is through the $dy\, dz$ faces only, and $\mathbf{S}$ is in the x direction. Thus

$$\int_{CS} \mathbf{S} \cdot d\mathbf{A} = (S_x\, dy\, dz)_{x+dx} - (S_x\, dy\, dz)_x$$

$$= [(S_x)_{x+dx} - (S_x)_x]\, dy\, dz$$

The term in brackets may be written $(\partial S_x/\partial x)\, dx$; so the last equation may be written

$$\int_{CS} \mathbf{S} \cdot d\mathbf{A} = \frac{\partial S_x}{\partial x}\, dx\, dy\, dz \tag{12.40}$$

We may now compare Eqs. (12.39) and (12.40) by means of Eq. (12.37) to find

$$\frac{\partial}{\partial x}(E_y H_z)\, dx\, dy\, dz = \frac{\partial S_x}{\partial x}\, dx\, dy\, dz$$

and since this equation holds for any arbitrary volume, it must be that

$$\frac{\partial}{\partial x}(E_y H_z) = \frac{\partial S_x}{\partial x}$$

Integration with respect to x gives

$$S_x = E_y H_z \tag{12.41}$$

plus a constant, which may be neglected.

For the general case, $\mathbf{S}$ is given by the vector product

$$\mathbf{S} = \mathbf{E} \times \mathbf{H} \qquad \text{joules/sec-m}^2, \text{ or watts/m}^2 \tag{12.42}$$

The Poynting vector $\mathbf{S}$ thus gives the magnitude of the energy flow. The direction of energy flow is perpendicular to the plane containing $\mathbf{E}$ and $\mathbf{H}$ and is in the direction of the vector $\mathbf{E} \times \mathbf{H}$. The Poynting vector can be written, alternatively, as $\mathbf{S} = (1/\mu_0)(\mathbf{E} \times \mathbf{B})$.

In Eq. (12.42), $\mathbf{E}$ and $\mathbf{H}$ refer to instantaneous values. In the case of sinusoidally varying fields, the average value of $\mathbf{S}$ is given by

$$\mathbf{S} = \mathbf{E}_{\text{eff}} \times \mathbf{H}_{\text{eff}}$$

or, since $\mathbf{E}_{\text{eff}} = \mathbf{E}_0/\sqrt{2}$ and $\mathbf{H}_{eff} = \mathbf{H}_0/\sqrt{2}$, where $\mathbf{E}_0$ and $\mathbf{H}_0$ are amplitudes,

$$\mathbf{S} = \tfrac{1}{2}(\mathbf{E}_0 \times \mathbf{H}_0)$$

A word of caution is necessary in regard to the application of $\mathbf{S} = \mathbf{E} \times \mathbf{H}$. This expression is valid only when applied to a closed surface surrounding a volume

$$\int_{cs} \mathbf{S} \cdot d\mathbf{A}$$

For example, suppose we take the static case of a charged capacitor placed between the poles of a magnet in an orientation such that $\mathbf{E} \perp \mathbf{H}$. The Poynting vector $\mathbf{S}$ evaluated over an area perpendicular to $\mathbf{S}$ is finite, and would indicate a flow of energy. But if the surface taken completely surrounds a volume, whether or not it includes part or all of the capacitor, the calculated net flow of energy into or out of the volume chosen would be zero.

12.9 Example, Poynting Vector

Within the limitation expressed above, the Poynting vector provides a valid method for calculating the flow of electromagnetic energy into or out of any volume. We show an example in which **E** and **H** are constant in time. Consider a cylindrical resistor (Fig. 12.10) of length

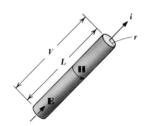

Fig. 12.10 Calculation of energy flow into a resistor. The Poynting vector S = E × H is directed inward at the surface of the resistor.

L, radius r, and resistance R, across which a potential difference V is applied. The rate at which energy is dissipated in this resistor is i^2R. We show that

$$\int_{CS} \mathbf{S} \cdot d\mathbf{A} = i^2R \tag{12.43}$$

That is, the flow of energy through the surface of the resistor, as measured by the integral of the Poynting vector, accounts for the rate of conversion of electric energy to heat within the resistor.

The calculation involves the determination of **E** and **H** over the surface of the resistor. **E** is pointed along the curved surface and has the value $V/L = iR/L$. Lines of **H** make circles around the resistor and, from Ampère's circuital law, have the value $H = i/2\pi r$ at the surface. Application of $\mathbf{S} = \mathbf{E} \times \mathbf{H}$ shows that **S** is pointed inward at the curved surface of the resistor (and is parallel to the end surfaces). Evaluation of the integral over the entire resistor surface then gives

$$\int_{CS} \mathbf{S} \cdot d\mathbf{A} = \int EH \, dA = \frac{iR}{L} \frac{i}{2\pi r} 2\pi rL = i^2R$$

Since **S** is parallel to the end surfaces, the integral over these surfaces is zero. We have proved the statement of Eq. (12.43).

12.10* Generation of Electromagnetic Waves

The problem of generation of electromagnetic waves can now be sketched. The complete solution to the problem shows that whenever

electric charges are accelerated, electromagnetic energy is radiated.
One experimental arrangement that is useful for the study of the problem is the oscillating dipole, shown in Fig. 12.11. If an ac source of

*Fig. 12.11 Oscillating di-
pole, showing crossed E
and H fields resulting from
currents and charges on
the vertical wires. The near
field of the dipole has an
oscillating Poynting vector
which moves energy in and
out from the dipole. At the
instant shown, the
Poynting vector is directed
outward at the point P. At
greater distances there is a
net flow of energy into a
propagating field, pro-
duced by the time-varying
E and H fields.*

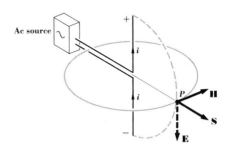

current is connected to wires as shown, charges will move back and
forth along the vertical wires, producing alternately an electric dipole
pointed up and then down. Currents also flow in the wire, producing
lines of **B** which periodically reverse direction. When the charges near
the ends of the wire are at a maximum, the current will be zero. Thus
the electric field **E** at some point P near the wire will be a maximum
when **B** is zero, and vice versa. **B** and **E** are 90° out of phase in time.
Since lines of **B** circle the current, and lines of **E** have a component
normal to the plane of **B**, the Poynting vector has a finite value
$\mathbf{S} = (1/\mu_0)(\mathbf{E} \times \mathbf{B})$. But at any point such as P, the fact that **E** and **B**
are 90° out of phase ensures that the direction of energy flow alternates
regularly between outward and inward directions; so the net energy
flow is zero. The *near field* of the oscillating dipole moves energy in and
out equally, and does not result in a radiated wave. This pulsating field
falls off as $1/r^3$, just as does the static field of a dipole, and is therefore
not in any case important at large distances.

There is another effect, however, that becomes more important
relative to this periodic ebb and flow of energy at positions farther
away from the dipole. This new effect produces the radiation of energy.
Our description of the **B** and **E** fields, just 90° apart in phase, is a
correct statement of the fields produced at a point P by the currents in

the wire and by the charges at its ends. But time-varying fields at any point in space have an additional source beyond that of the charge and currents of the dipole. The new source is local, and results from the in-phase **B** produced by the local time-varying **E**, and the in-phase **E** produced by the local time-varying **B**. That is, the two Maxwell equations for induced electric and magnetic fields [Eqs. (12.1) and (12.24)] produce **E** and **B** fields which are in phase with each other, as we found in our examination of the electromagnetic wave. Thus the total fields at a given point P in space are the vector sums of the out-of-phase components caused by charges and currents at the dipole and the fields induced locally by the local time-varying fields. The out-of-phase components produce the ebb and flow of energy near the dipole and fall off rapidly in energy density with distance, while the in-phase components provide the only net transfer of energy, and become the dominant fields at distances far from the dipole. The oscillating near field of the dipole acts to launch the wave which produces the radiation.

It is easy to see that the energy radiated by an oscillating dipole is proportional to the fourth power of the frequency. Since the **E** and **B** fields generated by the mechanisms of Maxwell's first two equations are proportional to the time rate of change of **H** and **E**, respectively, they are proportional to the frequency ω. But the energy in the wave is proportional to $(E^2 + H^2)$. This makes the energy radiated proportional to ω^4.

12.11*   Reflection of Electromagnetic Waves by a Conducting Plane

The reflection of light or other electromagnetic waves by metals is a commonly observed phenomenon. This reflection of nearly all light gives metals a shiny appearance and is the direct consequence of the high electrical conductivity of metals, which causes the tangential component of **E** at the metal surface to remain close to zero.

We show in Fig. 12.12 a plane wave **S** approaching a metal surface, and a wave S_1 reflected back. It is easy to see that E_1, the reflected electric vector, is of the same magnitude and 180° out of phase with the incident wave at the metal surface, since if this is true, the sum of **E** and E_1 at the surface will always be zero, as required. In this approximation we are assuming negligible loss of energy from the wave at the reflecting surface. The boundary conditions do not impose simi-

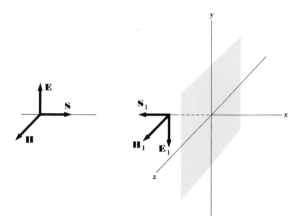

Fig. 12.12   Incoming wave S, normally incident on conducting surface in yz plane shown, gives rise to a reflected wave S₁. Phase reversal of E at surface is required to give net E∥ of zero at conducting surface.

lar zero-field conditions on the component of **H** parallel to the surface, as was shown in Chap. 10.

An interesting contrast occurs in the case of two kinds of polarized electromagnetic waves incident on a metal surface at an oblique angle. In the case of Fig. 12.13*a*, the electric vector is polarized parallel to the surface plane, and a 180° phase shift occurs in the reflected wave, as in the normal incidence case discussed above. But for the wave shown in Fig. 12.13*b*, where the **E** vector is polarized in a plane normal to the reflecting plane, no phase shift occurs, even though the same zero-field boundary condition holds.

Appendix L discusses the case of a wave incident on a metallic boundary, without neglect of the losses and the partial penetration of the wave into the metal. We derive the way in which the amplitude of the wave decreases as it travels into the metal.

12.12*   *Reflection and Refraction of Electromagnetic Waves at a Dielectric Boundary*

Another interesting and relatively simple problem is that of an electromagnetic wave incident normally on a dielectric boundary. We shall look at this, making the assumption that the energy absorbed in the dielectric is negligible. Some of the energy is reflected and some is

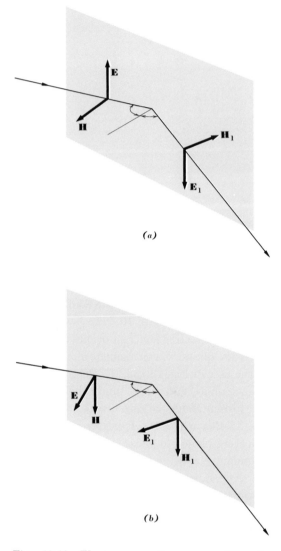

Fig. 12.13 Electromagnetic waves obliquely incident on a conducting surface. (a) E is polarized in the plane of the conductor, and the phase of the reflected wave is forced to reverse by the conducting boundary; (b) the phase E is not reversed by the conducting boundary.

transmitted into the dielectric. Our problem is to determine the relative intensities of the reflected and refracted waves when the incident wave is normal to a plane dielectric boundary. Figure 12.14 shows the

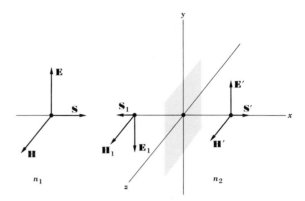

Fig. 12.14 Reflection and refraction of electromagnetic waves at a dielectric boundary.

geometry of the problem and the quantities involved. The boundary between the two media is the yz plane at $x = 0$. The electric, magnetic, and Poynting vectors of the incident (E,H,S), reflected (E_1,H_1,S_1), and refracted (E',H',S') plane waves are shown. The regions on either side of the boundary are characterized by the indices of refraction n_1 and n_2, respectively.

It was shown earlier, in Eq. (12.36), that

$$n = \sqrt{K}$$

where K is the dielectric constant of the material. This holds in all cases where $\mu = \mu_0$, as is assumed here.

In the diagram the E_1 vector for the reflected wave is drawn out of phase with the incident E, and H_1 has been made in phase with H. Clearly, either the E or the H vector of the reflected wave must be reversed in order that the Poynting vector be in the backward direction. For the moment let us consider our choice arbitrary.

A further requirement that must be satisfied is that the ratio between the E and H vectors in each wave must have the value found earlier,

$$\sqrt{\epsilon}\, E = \sqrt{\mu}\, H \qquad \text{or} \qquad H = n \left(\frac{\epsilon_0}{\mu_0} \right)^{\frac{1}{2}} E \qquad\qquad (12.44)$$

From this we have

$$H = n_1 \left(\frac{\epsilon_0}{\mu_0}\right)^{1/2} E \qquad H' = n_2 \left(\frac{\epsilon_0}{\mu_0}\right)^{1/2} E' \qquad H_1 = n_1 \left(\frac{\epsilon_0}{\mu_0}\right)^{1/2} E_1$$

Finally, the boundary conditions must be satisfied:

$$D_{n1} = D_{n2} \qquad B_{n1} = B_{n2}$$
$$E_{t1} = E_{t2} \qquad H_{t1} = H_{t2}$$

For the special case of plane waves normal to the surface, the conditions on D_n and B_n are inoperative since these quantities are both zero.

When we apply the boundary conditions on $\mathbf{E}$ and $\mathbf{H}$ and use in addition the relations between $\mathbf{E}$ and $\mathbf{H}$ in each wave, we can write

$$E - E_1 = E'$$
$$H + H_1 = H' \to n_1 E + n_1 E_1 = n_2 E'$$

Solution of these equations for E_1 and E' yields

$$E' = \left(\frac{2n_1}{n_2 + n_1}\right) E \qquad \text{and} \qquad E_1 = \left(\frac{n_2 - n_1}{n_2 + n_1}\right) E$$

When we solve instead for H' and H_1, we get, similarly,

$$H' = \left(\frac{2n_2}{n_2 + n_1}\right) H \qquad \text{and} \qquad H_1 = \left(\frac{n_2 - n_1}{n_2 + n_1}\right) H$$

E_1 and H_1 are both positive if $n_2 > n_1$. This means that the assumptions made in assigning directions to E_1 and H_1 were correct if $n_2 > n_1$ and that these directions will be reversed if $n_2 < n_1$. The flux of energy in, per unit area, is $\mathbf{S} = \mathbf{E} \times \mathbf{H} = EH$. The flux out is readily shown by the addition of $E_1 H_1 + E' H'$ to be equal to the same quantity. Thus conservation of energy is satisfied by this result.

For nonnormal incidence, the polarization direction needs to be taken into account in order to determine the division of energy into reflected and refracted beams. We leave this and other boundary-value problems for study in optics.

12.13* *Electromagnetic Waves in Waveguides*

The problem of conveying alternating currents from one place to another by using conducting wires becomes increasingly difficult as the frequency increases. There are two sources of difficulty. The first is the skin-depth effect discussed in Chap. 9. Eddy currents tend to confine the ac current to the outer skin of the conductor, causing the effective resistance to increase and resulting in large power loss along the wire. The second source of trouble lies in the fact that electromagnetic radiation increases as f^4, which results in much of the energy being radiated away instead of being conducted to the place where it is wanted. At frequencies above about 3,000 Mc/sec (at the lower end of the microwave frequency range) these two effects rule out the practical use of simple wire conductors for the transmission of electric energy. One solution to the problem of losses by radiation is to use a coaxial line such as shown in Fig. 12.15. The energy at high frequencies is

Fig. 12.15   Coaxial line used for high-frequency wave transmission. The lines of E are radial in the space between the conductors, and the lines of B are concentric circles about the center conductor.

transmitted as an electromagnetic wave passing down the space between the two conductors. Since the radiation cannot penetrate the outer conductor, no energy is lost by radiation. There is one difficulty at very high frequencies, however. It is necessary to support the inner conductor somehow, and this is usually done by filling all or part of the space between conductors with a dielectric material. The difficulty is that at high frequencies most practical dielectric materials absorb electromagnetic energy. As a result, coaxial guides are not satisfactory at the higher microwave frequencies.

For the higher microwave frequencies, say, above 24 kMc/sec, there is an elegant solution to the transmission problem. This is the use of hollow waveguides. These are like coaxial lines, except that the central conductor is omitted. In waveguides a suitable radiator sets up an electromagnetic wave that travels within the guide rather like a plane wave in free space. The big difference is that in the guide the wave is altered from a plane wave, as is required in order that the electric and magnetic boundary conditions at the surface of the conductor be satisfied. In general, there are many different modes or shapes of electromagnetic waves that can satisfy the boundary conditions and propagate energy down a guide. It is possible, however, to use a shape and size of guide that, for a limited range of frequencies, allows only one mode of transmission. We discuss the simplest, or *dominant*, mode in a rectangular guide such as shown in Fig. 12.16. In this mode the **E**

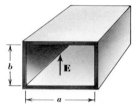

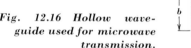

Fig. 12.16 Hollow wave-guide used for microwave transmission.

vector is polarized along the narrow dimension of the guide, is a maximum midway between the sidewalls, and falls to zero at the sidewalls.

It is a straightforward problem in electromagnetic theory to determine the possible electromagnetic waves that can propagate in such a hollow conducting guide. We need only combine Maxwell's equations with the boundary conditions at the metal surface to obtain the possible solutions. Appendix M shows how this can be done. Here we simply describe the propagating wave. We first discuss the configuration of the oscillating electric field of the wave. As stated above, the field falls off to zero at the sidewalls of the cavity. This is required to satisfy the condition that $E_\parallel$ is zero at a conducting surface. The E-field configuration is shown in Fig. 12.17, where electric field vectors (not lines of

Side view   End view

Fig. 12.17   Electric field vectors in waveguide.

force) are drawn. E varies sinusoidally down the guide, as shown in the side view. The electric field configuration is thus very similar to that in a polarized plane wave. The two modifications are that $E_\parallel$ goes to zero at the sidewalls and that the region of field is limited to the cross section of the guide. The modification in the magnetic field is more severe. It is still everywhere perpendicular to E, as in a plane wave, but because of the boundary condition, the B lines form closed loops in planes parallel to the broad face of the guide.

The boundary condition on the lines of varying B is that $B_\perp$ at the surface of a conductor goes to zero. This follows at once from the condition that $E_\parallel$ goes to zero. We argue that B must be perpendicular to E (from Maxwell's equations, as we showed in the discussion of a plane wave); then if $E_\parallel$ goes to zero, so must $B_\perp$. Thus the effect of the conducting boundary is to modify the infinite plane wave, in which lines of B form closed loops only at infinity, in such a way that the B loops are closed within the guide. Lines of B and E of a traveling wave are shown in Fig. 12.18. Use of the Poynting vector $\mathbf{S} = (1/\mu_0)(\mathbf{E} \times \mathbf{B})$ shows that this wave is traveling to the right.

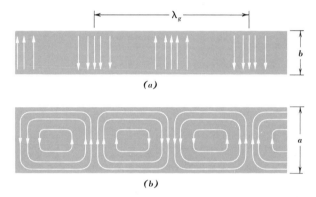

(a)

(b)

Fig. 12.18 **Lines of E and B in waveguide. (a) Lines of E, side view; (b) lines of B, top view.**

Two important features of electromagnetic waves in hollow guides are that the velocity with which energy travels along the guide is different from c, the velocity of a wave in free space, and that for each kind of mode there is a definite cutoff frequency below which waves cannot propagate through the guide. If we measure the characteristic of an electromagnetic wave in free space, we find that $\lambda_0 f = c$, where λ_0 is the wavelength in free space, f is the frequency and c is the velocity of light. If, however, we measure the wavelength λ in a waveguide, we find that for a given frequency f, λ is greater than is obtained in free space. (This measurement can be made by setting up standing waves by reflecting the wave at the end of the guide.) For the wave mode involved here, λ is related to λ_0 in free space by the equation

$$\lambda = \frac{\lambda_0}{[1 - (\lambda_0/2a)^2]^{1/2}} \qquad (12.45)$$

where a is the broad dimension of the guide. This result is derived in Appendix M.

At first glance we might think that $\lambda > \lambda_0$ seems to imply a velocity in the guide greater than the velocity of light in free space, in direct contradiction to relativity theory. However, the relativistic limitation on velocities refers to mass or energy transport. In a wave-guide or in any situation where the velocity depends on frequency, we must consider two kinds of velocity. The first is the *phase velocity* v_p, obtained by measuring the distance between peaks in the wave. This gives us the guide wavelength λ. The other is the velocity with which energy propagates, obtained by sending a short pulse of energy down the guide and measuring the time for the pulse to go a certain distance. This is called the group velocity v_g. In free space $v_p = v_g$, but in general,

$$v_p v_g = c^2 \tag{12.46}$$

as shown in Appendix M. Since the phase velocity in a guide is greater than c, it follows that the group velocity is less than c. From Eq. (12.46) we see that when the free-space wavelength λ_0 increases to $2a$, the guide wavelength becomes infinite and v_g goes to zero. That is, energy cannot be transmitted down the guide for frequencies lower than that corresponding to $\lambda_0 = 2a$. This limiting value is called the *cutoff frequency*.

12.14   *Comments on Chapter 12*

In this chapter the separate experimental laws of electricity and magnetism are brought together to exhibit the complementarity of electric and magnetic effects. We arrive at Maxwell's four relationships which provide the basis for understanding self-propagating electromagnetic waves.

Two equations rest on the inverse-square law of force between point charges and current elements in free space. Thus, for the electric field, we have

$$\int_{CS} \mathbf{E} \cdot d\mathbf{S} = \frac{1}{\epsilon_0} \int_V \rho \, dV \tag{2.9}$$

or in differential form,

$$\operatorname{div} \mathbf{E} = \frac{1}{\epsilon_0} \rho \tag{2.10}$$

In terms of **D** this becomes

$$\text{div } \mathbf{D} = \rho \tag{5.18}$$

For magnetic lines we have

$$\int_{cs} \mathbf{B} \cdot d\mathbf{S} = 0 \tag{8.20}$$

or

$$\text{div } \mathbf{B} = 0 \tag{8.21}$$

In terms of **H** in free space this is

$$\text{div } \mathbf{H} = 0$$

The third relation is equivalent to Faraday's induction law

$$\oint \mathbf{E} \cdot d\mathbf{l} = -\int \frac{\partial \mathbf{B}}{\partial t} \cdot d\mathbf{S} \tag{12.1}$$

or in differential form,

$$\text{curl } \mathbf{E} = -\frac{\partial \mathbf{B}}{\partial t} \tag{12.1a}$$

Both of these forms show that a time-varying **B** field gives rise to an electric field.

The fourth Maxwell equation is complementary to this third relation, above.

$$\oint \mathbf{B} \cdot d\mathbf{l} = \mu_0 \epsilon_0 \int \frac{\partial \mathbf{E}}{\partial t} \cdot d\mathbf{S} + \mu_0 \int \mathbf{j} \cdot d\mathbf{S} \tag{12.3}$$

or

$$\text{curl } \mathbf{B} = \mu_0 \epsilon_0 \frac{\partial \mathbf{E}}{\partial t} + \mu_0 \mathbf{j} \tag{12.3a}$$

The second terms on the right in these equations are in fact zero in free space, but are included here for completeness. The roles of **B** and **E** are exchanged in this new relation involving a time-varying quantity. The term $\epsilon_0(\partial \mathbf{E}/\partial t)$, or its equivalent $\partial \mathbf{D}/\partial t$, is known as the displacement current density. It plays a role similar to the real current density **j**. The last equation can be written

$$\text{curl } \mathbf{H} = \frac{\partial \mathbf{D}}{\partial t} + \mathbf{j} \tag{12.4a}$$

It is the pair of equations relating **B** to $\partial \mathbf{E}/\partial t$ and **E** to $\partial \mathbf{B}/\partial t$ which account for the propagation of electromagnetic waves.

The next section reviews the general theory of propagating waves. The central result, derived here on the basis of transverse waves on a string, is that any differential equation of the form

$$\frac{\partial^2 z}{\partial x^2} = \frac{1}{u^2}\frac{\partial^2 z}{\partial t^2} \tag{12.13b}$$

indicates a traveling wave moving along the x axis with a velocity u. The simplest equation for such a wave is

$$z = z_0 \cos \frac{2\pi}{\lambda}(x - ut) \tag{12.16}$$

where λ is the wavelength of the sinusoidal wave. More complicated traveling-wave forms satisfy the differential equation equally well.

$$\lambda f = u \tag{12.15}$$

gives the well-known relationship between wavelength, frequency, and velocity of a traveling wave.

Common practice in dealing with traveling waves is to introduce the wave vector

$$k = \frac{2\pi}{\lambda} \tag{12.17}$$

and the angular frequency

$$\omega = 2\pi f \tag{12.18}$$

Equation (12.15) then becomes

$$k = \frac{\omega}{u} \tag{12.19}$$

and the traveling-wave equation takes the simple form

$$z = z_0 \cos(\omega t \pm kx)$$

Even more useful is the complex form

$$z = z_0 e^{j(\omega t \pm kx)} \tag{12.23}$$

In Sec. 12.5 it was shown how Maxwell's equations lead to the differential equation for a traveling plane wave in free space, with **E** and **B** fields normal to each other and to the direction of propagation.

$$\frac{\partial^2 E_y}{\partial x^2} = \epsilon_0 \mu_0 \frac{\partial^2 E_y}{\partial t^2} \tag{12.28}$$

and

$$\frac{\partial^2 B_z}{\partial x^2} = \epsilon_0 \mu_0 \frac{\partial^2 B_z}{\partial t^2} \tag{12.29}$$

Comparison with Eq. (12.13b) shows that the propagation velocity in free space is

$$c = \frac{1}{\sqrt{\epsilon_0 \mu_0}} \tag{12.30}$$

The magnitudes of B_z and E_y are related in free space by

$$B_z = \sqrt{\mu_0 \epsilon_0}\, E_y \tag{12.33}$$

Attention is called to the short derivation of the equations for electromagnetic waves in Appendix K, using the differential forms of Maxwell's equations.

The free-space equations are easily modified to account for waves traveling in extended dielectric or magnetic media, as shown in Sec. 12.6. The index of refraction was defined as

$$n = \frac{c}{u}$$

For media in which the magnetic properties approximate those of free space, as in usual dielectric materials, it is shown that

$$n = \sqrt{K} \tag{12.36}$$

where K is the dielectric constant of the medium.

A study of the propagation of energy in a traveling electromagnetic wave shows that the transmitted energy per unit cross-section area per second, or power density, is given by the Poynting vector

$$\mathbf{S} = \mathbf{E} \times \mathbf{H} \quad \text{watts/m}^2 \tag{12.42}$$

A discussion of the generation of electromagnetic waves leads to the fact that accelerated charges are essential for the setting up of propagating waves.

In Secs. 12.11 and 12.12 and in Appendix L, problems involving electromagnetic waves at boundaries are discussed. These include the reflection of a wave by a conducting plane, reflection and refraction of a wave at a dielectric boundary, and, in Appendix L, the attenuation of a wave in a conducting medium. This latter problem shows how the skin depth arises for high-frequency currents in a metal.

The final section shows how plane waves are modified in a typical waveguide. Appendix M develops the relation between free space and guide wavelength, and discusses the contrast between phase and group velocity in dispersive media, that is, in any situations in which the velocity of a wave depends on its frequency.

PROBLEMS

With the addition of Maxwell's displacement current, the basic electromagnetic laws provide the basis for understanding self-propagating electromagnetic waves. These first problems relate to the differential equations which lead to traveling electromagnetic waves.

12.1A   Starting with Eqs. (12.26) and (12.27), which relate time and space variations of **E** and **B**, show that

$$\frac{\partial^2 B_z}{\partial x^2} = \epsilon_0 \mu_0 \frac{\partial^2 B_z}{\partial t^2}$$

12.1B   Show that the differential equation of Prob. 12.1A can be satisfied, for example, by a sine wave in B_z traveling in the negative x direction, if the velocity is given by

$$c = \frac{1}{\sqrt{\epsilon_0 \mu_0}}$$

12.1C   An ac generator is connected to a parallel-plate capacitor made of circular disks of area A. As a result, the charge q on the plates is $q = q_0 \sin \omega t$. The lines of B induced by the resulting displacement current are circles with centers on the axis of symmetry of the capacitor. Show that the magnetic field intensity at any point between the plates is given by

$$B = \mu_0 \frac{q_0 r \omega}{2A} \cos \omega t$$

where r is the distance from the axis of symmetry. Neglect edge effects.

This simple problem is presented to give familiarity with the frequencies of the well-known regions of the electromagnetic-wave spectrum.

★12.2A   Find the frequencies of electromagnetic waves having the following wavelengths in free space:
   a 10^3 m (long-wave radio)
   b   1 m (short-wave radio)
   c   3 cm (microwaves)

d 10⁻⁴ m (infrared)

d 10^{-4} m (infrared)

e 5,000 A (optical) (1 angstrom = 10^{-10} m)

f 0.1 A (x rays)

g 10^{-2} A (gamma rays)

It is important to become familiar with the various ways of expressing the parameters which describe traveling waves.

12.3A Using the definitions of the parameters involved, show how to convert the equation for a transverse sinusoidal traveling wave moving in the positive x direction,

$$z = z_0 \sin \frac{2\pi}{\lambda} (x - ut)$$

into one involving k, x, ω, and t. Complex notation may be used if you wish.

The Poynting vector relates the flow of energy in a traveling wave to the amplitudes of the transverse **E** and **B** fields.

★12.4A A plane radio wave travels in the x direction and is plane-polarized with its electric vector in the y direction. Its frequency is 1 Mc/sec. The average power propagated by the wave is 20 watts/m².
a Find the wavelength of the wave.
b Find the amplitudes of **E** and **B** for this wave.

12.4B Sunlight strikes the earth, outside its atmosphere, with an intensity of 2.0 cal/cm²-min. Calculate the peak values of **E** and **B** for sunlight at the earth.

Displacement currents are generally unimportant compared with real currents in conductors. They become important only at very high frequencies or in the absence of conductivity, as in an electromagnetic wave in free space.

12.5A Show that for frequencies at which vacuum tubes are ordinarily operated, the vacuum displacement current is negligible compared with the current carried by electrons. Take, for example, a tube with cathode and plate area each 1 cm², spaced 5 mm apart, passing 10 ma (rms) at a frequency of 10^6 cps. Assume parallel-plate geometry and that the cathode is at fixed potential and the rms ac voltage across the tube is 100 volts. What is the magnitude of the rms displacement current through the tube?

The boundary conditions imposed on an electromagnetic wave in a hollow conducting waveguide affect its propagation and produce a low-frequency limit for propagated waves.

*12.6A   Find the lowest frequency for which an electromagnetic wave can be transmitted through a rectangular waveguide whose inner dimension perpendicular to the **E** field is 1 cm.

12.6B   A rectangular guide has a width (perpendicular to the **E** field) of 1.0 cm. For the dominant mode [for which Eq. (12.45) holds], what is the guide wavelength for an electromagnetic wave for which the free-space wavelength is 1.25 cm? What is the phase velocity of this wave in the guide? What is the group velocity with which energy propagates in the guide?

13

*relativity and electromagnetism

13.1* Introduction

One of the basic assumptions of special relativity is that there is no favored "rest" frame of reference. There is no experiment that differentiates a state of absolute rest from one of uniform motion. In this chapter we show that, consistent with this assumption, the forces between charges are invariant in magnitude, regardless of the state of relative (uniform) motion of the charges and the observer. However, the division between electric and magnetic forces does depend on the relative motion of charges and observer. Thus the distinction between electric and magnetic force is not fundamental. That which one observer would call a magnetic force would be described as an electric force by another observer in a different reference frame. We approach this problem by investigating the development of special relativity. Special relativity was originally forced on physics by a crucial experiment first carried out by Michelson and Morley in 1881. In this experiment it was shown that the measured velocity of light is the same, no matter what the velocity of the observer and his apparatus. This result has consequences of great importance. In order to understand it and fit it into the known facts of physics, it was necessary to throw out many ideas that had never been critically examined and develop a completely new set of ideas about space, time, and matter. The revolution in thinking was led almost entirely by one man, Albert Einstein. Special relativity enables us to understand the unity of electricity and magnetism, as well as many other phenomena, from relativistic velocity effects to the famous equivalence of mass and energy.

13.2* *Classical Space and Time*

A brief description is first given of the point of view of classical physics regarding space and time, the assumptions which underlie newtonian mechanics. The ideas of Newton involve the assumption that the laws of motion, and indeed all the laws of physics, are the same for an observer at "rest" as for an observer moving with uniform velocity with respect to the rest system. That is, if an *inertial* reference system is defined as one in which Newton's laws describe the behavior of bodies, any other reference system which moves with constant velocity with respect to this first inertial system is also an inertial system. Thus a game of billiards played on a table in a railway car is the same whether the car is at rest with respect to the earth or is moving with a uniform velocity relative to the earth. The description of the motion of the balls in the reference frame of the car is the same in either case.

An equivalent statement of the assumption of newtonian mechanics is that a game of billiards played on a table on the train can equally well be described by a man standing by the table and by a man standing on the ground. As long as all velocities are modest compared with the velocity of light, Newton's laws are valid for both descriptions. But the descriptions are different, since the man on the ground can perfectly well say that before the game starts all the balls are moving at the velocity of the train, while the man on the train says they are at rest. This obvious difference of description is formalized by the galilean transformation, which we now explain. In Fig. 13.1 a point P is shown. Its position at a certain time, in the reference frame S', is given by $P(x_1', y_1', z_1')$, and it is moving with a velocity $u = dx'/dt$ in this frame. The position of the point can be equally well described in another reference frame S, which is itself moving with the same velocity u with respect to the frame S'. For simplicity, we assume motion in the x direction only. In this new frame the point is at rest, and can be

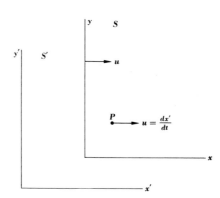

Fig. 13.1 Position and velocity described in two different inertial frames. The point P is initially at the position (x_1',y_1',z_1') in the reference frame S'. The z' coordinate is not shown. The point is moving with a velocity $u = dx'/dt$ in S'. In the reference frame S, which is itself moving with the same velocity u with respect to S', the point P is at position (x_1,y_1,z_1), and is at rest.

described by $P(x_1,y_1,z_1)$. It is a simple matter to transform from one frame to the other.

$$x = x' - ut$$
$$y = y'$$
$$z = z'$$
(13.1)

This is the galilean transformation, which describes the effect of changing from one inertial frame to another, in this case where the relative velocity of the two frames is u, along the x axis.

In general, the transformation of velocities from one to the other system is obtained by taking time derivatives. When the relative motion of the two frames is confined to the x direction, the transformation becomes

$$\frac{dx}{dt} = \frac{dx'}{dt} - u \quad \text{or} \quad v_x = v_x' - u$$
$$\frac{dy}{dt} = \frac{dy'}{dt}$$
$$\frac{dz}{dt} = \frac{dz'}{dt}$$
(13.2)

Thus any motion of a body as described in one frame can be transformed to a description in the other frame. Events can be described by Newton's laws equally well in either frame.

This simple transformation contains a pair of hidden assumptions. First, it is assumed that time intervals are the same in both systems. A further assumption, not brought out in this discussion, is that simultaneous events at two positions in one inertial frame are simultaneous in any other inertial frame. Second, it is assumed that lengths measure the same in any inertial frame. That is,

$$t' = t$$
$$l' = l$$

where l or l' is any distance measured by either observer, and t and t' are times as measured in the two frames. If we do not look too closely at the problem of verification of these last two assumptions, they certainly seem to match our experience. Time and space *seem* to be independent of the particular inertial frame used. It is in fact true that as long as we restrict our considerations to relative velocities which are much less than the velocity of light, the galilean transformation and the assumptions of a uniform space and time are completely satisfactory.

13.3*   *The Michelson-Morley Experiment*

At the time of the Michelson-Morley measurement, in 1881, of the velocity of light, it was recognized that light consists of electromagnetic waves, and numerous experiments had led to approximate values for the velocity. The particular interest of the Michelson-Morley experiment was that it was particularly designed to measure the possible effects of "ether drift" on the velocity of light. Eighteenth- and nineteenth-century physicists almost took it for granted that since light is a wave motion, there must be a medium which supports the waves. Thus the ether was invented as a substance which pervades all space and thus permits the existence of light waves. But the postulated existence of the ether suggested that just as the velocity of sound is modified by motion of the air as wind, and water-wave velocities are influenced by the flow of water, the measured velocity of light should be influenced by motion of the ether. It would therefore be expected that the measured velocity of light would depend on the motion of the ether with respect to the earth. Thus, unless the ether is always at rest with respect to the earth—an idea which is hardly compatible with the earth's yearly orbit around the sun—light velocities measured on earth should be different in different directions.

The new experiment was set up to compare the velocities of light in different directions. The device used was an *interferometer*, as shown in Fig. 13.2. In this apparatus light from a source hits a half-silvered mirror A, which reflects part of the light to B and transmits part to C.

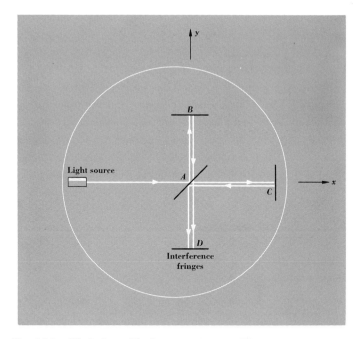

Fig. 13.2   Michelson-Morley experiment. This interferometer was used to look for possible differences in the velocity of light in different directions. Interference fringes appear at D when light reflected from mirrors B and C combines. The fringe pattern would shift on rotation of the apparatus if light velocities were different in x and y directions. No shift was detected.

Some of the light reflected at B and at C gets back to D, where an interference pattern is set up. Any change in the relative times taken by the light to traverse the two alternative paths shows up as a shift in the interference pattern at D. The entire apparatus is rotated through 90° to test whether the light velocity is affected by ether drag, which would cause a shift in the interference pattern.

We shall not discuss the quantitative details of the experiment, except to note that the velocity of the earth in its orbit around the sun is approximately 10^{-4} of the velocity of light.

Michelson and Morley showed that there is no measurable difference in the velocity of light in different directions on the earth. Repeated experiments since the original one have shown that the speed of light is independent of the motion of the earth within less than

1 part in 1,000 of the earth's orbital velocity around the sun. There are no effects from ether drift.

Many explanations of this very surprising negative result for the effect of ether drift were attempted, but until 1905 no really useful solution was found. In that year, the young Einstein, then twenty-six years old and a civil servant in the patent office in Berne, wrote a short but startling paper which got to the heart of the matter, and pointed the way to understanding this result. At the same time, the new theory of special relativity revolutionized concepts of space and time and made far-reaching changes in many aspects of physics.

13.4* Special Relativity

In order to understand the implications of the Michelson-Morley experiment and other experimental evidence, Einstein established two basic postulates:

1. The laws of electrodynamics and of mechanics are the same in all inertial frames. This includes the requirement that c, the velocity of light in free space, is invariant.

2. It is impossible to devise an experiment which defines a state of absolute motion. There is no special "rest" frame of reference.

This point of view was not new as applied to Newton's laws, since the galilean transformation had already shown that all systems moving with fixed velocity relative to one inertial system are also inertial frames. The crucial modification of Einstein was to add the statement that *the velocity of light is the same in all inertial frames*. This postulate directly contradicts galilean velocity-transformation equations, like

$$\frac{dx'}{dt} = \frac{dx}{dt} - u$$

which says that velocities are different in different inertial systems. The strength of Einstein's work was his ability to cast aside the unwarranted assumptions of the classical viewpoint of space and time, and arrive at the necessary modifications needed to accommodate the newly discovered experimental facts.

The result of Einstein's work was the theory of special relativity, which extends newtonian mechanics for situations involving very high velocities and which accommodates the phenomena of electricity and magnetism. In order to provide a framework of ideas which accommodates the invariance of light velocity in free space, it was necessary to reexamine intuitive ideas about simultaneity of events occurring at different points in space, and to question the universality of scales of time and distance.

In classical physics, the idea of the same pair of events seeming simultaneous to different observers in relative motion is taken for granted. This is an unwarranted assumption even though in situations involving small velocities it does not cause noticeable errors. Suppose we imagine a moving train, such as shown in Fig. 13.3. At the instant

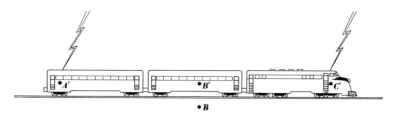

Fig. 13.3   The problem of simultaneity of two events. As seen by an observer at rest at B, lightning strikes the two ends of a train at A' and B' at the same instant. But for an observer with sufficiently accurate measuring instruments on the train at B', the two events do not occur at the same time. Because of the finite velocity of light and the motion of the train, the observer sees the lightning from C' before that from A'.

when the middle of the train is at B, an observer by the tracks at B sees lightning strike the two ends of the train at the same time. A man at B' on the train at its midpoint would not see the two events at the same time. This results from the fact that while the light signal is coming to him, his motion moves him toward the point where the front of the train was hit, and away from the rear end. The light from the rear-end lightning strike has to travel farther than that from the front of the train. For the observer on the train the two events will not seem simultaneous. Thus we must conclude that simultaneity is not invariant but depends on the reference frame. We could avoid this difficulty only if there were some way of transmitting information from one place to another instantaneously.

The problem of simultaneity is not the only one which becomes complicated when we examine the effect of moving reference frames. There is also an actual change in the scale of time and of distance. These effects are shown by considering a number of imaginary experiments which exhibit the ways in which ordinary classical ideas must be modified to satisfy Einstein's postulates. The procedure is to examine certain phenomena from different reference frames. The frame in which the apparatus or body is at rest is called its *proper* frame.

Experiment 1. Lengths perpendicular to the direction of motion. Imagine two rulers which are of the same length as measured in their proper frames. Let one ruler be moving with respect to the other, as shown in Fig. 13.4. Consider that the ruler L is at rest in frame S, and L' is at

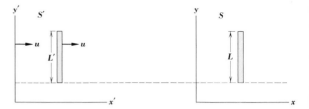

Fig. 13.4 *Argument to show that lengths perpendicular to the direction of motion are invariant. Ruler L' moves past ruler L so that the bottom ends coincide. If one ruler is shorter than the other, a scriber on the top end of the shorter ruler marks the longer one. Observers on S' and S must see the same results of the hypothetical experiment. The only possible interpretation is that the relative motion of ruler and observer cannot affect lengths in this case. Note that measurements of time are not involved in this length comparison. This argument does not hold for longitudinal motion.*

rest in frame S', but that the primed frame and ruler are moving relative to S with a velocity u in the x direction. For an observer on S', ruler L is moving, and for an observer on S, ruler L' is moving. It is arranged that as L' moves past L, the bottom ends of the two rulers coincide. Scribers are placed at the top end of each ruler, so that if lateral motion affects the length of the ruler, the scriber on the shorter ruler will mark the longer one. In this situation it is easy to show that the lengths L and L' cannot be affected by the motion, as follows: If the moving ruler is shorter, its scriber will mark the ruler at rest. But the result of the experiment cannot depend on which observer looks at it. The only way in which both observers can see the same result of the

experiment is for the two rulers to remain the same length, despite
their relative lateral motion. The same logic would apply if the moving
ruler were longer rather than shorter than the stationary one. This
special case of length measurement in directions perpendicular to the
direction of motion is particularly simple because time measurements
are not involved in the comparison. The conclusion here is that, for
motion along x,

$$y = y' \quad \text{and} \quad z = z'$$

just as in the galilean transformation.

Experiment 2. Time scale.   We next show that if Einstein's postulates are accepted, they lead to a dependence of measured time intervals
on the relative motion of the observer and the phenomena being
observed. Time intervals measure differently in different inertial reference frames. We choose an apparatus which in principle allows the
measurement of the time interval required for a light pulse to travel a
distance d from a light source to a mirror and back to a photocell
detector placed next to the source, as shown in Fig. 13.5. The apparatus

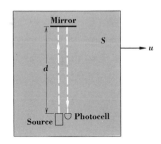

*Fig. 13.5 Measurement of
time intervals. For an observer moving with an ap-
paratus for measuring time
intervals, using the velocity
of a light pulse from
source to mirror and back,
the time interval is unaffected by motion of the
apparatus. For an observer
in the rest frame of the
apparatus, $\Delta t = 2d/c$. The
velocity of the reference
frame is to the right.*

moves with some velocity u in a direction perpendicular to the distance
d between source and mirror. The time interval for the light pulse to
travel from source to mirror and back to the photocell, as measured by
an observer in the proper frame S in which the apparatus is at rest, is
given by

$$\Delta t = \frac{2d}{c} \tag{13.3}$$

This *proper time* is independent of the velocity u, since the distance d is invariant as shown above, and the velocity of light c is also independent of uniform motion. Thus an observer moving with the apparatus cannot detect uniform motion of his frame; this inability is required by Einstein's postulate.

The experiment is now repeated, but this time the observer with his clock is in a frame S' in which the light and mirror are moving transversely with a velocity u in the x direction, perpendicular to the distance d between the source and mirror, as shown in Fig. 13.6. As seen

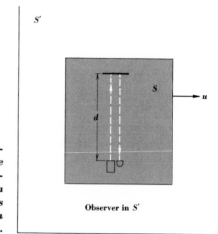

Fig. 13.6   Time-interval measurement by an observer in the S' frame, in which the apparatus moves transversely with a velocity u. The light path as seen by the observer is shown in Fig. 13.7.

by the observer in S', the path of the light is now not in the y direction, but as shown in Fig. 13.7, because of the transverse motion of the source during the light transit time. There is a problem for the observer, since he cannot be at the source and detector both at the beginning and end of the timing experiment. Thus he must be able to correct for the time lag required for information to travel from the source and photocell to him. He solves this problem by placing himself in the position O', just half way between the beginning and end positions of the moving source. Since the velocity of light is a universal constant in all inertial systems, he receives word that the pulse from the source has started toward the mirror with a time delay, but the same delay is involved in his learning that the reflected light pulse has arrived back at the detector. Thus his measurement of $\Delta t'$ is unaffected by the delayed information. The transit time $\Delta t'$ measured by this observer cannot be the same as was the time Δt measured in the rest system S. This is because

Fig. 13.7 Light path of time-interval apparatus as seen by an observer in the S' frame. The apparatus moves past the observer with a transverse velocity u. At the beginning of the time-interval measurement, the source and detector are at A. At the end of the measurement they are at B. Since the path is longer than that seen in the rest frame, and since c, the velocity of light, and d, the transverse length, are invariant, $\Delta t'$, the time interval measured by the observer, is different from that measured in the rest frame.

$\Delta t'$ (in moving frame)

$$= \frac{\Delta t \ (in \ rest \ frame)}{\sqrt{1 - u^2/c^2}}$$

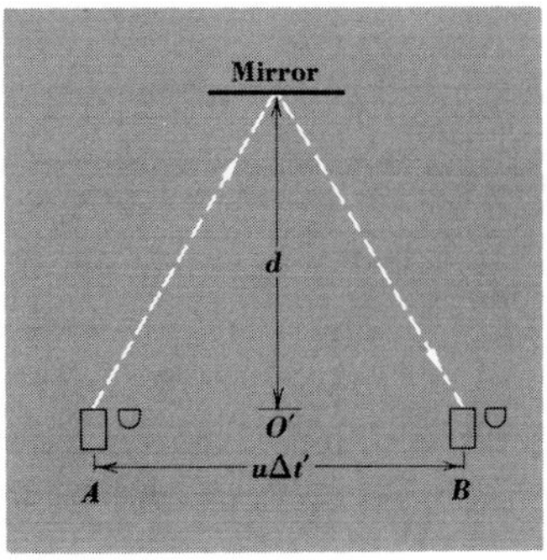

the light path as seen by the observer in S' is $2\sqrt{d^2 + (\frac{1}{2}u\,\Delta t')^2}$, as can be seen from Fig. 13.7. Since this is longer than $2d$, and since c is invariant, the time interval measured *must* be different for the observer in frame S'. It is given by

$$\Delta t' = \frac{2\sqrt{d^2 + (\frac{1}{2}u\,\Delta t')^2}}{c} \tag{13.4}$$

The results of Eqs. (13.3) and (13.4) can be used to solve for the relationship between the time intervals measured in the two reference frames. An easy way to do this is to square Eq. (13.4) and replace $4d^2/c^2$ by Δt^2 as given by Eq. (13.3). We thus find at once

$$\Delta t' = \frac{\Delta t}{\sqrt{1 - u^2/c^2}} \tag{13.5}$$

The transit time $\Delta t'$ measured in the frame in which the source is moving appears to be longer than Δt measured in a frame in which the source is at rest. But since the same event is being measured in both cases, we can only conclude that time intervals measure differently in the two frames! This phenomenon is known as *time dilation*. An example of this effect seen experimentally is the lifetime of high-velocity unstable nuclear particles such as mesons, which disintegrate in flight. The lifetime appears lengthened, as observed on the earth, by an amount which depends on the meson velocity. But the lifetime observed in the frame in which the meson is at rest is invariant.

We now simplify the equation by using the standard symbols for u/c, the ratio of the velocity of the moving system to the velocity of light.

$$\frac{u}{c} = \beta \tag{13.6}$$

and for the reciprocal square-root term,

$$\frac{1}{\sqrt{1 - \beta^2}} = \gamma \tag{13.7}$$

Equation (13.3) can then be written in either form

$$\Delta t' = \frac{\Delta t}{\sqrt{1 - \beta^2}} \quad \text{or} \quad \Delta t' = \gamma \, \Delta t \tag{13.5a}$$

The relativistic constant γ is a number which is close to unity for low relative velocities u/c, and goes to infinity as u approaches c. Figure 13.8 shows γ plotted against the velocity ratio β. The unavoidable con-

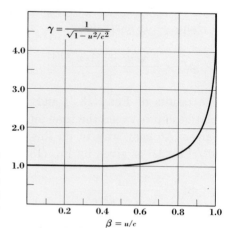

Fig. 13.8 The relativistic constant γ plotted against $\beta = u/c$. Relativistic effects are generally unimportant for velocities below half the velocity of light.

clusion of this imaginary experiment is that time intervals are not universal or invariant, but depend on the observer's frame of reference.

Experiment 3.   Lengths parallel to the direction of motion.   The problem of measuring lengths parallel to the direction of motion is very different from the perpendicular case examined in Experiment 1. The important difference is that if an observer is to compare the length of one ruler moving longitudinally with respect to another, the time at which the comparisons of the two ends are made is critical. The observer must measure both times and positions. This fact complicates the problem by the addition of time dilation. We examine it first from the point of view of an observer in the proper frame S of a ruler, in which the ruler is at rest, and then in a frame S' relative to which the ruler is moving. In the same spirit as in the time-interval experiments just discussed, an optical method is to be used to measure the length of the ruler.

Figure 13.9 shows the ruler with a source of a light pulse and detector, and a mirror, at opposite ends of the ruler. Since in the first

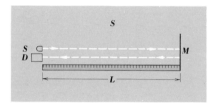

Fig. 13.9   Ruler with attached light source S, mirror M, and detector D, for idealized length measurement. For an observer in the rest, or proper, frame of the rod, Δt and the length L are related by $\Delta t = 2L/c$.

measurement, the observer moves with the ruler, we put him and the ruler in the frame S, and call the length of the ruler L. The measurement is made by the observer, who is at the source and detector. He measures the elapsed time Δt for the light to travel to the mirror and back. Then

$$\Delta t = \frac{2L}{c} \tag{13.8}$$

The second measurement is made by an observer in the frame S', and he calls the length of the moving ruler L'. In Fig. 13.10 we show the ruler in three positions as it moves past the observer. When the ruler is in position A, the light pulse starts toward the mirror. In position B it is shown at the instant when the light pulse arrives at the mirror, and in C, its position when the light has just returned to the detector. The observer stands at a position O' midway between the first

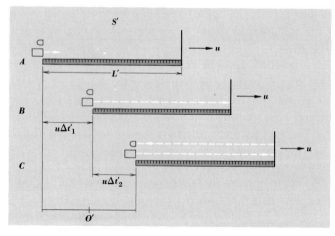

Fig. 13.10 *Ruler with attached light apparatus as seen by an observer in frame S'. Observer sees ruler moving longitudinally with a velocity u in the x' direction. Light measurement begins when the ruler reaches position A; is completed when ruler arrives in position C. Observer is at O', half way between detector positions at A and C. Calculation shows that the measured length in S' is given by*

$$L' \ (in \ moving \ frame) = L \ \sqrt{1 - \beta^2} = \frac{1}{\gamma} L \ (in \ rest \ frame).$$

The measured length of a longitudinally moving rod is less than its length measured in its rest frame.

and last positions, so that the time delay in measuring the beginning and the end of the experiment is the same.

The total time $\Delta t'$ for the light pulse to go from source to mirror and return is the sum of $\Delta t'_1$, the time to reach the mirror, and $\Delta t'_2$ to return back to the source. But as seen by the observer, the distance the light must travel to reach the mirror is

$$d_1 = L' + u \ \Delta t'_1$$

and to return is

$$d_2 = L' - u \ \Delta t'_2$$

because of motion of the ruler, as shown in Fig. 13.10. The light beam takes times $\Delta t'_1$ and $\Delta t'_2$ to move these distances, where

$$d_1 = c \ \Delta t'_1 \qquad d_2 = c \ \Delta t'_2$$

Combining these results, we find

$$\Delta t'_1 = \frac{L'}{c - u} \qquad \Delta t'_2 = \frac{L'}{c + u}$$

so

$$\Delta t' = \Delta t'_1 + \Delta t'_2 = \frac{2L'}{c(1 - u^2/c^2)} = \frac{2L'}{c(1 - \beta^2)} = \frac{\gamma^2 2L'}{c}$$

Comparing this result with that for the observer moving with the ruler and using the earlier time-dilation result, $\Delta t' = \gamma \, \Delta t$, we find

$$L' = L \sqrt{1 - \beta^2} = \frac{1}{\gamma} L \tag{13.9}$$

This result means that the length of a ruler moving parallel to its length, L', as measured by an observer in S', is less than its length L measured in its rest frame.

We are thus forced to accept change of lengths in the dimension parallel to the velocity. The two observers cannot agree on the measurements of lengths. This effect is unimportant for ordinary speeds, just as in the case of time dilation.

13.5* Relativistic Dynamics

The effects of motion on length and time make profound changes in the dynamics of moving bodies at velocities approaching that of light. We shall not investigate all these modifications in detail, but shall exhibit the most important effects and discuss how they come about.

If we examine a simple two-body collision as seen from different reference frames, we find that the classical momentum-conservation law does not hold in all inertial frames. That is, $\Sigma(m_0 v)$ is not always zero for a two-body collision in all reference frames, where m_0 is the mass of each body at rest. It can be shown, however, that if the momentum is defined as

$$p = \frac{m_0 v}{\sqrt{1 - \beta^2}} \tag{13.10}$$

then classical momentum conservation does hold. When $v \ll c$, this relativistic expression for momentum reduces to its classical value.

As a result of this modification in the expression for momentum, it is natural and convenient to identify the change with a change in the apparent mass of a body when its velocity approaches c. Thus, if mass is defined by

$$m = \frac{m_0}{\sqrt{1 - \beta^2}} = \gamma m_0 \tag{13.11}$$

the momentum can be written

$$\mathbf{p} = m\mathbf{v} = \frac{m_0\mathbf{v}}{\sqrt{1 - \beta^2}} = \gamma m_0\mathbf{v} \tag{13.12}$$

The meaning is that the dynamics of bodies, as modified by velocity-dependent effects on measures of length and time, can be simply described by an apparent change in mass of the bodies involved.

This modification of the expression for momentum can be applied to Newton's second law to give

$$\mathbf{F} = \frac{d\mathbf{p}}{dt} = \frac{d}{dt}\left(\frac{m_0\mathbf{v}}{\sqrt{1 - \beta^2}}\right) = \frac{d}{dt}(\gamma m_0\mathbf{v}) \tag{13.13}$$

This can be used to find the relativistic expression for energy by the argument which is outlined next.

For simplicity, only one-dimensional motion along the x axis is considered. We compute W, the work done when a force F in the x direction is applied to a free body over a distance x_1 to x_2.

$$W = \int_{x_1}^{x_2} F\, dx \tag{13.14}$$

Since this is to be a relativistic problem, we use Eq. (13.13) to express the effect of work done on the momentum of the body. The following steps carry out this calculation:

$$W = \int_{x_1}^{x_2} \frac{dp}{dt}\, dx = \int_{t_1}^{t_2} \frac{dp}{dt}\frac{dx}{dt}\, dt$$
$$= \int_{v_1}^{v_2} v\, dp = \int_{v_1}^{v_2} v\frac{dp}{dv}\, dv$$

Here v_1 and v_2 and t_1 and t_2 are the velocities and times of the body at x_1 and x_2.

We now substitute Eq. (13.13) to write

$$W = \int_{v_1}^{v_2} v\frac{d}{dv}\left(\frac{m_0 v}{\sqrt{1 - v^2/c^2}}\right) dv \tag{13.15}$$

This equation must be first differentiated as indicated, and the result then integrated. This gives the result, which we shall not carry out in detail,

$$W = \frac{m_0 c^2}{\sqrt{1 - v_2{}^2/c^2}} - \frac{m_0 c^2}{\sqrt{1 - v_1{}^2/c^2}}$$

showing that work done results in a change in the quantity

$$E = \frac{m_0 c^2}{\sqrt{1 - v^2/c^2}} \qquad\qquad (13.16)$$

as a result of the change in v. Since we are dealing with the effect of force on a free body, it is a conservative system. Therefore we can equate the work done to the change in the energy of the body. This brings us to the unusual nature of the relativistic energy. Even when the velocity v of a body is zero, its energy is not zero, but is

$$E = m_0 c^2 \qquad\qquad (13.17)$$

This is the well-known expression for the relativistic *rest energy* of a body.

The relativistic expression for the kinetic energy is obtained by subtracting the rest energy from the total energy.

$$KE = \frac{m_0 c^2}{\sqrt{1 - v^2/c^2}} - m_0 c^2 \qquad\qquad (13.18)$$

It is easy to show by expanding $(1 - v^2/c^2)^{-\frac{1}{2}}$ by means of the binomial theorem

$$\left(1 - \frac{v^2}{c^2}\right)^{-\frac{1}{2}} = 1 + \frac{1}{2}\frac{v^2}{c^2} + \frac{3}{8}\frac{v^4}{c^4} + \frac{5}{16}\frac{v^6}{c^6} + \cdots$$

that the kinetic energy expression can be written

$$KE = \tfrac{1}{2}m_0 v^2 + \tfrac{3}{8} m_0 \frac{v^4}{c^2} + \cdots$$

Thus, for velocities small compared with c, .the relativistic expression reduces to the classical expression $\tfrac{1}{2}m_0 v^2$.

13.6* Charge Invariance

After the discussions of the dependence of time, distance, and mass on velocity, we now enquire about electric charge. There is very firm experimental evidence that the amount of charge is is no way influenced by motion. That is, charge is relativistically invariant. A particularly satisfying demonstration of this is in the exact neutrality of hydrogen molecules and of the helium atom. Very sensitive experiments on hydrogen molecules in electric fields show that the two positive charges of the protons and the two negative charges of the electrons cancel out within 1 part in 10^{20}. Similar experiments show the same kind of cancellation between the two protons in the helium nucleus and the two electrons in helium atoms. Now the protons in these two cases have very different motions. In hydrogen atoms the two protons are separated by a distance of nearly an angstrom, and revolve relatively slowly about their center of gravity. In helium the two protons are tightly bound in the same nucleus, and move with very large kinetic energies. If charge were not invariant, at least one of the two bodies, He or H_2, would have a net charge which is not the case. Charge invariance is an important part of the argument in the discussion of relativistic effects on the electric field.

13.7* Relativistic Electric Field Effects

In view of the relativistic effect on the measured dimensions of moving objects, a modification is to be expected in the nature of the electric field of a charged particle as seen from a reference frame in which it is in motion. This effect can be easily determined by using the two results of charge invariance and length contraction. We start with a pair of oppositely charged parallel plates, as shown in Fig. 13.11. We

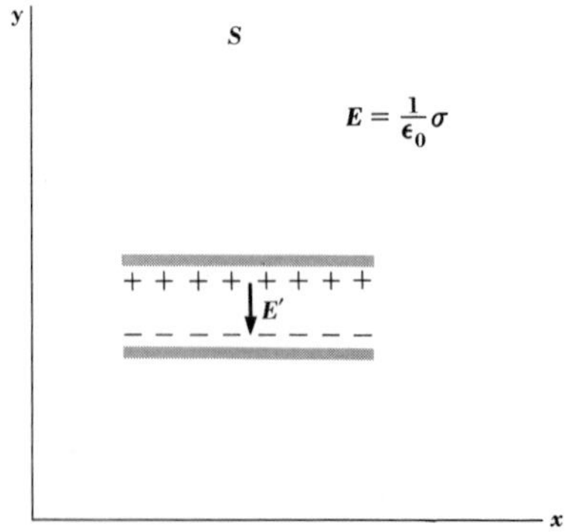

Fig. 13.11   Electric field between charged parallel plates at rest.

first consider the field E between the plates in a frame S in which the plates are at rest. The field is in a direction perpendicular to the x

axis and has a value which depends only on the charge density σ on the plates, according to

$$E = \frac{1}{\epsilon_0}\sigma \tag{2.10}$$

Viewed next from a frame in which the plates are moving in the x direction with a velocity u, as shown in Fig. 13.12, the field in this

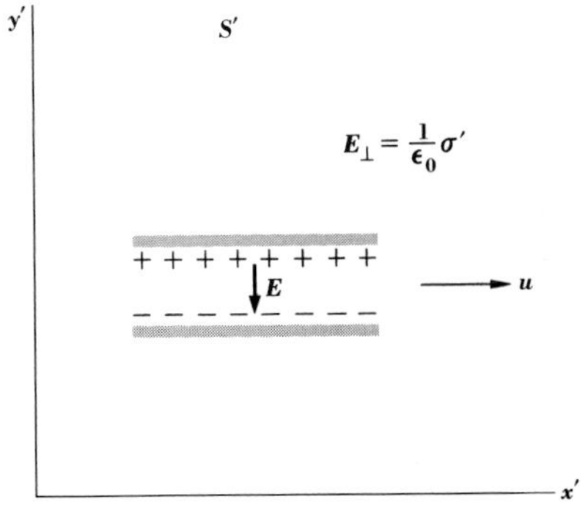

Fig. 13.12 *Electric field between charged parallel plates as viewed from frame in which plates are moving longitudinally. Length contraction of plates increases charge density to*

$$\sigma' = \frac{1}{\sqrt{1-\beta^2}}\sigma$$

Thus

$$E'_\perp = \frac{1}{\sqrt{1-\beta^2}}E_\perp$$

frame is

$$E' = \frac{1}{\epsilon_0}\sigma'$$

Is σ' the same when viewed from this frame? We know that charge itself is invariant, but we also know that the dimension L' of the plate in the x direction is reduced according to

$$L = \frac{1}{\sqrt{1-\beta^2}}L' \tag{13.7}$$

Since dimensions perpendicular to the direction of motion are unchanged, the total charge in the S' system is compressed into an area which is less by the ratio L'/L than the area in the rest frame. Therefore the charge density is increased to

$$\sigma' = \frac{1}{\sqrt{1-\beta^2}}\sigma$$

and the electric field perpendicular to the motion increases,

$$E'_\perp = \frac{1}{\sqrt{1-\beta^2}}E_\perp \tag{13.19}$$

The component of the field parallel to the motion is unchanged by the motion. This is apparent from Fig. 13.13. The effect of motion in

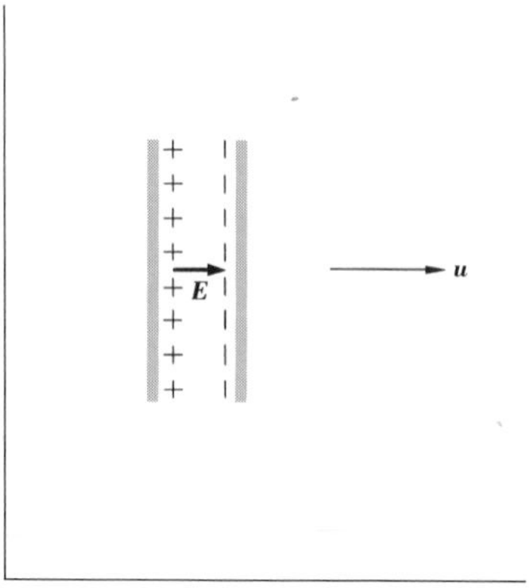

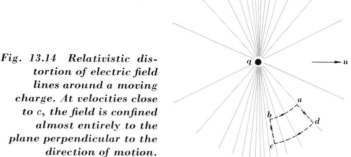

Fig. 13.13 The field component parallel to the direction of motion is unchanged, since length contraction changes only the spacing between plates. This does not affect the electric field. $E_\parallel = E_\parallel$.

the x direction is to decrease the spacing between the charged plates, but this has no effect on the field, and the plate area is not affected by the motion. Therefore

$$E'_\parallel = E_\parallel \tag{13.20}$$

These two results cause the "static" field configuration for a charge to be modified when viewed from a reference frame in which the charge is moving uniformly. This effect is illustrated in Fig. 13.14,

Fig. 13.14 Relativistic distortion of electric field lines around a moving charge. At velocities close to c, the field is confined almost entirely to the plane perpendicular to the direction of motion.

which shows the distortion of the lines of **E** around a moving charge q. The effect is unimportant, except for velocities which approach the velocity of light, for which β^2 approaches 1.

This field around a moving charge does not fulfill the requirement of zero circulation.

$$\oint \mathbf{E} \cdot d\mathbf{l} = 0 \qquad \text{or} \qquad \text{curl } \mathbf{E} = 0 \tag{3.4}$$

for a static electric field. The wider spacing of **E** lines along the path *ab* in Fig. 13.14 means lower field than along *cd*; so the line integral of the electric field of a moving charge is not zero around the closed path, as it is for the field of a charge at rest.

13.8* The Unity of Electric and Magnetic Fields

Now that we have looked at some of the relativistic effects of motion, we are in a position to ask some questions regarding the earlier discussions of electric and magnetic fields. For example, suppose we discuss the magnetic force on a charge q moving with velocity u in the magnetic field of a wire carrying a current i, as in Fig. 13.15. It was

*Fig. 13.15 Dependence of magnetic force on reference frame. In the frame in which the charge q is moving with a velocity u as shown, the magnetic force is as stated, where **B** is the field of the current i in the conductor. However, in the frame in which q is at rest, the magnetic force goes to zero. We show that this change in the magnetic force is just compensated by change in the electric force on q.*

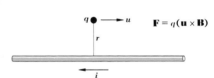

shown in Chap. 8 that the force on this moving charge is given by

$$\mathbf{F} = q(\mathbf{u} \times \mathbf{B}) \tag{8.32}$$

where **B** is the field caused by the current i. If we choose the frame S' in which u, the velocity of the charge q, is zero, the magnetic force on the charge clearly goes to zero! The embarrassment is that there can be nothing special about any particular inertial reference frame. The force must not depend on the frame chosen. But it certainly looks as though S' is a very special frame, different from all others. If there were no way out of this apparent difficulty, the ideas of relativity would fail completely. The whole idea of special relativity was to show that the experimental facts of electricity and magnetism are invariant under transformations between inertial frames. We are about to show that the force on charged particles is in fact relativistically invariant despite the seeming difficulty of the example of Fig. 13.15. We show that the force on a charge has only one value, no matter what inertial frame is used. But what part of the force is electric and what part is magnetic depends entirely on the frame used. We show, in fact, that viewed from the special frame in which q is at rest, the force is entirely due to what looks like an electrostatic field. The behavior of charged particles is independent of the reference frame, but the division between electric and magnetic forces is entirely a matter of the frame used.

The approach we take is to use the arrangement of the charge shown in Fig. 13.15, moving in the field of a wire-carrying current. We pick two reference frames, in one of which the force is exclusively magnetic and in the other, exclusively electric. But the effect of the forces on the charge is shown to be identical in both cases. Figure 13.16 shows

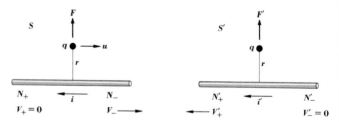

Fig. 13.16   Force on a charge at a distance r from a current. In the frame S the charge q moves with a velocity u. In S' the charge is at rest. For the case given, the magnetic force F in frame S is identical with the electric force $\mathbf{F}'$ as viewed from the rest frame of the charge. N_+, N_- and N'_+, N'_- are the positive and negative charge densities in the conductor, as viewed from the S and S' frames.

the nomenclature to be used. In the frame S, the charge q moves with a velocity u, and the wire is at rest. N_+ represents the number of positive ions per unit volume in the metal wire. These ions are at rest in the frame S; that is, $v_+ = 0$. Conduction electrons, N_- per unit volume, are moving to the right with an average drift velocity v_-. This motion produces a current i in the opposite direction. A is the cross-section area of the wire. The charge density is N_-e, where e is the electronic charge. We assume the net charge on the wire is zero, as viewed from the frame S. That is,

$$N_+|e| = N_-|e|$$

There is thus no electric force on the charge q in this reference frame.

The calculation of the magnetic force proceeds in the ordinary way, using

$$\mathbf{F} = q(\mathbf{u} \times \mathbf{B}) \qquad \text{newtons}$$

$$\mathbf{B} = \frac{\mu_0 i}{2\pi r} \qquad \text{webers/m}^2$$

$$i = N_- evA \qquad \text{amp}$$

By substitution

$$F = \frac{q\mu_0}{2\pi r} N_- eAv_- u$$

We simplify the problem for later comparison by taking the special case that $v_- = u$. Also, we replace μ_0 by $1/\epsilon_0 c^2$, using the relation

$$c^2 = \frac{1}{\epsilon_0 \mu_0}$$

Then we have, for the magnetic force on the moving charge q,

$$F = \frac{qe}{2\pi r \epsilon_0} \frac{N_- A u^2}{c^2} \qquad\qquad (13.21)$$

We compare this with the next calculation, made in the reference frame S', in which q is at rest.

Since in the frame S', q is at rest, there is no magnetic force. Since charge is invariant, q is unchanged. The wire and its positive ions move with a velocity to the left of $-u$, and the electrons have zero drift velocity. But if $N_+ = N_-$ in the rest systems, this is no longer true in S', because of the relativistic change of dimension along the direction of motion of the wire. The positive charges are contained in a shorter length; so their density increases to

$$N'_+ = \frac{N_+}{\sqrt{1 - \beta^2}}$$

Similarly, the density of electrons is changed. But N_- was the density in the S frame in which they were moving with a velocity u; so in S', in which they are at rest, they are stretched out, and the density is decreased.

$$N'_- = N_- \sqrt{1 - \beta^2}$$

The net charge per unit length in S' is thus

$$\sigma' = \frac{N_+|e|}{\sqrt{1 - \beta^2}} - N_-|e| \sqrt{1 - \beta^2}$$

$$= N_+|e| \frac{u^2/c^2}{\sqrt{1 - \beta^2}} \qquad \text{coul/m}$$

In this frame, the wire has a net positive charge. The magnitude of $\mathbf{F}'$, the force on q, is then given by

$$F' = \frac{q2\sigma'}{4\pi r\epsilon_0} = \frac{qe}{2\pi r\epsilon_0} \frac{N_- A u^2}{c^2} \frac{1}{\sqrt{1 - \beta^2}} \tag{13.22}$$

Except for the factor $1/\sqrt{1 - \beta^2}$, this electrostatic force is identical with that found for the magnetic force in the S frame. But even this factor is removed when we consider the problem more closely. The phenomenon which brings the two results into exact agreement is the relativistic effect on forces. The essential feature of a force, and the method by which we infer its value, lies in the change in momentum which it produces. But the change in momentum, Δp, depends on the impulse $F \Delta t$. Thus when we move to a new reference frame, time dilation comes into play, Δt is modified, and the change of momentum is modified. In the case discussed here, the force is perpendicular to the direction of motion of the frame; so dimensional changes are not involved. Only the time dilation need be considered. In the S' frame, the charge q is initially at rest; so the time dilation equation gives

$$\Delta t = \frac{\Delta t'}{\sqrt{1 - \beta^2}}$$

In the S frame the particle is moving, and time intervals measured in a frame in which a particle is moving appear to be longer than in the particle's rest frame.

$$\Delta t > \Delta t'$$

Thus, in the S' frame, the time interval t' is shorter and *less* momentum change occurs than would be expected in the S frame. In this way the rate of momentum change in the S' system, or the effective force in that system, is less by the factor $\sqrt{1 - \beta^2}$. The effect on momentum of the electric force in the frame S', as given in Eq. (13.22), becomes the same as the effect on momentum caused by the magnetic force in the frame S, as given by Eq. (13.21).

We have considered only two particular reference frames, although the conclusion is always the same. In cases in which u, the velocity of the test charge q, is not the same as the drift velocity v_- of the charge carriers, as was assumed above, the force calculation is more complicated. But in all cases, the interaction between charged particles is independent of which inertial frame is used, though the division between magnetic and electric forces depends on the frame. In all cases the behavior of a charged particle is correctly given by the relativistic equation

$$q(\mathbf{E} + \mathbf{v} \times \mathbf{B}) = \frac{d}{dt} \frac{m_0 v}{\sqrt{1 - v^2/c^2}} \tag{13.23}$$

where $\mathbf{E}$, $\mathbf{B}$, and $\mathbf{v}$ are measured in the same reference system. m_0 and q are the same in any reference system. The magnitudes of $\mathbf{E}$, $\mathbf{B}$, and $\mathbf{v}$ will depend on the reference system in which they are measured. This interchange between electric and magnetic forces when the reference frame is changed is a case in which even small velocities bring in a relativistic change in the description of forces. But relativistic changes in the dynamics of a moving charge become important only at velocities approaching that of light.

13.9* Comments on Chapter 13

Experiments by Michelson and Morley, since repeated in many forms, made clear that the velocity of light or other electromagnetic radiation in a vacuum is independent of the inertial reference frame in which it is observed. This observation required a major revision of older ideas regarding space and time. In order to accommodate the apparently simple experimental result, it was necessary to examine all the preconceived ideas about measurements of space and to question the supposed validity of the universality of time.

Of all the physicists who contributed to the reordering of ideas, Einstein played the most important role, in his development of special relativity. Einstein's strength was his ability to analyze exactly how far actual observation can justify the classical ideas of space and of universal time. The basic idea of special relativity is that the velocity of light places a ceiling on how fast information about events taking place at a distance can be received. By means of a series of "thought" experiments, Einstein swept away the foundations of classical space and time, and developed a consistent framework which rested solidly on observable facts.

In this chapter we demonstrated briefly the nature of the arguments which led to changes in the measure of time and space, two of the most important relativistic results.

Time dilation is described as follows: Let Δt be the time interval between two events as measured in the rest frame of the phenomenon being observed. In another inertial frame, in which the experiment is moving with a velocity u, the measured time interval between the same two events is *greater*, and is given by

$$\Delta t' = \frac{\Delta t}{\sqrt{1 - u^2/c^2}} \tag{13.5}$$

where c is the velocity of light. Using the notation

$$\beta = \frac{u}{c} \tag{13.6}$$

or

$$\gamma = \frac{1}{\sqrt{1 - \beta^2}} \tag{13.7}$$

the time dilation equation can be expressed

$$\Delta t' = \frac{\Delta t}{\sqrt{1 - \beta^2}} \quad \text{or} \quad \Delta t' = \gamma\, \Delta t \tag{13.5a}$$

The effect of relative motion on lengths can be described as follows: Lengths measured in the plane perpendicular to velocities with respect to the observer are unaffected. But lengths parallel to the direction of motion are *shortened* according to

$$L' = L\sqrt{1 - \beta^2} = \frac{1}{\gamma} L \tag{13.9}$$

where L is the length as measured in the rest frame.

On the basis of these effects on time and space, it is possible to

derive relativistic expressions for momentum, mass, and energy, which
we repeat here.

Momentum: $\mathbf{p} = m\mathbf{v} = \dfrac{m_0\mathbf{v}}{\sqrt{1 - \beta^2}} = \gamma m_0\mathbf{v}$ (13.12)

Mass: $m = \dfrac{m_0}{\sqrt{1 - \beta^2}} = \gamma m_0$ (13.11)

Rest energy: $E = m_0 c^2$ (13.17)

Kinetic energy: $KE = \dfrac{m_0 c^2}{\sqrt{1 - \beta^2}} - m_0 c^2$ (13.18)

All these relativistic effects are unimportant for velocities much
less than the velocity of light, as is made clear in Fig. 13.8, which
shows that the relativistic constant γ is very close to 1 until $\beta(= u/c)$
becomes greater than a few tenths.

One of the prime requirements of a relativistic theory was to ensure that electromagnetic theory be invariant when transformed from
one inertial system to another. Indeed, just the transformations we
have discussed make this true. But there are several particular consequences of relativity which need comment in connection with electromagnetism. The first is that electric charge is invariant under
relativistic transformation. The basis for this is from experimental
observation. One particular observation was discussed in this chapter,
but in a wide range of observable situations similar arguments can be
made. In all cases the crucial test is whether high-velocity internal
motion of, say, electrons affects the otherwise overall neutrality of a
system composed of equal numbers of positive and negative charges.
Many systems which have been studied confirm the relativistic invariance of charge.

A second consequence of the relativistic transformations is that
the *shape* of the electric field around a moving charge is modified. This
is the result of relativistic length dilation, as was argued in detail.
There is, of course, no effect for an observer moving with the charge.

We finally demonstrated for a particular situation that the description of the force on a charge moving in the field of other charges
is modified by the reference frame from which the charge is observed.
The inevitability of this change in description is obvious when we note
that the magnetic force on a charge is zero as observed in the rest
frame of the charge, since magnetic fields act only on moving charges.
We showed, however, that the dynamics of charged particles is independent of the observer's reference frame. Only the separation of the

force into electric and magnetic components is affected. This relativistic result revolutionizes our concept of electric and magnetic fields. From this point of view there is a single kind of force between charges, and the magnetic field is simply a convenient way of building into the theory the inevitable results of special relativity. It is only from habit that we continue to think in terms of separate electrostatic and magnetic fields.

PROBLEMS[1]

The first problems illustrate some of the most striking consequences of relativistic effects of velocity on time and space measurements.

*13.1A The π mesons are unstable particles which decay into other particles. A π^+ meson at rest decays approximately 2.6×10^{-8} sec after it is produced. This time may be called its *lifetime*.

   a A π^+ meson is moving with a speed of $0.8c$ with respect to an observer in a laboratory. He measures the lifetime of the particle; what result does he obtain?

   b What distance (measured in the laboratory) does the particle travel between production and decay?

13.1B In Relativityland, where the speed of light is 10 mph, a car drives down the street, passing an observer standing on a sidewalk. The car seems to the driver to be headed straight down the street, but to the observer it seems pointed off to one side. Which side? Explain.

*13.1C The Orient Express moves past a small-town station at a speed of 1.5×10^8 m/sec. It has mirrors attached to both ends; the (proper) length of the train is 100 m. After it passes, the stationmaster turns on a light. The light travels to both mirrors, and is reflected back to him. How much time elapses between the arrival of the two reflected light beams?

13.1D Describe a method by which the stationmaster in Prob. 13.3 can measure the length of the train as it passes. What result does he obtain?

These problems involve relativistic energies.

*13.2A Protons emerge from a synchrocyclotron with kinetic energy equal to about $0.49mc^2$. What is the speed of these particles? Compare your

---

[1] Most of these problems are taken from "Fundamentals of Mechanics and Heat," by Hugh D. Young, McGraw-Hill Book Company, New York, 1964. The material in chap. 14 of that book provides a very useful background and exposition of the mechanical aspects of special relativity.

result with that obtained from the nonrelativistic relation between mass and kinetic energy.

13.2B   What is the speed of a particle whose kinetic energy is equal to its rest energy? What percentage error is made if the nonrelativistic kinetic-energy expression is used?

*13.2C   A proton emerges from a particle accelerator with a speed of $0.75c$ and collides with another proton initially at rest.

    a What is the kinetic energy of the proton?

    b Find the velocity of a moving coordinate system such that in this system the total momentum of the two protons is zero.

    c What is the total kinetic energy with respect to this moving coordinate system?

Special relativity modifies some of the classical results of electromagnetic theory.

13.3A   Nonrelativistic mechanics predicts that a particle of mass m and charge q moving perpendicular to a uniform magnetic field **B** moves in a circle of radius R, where $R = mv/qB$. Derive the relativistic generalization of this result.

13.3B   A block of matter has an excess charge Q. It is moving with a relativistic velocity.

    a Does Gauss' flux theorem hold? Explain.

    b Does the law $\oint \mathbf{E} \cdot d\mathbf{l} = 0$ or curl $\mathbf{E} = 0$ hold? Explain.

14

motion of charged particles in electric and magnetic fields

14.1 Introduction

In Chaps. 2 and 8 we discussed the forces on charged particles, first in an electric, then in a magnetic field. Here we study a few cases in which moving charges are placed in combined electric and magnetic fields. This includes the motion of charges in crossed **E** and **B** fields and the magnetic mirror effect which accounts for the trapping of charged particles in the magnetic field which surrounds the earth. In addition, we describe briefly the behavior of highly conducting fluids in the presence of a magnetic field.

14.2 The Lorentz Force Equation

The effects of electric and magnetic fields are often combined in a single vector equation which gives the total force on a moving charge. This is written

$$\mathbf{F} = e[\mathbf{E} + (\mathbf{v} \times \mathbf{B})] \tag{14.1}$$

in the mks system. It is called the Lorentz force equation, and is, simply, the vector sum of the electric force $e\mathbf{E}$ and the magnetic force $e(\mathbf{v} \times \mathbf{B})$ acting on a charge e having a velocity $\mathbf{v}$.

It was shown in Chap. 8 that the effect of a magnetic field alone can be discussed most easily if the velocity $\mathbf{v}$ of the charge is separated into two components, $v_{\parallel}$, parallel to $\mathbf{B}$, and $v_{\perp}$, perpendicular to $\mathbf{B}$.

$$\mathbf{v} = \mathbf{v}_{\parallel} + \mathbf{v}_{\perp} \tag{14.2}$$

According to Eq. (14.1), the velocity component $\mathbf{v}_{\parallel}$ is not affected by the magnetic field. We saw that the magnetic force resulting from $\mathbf{v}_{\perp}$ produced circular motion in a plane perpendicular to $\mathbf{B}$ of radius

$$r = \frac{mv_{\perp}}{eB} \tag{8.34}$$

with an angular frequency

$$\omega_c = \frac{eB}{m} \tag{8.33}$$

ω_c is called the cyclotron (angular) frequency. When the velocity $\mathbf{v}$ has components both parallel and perpendicular to a uniform field $\mathbf{B}$, the motion of a charged particle is helical, with a constant radius and pitch, and with the axis of the helix along the field direction.

The fact that the cyclotron frequency is independent of the velocity of the charged particle has a number of interesting consequences. One of these was mentioned in Chap. 8, in the discussion of the cyclotron. As long as velocities remain well below those producing relativistic increase in the mass, the angular velocity of the charged particles being accelerated remains constant. Thus a constant-frequency accelerating potential can be used to accelerate the particles.

In another application to mobile charges in semiconductors and in metals, the cyclotron frequency of the charges can be measured by microwave-absorption techniques in a known external magnetic field. Knowing e and $\mathbf{B}$, it is possible to determine the *effective mass* of the mobile charges through Eq. (8.33). Here e is the charge on the electron. This effective mass generally differs from the free-electron value, often by factors greater than 10. This result is expected on the basis of momentum interchange between electrons acting as waves in the crystal and the regularly spaced positive ion lattice of the crystalline semiconductor or metal. The effective mass can be more or less than the free-electron mass, depending on circumstances. These experiments can be performed only at very low temperatures and on pure materials, since otherwise the scattering of the charged particles by impurities and thermal motions of the lattice prevent the particles from completing closed orbits between scattering events. Such experimental studies of effective mass have been useful in the development of the theory of conduction electrons in solids.

14.3   Crossed E and B Fields

We now discuss the motion of charged particles in some cases in which the uniform electric and magnetic fields are mutually perpendicular. To simplify the discussion we assume that the initial velocity of the charged particles is in the plane perpendicular to $\mathbf{B}$. As a result, all motion is limited to this plane, since the forces of both $\mathbf{B}$ and $\mathbf{E}$ are in this plane. At any time, then, if v is the velocity of the particle, the motion is governed by Newton's law, where the force is given by the Lorentz equation. Thus

$$m \frac{dv}{dt} = e[\mathbf{E} + (\mathbf{v} \times \mathbf{B})] \tag{14.3}$$

The resulting motion in the plane perpendicular to $\mathbf{B}$ is uniform circular motion, superposed on a uniform translational velocity. This can be shown by the following argument. We first write the total particle velocity as the vector sum of two terms, $\mathbf{v}'$, a velocity of uniform circular motion, and another constant term, $(\mathbf{E} \times \mathbf{B})/B^2$. Thus

$$\mathbf{v} = \mathbf{v}' + \frac{\mathbf{E} \times \mathbf{B}}{B^2} \tag{14.4}$$

We must now demonstrate that $\mathbf{v}'$ is in fact a velocity describing uniform circular motion. Upon substituting this value of v into Eq. (14.3), we find

$$m \frac{dv'}{dt} = e[\mathbf{E} + (\mathbf{v}' \times \mathbf{B}) + \frac{1}{B^2} (\mathbf{E} \times \mathbf{B}) \times \mathbf{B}] \tag{14.5}$$

The meaning of $(\mathbf{E} \times \mathbf{B}) \times \mathbf{B}$ can be understood by examining Fig. 14.1. When $\mathbf{E}$ is along the x direction and $\mathbf{B}$ is along the y direction, the vector $(\mathbf{E} \times \mathbf{B})$ is in the z direction. Taking the cross product of this vector with $\mathbf{B}$, we find that the resultant vector points in the $-x$ direction. Thus $(\mathbf{E} \times \mathbf{B}) \times \mathbf{B} = -B^2\mathbf{E}$, or

$$\frac{1}{B^2} (\mathbf{E} \times \mathbf{B}) \times \mathbf{B} = -\mathbf{E}$$

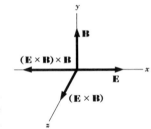

**Fig. 14.1   Diagram illustrat-
ing the direction of the
vector (E × B) × B.**

This substitution then reduces Eq. (14.5) to

$$m\frac{dv'}{dt} = e(\mathbf{v'} \times \mathbf{B})$$ (14.6)

This equation verifies that $\mathbf{v'}$, as defined in Eq. (14.4), represents uniform circular motion in the field $\mathbf{B}$. But according to that equation there is an additional uniform linear velocity term, $(\mathbf{E} \times \mathbf{B})/B^2$, which is in the z direction, as shown in Fig. 14.1. The magnitude of this drift velocity is $\mathbf{E}/\mathbf{B}$. The nature of the total motion is shown in Fig. 14.2.

**Fig. 14.2   Effect of an elec-
tric field on the circular
motion of charged particles
in a uniform magnetic
field. A drift velocity is
added to the circular mo-
tion as shown.**

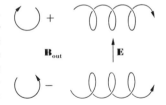

It is notable that an electric field $\mathbf{E}$ applied normal to $\mathbf{B}$ produces a drift in a direction perpendicular to $\mathbf{E}$. In the more general case where $\mathbf{E}$ has a component parallel to $\mathbf{B}$, this component adds an acceleration to the component of velocity parallel to $\mathbf{B}$.

A second case of interest is that of a gravitational field perpendicular to the uniform $\mathbf{B}$ field. This contrasts with the previous electric field case in that the extra force is changed from the sign-dependent $e\mathbf{E}$ to $mg_\perp$, where $mg_\perp$ is the gravitational force perpendicular to $\mathbf{B}$. When we make this change in the equation for the drift velocity v_D, we find

$$v_D = \frac{mg_\perp}{eB} = \frac{g_\perp}{\omega_c}$$ (14.7)

The drift velocity is in the direction of $m\mathbf{g}_\perp \times \mathbf{B}$ for a positive particle and is reversed for a negative particle. Figure 14.3 shows the nature of the motion.

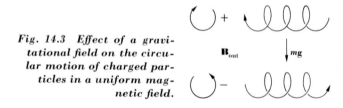

Fig. 14.3 Effect of a gravi-tational field on the circu-lar motion of charged par-ticles in a uniform mag-netic field.

A final case of interest is that of the motion of charges in an inhomogeneous field. Figure 14.4 shows the kind of motion that results

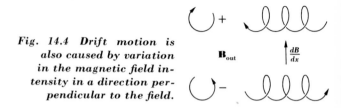

Fig. 14.4 Drift motion is also caused by variation in the magnetic field in-tensity in a direction per-pendicular to the field.

when **B** varies linearly in the x direction perpendicular to the direction of **B**. The qualitative nature of this motion is easily understood on the basis that the curvature is greater in the region of higher magnetic field and less in the lower field region. As a consequence, the circular motion in a uniform field is distorted as shown.

14.4* Motion in a Converging Magnetic Field

Our next task is to discuss the interesting case of particle motion in a region in which magnetic lines are converging. That is, **B** is increasing as we move along the direction of lines of force. Before examining this situation, however, we consider an important theorem regarding circu-lar motion of a charged particle in a magnetic field. This theorem states that if **B** varies slowly in space and time, the magnetic moment result-ing from particle motion in the field is constant. Let the magnetic moment resulting from circular charge motion in the field be μ. Then

$$\mu = iA = e\frac{\omega_c}{2\pi}\pi r^2 = \frac{\frac{1}{2}mv_\perp{}^2}{B} \tag{14.8}$$

We prove the theorem first for the case of **B** uniform in space but varying with time. The time variation of flux within the area of the circular path gives rise to an induced emf ε according to Faraday's law, and we can write

$$\varepsilon = \oint \mathbf{E} \cdot d\mathbf{l} = - \int \frac{\partial \mathbf{B}}{\partial t} \cdot d\mathbf{S} \tag{12.1}$$

The rate at which work is done on the moving charge is

$$\frac{dW}{dt} = \frac{d}{dt}\left(\frac{1}{2} mv_\perp{}^2\right) = \varepsilon i = \frac{e\omega_c}{2\pi}\pi r^2 \frac{dB}{dt} \tag{14.9}$$

We have evaluated ε from Eq. (12.1) and used $i = e\omega_c/2\pi$ for the current due to the rotating charge. Comparison with Eq. (14.8) shows that

$$\frac{dW}{dt} = \frac{d}{dt}\left(\frac{1}{2} mv_\perp{}^2\right) = \mu \frac{dB}{dt} \tag{14.10}$$

When we multiply Eq. (14.8) by B, we get $\mu B = \frac{1}{2}mv_\perp{}^2$. Differentiation of this with respect to time gives

$$\frac{d}{dt}(\mu B) = \mu \frac{dB}{dt} + B \frac{d\mu}{dt} = \frac{d}{dt}\left(\frac{1}{2} mv_\perp{}^2\right)$$

But in view of the result of Eq. (14.10), the term $B\, d\mu/dt$ must equal zero; so μ is a constant, and we have proved the point we were after.

The case of **B** constant in time but increasing as we move along lines of **B** is now considered. Figure 14.5 shows the helical path of a

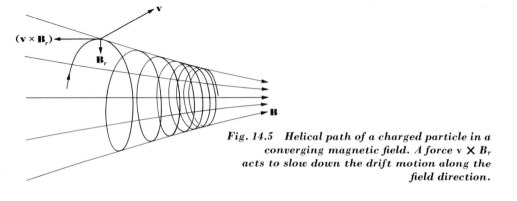

Fig. 14.5 *Helical path of a charged particle in a converging magnetic field. A force* v × B$_r$ *acts to slow down the drift motion along the field direction.*

charged particle in a converging magnetic field, and we discuss the nature of the motion in this situation. The proof that, in this case also, the magnetic moment of the circular motion is constant will not be given. It is true, however, as long as changes in **B** are small over distances comparable with the radius of circular motion, and we use the result in the following discussion.

Whenever there is a radial component B_r pointing toward the guiding center of the helical path, there is a force acting to decelerate the motion along the axis of the spiral, given by $\mathbf{v} \times \mathbf{B}_r$. This tends to retard the drift velocity in the field direction. The motion in the field direction not only is decreased but actually goes to zero and then reverses. Converging lines of **B** can thus reflect the motion (whence the term *magnetic mirror*). However, since the total magnetic force is always perpendicular to the velocity of the particle, no work is done on the particle, and therefore its velocity stays constant in magnitude. Thus, if **v** is the total velocity of the particle and $\mathbf{v}_D$ is its velocity component along the axis of the helix and $\mathbf{v}_\perp$ is the velocity perpendicular to the axis, we have

$$\mathbf{v} = \text{const} = \mathbf{v}_\perp + \mathbf{v}_D \tag{14.11}$$

Thus, as $\mathbf{v}_D$ decreases, $\mathbf{v}_\perp$ must increase so as to keep **v** constant in magnitude. From Eq. (14.8) for the magnetic moment of the circular motion, we see also that if μ is to remain constant, $v_\perp^2/B$ must stay constant, so that the fractional increase of $v_\perp^2$ is proportional to the fractional increase in **B**. If we call θ the angle made by the helical motion with respect to the axis of the helix, or the angle by which the particle advances along the helix (Fig. 14.6), we can write

$$\frac{v_\perp}{v} = \sin\theta \qquad \text{or} \qquad \frac{v_\perp^2}{v^2} = \sin^2\theta \tag{14.12}$$

The value of θ changes as the particle moves along the helix. When, at some point where the field is $\mathbf{B}_0$, the value of θ is θ_0, and for some point farther along, the field is **B** and the angle is θ, we can compare the angles of advance in the two locations, using Eqs. (14.11) and (14.12), which give

$$\frac{\sin^2\theta_0}{B_0} = \frac{\sin^2\theta}{B} \qquad \text{or} \qquad \sin^2\theta = \frac{B}{B_0}\sin^2\theta_0 \tag{14.13}$$

When the particle has moved far enough along the helix so that $B/B_0 = 1/\sin^2\theta_0$, $\sin^2\theta = 1$. This means that $v_\perp = v$; so all the

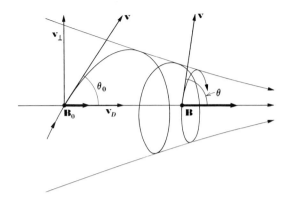

*Fig. 14.6   Helical path in a converging field
showing change in angle of advance from θ_0
to θ when field has changed from B_0 to B.*

motion is perpendicular to the axis of the helix, and the drift velocity has become zero. However, there is still a backward force; so the drift reverses after stopping, and we find that the particle motion has been reflected by the converging lines of **B**. The kinetic energy of the particle remains constant during this reflection process.

This reflection of the spiral motion of charged particles in converging lines of magnetic field is of importance in the explanation of the recently discovered high density of charged particles, called the Van Allen belt, which surrounds the earth out to distances four or five times the radius of the earth. Information on this region of high radi-

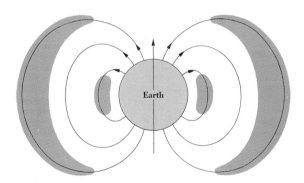

*Fig. 14.7   The Van Allen belt of charged particles
captured by the earth's magnetic field. The
inner torus contains mostly protons, and the
outer one contains mostly electrons.*

ation intensity was obtained in 1958 from the flights of the satellites Explorer I, III, and IV and Sputnik III and Mechta.[1] The existence of this high radiation intensity is explained by the trapping of high-energy protons and electrons of cosmic origin by the geomagnetic field. Figure 14.7 is a sketch of the form of the region, which consists of an inner region of high proton density and a more distant region containing electrons. These regions encircle the earth, and they tend to follow the curvature of the lines of magnetic field around the earth. The trapping of the charged particles is easily understood on the basis of the mirror effect.[2] Figure 14.8 is a sketch (not to scale) of the way

Fig. 14.8 Helical path of charged particle captured in earth's magnetic field. Particle spirals back and forth between the two magnetic mirrors formed by converging field lines. Drawing is not to scale.

in which the converging lines of magnetic field produce reflections of the helical motion of charged particles and hence effectively trap them. The theory of this effect has long been understood, and was confirmed when the experimental data were obtained from satellite observations.

Another application of the mirror effect was postulated by Fermi and Alfvén to account for the acceleration in space of cosmic-ray particles. Fermi suggested that in interstellar clouds the magnetic field could be greater than in the intervening regions. If that were so, particles in the region between two clouds could be trapped by the converging fields. If the two clouds are moving toward each other, it can be shown that the particles gain kinetic energy each time they are re-

[1] Information on this work and further references can be found in J. A. Van Allen, The Geomagnetically Trapped Corpuscular Radiation, *J. Geophys. Res.*, **64**:1683–1689 (1959).

[2] An extensive treatment of this and other problems in magnetohydrodynamics is given in H. Alfvén, "Cosmic Electrodynamics," Oxford University Press, New York, 1950.

flected by the magnetic mirror. This mechanism would explain at least one of the causes of very high energy charged particles in cosmic rays.

14.5*   *Magnetohydrodynamic Waves*

We now turn from the discussion of single-particle motion in a magnetic field to a consideration of some of the characteristics of the motion of a fluid of such high ion density that it is highly conducting. We consider the case of a *plasma* in which the density of positive and negative particles is equal. If a magnetic field is present, moving charges (hydrodynamic motion) give rise to induced E fields, which in turn give rise to current. These currents are acted upon by the magnetic field, and the resultant forces change the state of motion. This connection between mass motion and electromagnetic fields can set up *magnetohydrodynamic* waves.

We can see this by means of a crude model. Suppose a conducting fluid is immersed in a uniform magnetic field. Suppose, to begin with, that all the fluid is at rest except for a column moving with constant velocity v in the negative direction, into the paper (Fig. 14.9). Con-

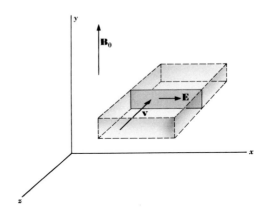

Fig. 14.9   A column of highly conducting fluid moving perpendicular to a magnetic field, B_0, *showing induced electric field* **E** *in moving column.*

sider this column to be of infinite extent along the z direction. We wish to show how electric and magnetic forces resulting from the motion of this column cause consequent motion of other parts of the fluid, and in fact set up waves of motion that propagate through the medium.

We have seen in Sec. 9.5 that when a conductor moves with a velocity v perpendicular to a magnetic field **B**, magnetic forces act on charges in the conductor. These forces, given by $F = qvB$, separate opposite charges until an electric field E is set up in the conductor, which acts in opposition to the magnetic forces. In equilibrium, then, there is an electric field set up in the conductor given by

$$E = -\frac{F}{q} = -vB$$

The exact statement of relative directions is

$$\mathbf{E} = -(\mathbf{v} \times \mathbf{B}) \tag{14.14}$$

As a result of this field, currents are set up in the moving conducting fluid as well as in the adjacent stationary fluid, somewhat as sketched in Fig. 14.10. Though we have considered equal densities of

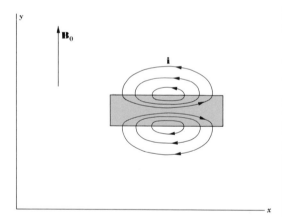

Fig. 14.10   Current resulting from induced electric field sets up forces that retard moving column and accelerate adjacent regions. This action sets up magnetohydrodynamic waves.

positive and negative carriers, they move in opposite directions to give currents in the same direction. Even though the net charge is zero, both signs of charge contribute to the current.

These currents will interact with the magnetic field, and as a result there are forces acting on the charges of the fluid. The force on each current element is

$$d\mathbf{F} = i\,d\mathbf{l} \times \mathbf{B} \tag{8.3}$$

Since the current inside the moving column of fluid is in the positive x direction, Eq. (8.3) gives a force in the positive z direction, out of the paper, which opposes the original motion in the negative z direction. In the adjacent static columns of fluid, above and below the moving column in the diagram, the current is in the opposite direction; so the force is in the negative z direction. Thus the original column tends to be slowed down, and adjacent columns tend to gain velocity in the original direction of motion. The events described show how this kind of electromagnetic coupling provides a mechanism by which motion in one region is transferred to surrounding regions. It is this action which is responsible for magnetohydrodynamic waves.

14.6* *Flow of a Conducting Medium in a Magnetic Field*

We now discuss the interaction between the flow of a conducting fluid and a magnetic field. Motion of the fluid perpendicular to the lines of magnetic field is seriously impeded by the circular motion of the charges, while motion parallel to the field is unaffected. In a highly conducting medium, in fact, we can assume that the magnetic lines are "frozen" in the fluid and move along with any transverse motion of the fluid. In effect, a magnetic field tends to *contain* a plasma and prevent it from diffusing outward.

A great deal of work is now being done to investigate this situation in connection with attempts to produce controlled nuclear fusion energy. The problem is to raise the temperature of a plasma, which will undergo fusion with a consequent release of energy, to a value high enough ($\approx 10^8\ °\mathrm{K}$) to allow the process to occur. The hope is that, by means of a magnetic field, the plasma can be confined to a volume away from the surface of the container, so as to prevent the loss of heat that occurs if the plasma is in contact with the walls. The difficulty is that many possible field configurations turn out to be unstable and thus are ineffective in containing the plasma. It remains to be seen whether or not there is a practical solution to this problem.

14.7 *Comments on Chapter 14*

In this chapter the electric and magnetic force equations are applied to freely moving charged particles. The Lorentz force equation combines the effects of both **E** and **B** fields in a single equation

$$\mathbf{F} = e[\mathbf{E} + (\mathbf{v} \times \mathbf{B})] \tag{14.1}$$

Motion which is limited to planes perpendicular to the **B** field is caused to be circular by the magnetic force. The circular motion has a radius characterized by

$$r = \frac{mv_\perp}{eB} \tag{8.34}$$

and a cyclotron frequency

$$\omega_c = \frac{eB}{m} \tag{8.33}$$

The parallel component of velocity is unaffected by the magnetic field.

In crossed **E** and **B** fields, cycloidal motion results. Similar motion results when the **E** field is replaced by a gravitational field or by a magnetic field gradient, dB/dx.

In a converging magnetic field the helical motion converges to a smaller radius, and the component of motion along the field is reduced. This allows for reflection of spiral trajectories in a converging field, with no loss of kinetic energy. This phenomenon is called the magnetic mirror, and is responsible for the trapping of charged particles in the magnetic field surrounding the earth.

There follows a short discussion of magnetohydrodynamic waves which can occur in highly conducting fluids in a magnetic field. The restoring forces which produce wave motion are a result of Faraday induction electric fields. The chapter concludes with mention of the influence of a magnetic field on the motion of a highly conducting fluid or plasma. Since translational motion of charges in the plane perpendicular to the field is inhibited by the circular motion caused by the magnetic field, transverse motion of the plasma is inhibited, and when it occurs it tends to carry the magnetic lines of force with it.

15

*electric and magnetic quantum effects

15.1* Introduction

In this chapter we give a brief discussion of the impact of *quantum mechanics* on classical electricity and magnetism. We find that there are situations in which electromagnetic radiation is best described in terms of *particles* rather than by waves. Historically, it was with great difficulty that physicists attempted to reconcile the particle nature of radiation with its wavelike properties. Nowadays it is realized that there is no real contradiction in these two aspects, though it is to be expected that different kinds of experiments bring out different aspects. In the following discussion we give some brief descriptions of certain experiments. Further studies are more appropriate to another course, in which a framework of quantum theory can be built up and the problem can be examined in more detail.

15.2* The Photoelectric Effect

The discovery of the photoelectric effect near the end of the nineteenth century gave one of the most direct cases in which classical theory failed to give a sensible explanation of the observed phenomena. The effect has to do with the ejection of electrons from a metal surface when electromagnetic radiation (light) is incident on the surface. Einstein's explanation of the effect in 1905 was based on the quantum theory of Planck, first published in 1900. On the basis of what had gone before, there was no indication that the very surprising results of the experiments would occur. There were at the time, however, quite a number of experiments pointing in the same direction as the photoelectric effect.

At the time of this development the idea of a work function was well understood. It was clear that, to remove an electron from a metal, enough energy has to be given it to allow it to escape over the potential barrier that ordinarily keeps it in the metal. There are a number of known ways of providing this energy. One method of considerable importance is to heat the metal to such an extent that the thermal kinetic energy of the conduction electrons allows some of the most energetic electrons to escape from the surface. This is called *thermionic emission*, and is the usual source of electrons in vacuum tubes at present. Another method is called *secondary emission*. When the surface of a metal is bombarded by atoms, ions, or electrons with sufficiently high kinetic energies, a conduction electron can be given enough kinetic energy to allow it to escape. Finally, if a very high negative potential is applied to a metal, the electric field produced at the metal surface may be sufficient to pull the electron over the potential barrier and give what is called *field emission*. This requires fields of the order of 10^6 volts/cm at the surface.

It might be expected that if an electromagnetic wave were incident on a metal surface, there would be conditions under which the oscillatory **E** field of the wave could impart enough energy to an electron to allow it to escape. This is indeed the photoelectric effect, but the details are surprisingly different from those which can be predicted by any classical theory. The first observations of this effect were made in 1887 by Hertz, who found that the sparking in air between two highly charged electrodes occurs at lower voltage when the electrodes are illuminated. However, these experiments were not carried far, since at that time electrons were not yet known.

An experiment like the later one of Lenard in 1902 brings out the contrast between the expected and actual behavior of electromagnetic waves. Figure 15.1 shows two electrodes placed in a glass envelope that can be evacuated. One electrode is grounded, and the other is

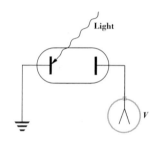

Fig. 15.1   Apparatus used in photoelectric-effect experiment. Electrons emitted from electrode by light quanta drift through evacuated tube to opposite electrode until potential builds up sufficiently to hold them off.

connected to an electroscope that measures the potential of the second electrode with respect to ground. When the first electrode is illuminated, energy is imparted to some electrons, which allows them to escape from the metal with some remaining kinetic energy $W = \frac{1}{2}mv^2$. Those electrons which happen to be traveling toward the second electrode travel through the vacuum and are collected on it. This process continues until the charge collected builds up a potential that prevents the electrons from arriving. When this potential is reached, the electrons are repelled to the walls or fall back to the illuminated electrode. Figure 15.2 shows a time plot of the way in which equilibrium is

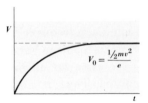

Fig. 15.2   Buildup of charge to equilibrium value in photoelectric-effect experiment. The potential ceases to change when emitted electrons no longer have sufficient energy to reach the second electrode.

reached at the second electrode. Equilibrium occurs when the initial energy of the emitted electrons, $W = \frac{1}{2}mv^2$, just equals the potential energy eV, which they must gain to reach the second electrode. Thus

$$V_0 = \frac{\frac{1}{2}mv^2}{e} \tag{15.1}$$

where V_0 is the equilibrium potential of the electrode. [Actually, the applied potential necessary to stop the electrons is modified by the work functions of the electrodes. Thus, if the potential as read on a voltmeter connected between the two plates is called V_s, the effective potential difference is $V_0 = V_s + (\Phi_2 - \Phi_1)/e$, where Φ_1 and Φ_2 are the work functions of the emitter and collector plates, expressed in volts.] On a classical basis we expect that if the brightness of the illumination is increased, giving a larger magnitude to the electric field vector in the electromagnetic wave, the electrons will get more initial energy and V_0 will be increased. The fact is that the only result of increasing the illumination intensity is that the equilibrium value is reached more rapidly. That is, more electrons are emitted in a given time, but their energy is unchanged. This result is perhaps only a little less surprising than the further discovery that the only factor that produces a change in V_0 is the frequency f of the incident light. Figure 15.3 shows a plot of the potential V_0 related to the frequency of the

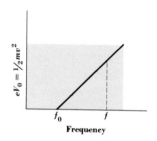

Fig. 15.3 Electron energy versus frequency of illuminating light in photoelectric experiment. Only the frequency of the light, not its intensity, dictates the maximum energy of emitted electrons.

illumination on a given metal. This result means that the kinetic energy given the electrons is proportional to the excess in frequency over a minimum frequency f_0.

f_0 is found to vary from metal to metal, but the slope of the curve is the same for all metals. At frequencies below f_0 no electrons are emitted. Thus, not only is $\frac{1}{2}mv^2 \propto (f - f_0)$, but the proportionality constant is independent of the metal used. We may write

$$\frac{1}{2}mv^2 = h(f - f_0) \tag{15.2}$$

where h is the constant of proportionality. This is found to be Planck's quantum constant ($h = 6.62 \times 10^{-34}$ joule-sec). When we let $hf_0 = W_0$, we may write this relationship

$$hf = \frac{1}{2}mv^2 + W_0 \tag{15.3}$$

Einstein interpreted this as follows: An amount of energy hf is given by the radiation to one electron. Of this one part, W_0, depends on the kind of metal; this is used in getting the electron out of the metal while the rest is converted into kinetic energy of the liberated electron. The energy W_0 is the work function for the metal. We are thus entitled to think of the energy in the electromagnetic waves as consisting of discrete *quanta*, each having an energy

$$W = hf \tag{15.4}$$

The discrete, or particle-like, nature of the energy content is forced on us if we are to understand how the electromagnetic wave is able to impart its energy to a *single* electron in the metal rather than to share it among many. The experiment indicates that the radiation energy either is not imparted to the electron or gives up the entire quantity *hf* to a single electron. It is usual to speak of these quanta of radiation as *photons*. In so doing, we are emphazing their particle-like properties.

15.3* Atomic Radiation

Another major development in the application of quantum ideas came in 1913 with the atomic structure theory of Niels Bohr. Bohr combined the quantum hypothesis of Planck with the Rutherford nuclear model of the atom to account for the discrete frequencies of the electromagnetic radiation from hydrogen and hydrogen-like atoms which had been observed by nineteenth century spectroscopists. In the Bohr theory, as in the more elaborate modern quantum theory, the energy levels of electrons which surround the nucleus of an atom are quantized. The shifting of an electron from one allowed energy level in an atom to a lower energy vacant level releases a quantum of radiation (a photon), which satisfies the relation

$$\Delta W = hf \tag{15.5}$$

where ΔW is the energy difference between the two states.

The study of emission and absorption of photons by atoms has allowed the untangling of the great mass of data giving the frequencies of radiation from atoms, and has provided the basis for the modern model of the atom.

15.4* X-rays and γ Rays

In 1895 a very energetic kind of radiation was discovered by Roentgen and was found to penetrate matter that is opaque to ordinary light. These *x-rays* are produced when a high-velocity beam of electrons impinges on a metal electrode. A tube for the production of x-rays is shown in Fig. 15.4. Potential differences of from 30 up to 100 kv or more are applied between the electron source and the metal anode. The

Electron source
(cathode)

Target
(anode)

*Fig. 15.4   X-ray tube. Elec-
trons emitted thermally
by cathode are accelerated
by the applied voltage and
are suddenly stopped at
the anode. X-rays are
emitted at the anode.*

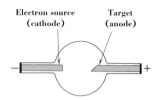

tube is evacuated, so that the electrons reach high energies before they collide with the anode. X-rays emerging through the glass walls of the tube were at first studied by their ability to ionize gases and to produce exposure on a photographic plate. By this means their absorption by various materials was investigated.

One process which occurs is that a high-energy electron can knock an electron from a deep-energy level in an atom of the metal completely out of the atom. When another electron falls back into this level, the energy released by this sudden decrease in potential energy is emitted as a quantum of electromagnetic energy, and an x-ray is the result. Another process producing x-rays is the sudden stopping of the high-energy electrons by impact with the metal. This sudden deceleration can result in the direct transfer of the kinetic energy of the electron into an electromagnetic quantum, or x-ray.

In 1913, von Laue reasoned that if x-rays were electromagnetic waves, they should exhibit interference effects typical of waves, as observed in the diffraction of light by a grating. He therefore sent a beam of x-rays through a salt crystal, in which the periodic spacing between atoms caused it to act as a diffraction grating. He found a diffraction pattern on a photographic film placed in the beam beyond the crystal that not only showed the expected pattern due to wave interference, but also made possible a measurement of the wavelength of the x-rays. The necessary knowledge of the spacing between atoms in the crystal (the lattice constant) he obtained from the density of the crystal and Avogadro's number. Whereas the wavelength range of visible light lies between the limits of about 4,000 and 7,000 A (one angstrom is equal to 10^{-10} m), x-rays lie in the wavelength range between about 0.01 and 100 A. Use of the relation $\lambda f = c$, where λ is the wavelength, f the frequency, and c the velocity of travel of the waves, gives frequencies between approximately 10^{20} and 10^{16} cps for x-rays.

The use of diffraction patterns of single crystals not only has provided an accurate tool for measuring x-ray wavelengths, but also has given very detailed information about the spacing and arrangement of atoms in solids.

Another process that releases high-energy quanta occurs in nuclei of atoms. One of the processes by which energy is given off by unstable nuclei is the emission of γ rays. These are like x-rays, except that they result from nuclear events and are often of still higher energy.

15.5*   The Compton Effect

There is a kind of interaction between x-rays and matter that exhibits very clearly the particle-like nature of electromagnetic radiation. This interaction was first observed by A. H. Compton in 1923. When x-rays are incident on a thin foil of metal, some of the energy of the x-ray can be given to an electron and cause it to be ejected from the metal. It can happen that not all the energy is transferred to the electron, and as a result, the x-ray proceeds with less than its original energy (and therefore has a lower frequency). The special feature here is that if we treat the x-ray as a particle, with energy hf and momentum $p = hf/c$, then the event is completely described as a particle collision process between a photon and an electron. That is, both momentum and energy are conserved, and if direction and energy of the emitted electron are known, the direction and frequency of the scattered x-rays can be calculated. The relatively small energy used to free the electron from the metal is insignificant compared with the very much greater energy of the incident x-ray, and so may be neglected in making the energy and momentum balance.

15.6*   Electron Waves

Present knowledge of atomic structure indicates that in the atom and in solids, it is useful to attribute wavelike properties to particles. The experiments of Davisson and Germer and of G. P. Thomson in 1927 have demonstrated this for electrons in a very revealing way. In these experiments, a beam of electrons is incident on a thin film of matter, and the pattern of electrons that comes through the film is found to exhibit the typical diffraction pattern of waves, exactly like the diffraction patterns of x-rays. In Sec. 7.3, which discussed the physics of metallic conductivity, experiments which demonstrate the wavelike properties of electrons were mentioned. Similar experiments show that wave properties are exhibited by all matter. Hydrogen molecules, helium atoms, protons, and neutrons demonstrate their wave properties in crystal diffraction experiments. In all cases, the de Broglie relationship between wavelength and particle momentum holds. That is,

$$\lambda = h/p$$

where λ is the particle wavelength, h is Planck's constant, and $p = mv$ is the momentum of the particle. The existence of *matter waves* emphasizes the particle-wave duality which is a central aspect of quantum theory.

15.7* *Magnetic Quantization, the Stern-Gerlach Experiment*

During the period of growth of the quantum theory, there were a series of surprises for physicists, which have perhaps not been equaled before or since. One of these relates to atomic magnetism. We have already described the sources of magnetism in atoms, the orbital motion of electrons, electron spin, and nuclear magnetism. The experiments of Stern and Gerlach in 1921 were set up to measure the magnetic moments of individual atoms. Prior to this, magnetic measurements had been confined to susceptibility measurements on bulk matter. The principle of the experiment is to measure the deflection of a beam of neutral atoms due to an inhomogeneous magnetic field through which they pass. Figure 15.5 shows a schematic drawing of the experimental arrangement.

This experiment can be used to measure the magnetic moments of atoms. A highly collimated beam of atoms is emitted from the oven source at one end of the apparatus. The atoms travel through an evacuated chamber in a divergent magnetic field produced by appropriately shaped poles of an electromagnet. After passing through the field, the beam hits a fluorescent screen or a photographic plate, which records its position. There is a net force on a magnetic dipole in a nonuniform magnetic field. It is convenient to describe this effect using the polar model of a magnetic dipole (the equivalent of an electric dipole in a divergent electric field). Such a dipole is shown in Fig. 15.6, using q_m for the effective pole strength (where q_m is defined as in Sec. 10.13) and l for the pole separation. The upward components of the field at the two poles are H_1 and H_2, respectively. Now since the force on each pole is $q_m\mu_0 H_1$ and $-q_m\mu_0 H_2$, the net force is $q_m\mu_0(H_1 - H_2)$, in this case in the downward direction. With the dipole oriented in the opposite direction, the force would be upward. For other orientations, the net

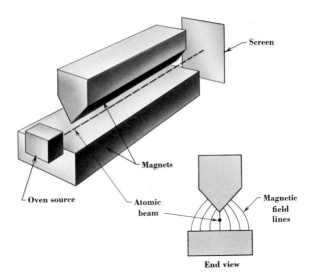

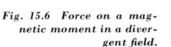

End view

Fig. 15.5 *Atomic-beam apparatus. Neutral atoms from the oven source move through the divergent magnetic field to the screen where they are detected. Force of divergent field on atomic magnetic dipoles causes vertical deflection of beam.*

force is less since there is less difference between H_1 and H_2 if the dipole is not aligned along the direction of maximum field gradient. The effect of the divergent field is thus expected to be a lengthening of the spot made on the screen by the beam in the absence of the field. Some atoms would be deflected upward and some downward, to a greater or lesser extent, depending on their speed and their orientation in space as they travel through the magnetic field. Figure 15.7 shows three patterns on the screen, the first with no field, the second the expected pattern with the field turned on, and the third the actual pattern observed with, say,

Fig. 15.6 *Force on a magnetic moment in a divergent field.*

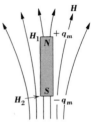

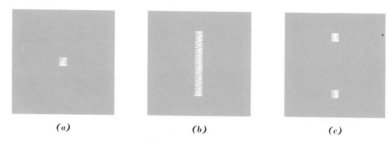

Fig. 15.7   Atomic-beam traces. (a) Beam in absence of magnetic field; (b) classical expectation for beam after passing through divergent H field; (c) experimental result for beam after passing through divergent H field.

lithium atoms. Instead of all possible orientations, only two occur, one parallel to the field and one antiparallel.

This result is another of the phenomena explained by quantum theory. It results from the quantization of the possible orientations of a magnetic dipole in a magnetic field. Another description that amounts to the same thing is to say that the energy levels allowed for the dipole in a field are quantized. Since it takes work to turn a dipole from the direction in which it is aligned with the field into the antiparallel direction, its orientation is expressible in terms of an energy, and it is this energy that is quantized. In the example shown, only two orientations are allowed, although in other situations there may be more. This same technique has been applied to magnetic nuclei by Stern and Rabi, and is at present much used in the exact determination of nuclear magnetic moments.

The quantum-mechanical behavior of magnetic dipoles of electrons and nuclei is the basis of an active field of research in solid-state physics at the present time. Samples are placed in a magnetic field where radiation in the high-frequency, or microwave, region is present. Transitions of the magnetic dipoles from one magnetic state to another are induced by the radiation, and result in energy loss from the radiation field to the sample. Results of these experiments give information about the dipoles themselves and about the matter in which they occur. These are called *magnetic-resonance* experiments.

15.8*   Comments on Chapter 15

In this chapter we touched briefly on some of the phenomena where electromagnetic effects are intimately connected with quantum aspects of physics. The photoelectric effect was the first experiment that showed that the classical theory of electromagnetic waves must be modified to accept photons, the quanta of radiation. The study of line spectra of the electromagnetic radiation from atoms showed unequivocally that the energy levels of electronic states in atoms are quantized. X-rays and γ rays were shown to be electromagnetic waves, and they also exhibited quantum characteristics. The Compton effect, which demonstrated that the energy of photons could be degraded when atomic electrons accept part of the energy and are emitted by the atom, gave another example of the particle-like nature of electromagnetic energy.

Crystal-diffraction experiments on electrons and on protons showed that these particles and others, under suitable conditions, exhibit wavelike properties. Thus the wave-particle duality seems to extend throughout nature.

We discussed the quantization of magnetic states as first shown in atomic beam experiments. This magnetic quantization makes possible the several kinds of magnetic resonance experiments that have added much to the understanding of solids.

16

*vacuum tubes and semiconductor devices

16.1*   Introduction

In this chapter we consider the basic characteristics of three devices of primary importance in practical electronics. These are the vacuum tube, the transistor, and a special high-frequency tube, the klystron. The vacuum tube and transistor are basically similar in function in that the current through them can be controlled by an electric signal. The entire field of electronics depends on the control characteristics of these devices. The many special types of tubes and transistors allow for a multitude of electronic circuits that perform very diverse functions. It is appropriate here to discuss only their basic design and a few typical applications. The klystron is discussed as one example of devices that operate at very much higher frequencies than conventional vacuum tubes. They are the most important sources of microwave-frequency signals, and are becoming of major importance in the communication field. The availability of electric power at microwave frequencies has allowed the development of many new fields of investigation in experimental physics.

16.2*   The Vacuum Tube

The principal function of the vacuum tube is to control the flow of current in a circuit. This control is possible with negligible expenditure of power. As a result, the vacuum tube can be used to rectify or amplify an ac signal or to operate as an oscillator in appropriate circuits and thereby produce an ac signal from a dc source of power. In a vacuum tube, thermionic emission from a hot *cathode* in a vacuum provides a constant source of electrons that carry a negative current to a *plate*, or *anode*, held at a positive potential with respect to the cathode. Control of this current is obtained through the operation of one or more *grids* whose potential is controlled by external circuits. We begin with a discussion of the relationship between the vacuum current and the potential applied between cathode and plate.

The electron current in a vacuum is limited by the rate at which electrons can be emitted by the cathode. This depends on the temperature of the cathode, but in practice the controlling factor is the *space charge* in the cathode region. The effect can be explained qualitatively as follows: In the absence of electron emission, there is a field at the cathode due to the potential difference applied between plate and cathode. When electrons are emitted by the cathode, this field accelerates the electrons toward the plate, and there is a distribution of electrons in the cathode region. Their presence alters the field distribution and lowers the field near the cathode, which in turn allows more electrons to collect in the cathode region. This process continues until the field at the cathode surface actually reverses. In steady state, the kinetic energy of the emitted electrons just overcomes the negative field, and there exists a steady-state *space-charge-limited* current. A simple quantitative analysis of this situation, which we shall not develop here, shows that the current is proportional to $V^{3/2}$, where V is the plate-to-cathode potential difference. To a good approximation this law holds for any electrode shape. The vacuum tube does not behave as an ohmic resistance, since the current is *not* proportional to the applied voltage.

We first investigate the properties of a vacuum-tube *diode*, which has only a cathode and plate and is used primarily as a *rectifier*. Figure 16.1 shows a plot of the current through a vacuum-tube diode as a function of the voltage across it. Positive current flows when the plate is positive with respect to the cathode. The current is zero when the potential is applied in the opposite direction, since no carriers are available from the plate, and electrons emitted by the cathode are

Fig. 16.1 *Current-voltage
characteristic for a vac-
uum-tube diode. Positive
voltage means plate is positive with respect to cathode. Positive current is directed from plate to cathode, corresponding to electron flow from cathode to
plate. The asymmetry of
this curve produces the
rectifier action of the diode.*

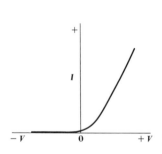

held there by the applied field. Figure 16.2 shows a simple circuit in which a diode is used as a *half-wave rectifier*. In this circuit an ac voltage is converted to a dc voltage. The cathode is heated by a heater filament connected to a low-voltage external supply, usually a transformer. This supplies the heat to cause the cathode to emit electrons. The cathode is usually coated with a metal oxide that lowers the temperature required to give electron emission. On the half-cycle of the ac voltage during which the plate is positive, current flows through the tube. On the negative half-cycle, however, no current can flow, since electrons are repelled by the negative plate voltage. The result of this action is the output signal shown, in which the negative half-cycles are missing. The average value of the half-wave-rectified voltage output is no longer zero, and if a suitable filter is added (see Sec. 11.10), a net dc voltage is obtained. The simplest filter would be obtained by connecting a capacitor across the output.

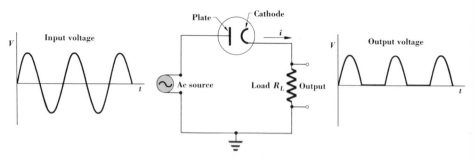

Fig. 16.2 *Half-wave rectifier circuit. Cathode heater is not shown. The ac signal appears on the plate of the tube. Since electrons can flow only when the plate is positive with respect to the cathode, current flows only during the positive half-cycle of the ac voltage on the plate. As a result the output voltage across the load resistor is rectified as shown.*

A full-wave rectifier circuit using a center-tapped transformer is shown in Fig. 16.3. The two tubes required are often placed in the

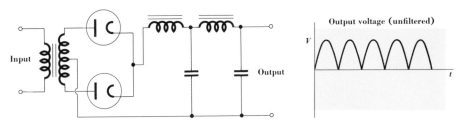

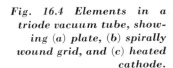

Fig. 16.3 Full-wave rectifier, using center-tapped transformer, with filter circuit in output. Cathode heaters are not shown. Output voltage is shown for a sinusoidal input, before filtering. The diodes operate on alternate half-cycles of the ac input voltage. The pair of LC filter circuits removes most of the time variation from the unfiltered output of the diodes.

same vacuum envelope and use a common cathode. Also shown is a more complicated filter circuit such as is used for minimizing the remaining ac ripple. On alternate half-cycles the current passes through that tube which has a positive potential on its plate, while the other tube ceases to conduct. The heater connections are omitted in the diagram. Such a rectifier circuit is the usual source of dc voltage needed for amplifiers, oscillators, and other electronic devices.

In a *triode*, shown schematically in Fig. 16.4, a single control grid is placed between cathode and plate. The control grid is an open net-

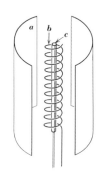

Fig. 16.4 Elements in a triode vacuum tube, showing (a) plate, (b) spirally wound grid, and (c) heated cathode.

work of wire through which most of the electrons pass on their way to the positive plate. However, when a negative potential (relative to the cathode) is applied to the grid, the field set up modifies the space-charge-limited current and tends to prevent electrons from reaching the plate, thus reducing the current. The magnitude of the plate current can thus be controlled from zero to a maximum value by varying the grid potential. Since practically no current goes to the grid, this can be done with a very small expenditure of electric power. Figure 16.5 shows a plot of plate current versus grid voltage when the plate

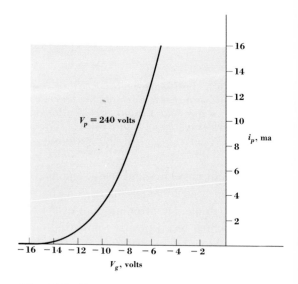

$V_p = 240$ volts

i_p, ma

V_g, volts

Fig. 16.5   Plate current versus grid voltage in a triode. Plate voltage held constant.

voltage is held constant. This plot shows that some current goes to the plate even when the grid is quite negative with respect to the cathode. This is due partly to the open structure of the grid, which allows some lines of force to penetrate through the grid from plate to cathode even when the grid is negative. Another factor involved is the finite kinetic energy of the electrons evaporated from the cathode, which enables them to overcome a small retarding potential. Figure 16.6 shows the more conventional plot of the characteristics of a triode, from which Fig. 16.5 was obtained. The current through the tube depends on both the grid and plate potential.

Figure 16.7 shows a typical circuit in which a triode is used as an ac amplifier. We use this to give a qualitative picture of the process of amplification. Let us imagine an ac signal (not necessarily sinusoidal), having an average amplitude of about 0.1 volt. If the reactance $1/C_g\omega$

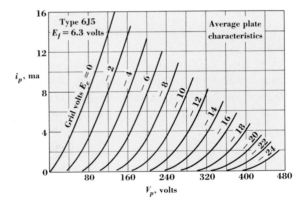

Fig. 16.6   **Triode plate current versus plate voltage**
for various grid voltages. (*From RCA Receiving*
Tube Manual, copyright 1950, Technical Series
RCI, fig. 92CM-4771T, p. 147.*)

is very small compared with the grid resistance R_g, most of the voltage
will appear across R_g and on the grid of the tube. The cathode resistance R_c and the plate resistance R_p will have been chosen to put the
tube in its operating range (where the current is sensitive to the grid
voltage). The capacitor C_c across the cathode resistor is large enough to
hold the cathode at a nearly constant voltage despite the rapid varia-

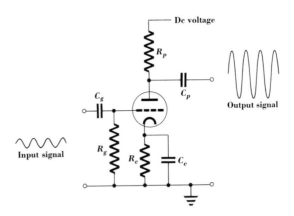

Fig. 16.7   **A triode used in a typical amplifier**
circuit. A dc grid bias voltage is provided by
R_c, through which the cathode current
passes. The capacitor C_c holds the bias volt-
age constant.

tion of the current through the tube due to the ac signal. That is, the time constant of the R_cC_c circuit is long compared with the period of one cycle at the signal frequency. The small grid signal causes a variation in the tube current; this causes the voltage drop across the plate resistance R_p to vary, and the resulting ac signal at the output becomes, perhaps, one hundred times the input signal, say, 10 volts. By placing a series of tube stages one after the other, large amplifications can be obtained.

A self-excited oscillator is shown in Fig. 16.8. A *tank* circuit, consisting of an inductance and a capacitance and having a natural

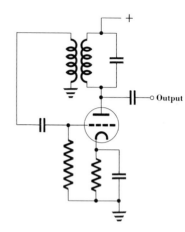

Fig. 16.8 *A triode used in a self-excited oscillator circuit. Inductive coupling from the LC resonant circuit in series with the plate feeds an ac signal to the grid. The resulting ac current to the plate maintains oscillation in the resonant circuit. The frequency of the ac output signal depends on the resonant frequency of the LC circuit.*

frequency of oscillation, feeds back a small amount of signal to the input grid. If the phase of this signal is correct, the consequent variation of current in the tube reinforces the oscillations in the tank circuit, and they become self-maintaining. There are many alternative oscillator designs, but in all cases the function of the tube is to feed back enough energy to the oscillating circuit to make up for the losses that would otherwise cause it to stop oscillating.

More complicated tubes have extra electrodes that modify the characteristics of the tubes for special applications. Discussion of such tubes as tetrodes and pentodes is omitted here, though they are of great importance in electronic devices. We also omit discussions of such special-purpose tubes as beam-power tubes and of gas-filled tubes such as thyratrons and voltage regulators. The interested student may easily inform himself of the characteristics of the multitude of types of tubes by studying one of the several tube manuals readily available.

Our purpose here has been to give only the briefest qualitative description of the principles involved.

16.3* Semiconductor Devices

In Chap. 7 the energy gap in the mobile electron energy distribution in semiconductors was discussed briefly. It was shown that by introducing impurity atoms into pure semiconductors these materials can be made good conductors at room temperature. Conductivity is caused by the presence of mobile carriers, both electrons (− charge) and holes[1] (+ charge). By adjusting the number and kind of impurity atoms which are introduced as the crystal is grown from the liquid melt, the carriers in a particular specimen can be predominantly either electrons or holes (*n*- or *p*-type material). Useful devices are constructed by placing successive regions of opposite type next to each other and by making appropriate electrical connections to the various regions of the combined specimens. A common practice is to grow one type of material from the melt, after which another kind of impurity is added to reverse the type. Thus *n* and *p* regions are joined by a transition region. A qualitative understanding of how these devices operate can be gained by looking first at a semiconductor junction diode and then at a three-element junction transistor.

16.4* Junction Diode

A junction diode operates as a current rectifier. That is, when a given voltage is applied across the device, a much larger current flows for one direction of applied voltage than for the other. The device consists of an *n*-type region adjacent to a *p*-type region, with current leads to each region, as shown in Fig. 16.9. If the two regions were not connected,

---

[1] As explained in Chap. 7, when an energy band in a semiconductor is almost completely full of electrons, conduction occurs through the effective motion of unoccupied states. This is called conduction by holes. Holes act as positively charged carriers.

Fig. 16.9 A pn junction diode. One region is connected to the other through a transition region called a junction. Current leads are shown.

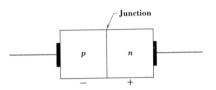

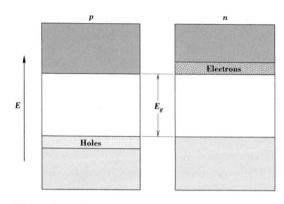

Fig. 16.10 *Separate* p *and* n *semiconductor specimens, showing energy gap* E_g *and high concentration of mobile holes in the* p *material and of mobile electrons in the* n *material. Both specimens are normally electrically neutral.*

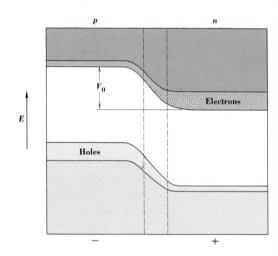

Fig. 16.11 *A junction diode, showing energy-band diagram.* p *and* n *specimens are connected by a junction. Diffusion of holes from the* p *region and of electrons from the* n *region produces a net charge on each region. This leads to a potential difference* V_0 *between the two regions in steady state.*

the concentration of mobile electrons would be high in the n region and the concentration of mobile holes would be high in the p region, as shown in the energy diagram, Fig. 16.10. Each region would be electrically neutral. However, when the two regions are connected together, there is a net migration of electrons into the p region and of holes into the n region, caused by diffusion of each kind of charge carrier from the region of high concentration to the other region. This process of net charge transfer continues until a steady state has been reached, as shown in Fig. 16.11. In this steady-state condition, V_0, the potential difference produced by net charge transfer, has reached a value such that the diffusion of electrons from the n to the p region is just equal to the back diffusion of electrons from the p to the n region, as aided by the potential difference V_0. Thus a self-bias develops as a result of the thermal generation and diffusion of carriers. In the steady state, the rate of generation of carriers is just matched by their rate of recombination. At the same time, diffusion of holes from the p region to the n region acts similarly to produce a similar potential difference in the same direction. In the energy diagram of Fig. 16.11, electron energy increases in the upward direction and hole energy increases in the downward direction.

What will happen if the two regions are electrically connected externally, as shown in Fig. 16.12? Since the two regions are at different

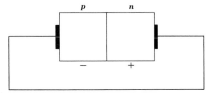

Fig. 16.12 *A junction diode, shorted externally. No net current flows. See explanation of Fig. 16.13.*

potentials, it might be thought at first that the diode would act as a battery and a current would flow. This would be thermodynamically incorrect, since it would imply a source of energy with no temperature difference required. But it can also be ruled out by imagining a circular pair of p and n specimens connected at both ends, as shown in Fig. 16.13. In steady state the p region would assume a negative potential with respect to the n region by virtue of the potential difference set up by diffusion at both junctions, but no current would flow. The circuit is

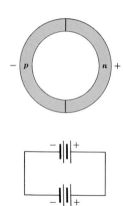

Fig. 16.13 Diagram of a double pn junction and its equivalent circuit. The two junctions behave as two batteries connected oppositely in a closed circuit. Thus the two specimens are held at different potentials but no current flows. The shorted junction diode of Fig. 16.12 is equivalent to this circuit, since the external wire completes the second junction.

equivalent to two batteries connected in opposite directions, as shown. Figure 16.12 is equivalent to this arrangement, since the external wire simply acts to complete the second junction.

We may now consider the rectifying action of the junction diode, as shown in Fig. 16.14, for the two possible directions of applied potential. In (a) the potential is applied in the *forward* direction. It acts to reduce the potential difference between the regions. This allows a larger rate of flow of electrons and holes, and results in a net current as long as the potential is applied. The current is approximately linear with respect to applied voltage.

In (b) the potential is applied in the *reverse* direction. The increased potential difference further decreases the diffusion of both electrons and holes, but results in almost negligible reverse current. The reason for the very small reverse current is easily explained. Consider the charge flow produced by electrons. Since the dominant source of mobile electrons is in the n region, and electrons in the p region are largely the result of diffusion from the n region, increasing the potential difference can result in increased current only by increasing the back flow of electrons from the p to the n region. But this can have only a small effect, since the concentration of electrons in the p region is in any case small. A similar argument applies to hole transport. Figure 16.15 shows a typica current-voltage curve for a junction diode. Also shown is the conventional circuit symbol for the diode. The arrow gives the direction of forward (positive) current. This behavior of the junction diode is similar to that of the vacuum-tube diode (Fig. 16.2). A major advantage of the junction diode is that it requires no hot cathode to provide the mobile carriers.

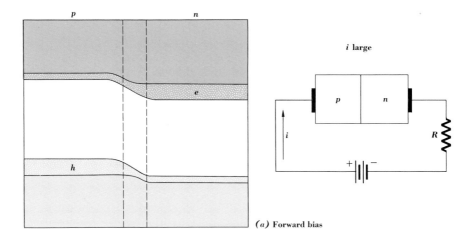

(a) Forward bias

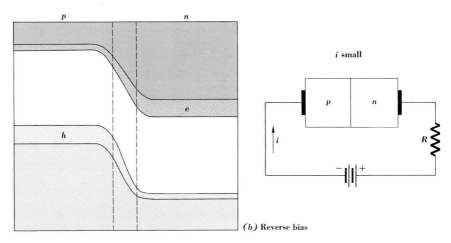

(b) Reverse bias

Fig. 16.14 *A source of emf connected to a junction diode. (a) The battery is connected in the forward direction. This lowers the potential difference between the two regions and gives a large forward current. (b) The battery is applied in the reverse direction. Only a small reverse current is developed.*

16.5* Junction Transistor

The junction transistor is made of two junctions, each having properties similar to those of the junction diode. Figure 16.16 shows an *npn* transistor and its energy diagram. This combination of two junctions is symmetric, and is provided with three contacts, one to each region.

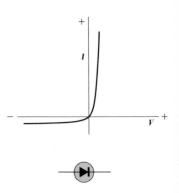

Fig. 16.15 I-V curve for a
junction diode, and con-
ventional diode symbol.
The arrow gives the direction of the forward (positive) current. Compare
this curve with Fig. 16.2,
which shows the similar
behavior of a vacuum-tube
diode.

The energy diagram shows the natural bias generated by diffusion across the junctions. The three regions are called the *emitter*, *base*, and *collector*. In the design shown, emitter and collector have the same shape, though in other kinds of transistors they may be of different shapes, with different areas of transition region connecting them to the base.

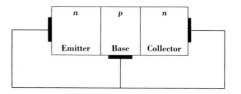

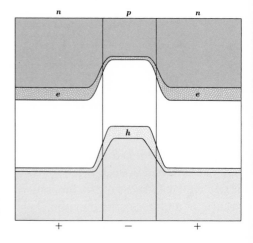

Fig. 16.16 npn transistor,
showing energy diagram
and steady-state biases
induced by charge diffusion.

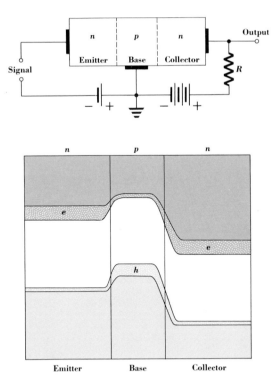

Fig. 16.17   npn transistor connected as a common-base amplifier. A forward bias is placed on the emitter, and a reverse bias on the collector. The signal voltage between emitter and base controls the collector current. Electrons provide the major current source.

Figure 16.17 shows the modification in this situation when external potentials are applied. Most of the applied voltage appears across the transition layers at the junctions, since these regions have a much higher resistivity than do the pure n and p regions. With potentials applied as shown in the figure, there is a forward bias placed on the left-hand junction (emitter to base), and a reverse bias on the right-hand junction (base to collector). As a result, there is a continual flow of electrons from emitter to base. The thickness of the p-type base region is so small that most of the electrons move through the base by diffusion and into the collector region without combining with holes in the base region. Further diffusion through the collector region brings the electrons to the collector electrode. Since the emitter current depends on

*Fig. 16.18 Simplified cir-
cuit diagram of an npn
transistor connected as a
common-base amplifier.
Bias voltages are omitted
from the diagram. The
convention adopted for
positive direction of electrode currents is shown.
The arrow on the emitter
electrode points in the direction of true positive
current.*

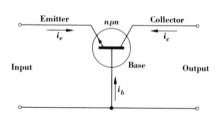

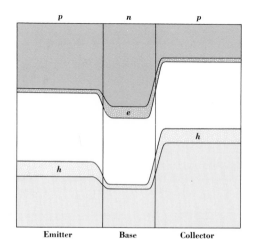

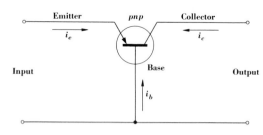

*Fig. 16.19 Energy diagram of a pnp transistor
operated as a common-base amplifier.
Holes provide the major source of current.
Bias voltages are the opposite of those
shown for the npn transistor in Fig. 16.17.
Also shown is a simplified circuit diagram
of the arrangement.*

the forward-bias voltage, the collector current varies with the signal input. For a *small-signal* (ac) input voltage between emitter and base, there is a power gain in the output signal across the load resistance. This gain results from the relative insensitivity of the collector current to changes in the reverse-bias potential between base and collector.

Figure 16.18 shows a simplified circuit diagram of the *npn* transistor in this arrangement, called the *common-base transistor amplifier*. Bias voltages are not shown. Electron current dominates in the *npn* transistor, though there is a small contribution from the low density of holes moving in the opposite direction from the collector to the emitter. The arrow on the emitter electrode symbol indicates the direction of flow of positive current. Also shown in the diagram is the convention adopted for positive current through the three electrodes. i_e is negative here, while i_c is positive.

The *pnp* transistor can be operated similarly in the common-base amplifier circuit. For this, the bias voltages are reversed, and the current flows in the opposite direction, as shown in Fig. 16.19. This current is predominantly due to the transport of holes. The arrow on the emitter is reversed, to correspond to the true current direction. However, the positive-electrode-current convention is the same here as for the *npn* transistor.

In Fig. 16.20 we show two other commonly used amplifier circuits in which either type of transistor can be used, with appropriate bias

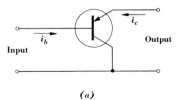

(*a*)

Fig. 16.20 pnp transistor in alternate amplifier cir-cuits. (a) Common-emitter circuit; (b) common-col-lector circuit. Bias voltages are not shown.

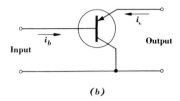

(*b*)

voltages (not shown). Figure 16.20*a* is called a *common-emitter* circuit, while Fig. 16.20*b* is called a *common-collector* circuit. Figure 16.21

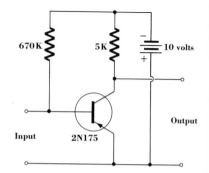

Fig. 16.21 Practical common-emitter amplifier circuit showing how bias voltages can be obtained from a single voltage source.

shows how proper bias voltages can be obtained from a single voltage source, as applied to a practical common-emitter amplifier.

The several kinds of circuits shown, and the fact that they can operate with either polarity through the choice of *pnp* or *npn* transistors, make possible a completely new flexibility in the design of amplifiers.

Some other semiconductor devices of ingenious design and great interest are as follows: The *Zener diode* is a voltage-regulator device in which a large reverse-bias voltage is applied to a junction diode. At high enough applied voltage, each mobile electron produces many others by an ionization process as it is driven through the junction region by the applied field. With a suitable series resistance, the voltage across the device is constant over a wide range of currents. The *silicon-controlled rectifier* is an on-off device involving four parallel *pn* junctions, which can be used to control large amounts of power with little absorption of power by the device itself. A *gate* electrode controls the operation of a junction rectifier.

The *tunnel diode* contains a very thin *pn* junction which allows electrons to tunnel through a potential barrier to produce a negative-resistance characteristic. That is, increased voltage results in decreased current through the junction. This property provides a convenient element for constructing very high frequency oscillators. The *field-effect transistor* provides a high input impedance which is useful for certain applications, and has the additional feature that it will operate at much higher frequencies than the junction transistor. The *parametric diode* is a *pn* junction operated in reverse bias which acts as a variable capacitor. Increase in the reverse bias reduces the junction capacitance by increasing the effective width of the insulating junction. This device has many interesting applications such as in automatic tuning of radio receivers. The term *integrated circuit* is applied to many devices which combine a number of semiconductor functions in a single multiple-element unit. The opportunities for miniaturized circuits which they provide represent a rapidly growing field of interest in electronics.[1]

16.6* The Klystron

During World War II there was a great development of equipment utilizing very high frequency ac circuits having frequencies from 1,000 to, say, 24,000 megacycles per second (Mc/sec). The development of power sources and detectors of power in this microwave frequency range made radar possible, and has also opened up many new fields in experimental physics. In this section we limit discussion to a brief description of one of the most important methods of generating these very high frequencies, the klystron tube.

There are a number of reasons why a conventional vacuum tube becomes unsatisfactory as an oscillator or amplifier at frequencies above a few hundred megacycles per second. A major difficulty lies in the small but unavoidable capacitances between control electrodes in the tube. Since the impedance of these capacitances depends on $1/\omega C$, when frequencies get too high the capacitance has the effect of shorting out the high-frequency voltage. A second difficulty arises when the transit time for electrons to travel from cathode to plate becomes comparable with a period of the high-frequency signal. Under these conditions the rapidly varying electron density in the electron beam induces high-frequency currents in the grid that prevent effective control of the current. This difficulty limits conventional tubes to frequencies below about 100 Mc/sec. Present-day schemes for getting around this difficulty actually take advantage of transit-time effects.

As an example of a microwave generator we discuss the *reflex klystron*. The heart of this tube is a resonant cavity. This is a metal box, in this case in the shape of a toroid, which acts at very high frequencies like an LCR circuit. That is, an electromagnetic wave can be set up inside the cavity at a resonance frequency, just as an LCR circuit oscillates. Oscillations in an LCR circuit are damped by resistive losses. In a cavity, losses result from currents induced in the walls by

[1] A very good elementary discussion of many of these devices and others can be found in J. J. Brophy, "Basic Electronics for Scientists," McGraw-Hill Book Company, New York, 1966.

the oscillating electromagnetic waves within the cavity. In the klystron, the cavity is excited and kept in oscillation by a pulsed electron beam. A schematic diagram of a klystron is shown in Fig. 16.22.

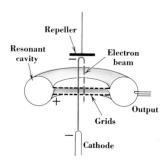

Fig. 16.22   The electron beam, after dc acceleration, is bunched after it passes through the microwave field between the grids. Upon reflection by the repeller electrode the electron bunches pass back through the cavity just out of phase with the microwave field. Their loss of kinetic energy maintains the electromagnetic energy in the cavity. Power is coupled out of the cavity by an antenna.

The electron beam acts to maintain electromagnetic oscillations in the cavity. In a reflex klystron, an electron beam is caused to pass twice through the resonant cavity. In their first passage the electrons are speeded up or slowed down by the oscillating field in the cavity, depending on the phase of the oscillating field at the time of electron passage through the cavity. The beam is then reflected by a dc potential on a repeller electrode, and passes back through the cavity. At the time that the beam makes its second passage through the cavity, the electrons have been bunched in space as a result of their previously modified velocities. In the operating condition, the pulses of electrons arrive back in the cavity at times so that they are retarded by the microwave field. The kinetic energy they lose goes into the oscillating electromagnetic wave in the cavity. This is the mechanism which maintains the oscillations and makes up for the energy losses in the cavity walls, and also the microwave radiation which is coupled out of the cavity for use.

Figure 16.23 shows a plot of the microwave power output and of the microwave frequency as a function of repeller voltage for a fixed cathode-grid voltage. Several *modes* of oscillation are shown. In the mode giving the largest power, bunched electrons arrive back at the cavity just one period after passing through the cavity and being reflected back by the repeller voltage. At the peak of this power-output

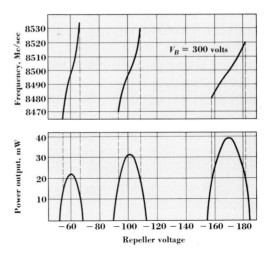

Fig. 16.23   Power output in several modes of a klystron oscillator versus repeller voltage. V_B is the (fixed) cathode-grid voltage. The frequency plot shows the appreciable electronic tuning available.

curve the electron bunches arrive exactly in phase with the natural cavity oscillations, and the system oscillates at the natural frequency of the cavity. For slightly greater or lesser repeller voltages the electrons arrive at the cavity slightly ahead of or behind the unperturbed phase of the cavity. As a result the frequency of the system is slightly increased or decreased, as shown in the frequency plot. This is the mechanism by which electrical tuning of the klystron is accomplished. Other modes of oscillation allow two or more cycles to pass between electron passages through the cavity. These modes give somewhat less power than the first mode discussed. Additional tuning is provided by a mechanical arrangement which slightly distorts the shape of the microwave cavity and thereby changes its natural oscillation frequency.

16.7*   Comments on Chapter 16

This chapter might have been called "current- and voltage-control devices." Vacuum tubes and semiconductor devices are at the heart of modern electronics because of the many ways in which they can be used to control the currents which flow in circuits. They are combined with appropriate passive devices, that is, resistors, inductors, and capacitors, to provide rectifiers, amplifiers, oscillators, and many other important electronic circuits.

We have touched briefly on the nomenclature and parameters which describe their behavior. The method by which a low-energy signal on a vacuum-tube grid controls the current through the tube is qualitatively simple, involving as it does the behavior of electrons in an electric field. The ideas involved in the control of mobile carriers in semiconductor devices are more complicated, but the devices themselves tend to be more adaptable to special functions than are vacuum tubes. The absence of the requirement for a heated cathode and the small size of the semiconductor device open up many new applications of great practical importance.

We touched briefly on the simplest transistor design and described a few of the special devices in common use. There are many good sources of detailed information on the newly available devices which are already playing important roles in electronics.

The chapter concludes with a very brief description of the klystron tube, probably the most important source of very high frequency electromagnetic radiation.

PROBLEMS

The behavior of a vacuum tube or transistor in a circuit can be determined graphically from empirical current-voltage curves. This is illustrated for a vacuum-tube triode in the following problem.

$\star$16.1A   In Fig. P16.1, a tube with characteristics as shown in Fig. 16.6 is connected to a 240-volt dc supply through a plate resistance $R_p = 30,000$ ohms. We wish to investigate the effect of a change in the grid voltage V_g on the plate voltage V_p.

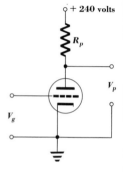

Fig. P16.1

a Using Fig. 16.6, plot the *load line* for this triode for the given values of applied voltage and R_p. To do this, we plot two or more points on Fig. 16.6 that give the voltage V_p across the tube for various plate currents. Thus, for zero current, there will be no voltage drop across the plate resistor; so V_p = 240 volts. Similarly, when i_p = 8 ma, the voltage across the tube will be V_p = 240 − iR_p = 240 − (8 × 10^{-3} × 30,000) = 0. The straight line between these two points is called the load line. For the circuit shown, this tube will operate along this line.

b Using the load line, find graphically the change in plate voltage when the grid voltage is changed from −6 to −4 volts.

16.1B Give a qualitative discussion to explain why, in an amplifier circuit such as shown in Fig. P16.1, there is a phase shift of 180° between input and output signals.

The behavior of semiconductor devices depends on the contrasting properties of *n*- and *p*-type materials.

16.2A Explain why an *n*- and a *p*-type semiconductor, brought into contact, suffer a change in electrostatic potential. Which becomes more positive, and why?

17

units of measurement

17.1 Introduction

In this book we use the meter-kilogram-second (mks) system of units, which is rather well known and has certain convenient features. However, since much of the important literature in physics and in engineering has been written in *electrostatic* and *electromagnetic cgs* units, it is essential for the student to have some knowledge of these systems. Furthermore, a considerable amount of contemporary writing is in the cgs system; so there is a continuing need for an understanding of both systems.

The important features of the mks system as we have used it are as follows:

1. All experiments, whether purely electric, purely magnetic, or a combination, use the same units. In contrast with this, in the cgs system two subsystems are developed, requiring conversion from one to the other in some situations.

2. In most cases the quantities used in the mks system are identical with the *practical* quantities of electricity and magnetism, such as amperes, volts, ohms, and farads, which have been for a long time the most com-

mon units in practical measurements in both physics and engineering. In the cgs system, the absolute quantities derived from the basic equations must usually be converted to practical units.

3.   We have used the *rationalized* mks system, which brings the factor 4π into the equations. Its presence there gives a somewhat simpler form to many of the frequently used derived equations.

4.   The mks system uses meters, kilograms and newtons instead of centimeters, grams and dynes as in the cgs system.

In this chapter we examine the cgs system, and also the related *gaussian* system, and show the relationship between these and the mks system.

17.2   Measuring Systems Compared

In setting up a system of electrical units, the first step is to decide on units of length, mass, and time. This leads to units of force, work, and power. As shown in Table 17.1, the two alternatives in practice are the mks and cgs systems.

Once the choice is made, the unit of charge q, or the unit of current i, must be chosen. Since i is dq/dt, and since the second is used in both systems as the unit of time, the relation between q and i in a given system is fixed. With the choice of mechanical units made and with unit charge defined, all other electrical quantities follow. Certain derived quantities relating to properties of matter depend further on the form of equations used for their definition.

Units of charge and of current are defined by force equations in the several systems of units. A complication exists in any system because there are two ways in which the unit of charge can be defined. Coulomb's law for the electrostatic force between two point charges can be taken as the basis of unit charge. This relates unit charge to an

Table 17.1

	MKS	*CGS*
Length	**Meter**	$= 10^2$ **cm**
Mass	**Kilogram**	$= 10^3$ **grams**
Time	**Second**	$=$ **second**
Force	**Newton**	$= 10^5$ **dynes**
Work	**Joule (newton-meter)**	$= 10^7$ **ergs (dyne-cm)**
Power	**Watt (joules/second)**	$= 10^7$ **ergs/sec**

experimentally measured electrostatic force. Alternatively, the measured magnetic force between current elements can be used to define unit current. Then, since i is dq/dt, this fixes the unit of charge on the basis of the measured magnetic force. See, for example, Eq. (8.13), which applies to the force between two current loops.

How can the two experimental ways by which unit charge is defined be accommodated? Each system of units handles the problem differently. The *cgs system* solves the problem by defining one charge unit for electrostatic problems and another for magnetic problems. A modified cgs system, called the *gaussian system*, defines an electrostatic unit of charge, just as in the cgs system, and further defines the proportionality constant in magnetic equations so that they are correct when the electrostatic charge unit is used in them. The *mks system*, as we have seen, sets the proportionality constants in the electric and magnetic equations so that the charge unit is the same. Furthermore, this charge unit is the same as in the *practical system* of coulombs, amperes, volts, ohms, henrys, and farads.

17.3   The CGS System

We begin a discussion of the several systems with the oldest one in common use. As suggested above, the cgs system is really two systems, one for electrostatic and the other for magnetic problems. The relation between the two is dictated by the relative strengths of the electrostatic force between charges and the magnetic force between current elements.

The electrostatic system, called esu (electrostatic units), defines unit charge by Coulomb's law, written

$$F = \frac{q_1 q_2}{r^2} \tag{17.1}$$

When q_1 and q_2 are made equal, they are unit charges, called esu, or *statcoulombs*, if at one centimeter separation the force between them is one dyne. From this definition is derived that for unit electric field,

$$\mathbf{E} = \frac{\mathbf{F}}{q} \qquad \text{dynes/esu, or dynes/statcoul} \tag{17.2}$$

and for potential difference,

$$V = -\int \mathbf{E} \cdot d\mathbf{l} \qquad \text{ergs/esu, or statvolts} \tag{17.3}$$

For magnetic problems the unit of current, called emu (electro-magnetic units), or abcoulombs, is defined by an equation like Eq. (8.1), with the constant of proportionality set equal to 1. When this is integrated to give the force per unit length between two parallel wires carrying equal currents i and separated by a distance r, we find

$$\frac{F}{l} = \frac{2i^2}{r} \tag{17.4}$$

This is similar to Eq. (8.13), except for the constant of proportionality, and provides the definition of unit current,

$$\frac{F}{l} \text{ dynes/cm} = \frac{2i^2}{r} \text{ emu}^2/\text{cm} \tag{17.5}$$

The emu of current is also called the *abampere*. The abampere corresponds to a charge transfer of

1 abcoul/sec, or 1 emu/sec

and thus defines the unit of charge for magnetic problems.

The magnetic field in emu units is obtained through

$$d\mathbf{B} = \frac{i \, d\mathbf{l} \times \hat{\mathbf{r}}}{r^2} \qquad \text{gauss} \tag{17.6}$$

The force on a moving charge in an electric and magnetic field is given by

$$\mathbf{F} = q\mathbf{E} + q'(\mathbf{v} \times \mathbf{B}) \tag{17.7}$$

where q is measured in esu, or statcoulombs, and q' is in emu, or abcoulombs.

Experiments which compare electric and magnetic forces show that

3×10^{10} statcoul $= 1$ abcoul

The esu unit of charge is thus very small compared with the emu unit. The number 3×10^{10} is more accurately

$$c = 2.997930 \times 10^{10} \text{ cm/sec} \tag{17.8}$$

the velocity of electromagnetic waves in free space. For most purposes the approximate value is satisfactory.

17.4   The Gaussian System

For electrostatic problems the gaussian system is identical with the esu system, though the unit of charge is usually called the gaussian unit rather than statcoulomb, or esu. Magnetic problems, however, are handled by a simple modification of all magnetic equations to give correct results when the electrostatic charge unit is used. The modification simply involves replacing the i of the emu equations by i/c, where the new i is to be measured in esu, or gaussian, units. This follows at once from the relation between esu and emu units.

In the gaussian system we thus write

$$\frac{F}{l} = \frac{2i^2}{c^2 r}$$

instead of Eq. (17.4). Similarly, we use for the magnetic field equation

$$dB = \frac{1}{c} \frac{i\, dl \times \hat{r}}{r^2} \qquad \text{gauss} \tag{17.9}$$

Other magnetic equations involving i or q are similarly modified. Equation (17.7) becomes

$$\mathbf{F} = q\mathbf{E} + \frac{q}{c}(\mathbf{v} \times \mathbf{B}) \tag{17.10}$$

The gaussian system very conveniently avoids the confusion of the two kinds of charge units in the conventional cgs system.

17.5   MKS System

For comparison we repeat here the defining equations of the mks system, as used in this book. The duality of charge unit determination is handled by using constants other than unity for both electrostatic and magnetic equations. A special advantage of the system is that the commonly used practical units (volts, amperes, ohms, farads, and henrys) also appear here. This is achieved, however, by using mks units of length, mass, force, etc.

The equation defining unit charge by means of electrostatic force is

$$F \text{ (newtons)} = \frac{1}{4\pi\epsilon_0} \frac{q_1 q_2}{r^2 \text{ (meters}^2)} \tag{17.11}$$

The charge unit is called the coulomb, and as we learned in Chap. 1,

$$\frac{1}{4\pi\epsilon_0} = 9 \times 10^9 \text{ newton-m}^2/\text{coul}^2$$

ϵ_0 is called the permittivity of free space.

Electric field and potential are obtained in the same way as in the cgs system, with appropriate changes to mks units.

$$\mathbf{E} = \frac{\mathbf{F}}{q} \qquad \text{newtons/coul}$$
$$V = -\int \mathbf{E} \cdot d\mathbf{l} \qquad \text{joules/coul}$$

The magnetic force equation is written as in Eq. (8.1), in which the constant of proportionality is-

$$\frac{\mu_0}{4\pi} = 10^{-7} \qquad \text{webers/amp-m}$$

μ_0 is called the permeability of free space. When the potential equation is integrated to give the force per unit length between two long parallel wires, we find

$$\frac{F}{l} = \frac{\mu_0}{4\pi} \frac{2i^2}{r} = \frac{\mu_0 i^2}{2\pi r} \tag{8.13}$$

This equation defines the mks unit of current, the ampere, and hence the unit of charge, the coulomb, through the relation

1 amp = 1 coul/sec

Thus the coulomb, obtained from a magnetic experiment, is also the basis for charge in electrostatic equations.

The expression for the magnetic field of a current becomes, in the mks system,

$$d\mathbf{B} = \frac{\mu_0}{4\pi} \frac{i\, d\mathbf{l} \times \hat{\mathbf{r}}}{r^2} \qquad \text{webers/m}^2 \tag{8.2}$$

The unit magnetic field, weber per square meter, shows explicitly that magnetic field intensity is measured by flux density. This is also true of the electric field intensity, but it does not appear explicitly in the defining units, for purely historic reasons.

The total force equation in mks units becomes

$$\mathbf{F} = q\mathbf{E} + q(\mathbf{v} \times \mathbf{B}) \qquad \text{newtons} \tag{17.12}$$

The constant $\mu_0/4\pi$ is included in the definition of $\mathbf{B}$, as shown above.

17.6 Units Compared

It is now possible to relate the magnitudes of fundamental units in the various systems, using the defining equations as exhibited, and the relationships given in Table 17.1.

In order to compare the size of mks and esu units of charge we imagine the same Coulomb's law measurement in each system. For simplicity we use two equal charges q, separated by 1 m. The size of the charges is such that the measured force between them is 1 newton. According to Eq. (17.11), the force equation in mks units is written

$$1 \text{ newton} = 9 \times 10^9 \frac{N^2_{\text{mks}} \text{ coul}^2}{1 \text{ m}^2} \tag{17.13}$$

where N_{mks} is the number of coulombs required. Solving this equation gives the number of coulombs required to produce the stated force.

$$N^2_{\text{mks}} = \frac{1}{9 \times 10^9} \tag{17.14}$$

In the esu system, the equation is

$$10^5 \text{ dynes} = \frac{N^2_{\text{esu}} \text{ esu}^2}{10^4 \text{ cm}^2} \tag{17.15}$$

or

$$N^2_{\text{esu}} = 10^9 \tag{17.16}$$

This gives the number of esu charge units to produce the stated force. The ratio of the number of charges involved, as measured in the two systems, can be obtained by dividing Eq. (17.16) by Eq. (17.14) and taking the square root.

$$\frac{N^2_{\text{esu}}}{N^2_{\text{mks}}} = 10^9 \times 9 \times 10^9$$

or

$$N_{\text{mks}} \text{ coul} = \frac{1}{3 \times 10^9} N_{\text{esu}} \text{ esu} \tag{17.17}$$

Thus it takes many fewer coulombs than esu to measure the same charge, or

$$1 \text{ coul} = 3 \times 10^9 \text{ esu, or statcoul}$$

Similarly, since esu and gaussian charge units are the same,

$$1 \text{ coul} = 3 \times 10^9 \text{ gaussian units}$$

The relation between electric fields measured in mks and cgs units is similarly obtained, using

$$E_{esu} = \frac{F \text{ (in dynes)}}{q \text{ (in esu)}}$$

and

$$E_{mks} = \frac{F \text{ (in newtons)}}{q \text{ (in coulombs)}}$$

If the field is 1 newton/coul, the number of mks units of field

$$N_{mks} = 1$$

In cgs units

$$N_{esu} = \frac{10^5 \text{ dynes}}{3 \times 10^9 \text{ esu}} = \frac{1}{3 \times 10^4}$$

The ratio of the number of units required in each system is

$$\frac{N_{mks}}{N_{cgs}} = \frac{3 \times 10^9}{10^5} = 3 \times 10^4$$

The field unit in mks is thus smaller than the esu unit; so

$$1 \text{ volt/m} = \frac{1}{3 \times 10^4} \text{ statvolt/cm}$$

Comparison of unit potential difference in the two systems is made through $V = \text{work/unit charge}$. Thus to describe a potential difference of 1 volt, we write in mks units

$$N_{mks} = \frac{1 \text{ joule}}{1 \text{ coul}} = 1$$

where N_{mks} is the number of units of potential difference. The same potential difference described in esu is

$$N_{esu} = \frac{10^7 \text{ ergs}}{3 \times 10^9 \text{ esu}} = \frac{1}{300}$$

The ratio of numbers of units in the two systems is then

$$\frac{N_{esu}}{N_{mks}} = \frac{1}{300}$$

Fewer esu units are required; so the esu unit is the largest, or

$$1 \text{ statvolt} = 300 \text{ volts}$$

Other derived units are similarly compared. We give the arguments for resistance R and capacitance C in brief outline.

$$R = \frac{V}{I}$$

$$N_{mks} = \frac{1 \text{ volt}}{1 \text{ amp}} = 1$$

$$N_{esu} = \frac{\frac{1}{300} \text{ esu}}{3 \times 10^9 \text{ esu}} = \frac{1}{9 \times 10^{11}}$$

or

$$\frac{N_{mks}}{N_{esu}} = 9 \times 10^{11}$$

The mks resistance unit is thus smaller than the esu unit.

$$9 \times 10^{11} \text{ ohms} = 1 \text{ statohm (esu)}$$

$$C = \frac{Q}{V}$$

$$N_{mks} = \frac{1 \text{ coul}}{1 \text{ volt}} = 1$$

$$N_{cgs} = \frac{3 \times 10^9 \text{ esu}}{\frac{1}{300} \text{ statvolt}} \; 9 \times 10^{11}$$

or

$$\frac{N_{mks}}{N_{esu}} = \frac{1}{9 \times 10^{11}}$$

Thus

$$1 \text{ farad} = 9 \times 10^{11} \text{ cm (esu)}$$

Since the mks system involves the constant $1/4\pi\epsilon_0$ in all force or field equations, the forms of all derived equations involving electrostatic forces or fields or potentials differ from the cgs equations. We illustrate this with a few examples.

Potential of a point charge:

$$V_{mks} = \frac{1}{4\pi\epsilon_0} \frac{q \text{ couls}}{r \text{ m}}$$

$$V_{esu} = \frac{q \text{ statcouls}}{r \text{ cm}}$$

Potential difference between two points in the field of a long line of charge:

$$V_{mks} \text{ (volts)} = \frac{\sigma}{2\pi\epsilon_0} \ln \frac{R_A}{R_B}$$

$$V_{cgs} \text{ (statvolts)} = 2\sigma \ln \frac{R_A}{R_B}$$

Capacitance of parallel plates:

$$C_{\text{mks}} \text{ (farads)} = \frac{A\,\epsilon_0}{d}$$

$$C_{\text{esu}} \text{ (esu)} = \frac{A}{4\pi d}$$

When matter is present, the mks equations are modified by replacing ϵ_0 by $\epsilon = K\epsilon_0$, where K is the dielectric constant. In the esu system, K is placed in the denominators of the equations for V, and in the numerators of the capacitance equation. In general, $4\pi\epsilon$ in the mks equations is replaced by K to change them to cgs equations.

Table 17.2 shows a comparison between some important equations in mks, esu, and gaussian cgs units.

We next compare cgs and mks units for currents and magnetic fields. The magnetic force equations as written in the cgs system (emu)

Table 17.2

	MKS†	*ESU*†	*Gaussian*†
Gauss' law	$\displaystyle\int \mathbf{E}\cdot d\mathbf{S} = \frac{1}{\epsilon_0}\sum q$	$\int\mathbf{E}\cdot d\mathbf{S} = 4\pi\Sigma q$	$\int\mathbf{E}\cdot d\mathbf{S} = 4\pi\Sigma q$
	$\text{div } \mathbf{E} = \dfrac{1}{\epsilon_0}\rho$	$\text{div } \mathbf{E} = 4\pi\rho$	$\text{div } \mathbf{E} = 4\pi\rho$
Field quantities	$\mathbf{D} = \epsilon_0\mathbf{E} + \mathbf{P}$	$\mathbf{D} = \mathbf{E} + 4\pi\mathbf{P}$	$\mathbf{D} = \mathbf{E} + 4\pi\mathbf{P}$
	$\mathbf{P} = \epsilon_0\chi\mathbf{E}$	$\mathbf{P} = \chi\mathbf{E}$	$\mathbf{P} = \chi\mathbf{E}$
	$\mathbf{D} = \epsilon\mathbf{E}$	$\mathbf{D} = K\mathbf{E}$	$\mathbf{D} = K\mathbf{E}$
Dielectric constant‡	$\epsilon = \epsilon_0 K$	$K = 1 + 4\pi\chi$	$K = 1 + 4\pi\chi$
	$K = 1 + \chi$		
Stored energy	$\dfrac{\epsilon_0 E^2}{2}$ **joules**	$\dfrac{E^2}{8\pi}$ **ergs**	$\dfrac{E^2}{8\pi}$ **ergs**

† In each case, E must be measured in appropriate units.

‡ The absence of ϵ_0 from the esu equations eliminates the use of permittivity ϵ, leaving only the dielectric constant K. Since the dielectric constant relates to the ratio of capacitance of a capacitor with and without a dielectric filling, it is the same in all units. As a result, the susceptibility of a dielectric per unit volume (cubic meter) in the mks system is just 4π times the susceptibility per unit volume (cubic centimeter) in esu.

and in the mks system are

$$\frac{F}{l} \text{ dynes/cm} = \frac{2i^2 \text{ emu}^2}{r \text{ cm}}$$

$$\frac{F}{l} \text{ newtons/m} = \frac{\mu_0}{4\pi} \frac{2i^2 \text{ amp}^2}{r \text{ m}} = 10^{-7} \frac{2i^2}{r}$$

The ratio of unit currents in the two systems can be obtained by comparisons of the same kind as those made above. We take the physical situation which gives a force of one newton per meter in mks units and compare with the same situation measured in emu. Thus

$$N_{\text{mks}}^2 = \frac{1 \text{ newton}}{1 \text{ m}} \times 10^7 \times \frac{1 \text{ m}}{2} = \frac{10^7}{2}$$

where N_{mks} is the number of amperes to give the stated force. In cgs units this becomes

$$N_{\text{emu}}^2 = \frac{10^5 \text{ dynes}}{2} = \frac{10^5}{2}$$

The ratio

$$\frac{N_{\text{mks}}}{N_{\text{emu}}} = \frac{10^7}{10^5} = 10$$

shows that more mks units are required than cgs units; so

10 amp = 1 emu, or abamp

Magnetic fields can be similarly compared in the two systems.

$$dB \text{ gauss} = \frac{i \, d\mathbf{l} \times \hat{\mathbf{r}}}{r^2} = \frac{i}{r^2} \qquad \text{abamp/cm}^2$$

$$dB \text{ webers/m}^2 = \frac{\mu_0}{4\pi} \frac{i \, d\mathbf{l} \times \hat{\mathbf{r}}}{r^2} \qquad \text{amp/m}^2$$

We take unit current and length in the mks system for the physical arrangement. This gives

$$N_{\text{mks}} = 10^{-7}$$

and

$$N_{\text{emu}} = \frac{\frac{1}{10} \text{ abamp}}{10^2 \text{ cm}} = \frac{1}{10^3}$$

The ratio of numbers of unit fields in each system is thus

$$\frac{N_{\text{mks}}}{N_{\text{emu}}} = \frac{10^{-7}}{10^{-3}}$$

Table 17.3

MKS	EMU†	Gaussian†
$d\mathbf{B} = \dfrac{\mu_0}{4\pi}\dfrac{i\,dl \times \hat{\mathbf{r}}}{r^2}$	$d\mathbf{B} = \dfrac{i\,dl \times \hat{\mathbf{r}}}{r^2}$	$d\mathbf{B} = \dfrac{i\,dl \times \hat{\mathbf{r}}}{cr^2}$
$\oint \mathbf{B}\cdot dl = \mu_0 i$	$\oint \mathbf{B}\cdot dl = 4\pi i$	$\oint \mathbf{B}\cdot dl = \dfrac{4\pi i}{c}$
$\text{curl }\mathbf{B} = \mu_0\mathbf{j}$	$\text{curl }\mathbf{B} = 4\pi\mathbf{j}$	$\text{curl }\mathbf{B} = \dfrac{4\pi\mathbf{j}}{c}$
$\dfrac{1}{2}\dfrac{B^2}{\mu_0}$ joules	$\dfrac{B^2}{8\pi}$ ergs	$\dfrac{B^2}{8\pi}$
$\mathbf{B} = \mu_0(\mathbf{H} + \mathbf{M})$	$\mathbf{B} = \mathbf{H} + 4\pi\mathbf{M}$	$\mathbf{B} = \mathbf{H} + 4\pi\mathbf{M}$
$\mu = \mu_0(1 + \chi)$	$\mu = 1 + 4\pi\chi$	$\mu = 1 + 4\pi\chi$
$\mathbf{B} = \mu\mathbf{H}$	$\mathbf{B} = \mu\mathbf{H}$	$\mathbf{B} = \mu\mathbf{H}$

† In emu and gaussian units, $\mu_{\text{vac}} = 1$ and $B_{\text{vac}} = H_{\text{vac}}$.

By the usual argument as above, we find

1 weber/m² = 10^4 gauss

In Table 17.3 we give some comparisons between mks, emu, and gaussian equations.

17.7   Conversion Table

To convert a quantity that has been calculated or measured in practical (or mks) units to esu (or emu), multiply it by the corresponding factor given in the appropriate column of Table 17.4.

Table 17.4

		Factor	
Quantity	Practical (or mks) unit	esu	emu
Charge	**Coulomb**	3×10^9	10^{-1}
Current	**Ampere**	3×10^9	10^{-1}
Potential	**Volt**	$1/300$	10^8
Power	**Watt**	10^7	10^7
Resistance	**Ohm**	$1/(9 \times 10^{11})$	10^9
Inductance	**Henry**	$1/(9 \times 10^{11})$	10^9
Capacitance	**Farad**	9×10^{11}	10^{-9}

Thus, if a measured quantity is 1 volt, this is $1/300$ of the (larger) esu unit of voltage ($1/300$ statvolt), or 10^8 emu units (or abvolts). Similarly, if a calculated quantity were, say, 20 statvolts, this would be 6,000 volts.

The mks and cgs systems represent the major classifications of unit systems, but there are a number of other minor variants in the literature. The mks system we have used is called the rationalized mks system. The unrationalized mks system is obtained from the rationalized system by making the following substitutions:

$4\pi\epsilon_0$ is replaced by ϵ_0

$4\pi\epsilon$ is replaced by ϵ

$\dfrac{\mu_0}{4\pi}$ is replaced by μ_0

$\dfrac{\mu}{4\pi}$ is replaced by μ

D is replaced by $\dfrac{D}{4\pi}$

H is replaced by $\dfrac{H}{4\pi}$

In addition, the definitions of some of the derived quantities such as χ, D, and P, M, and H may be different by factors of μ_0 or ϵ_0 in some literature.

appendix A

the divergence theorem

The material in these appendixes goes somewhat beyond the level of most beginning courses in electricity. There are several good reasons for including it and for making some reference to it in the main body of this book. The properties of vector fields and the vector differential operators we discuss are essential to the further development of electrical and other physical theories involving vector fields. All students who go on to more advanced studies in electricity will have as an early task the mastering of these ideas. It seems clear that an early presentation can greatly assist in their later use. Furthermore, students working at the level of this book are already in a position to appreciate the great power of the mathematical-physical reasoning involved.

In this appendix we develop the *divergence theorem*, and express it in a form useful in Chap. 2 to convert the integral form of Gauss' flux theorem into the corresponding differential form. Gauss' divergence theorem, a mathematical theorem not related to his flux theorem of physics, evaluates the limiting case of what happens to the surface integral of a vector field over a closed volume when the volume is shrunk to zero. We discuss this in terms of a general vector field, which we shall call $\mathbf{F}(x,y,z)$.[1] Later, we apply the result to the special case of an electric field $\mathbf{E}(x,y,z)$.

We write the surface integral of the vector $\mathbf{F}$ over a closed surface

$$\int_{cs} \mathbf{F} \cdot d\mathbf{S}$$

where $d\mathbf{S}$ is an element of surface area, a vector quantity normal to the surface and pointed outward from the enclosed volume. We may call this integral the flux of the vector $\mathbf{F}$ out of the volume. If $\mathbf{F}$ is finite, the limit of the surface integral $\int_{cs} \mathbf{F} \cdot d\mathbf{S}$ is zero when the volume, and thus the surface area, approaches zero. That is, if the volume is shrunk to zero, $d\mathbf{S}$ itself must go to zero; so the integral, that is, the flux, must do likewise. Thus the value of the surface integral, or flux, is of no great interest as we shrink to zero volume. But suppose that, instead, we take the *ratio* of the flux to the volume involved, or the flux per unit volume, as the volume is allowed to shrink about any given point. We might well expect this ratio to approach a limiting value as the volume shrinks toward zero. This is indeed true for all vector fields of practical importance.

This limiting value of the flux per unit volume as the volume approaches zero is called the *divergence* of the field, usually written div $\mathbf{F}$. Its value may be different at each point in space, and its values at all points characterize an important property of any vector field. We may define the divergence formally by the expression

$$\operatorname{div} \mathbf{F} = \lim_{V \to 0} \left(\frac{1}{V} \int_{cs} \mathbf{F} \cdot d\mathbf{S} \right)$$

where V is the volume over which the surface integral is evaluated.

We evaluate the surface integral by subdividing the volume over which it is taken into a limitless number of infinitesimal volumes. The crucial step in the argument is that the net flux out of the entire volume is the same as the sum of the fluxes out of each tiny volume individually. This is apparent when we imagine the first division of the original macroscopic volume into two parts, as suggested in Fig. A.1. Here we note the new surface area S_{12} produced by the breaking up of the volume into two parts. But the flux *out* of one volume (say, 1) over this new surface is just the flux *into* the other volume (2), over the same surface. This is by virtue of the common value of $\mathbf{F}$ on the two

---

[1] $\mathbf{F}(x,y,z)$ means, simply, that the vector field $\mathbf{F}$ is a function of position only, and hence of x, y, and z.

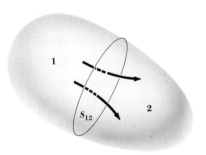

*Fig. A.1   The net flux of a vector **F** out of a volume is unaffected by breaking up the volume into two or more parts. The flux of **F** out of region 1 is just equal to the flux into region 2.*

sides of the surface and the fact that the vectors $d\mathbf{S}$ over the new surface have opposite sign for the two volumes, since the surface vector *out* of one volume points *in* to the other.

The same argument applies no matter how many divisions are made; so we can write

$$\int_{CS} \mathbf{F} \cdot d\mathbf{S} = \int_{CS_1} \mathbf{F} \cdot d\mathbf{S}_1 + \int_{CS_2} \mathbf{F} \cdot d\mathbf{S}_2 + \int_{CS_3} \mathbf{F} \cdot d\mathbf{S}_3 + \cdots$$

$$= \sum_{i=1}^{N} \int_{CS_i} \mathbf{F} \cdot d\mathbf{S}_i$$

where the right-hand sum is over all the pieces into which the original volume is divided.

Each term indicated by a value of the subscript i from 1 to N indicates the integral over one of the subvolumes into which the original volume is divided. As the volume is subdivided on a finer and finer scale, the value of each flux term becomes smaller and smaller, but by the reasoning given regarding the division into the first two subvolumes, this sum of an infinite number of terms has a fixed value, since the total flux is not affected by subdivision.

A simple restatement of the right-hand term in the last equation brings us near the end of the argument. Thus we multiply and divide each flux term by the volume V_i of the region over which the integral is taken, to obtain

$$\int_{CS} \mathbf{F} \cdot d\mathbf{S} = \sum_{i=1}^{N} V_i \left(\frac{\int_{CS_i} \mathbf{F} \cdot d\mathbf{S}_i}{V_i} \right) \qquad\qquad (A.1)$$

But the term in parentheses, when we go to the limit $N \to \infty$, $V_i \to 0$, is, by its definition, the divergence of $\mathbf{F}$. As we go to the limit the summation becomes an integration, and V_i becomes the volume element

dV. This brings us to the final statement, Gauss' theorem, often called the divergence theorem:

$$\int_{cs} \mathbf{F} \cdot d\mathbf{S} = \int_{V} \text{div } \mathbf{F} \, dV \qquad (A.2)$$

In order for this to be true, it is only necessary that the vector field be such that there *is* such a limit as defined by the definition of the divergence.

We now take the additional step of finding the expression for div $\mathbf{F}$ in cartesian coordinates. In these coordinates we can express the value of the vector $\mathbf{F}$ at each point in space in terms of three scalar functions $F_x(x,y,z)$, $F_y(x,y,z)$, and $F_z(x,y,z)$. The total flux of $\mathbf{F}$ through a given volume will then be the sum of the fluxes of F_x, F_y, and F_z. For convenience, we take for the elementary volume a cube of sides dx, dy, and dz, as shown in Fig. A.2. We first determine the flux

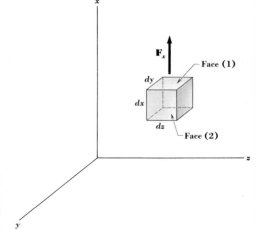

Fig. *A.2   The net flux of F_x out of the elementary cube depends on the difference between F_x at face 1 and at face 2 of the cube.*

of F_x out of the volume. Clearly, only the top and bottom $dy\,dz$ faces are involved in the flux of F_x, since all other faces of the cube are parallel to F_x.

If the value of F_x were the same at the top and bottom faces, the net flux of F_x out of the volume would be zero (since the outward normals dS at the top and bottom are opposite). Thus any net flux results from the variation of F_x over the distance dx between the top face 1 and the bottom face 2. We may write for the net flux of F_x

$$F_{x_1} dS_1 - F_{x_2} dS_2 = (F_{x_1} - F_{x_2}) \, dy \, dz$$

where the subscripts refer to F_z at the top and bottom faces. The negative sign expresses the downward direction of dS_2.

We next express F_{x_2} in terms of F_{x_1} and the rate of change of F_x with x. Thus

$$F_{x_2} = F_{x_1} - \frac{\partial F_x}{\partial x} \, dx$$

The justification of this is apparent from the plot of Fig. A.3. F_{x_2} is obtained by subtracting the slope[1] of F_x with respect to x times dx, the

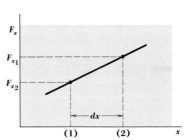

Fig. A.3 The value of F_z at face 2 is obtained from its value at face 1 through $F_{x_2} = F_{x_1} - (\partial F_x/\partial x) \, dx$.

distance between faces, from F_{x_1}. Only the first-order approximation, which assumes that F_x varies linearly with x, is necessary since only the linear term will be important when the volume (and dx) shrinks to zero.

With this simple argument we may write the net flux of F_x out of the cube

$$F_{x_1} - F_{x_2}$$

or

$$F_{x_1} - F_{x_1} + \frac{\partial F_x}{\partial x} \, dx \, dy \, dz = \frac{\partial F_x}{\partial x} \, dx \, dy \, dz$$

Similar arguments applied to the other components of **F** give similar expressions; so we may write the total net flux of the vector $\mathbf{F}(x,y,z)$ out of the cube

$$\text{Total flux of } \mathbf{F} = \left(\frac{\partial F_x}{\partial x} + \frac{\partial F_y}{\partial y} + \frac{\partial F_z}{\partial z} \right) dx \, dy \, dz$$

Since the divergence of **F** is just this flux divided by the cube volume,

[1] Use is made of the *partial* derivative, $\partial F_x/\partial x$, in order to make clear that although F_x is a function of x, y, and z, we are interested here only in its variation with x when y and z are held constant.

we have

$$\text{div } \mathbf{F} = \frac{\partial F_x}{\partial x} + \frac{\partial F_y}{\partial y} + \frac{\partial F_z}{\partial z} \tag{A.3}$$

This is the expression for div $\mathbf{F}$ in cartesian coordinates. The expression is different in other coordinate systems, but in all cases the terms involve the rates of change of components of the vector with respect to position, as they do here. We now see that the requirement that a vector field have a definable divergence is simply that the slopes of the components be finite.

The divergence theorem stems originally from the study of fluid flow, but its application to electric phenomena is of major importance. It is used in Sec. 2.7 to convert the integral form of Gauss' flux theorem to the differential form.

appendix **B**

the curl of a vector field, and Stokes' theorem

This appendix is written in order to introduce the reader to some necessary mathematical ideas which lie behind some more sophisticated statements of properties of a vector field.

In this case we develop the ideas which allow us, in Chap. 3, to transform the integral form of the conservative field statement, that the circulation around any path is zero, or

$$\oint \mathbf{E} \cdot d\mathbf{l} = 0 \tag{3.3}$$

into the limiting differential form

$$\text{curl } \mathbf{E} = 0 \tag{B.1}$$

and to understand its significance. The mathematical part of this problem depends on the mathematical Stokes' theorem, which we now consider.

We begin by considering the line integral around a closed path (Fig. B.1a), $\oint \mathbf{F} \cdot d\mathbf{l}$, like Eq. (3.3) quoted above, except that we have replaced the electric field by a general vector field $\mathbf{F}$. We investigate

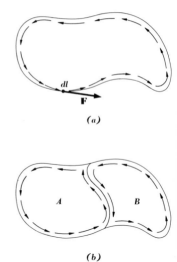

(a)

(b)

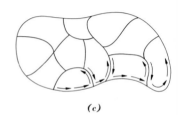

Fig. B.1   The circulation $\oint \mathbf{F} \cdot dl$ around a path is equal to the sum of the circulations around sub-areas made by subdividing the original area.

(c)

what happens when we let the path length of this closed line integral, the *circulation*, reduce to zero. The happy result is that although the limit of this line integral approaches zero as the path length is shrunk toward zero, the circulation *per unit area* enclosed approaches a finite limit, at least in the case of well-behaved vector fields.

The first step is to show that if a surface surrounded by a closed path is divided into any number of subareas, the sum of the circulations around each subarea is equal to the circulation around the original closed path. This is easily demonstrated using Fig. B.1. Comparing (a) and (b), we see that when we add the circulations around the subareas A and B, the extra contribution from the line segment dividing the original area into two parts cancels out, since the two line integrals over the new segment have the same magnitude but opposite signs. The same reasoning will apply, no matter how many subdivisions are made. This idea can be stated formally as

$$\oint \mathbf{F} \cdot d\mathbf{l} = \oint_1 \mathbf{F} \cdot d\mathbf{l}_1 + \oint_2 \mathbf{F} \cdot d\mathbf{l}_2 + \cdots$$

$$= \sum_{i=1}^{N} \oint_i \mathbf{F} \cdot d\mathbf{l}_i \qquad\qquad (B.2)$$

where each term in the sum of circulations around subareas of the original macroscopic area is indicated by a particular value of the subscript i. The area defined by the path of the line integral is not limited in any way but by the path itself. Any surface, flat or curved, which is bounded by the closed path satisfies this rule.

Now we take the limit of the ratio of the circulation around an area to that area as the path shrinks toward zero. We can readily see that, in general, the value of this ratio can depend on the orientation of the area. The ratio is actually a vector quantity, and as a result we can fully determine it if we find its components in three mutually perpendicular directions, since a vector in space is fully defined by three such perpendicular components.

On the basis of the discussion above, it is not difficult to see that a *component* of the desired ratio of circulation to area is given by the following equation:

$$\lim_{a_i \to 0} \left(\frac{\oint \mathbf{F} \cdot d\mathbf{l}_i}{\mathbf{a}_i \cdot \hat{\mathbf{n}}} \right)$$

Here a_i is the area surrounded by the closed path l_i. The denominator deserves a short explanation: The area is a vector quantity, since it can be oriented with its normal in any desired direction; so, by taking the scalar product between this vector and $\hat{\mathbf{n}}$, an arbitrarily oriented unit vector (which we orient successively along x, y, and z directions), we get a scalar quantity which measures the area normal to an arbitrary direction, or, what amounts to the same thing, the projection of the area normal to an arbitrary direction. So the limit of the quantity in parentheses can be evaluated for any orientation given to the unit vector $\hat{\mathbf{n}}$. The terms we get for any three mutually perpendicular directions of $\hat{\mathbf{n}}$ are the three components of a vector known as the *curl*. The sign of vector **a** is taken so that it points according to the right-hand-screw method with respect to the direction of the circulation integral, as shown in Fig. B.2.

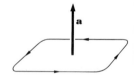

Fig. B.2 The sign of the vector a representing the area around which the circulation is taken is chosen according to the right-hand rule.

The relation between any component of the vector, as given by the limit of the parentheses, and the curl vector itself is written

$$(\text{curl } \mathbf{F}) \cdot \hat{\mathbf{n}} = \lim_{a_i \to 0} \left(\frac{\oint \mathbf{F} \cdot d\mathbf{l}_i}{\mathbf{a}_i \cdot \hat{\mathbf{n}}} \right) \tag{B.3}$$

Clearly, both sides of the equation represent components of a vector in the direction of $\hat{\mathbf{n}}$. Components of the curl along x, y, and z are found by letting the unit vector $\hat{\mathbf{n}}$ go to $\hat{\mathbf{x}}$, $\hat{\mathbf{y}}$, and $\hat{\mathbf{z}}$, successively.

To complete the formal statement of Stokes' theorem, we turn back to the expression for the circulation around the original macroscopic path,

$$\oint \mathbf{F} \cdot d\mathbf{l} = \sum_{i=1}^{N} \oint \mathbf{F} \cdot d\mathbf{l}_i = \sum_{i=1}^{N} \mathbf{a}_i \cdot \hat{\mathbf{n}} \left(\frac{\oint \mathbf{F} \cdot d\mathbf{l}_i}{\mathbf{a}_i \cdot \hat{\mathbf{n}}} \right) \tag{B.4}$$

We have equated the summed circulations to an equivalent expression on the right, obtained simply by multiplying and dividing by $\mathbf{a}_i \cdot \hat{\mathbf{n}}$. However, if we take the limit of the right-hand term as the number of area subdivisions is increased and as each subarea approaches zero in size, then, according to our definition of the term in parentheses, the right-hand term may be written

$$\int (\text{curl } \mathbf{F} \cdot \hat{\mathbf{n}})(d\mathbf{a} \cdot \hat{\mathbf{n}})$$

The summation has turned into an integral, and the finite $\mathbf{a}_i$ has become the infinitesimal $d\mathbf{a}$. The first term, $(\text{curl } \mathbf{F} \cdot \hat{\mathbf{n}})$, is simply the component of the vector curl $\mathbf{F}$ in the direction $\hat{\mathbf{n}}$, while the second term, $(d\mathbf{a} \cdot \hat{\mathbf{n}})$, is just the projected area $d\mathbf{a}$ normal to the same direction, $\hat{\mathbf{n}}$. The integral is thus just the surface integral of the vector-quantity curl $\mathbf{F}$, or

$$\int_S \text{curl } \mathbf{F} \cdot d\mathbf{a}$$

But this integral over the area bounded by the original path is, by

Eq. (B.4),

$$\oint \mathbf{F} \cdot d\mathbf{l} = \int_S \text{curl } \mathbf{F} \cdot d\mathbf{a} \tag{B.5}$$

This is Stokes' theorem. It says that the line integral, or circulation of a vector field $\mathbf{F}$ around a fixed macroscopic path, is equal to the surface integral of a new vector quantity, curl $\mathbf{F}$ over a (any) surface bounded by the path. As stated in Eq. (B.3), the quantity called the curl is the limiting value of the circulation per unit area as the area approaches zero. We have found a relationship between the line integral of a vector quantity over a finite path and a new point function, the curl of the vector. There is a close analogy to the divergence theorem (Appendix A) in which we started with a surface integral over a closed surface and found its connection with the integral of a new point function, the divergence, over the enclosed volume.

We now use the definition of the curl [Eq. (B.3)] to find an explicit expression for the curl in terms of cartesian coordinates. Since the curl of a vector is itself a vector, the expression will be a vector, and we find it by finding its three mutually perpendicular components. We can for convenience take a small elementary cube and calculate the circulation around the edges of three perpendicular faces.

We start by a calculation of the circulation about a face in the xy plane (Fig. B.3). This gives us the z component of the curl. The

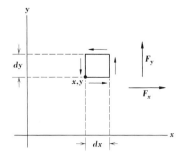

Fig. B.3   Calculation of the circulation around an area $d_x d_y$ in terms of F_x and F_y.

component F_x is the quantity involved in calculating the line integral along the x direction, and we see that if F_x has the same value along the bottom edge as along the top, the net contribution from the top- and bottom-edge line integrals will be zero (since one will be the negative of the other). Similar reasoning applies to the F_y component along the two side edges.

Indeed, if we consider only linear variations of F_x with y (and these are sufficient since dx and dy are infinitesimals), the contribution to the line integrals from the bottom and top segments is

$$(F_x)_y \, dx + (F_x)_{y+dy}(-dx)$$

The minus sign results from the negative direction of travel along the top segment.

But $(F_x)_{y+dy} = (F_x)_y + \dfrac{\partial F_x}{\partial y} \, dy$, giving

$$\left[(F_x)_y - (F_x)_y - \frac{\partial F_x}{\partial y} \, dy \right] dx = - \frac{\partial F_x}{\partial y} \, dy \, dx$$

Similarly, the side segments contribute

$$\frac{\partial F_y}{\partial x} \, dx \, dy$$

Thus the area $dx \, dy$ contributes a total circulation

$$\left(\frac{\partial F_y}{\partial x} - \frac{\partial F_x}{\partial y} \right) dx \, dy$$

or dividing by the area $dx \, dy$ and taking the limit, the component of the curl in the z direction is $\hat{z}(\partial F_y/\partial x - \partial F_x/\partial y)$. Similar considerations for the other two kinds of faces give us for the vector quantity

$$\text{curl } \mathbf{F} = \hat{x}\left(\frac{\partial F_z}{\partial y} - \frac{\partial F_y}{\partial z} \right) + \hat{y}\left(\frac{\partial F_x}{\partial z} - \frac{\partial F_z}{\partial x} \right) + \hat{z}\left(\frac{\partial F_y}{\partial x} - \frac{\partial F_x}{\partial y} \right) \tag{B.6}$$

Thus, the curl is a rather special kind of spatial derivative. If, for example, the vector field were to represent the velocity vector in a fluid, a simple whirlpool motion would have a curl unless the fluid rotated as a rigid body. It is possible, with this recipe for the curl and with Stokes' theorem, to show how a conservative field can be characterized in terms of its curl. We do this in Sec. 3.4.

appendix C

Laplace's and Poisson's equations

Here we develop another generalized statement which follows from the nature of the electric field, this one about how the potential can vary in space. We may find this rule, as expressed in cartesian coordinates, by starting with the differential form of Gauss' flux theorem,

$$\text{div } \mathbf{E} = \frac{1}{\epsilon_0} \rho \tag{2.10}$$

which in rectangular coordinates is

$$\frac{\partial E_x}{\partial x} + \frac{\partial E_y}{\partial y} + \frac{\partial E_z}{\partial z} = \frac{1}{\epsilon_0} \rho \tag{2.10a}$$

But since $E_x = -\partial V/\partial x$, etc., as shown in Chap. 3, by substitution we find

$$\frac{\partial^2 V}{\partial x^2} + \frac{\partial^2 V}{\partial y^2} + \frac{\partial^2 V}{\partial z^2} = -\frac{1}{\epsilon_0} \rho \tag{C.1}$$

This is called Poisson's equation.

The sum of the second derivatives on the left-hand side of the equation is called the *laplacian*. [We show in Appendix D that in terms of the vector operator ∇ ("del"), it is written $\nabla^2 V$.] This quantity tells about the local variation of the potential V and, as we see, puts limitations on the sums of the second partial derivatives of V.

In a region of space where there is no net charge, the right-hand term is zero; so the laplacian is zero. This very important equation,

$$\frac{\partial^2 V}{\partial x^2} + \frac{\partial^2 V}{\partial y^2} + \frac{\partial^2 V}{\partial z^2} = 0 \tag{C.2}$$

is called Laplace's equation.

Although we make minimal use of Poisson's and Laplace's equations in this book, they are essential for the more sophisticated methods of solving field and potential problems. Simple examples of the use of Laplace's equation are given in Appendixes E and F.

appendix D

vector differential operators

D.1 Gradient, Divergence, and Curl

In more advanced work there is need for the simplicity allowed through the use of the vector differential operator $\boldsymbol{\nabla}$ (called "del"). The main reason for knowing about this operator is that its use makes for great economy of notation. In addition, as we show, it helps to consolidate ideas about the vector quantities gradient, divergence, and curl.

For simplicity we consider only the case for rectangular cartesian coordinates, though the operator notation can be applied in any system of coordinates. Also, we replace the unit vectors $\hat{\mathbf{x}}$, $\hat{\mathbf{y}}$, and $\hat{\mathbf{z}}$ by the notation $\mathbf{i}$, $\mathbf{j}$, and $\mathbf{k}$.

We begin, then, by *defining* the vector operator $\boldsymbol{\nabla}$:

$$\boldsymbol{\nabla} = \mathbf{i}\,\frac{\partial}{\partial x} + \mathbf{j}\,\frac{\partial}{\partial y} + \mathbf{k}\,\frac{\partial}{\partial z}$$

This has no meaning of itself, that is, until it is allowed to operate on some quantity. It can operate with interesting and useful results on either scalar or vector quantities. For example, let it operate on a scalar quantity V, which might well be a potential. This means, simply, that we place V in the blank spaces to get

$$\boldsymbol{\nabla} V = \mathbf{i}\frac{\partial V}{\partial x} + \mathbf{j}\frac{\partial V}{\partial y} + \mathbf{k}\frac{\partial V}{\partial z} \tag{D.1}$$

As shown in Chap. 3, if V is the potential, Eq. (D.1) is the vector quantity, the *gradient* of V.

$$\boldsymbol{\nabla} V \equiv \text{grad } V \tag{D.2}$$

When the vector operator is applied to a vector quantity, we must decide whether it will be to form the scalar product (to give a scalar quantity) or to form a cross product (to give a vector quantity). Both are useful, and we first show the scalar product, by operating on a vector **E**, which could be the electric field. We write the scalar product

$$\boldsymbol{\nabla} \cdot \mathbf{E} = \left(\mathbf{i}\frac{\partial}{\partial x} + \mathbf{j}\frac{\partial}{\partial y} + \mathbf{k}\frac{\partial}{\partial z}\right) \cdot (\mathbf{i}E_x + \mathbf{j}E_y + \mathbf{k}E_z)$$

The field **E** has been written out in terms of its components in the three perpendicular directions **i**, **j**, and **k**. When we carry out the operations, we find

$$\boldsymbol{\nabla} \cdot \mathbf{E} = \frac{\partial E_x}{\partial x} + \frac{\partial E_y}{\partial y} + \frac{\partial E_z}{\partial z}$$

This follows from the fact that factors other than zero come only from terms involving $\mathbf{i} \cdot \mathbf{i}$, etc., since terms like $\mathbf{i} \cdot \mathbf{j}$ vanish. The result is a scalar quantity, as expected for a scalar product, which is identical with the divergence of **E** (Appendix A). Thus

$$\boldsymbol{\nabla} \cdot \mathbf{E} \equiv \text{div } \mathbf{E} \tag{D.3}$$

The cross product of the vectors $\boldsymbol{\nabla}$ and **E** is

$$\boldsymbol{\nabla} \times \mathbf{E} = \left(\mathbf{i}\frac{\partial}{\partial x} + \mathbf{j}\frac{\partial}{\partial y} + \mathbf{k}\frac{\partial}{\partial z}\right) \times (\mathbf{i}E_x + \mathbf{j}E_y + \mathbf{k}E_z)$$
$$= \mathbf{i}\left(\frac{\partial E_z}{\partial y} - \frac{\partial E_y}{\partial z}\right) + \mathbf{j}\left(\frac{\partial E_x}{\partial z} - \frac{\partial E_z}{\partial x}\right) + \mathbf{k}\left(\frac{\partial E_y}{\partial x} - \frac{\partial E_x}{\partial y}\right) \tag{D.4}$$

This is a vector, and results from the fact that $\mathbf{i} \times \mathbf{j} = \mathbf{k}$, etc., and $\mathbf{i} \times \mathbf{i} = 0$, etc., as required for the cross product. As shown in Appendix B, the quantity given is the curl; so we have

$$\boldsymbol{\nabla} \times \mathbf{E} \equiv \text{curl } \mathbf{E} \tag{D.5}$$

D.2   Formal Derivation of Equations of Poisson and Laplace

Use of the vector operator ∇ provides a concise approach to Poisson's and Laplace's equations. Thus the differential form of Gauss' theorem is written

$$\nabla \cdot \mathbf{E} = \frac{1}{\epsilon_0} \rho \qquad\qquad (D.6)$$

and the gradient relationship between $\mathbf{E}$ and V is written

$$\mathbf{E} = -\nabla V \qquad\qquad (D.7)$$

Combining these, we get

$$\nabla \cdot \nabla V = -\frac{1}{\epsilon_0} \rho$$

But

$$\nabla \cdot \nabla V = \nabla^2 V = \frac{\partial^2 V}{\partial x^2} + \frac{\partial^2 V}{\partial y^2} + \frac{\partial^2 V}{\partial z^2} \qquad\qquad (D.8)$$

as we can verify by writing the scalar product explicitly:

$$\nabla \cdot \nabla V = \left(\mathbf{i} \frac{\partial}{\partial x} + \mathbf{j} \frac{\partial}{\partial y} + \mathbf{k} \frac{\partial}{\partial z} \right) \cdot \left(\mathbf{i} \frac{\partial V}{\partial x} + \mathbf{j} \frac{\partial V}{\partial y} + \mathbf{k} \frac{\partial V}{\partial z} \right)$$

We have thus arrived at Poisson's equation,

$$\nabla^2 V = -\frac{1}{\epsilon_0} \rho \qquad\qquad (D.9)$$

or in a charge-free region, Laplace's equation,

$$\nabla^2 V = 0 \qquad\qquad (D.10)$$

The quantity ∇^2 is known as the laplacian operator.

appendix E

conducting sphere in a uniform electric field

We examine here, as an example of the general electrostatic boundary-value problem, the case of an uncharged conducting sphere placed in an otherwise uniform electric field.

A useful way of formulating the problem is to look for a solution having the following attributes: (1) It obeys Poisson's or Laplace's equation, depending on whether or not there is space charge. We limit ourselves to a case involving conductors in a vacuum; so $\nabla^2 V = 0$ (Appendix D). (2) It gives equipotential surfaces as required by the problem. (3) It behaves appropriately at infinity.

According to the uniqueness theorem,[1] which we are stating without proof, we have a guarantee that any solution that does all these things is the only solution. As shown in Fig. E.1, we let the field far from the sphere be E_0 (this is also the field in the absence of the sphere) and the radius of the sphere be a, and we assume the net charge on the sphere to be zero. There is an equipotential plane cutting through the

[1] A proof of the uniqueness theorem for static electric and magnetic fields is given, for example, in W. V. Houston, "Principles of Mathematical Physics," 2d ed., McGraw-Hill Book Company, New York, 1948, pp. 271–273.

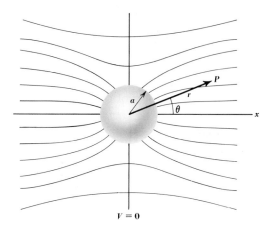

Fig. E.1   Conducting sphere in a uniform external field.

middle of the sphere and perpendicular to the electric field direction. We define this plane to be at zero potential. The problem now is to find an expression for the potential such that $\nabla^2 V = 0$, the sphere is an equipotential surface, and at points far away the potential is the same as in the absence of the perturbing effects of the sphere, that is, the potential consistent with a uniform field. Using cylindrical coordinates for convenience, at points far away from the sphere, $V = -E_0 x$, or $V = -E_0 r \cos \theta$. Thus, whatever our final expression for V, it must reduce to this for large r. Another consideration is that the surface of the sphere must be at a constant potential of zero. Thus an added term must also contain $\cos \theta$, so that for all positions on the sphere, the sum of the terms can be zero. However, for large r this second term must approach zero. An expression to try is one containing $\cos \theta / r^2$. We try $V = -E_0 r \cos \theta + (A/r^2) \cos \theta$, where A is a constant to be determined. Both terms are *harmonic functions*, all of which are solutions of $\nabla^2 V = 0$. When we set $V = 0$ for $r = a$, to satisfy the boundary condition at the surface of the sphere, we find $A = E_0 a^3$; so the expression becomes $V = -E_0 r \cos \theta + (E_0 a^3 / r^2) \cos \theta$. This expression is valid for all $r > a$. Boundary conditions are satisfied if we use for the second term in the potential $(E_0 a^2 / r) \cos \theta$. However, this term would not satisfy Laplace's equation and therefore is ruled out. Discussion and development of the possible forms of solutions to Laplace's equation are found in more advanced treatments of this subject. Since this expression fits the boundary conditions at $r = a$ and at $r = \infty$ and satisfies Laplace's equation, it must be the solution to the problem.

The second term, $(E_0 a^3 / r^2) \cos \theta$, amounts to the perturbation of the original uniform field by the conducting sphere. It corresponds to the effect of a dipole of dipole moment $p = 4\pi\epsilon_0 E_0 a^3$ placed at the position of the center of the sphere, with its axis along x.

The field at the surface of the sphere is obtained by taking the appropriate derivative of V. Since the field is normal to a conducting surface, it is along r for a conducting sphere. Thus

$$E = -\frac{\partial V}{\partial r} = E_0 \cos \theta + \left(\frac{2E_0 a^3}{r^3}\right)_{r=a} \cos \theta = 3E_0 \cos \theta$$

Along the x axis the field at the surface is $3E_0$. At points on the sphere where $\theta = 90°$, both V and E are zero.

appendix F

dielectric sphere in a uniform electric field

Here we discuss, partly without proof, the way in which a dielectric body perturbs a uniform field in which it is placed. We begin with the study of a dielectric sphere placed in a uniform field $\mathbf{E}_0$, as shown in Fig. F.1. This is related to the problem of the spherical conductor in a

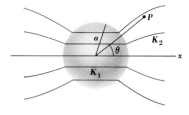

Fig. F.1 Dielectric sphere inserted in a uniform electric field. Lines of D are shown. $K_1 > K_2$.

uniform field as discussed in Appendix E. However, the boundary condition at the surface of the sphere is now different, and the field inside the dielectric sphere is not zero as it was in the conducting sphere. We keep the problem general by assigning dielectric constant K_1 to the sphere and K_2 to the region outside the sphere. The potential functions are V_1 inside the sphere $(r \leq a)$ and V_2 outside $(r \geq a)$. The solution to this problem must satisfy the following requirements:

1. $\nabla^2 V_1 = 0$ and $\nabla^2 V_2 = 0$; that is, both inside and outside, Laplace's equation must be satisfied. As in the case of the conducting sphere studied in Appendix E, the potential function required is made up of harmonic functions.

2. $V_2 + E_0 r \cos \theta$ must remain finite at infinity. The original uniform field has a potential given by $-E_0 x$ or $-E_0 r \cos \theta$ when we assume zero potential at the center of the sphere. V_1 must therefore contain this negative term. The requirement is then simply that the additional term or terms due to the presence of the sphere must become negligible at large distances.

3. V_1 must remain finite for all $r \leq a$ (inside the sphere).

4. $V_2 = V_1$ for $r = a$ at all angles θ. If this were not true, V would be a step function at the surface. This sudden change in V would require the rate of change of V to be infinite at the discontinuity. This would require infinite field.

5. $K_1 \partial V_1 / \partial r = K_2 \partial V_2 / \partial r$ at $r = a$ for all θ. This is simply the boundary condition $D_{n1} = D_{n2}$, which can be written $K_1 E_{n1} = K_2 E_{n2}$.

On the basis of our earlier result for the conducting sphere, we try the following solutions, which are made up of harmonic functions and which therefore are guaranteed to satisfy Laplace's equation.

$$V_2 = -E_0 r \cos \theta + \frac{A}{r^2} \cos \theta \tag{F.1}$$

$$V_1 = Br \cos \theta \tag{F.2}$$

Even without specifying the constants A and B, these solutions satisfy requirements 1 to 3. In order to satisfy requirement 4 and keep V single-valued at the surface, we set

$$-E_0 a + \frac{A}{a^2} = Ba \tag{F.3}$$

In order to satisfy requirement 5, we take $K_1(\partial V_1 / \partial r) = K_2(\partial V_2 / \partial r)$ to get

$$K_2\left(-E_0 - \frac{2A}{a^3}\right) = K_1 B \tag{F.4}$$

If we solve (F.3) and (F.4) for A and B, we find

$$A = \frac{K_1 - K_2}{K_1 + 2K_2} E_0 a^3$$

$$B = \frac{-3K_2}{K_1 + 2K_2} E_0$$

For a sphere in a vacuum we put $K_2 = 1$, and for a spherical cavity in a dielectric we put $K_1 = 1$. For all cases, the potential inside the sphere can be written $V_1 = Bx$. This means that the field inside the sphere is uniform. For the dielectric sphere in a vacuum, the original uniform field E_0 has been reduced to a value $[3/(K_1 + 2)]E_0$. This reduction is due to the uniform field of the polarization charges on the surface of the sphere acting in opposition to the original field. The size of this depolarization field E_{dep}, which acts in opposition to the original field E_0, is given for this case by

$$E_{dep} = E_0 - E_2 = \left(1 - \frac{3}{K_1 + 2}\right) E_0 = \left(\frac{K_1 - 1}{K_1 + 2}\right) E_0 \tag{F.5}$$

This opposing field may be expressed in terms of a *depolarizing factor L* relating the field to the state of polarization of the dielectric,

$$\epsilon_0 E_{dep} = LP \tag{F.6}$$

ϵ_0 is included in order to satisfy dimensional requirements.

The value of L for a sphere is obtained when we note that

$$P = \epsilon_0 (K - 1)E \tag{F.7}$$

where the subscript on K is omitted for convenience, and E is the macroscopic field inside the dielectric. This equation follows from Eqs. (5.8) and (5.14). Substitution in Eq. (F.6) gives

$$L = \frac{(K - 1)/(K + 2)}{3(K - 1)/(K + 2)} = \frac{1}{3} \tag{F.8}$$

In this case the potential V_2 outside the dielectric sphere consists of a term $-E_0 r \cos\theta$ from the original unperturbed uniform field plus a term $(A/r^2) \cos\theta$. This latter term gives rise to a dipole field, the same as we found for a dipole in Example 3.11b. Thus the field outside a uniformly polarized dielectric sphere in an originally uniform field is just the original uniform field, superposed on which is a dipole field due to the polarized sphere.

For convenience we have drawn lines of **D** rather than lines of **E** in Fig. F.1, since lines of **D** are continuous across the boundary of the dielectric, while lines of **E** are not. Although **D** inside the dielectric sphere is increased over the value in the original uniform field, **E** is decreased, as a result of the depolarization field.

In choosing a sphere, we have taken one of the few shapes to which a depolarization factor accurately applies, since in general the field inside a dielectric body immersed in a uniform field is not uniform inside the body. Using isotropic material, only specimens having the shape of a general ellipsoid have uniform internal fields. When one of the principal axes of the ellipsoid is parallel to the applied field, the polarization and the depolarizing field are along the same line as the original external field (assuming an isotropic dielectric).

the Maxwell loop method
for circuit equations[1]

A simple and systematic method for obtaining circuit equations for complicated networks is described. It may be preferred over the method described in Sec. 6.6. This method is known as the Maxwell's loop method. It differs from the method described earlier in its treatment of current in paths which are common to more than one loop. This treatment is illustrated by the use of Fig. 6.17. The steps to be taken in applying Kirchhoff's rules are listed as follows. Except for the current nomenclature in paths common to two or more loops, it is seen that the two methods are essentially the same.

    1. A clockwise direction is arbitrarily chosen for each path around a loop.

    2. A direction is chosen for loop current around each loop. Most simply, this is also taken clockwise. The current in any path which is common to two loops is considered to be the algebraic sum of the currents in the two loops. The current in each common path is given a sign consistent with

---

[1] This appendix follows very closely material developed by J. C. Street and suggested by him to the author.

the current in the rest of each loop. Thus the current through R_b in the circuit shown is taken as $i_1 - i_2$ for loop 1. This makes i_1 consistent in direction with the current i_1 in other parts of loop 1. For loop 2, the current through R_b is $i_2 - i_1$, making i_2 consistent with the current in the remainder of loop 2. i_1 and i_2 have opposite signs because of the choice of directions of loop current in each loop. The choice of $i_1 - i_2$ for the current through R_b is also consistent with the first circuit equation applied at point a or b, given the directions of i_1 and i_2 assumed in the rest of the circuit.

3.   The sum of the emfs in each loop is now equated to the sum of the potential drops in that loop, following the rules for the signs of these terms as given in Sec. 6.6. Thus we find

$$\mathcal{E}_1 = r_1 i_1 + R_a i_1 + R_b(i_1 - i_2)$$
$$\mathcal{E}_2 = r_2 i_2 + R_c i_2 + R_b(i_2 - i_1)$$

In the case of this example, $\mathcal{E}_1$ is positive and $\mathcal{E}_2$ is negative, but for simplicity we contain the sign in the emfs until final substitution. Thus $\mathcal{E}_2$ will be finally replaced by a negative number.

Rearrangement of the equations above gives

$$\mathcal{E}_1 = (r_1 + R_a + R_b)i_1 - R_b i_2$$
$$\mathcal{E}_2 = -R_b i_1 + (r_2 + R_c + R_b)i_2$$

In loop 1, the factor multiplying i_1 is just the series resistance around loop 1, and similarly, the factor multiplying i_2 for loop 2 is the series resistance around loop 2. In order to simplify we write the series sum for each loop as

$$R_{11} = r_1 + R_a + R_b$$
$$R_{22} = r_2 + R_c + R_b$$

The factor multiplying $-i_2$ in loop 1 and that multiplying $-i_1$ in loop 2 is R_b, the resistance common to both loops. We denote this common resistance by

$$R_{21} = R_{12} = R_b$$

The two loop equations now become

$$\mathcal{E}_1 = R_{11} i_1 - R_{12} i_2$$
$$\mathcal{E}_2 = -R_{12} i_2 + R_{22} i_2$$

where $\mathcal{E}_1$ and $\mathcal{E}_2$ represent the total emf around each loop, with appropriate sign.

This scheme can be generalized to give the appropriate equations for any combination of loops. It is the generalized equation which is of most practical use. This is illustrated by means of the example in

Fig. 6.17. We extend the generalized nomenclature to write down at once the equations for this circuit.

$$\mathcal{E}_1 = R_{11}i_1 - R_{12}i_2 - R_{13}i_3$$
$$\mathcal{E}_2 = -R_{12}i_1 + R_{22}i_2 - R_{23}i_3$$
$$\mathcal{E}_3 = -R_{13}i_1 - R_{23}i_2 + R_{33}i_3$$

The terms on the diagonal are the series resistance sums around each loop.

$$R_{11} = r_1 + R_b + R_a$$
$$R_{22} = r_2 + R_c + R_b$$
$$R_{33} = r_3 + R_d + R_c + R_a$$

The off-diagonal terms involving the resistors shared by the loops are

$$R_{12} = R_{21} = R_b$$
$$R_{13} = R_{31} = R_a$$
$$R_{23} = R_{32} = R_c$$

In this scheme all resistances are positive. These results may be derived in detail as in the first example. The emfs are again interpreted as the total emf around each loop, taken with appropriate sign.

The full advantage of this method is obtained by writing down a general equation for the solution of the problem.

$$\mathcal{E}_j = -R_{j1}i_1 - R_{j2}i_2 - \cdots + R_{jj}i_j - R_{j(j+1)}i_{j+1} - \cdots - R_{jm}i_m$$

Once the set of equations is written down according to this scheme, the solutions for the currents may be obtained by substituting the numbers for emfs and resistance and solving by substitution or by determinants.

appendix **H**

complex numbers

In Chap. 11 it is shown that complex-number notation provides an attractive means of dealing with ac circuit problems. Here we give a few aspects of the development of complex numbers.

For our purposes the most interesting approach to complex numbers is to describe the *complex plane*, a two-dimensional space, such as shown in Fig. H.1. This space is a plane characterized by an origin

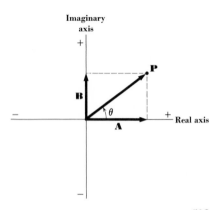

Fig. H.1   The complex number P in the complex plane is the vector sum of the real number A and the imaginary number B.
$$\mathbf{P} = A + jB.$$

and two axes at right angles to each other, the *real* axis (horizontal) and the *imaginary*[1] axis (vertical).

Complex numbers in the complex plane are ordered pairs of numbers which describe all points in the infinite plane in terms of vectors from the origin. Thus the point P shown in Fig. H.1 is described by the vector from the origin. This vector is the vector sum of the *real number* represented by the length A parallel to the real axis and the *imaginary number* represented by the length B parallel to the imaginary axis. In order to denote an imaginary number, represented by a point on the imaginary axis, we multiply the real number representing the magnitude (length) of B by the quantity j. Thus, if A and B are the magnitudes of the two numbers the complex number **P** is given by

$$\mathbf{P} = A + jB \tag{H.1}$$

where A is a real number and jB is an imaginary number. Clearly, any quadrant in the complex plane can be reached by appropriate combinations of $+$ and $-$ signs used with the two terms.

We now turn to the quantity $j = \sqrt{-1}$, which is at the heart of complex-number theory. From this simple definition comes a whole set of properties which account for the great usefulness of complex numbers. We first show two simple arithmetical properties of j.

(1) $j \cdot j = -1$

(2) $\dfrac{1}{j} = \dfrac{j}{j \cdot j} = \dfrac{j}{-1} = -j$

A complex number is a vector quantity, and hence can be characterized by a *modulus* (magnitude) and a direction. The square of the modulus can be obtained by multiplying the complex number by its *complex conjugate*. This quantity is the complex number with reversed signs on all terms containing j. Thus if, as in Eq. (H.1), the number is

$$\mathbf{P} = A + jB$$

its complex conjugate is

$$\mathbf{P}^* = A - jB \tag{H.2}$$

---

[1] The use of this word has lent an unnecessary air of mystery to complex numbers. There is nothing imaginary about this axis, as we shall see. The basic requirement is for two perpendicular axes and the associated ideas we are developing briefly here.

Thus

$$\mathbf{PP}^* = A^2 + B^2$$

This is always a real positive number.

$\sqrt{\mathbf{PP}^*}$ is the modulus of $\mathbf{P}$ in Fig. H.1.

It follows that

$$A = \tfrac{1}{2}(\mathbf{P} + \mathbf{P}^*)$$

and

$$jB = \tfrac{1}{2}(\mathbf{P} - \mathbf{P}^*)$$

Complex numbers obey the same commutative, associative, and distributive laws that real numbers do. Thus, if z_1 and z_2 and z_3 are any complex numbers, the following rules hold (and are easy to show):

$z_1 + z_2 = z_2 + z_1$	commutative law of addition
$z_1 z_2 = z_2 z_1$	commutative law of multiplication
$(z_1 + z_2) + z_3 = z_1 + (z_2 + z_3)$	associative law of addition
$(z_1 z_2) z_3 = z_1 (z_2 z_3)$	associative law of multiplication
$(z_1 + z_2) z_3 = z_1 z_3 + z_2 z_3$	distributive law of multiplication

The rules for subtraction are also similar to those for real numbers, with the proviso that the real and imaginary terms are treated separately. Thus

$$\mathbf{P}_2 - \mathbf{P}_1 = (A_2 - A_1) + j(B_2 - B_1)$$

Division of complex numbers is accomplished as follows:

$$\frac{A_2 + jB_2}{A_1 + jB_1} = \frac{A_2 + jB_2}{A_1 + jB_1} \times \frac{A_1 - jB_1}{A_1 - jB_1}$$

$$= \frac{(A_2 A_1 + B_2 B_1) + j(A_1 B_2 - A_2 B_1)}{A_1^2 + B_1^2}$$

The method involves multiplying the denominator by its complex conjugate so as to make the denominator a real number.

Many of the useful properties of complex numbers are most easily expressed and used if we convert the number into *polar* form. We now show that an equivalent expression to $\mathbf{P} = A + jB$ is

$$\mathbf{P} = Ne^{j\theta} \tag{H.3}$$

in which the modulus N is a real number, also written $|P|$, and θ is an angle expressed in radians. To obtain this result, we need merely to write the series expansion for the exponential e^x,

$$e^x = 1 + x + \frac{x^2}{2!} + \frac{x^3}{3!} + \frac{x^4}{4!} + \cdots$$

and note that

$$\sin x = x - \frac{x^3}{3!} + \frac{x^5}{5!} - \frac{x^7}{7!} + \cdots$$

and

$$\cos x = 1 - \frac{x^2}{2!} + \frac{x^4}{4!} - \frac{x^6}{6!} + \cdots$$

are series expansions for $\sin x$ and $\cos x$. Substitution of $j\theta$ for x then gives

$$e^{j\theta} = \cos \theta + j \sin \theta \tag{H.4}$$

which is known as Euler's formula.

Using Euler's formula, the complex number P can be written

$$\mathbf{P} = A + jB = N \cos \theta + jN \sin \theta = Ne^{j\theta}$$

Reference to Fig. H.1 shows the geometric interpretation of this result. It is apparent that

$$\tan \theta = \frac{B}{A}$$

The modulus of a complex number is easily obtained using the polar form.

$$\mathbf{PP}^* = Ne^{j\theta}Ne^{-j\theta} = N^2$$

One of the attractions of the polar form is the simplicity of manipulation of exponential functions of both real and complex variables. A few important facts about exponential function of real or complex variables are

$$e^{a+b} = e^a e^b$$

$$\frac{d}{dx} e^{kx} = ke^{kx}$$

$$\int e^{kx} k \, dx = e^{kx}$$

These relations hold for both real and complex numbers in the exponents.

If the quantities in the exponents are real, we have the following useful limiting values:

$$e^{-\infty} = 0 \qquad e^0 = 1 \qquad e^{\infty} = \infty$$

The meaning of numbers involving imaginary exponents is obtained by Euler's formula. The following special cases are illustrated in Fig. H.2.

θ	0	$\dfrac{\pi}{2}$	π	$\dfrac{3\pi}{2}$	2π
$e^{j\theta}$	1	j	-1	$-j$	1

From Euler's formula it is apparent that increasing values of the argument θ, which is multiplied by j in $e^{j\theta}$, have the effect of rotating the complex vector in the positive (counterclockwise) direction.

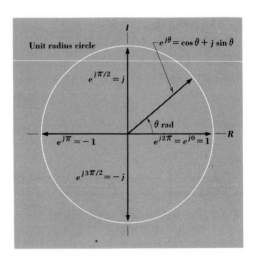

Fig. H.2   Complex numbers expressed in exponential form.

Another important property, easily demonstrated, is that when a complex number is multiplied by j, this has the effect of rotating the complex-number vector ahead by 90° in the complex plane. We prove this now, using Fig. H.3. Starting with the number

$$\mathbf{P} = Ne^{j\theta} = N(\cos\theta + j\sin\theta)$$

let

$$\mathbf{P}' = j\mathbf{P} = jNe^{j\theta} = N(-\sin\theta + j\cos\theta)$$

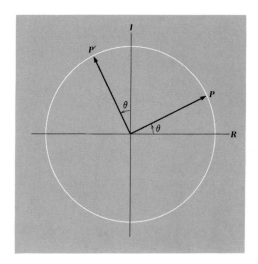

**Fig. H.3   Multiplication of
a complex number P by j
moves it forward by 90° in
the complex plane. Multi-
plication by −j moves it
by −90°.**

From the figure it is apparent that **P′** is 90° ahead of **P**. Multiplication
by −*j* has the effect of rotating **P** by −90°, as can be shown by the
same kind of argument.

In ac circuit work, advantage is taken of the foregoing properties
of complex numbers by letting the angle θ increase uniformly with
time according to

$$\theta = \omega t$$

where $\omega = 2\pi f$, the angular frequency of a sinusoidal function. Euler's
equation then becomes

$$e^{j\omega t} = \cos \omega t + j \sin \omega t$$

Thus a sinusoidal voltage can be represented by

$$v(t) = V_0 e^{j\omega t}$$

In this form, complex notation provides a concise description of rotating
generating vectors for sinusoidal functions of time, as discussed in
Chap. 11.

In Appendix J, use is made of complex exponential notation in
the description of traveling waves. Here again the notation is of
great advantage in its simplification of mathematical description.

appendix I

transient currents and voltages in a series LCR circuit

In Chap. 11 it is mentioned that many mechanical systems have simple electrical analogues. Here we discuss the transient behavior of a series *LCR* circuit. Its behavior is analogous to that of a damped mechanical oscillator. The behavior is parallel to what happens if a simple pendulum is displaced from its equilibrium position and then released. Depending on the amount of friction, or damping, the pendulum will either oscillate back and forth, with a gradually decreasing amplitude, or will move toward its equilibrium position without oscillations. We discuss the electrical analogue shown in Fig. I.1.

Initially, we charge the capacitor with a charge q, producing a

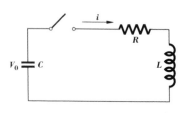

Fig. I.1 LCR circuit.

voltage across the plates

$$V_0 = \frac{q_0}{C} \tag{I.1}$$

At $t = 0$, the switch is closed and the charge q begins to leak off around the circuit through the inductance L and the resistor R. Positive current will be defined clockwise as shown. Since a positive current leads to a decreasing positive charge on the capacitor, we have

$$i(t) = -\frac{dq}{dt} \tag{I.2}$$

The current has been written as $i(t)$ to emphasize that i varies with time. The potential across the capacitor also changes with time, and can be written

$$v_C(t) = \frac{q(t)}{C} \tag{I.3}$$

The time rate of change of v_C is related to the current by differentiating Eq. (I.3) and substituting from Eq. (I.2).

$$\frac{dv_C}{dt} = \frac{1}{C}\frac{dq}{dt} = -\frac{1}{C}i(t) \tag{I.4}$$

According to the circuit equation,

$$v_C(t) - L\frac{di}{dt} = i(t)R \tag{I.5}$$

The sign of $L\,di/dt$ has been chosen correctly, because, when the switch was closed, the current was zero and increasing. Thus di/dt is initially positive. From the negative sign of Faraday induction it is clear that the voltage across the inductance will be in the direction to tend to decrease di/dt, thus conforming with Eq. (I.5).

Substitution of Eq. (I.4) and its derivative in Eq. (I.5) gives

$$\frac{d^2v_C}{dt^2} + \frac{R}{L}\frac{dv_C}{dt} + \frac{1}{LC}v_C = 0 \tag{I.6}$$

This is a second-order differential equation with constant coefficients. We are in search of an expression for v_C, the voltage across the capacitor, as a function of time. In view of the work in Chap. 11, it is a reasonable guess to expect damped oscillatory variation of v_C, and we try such a solution. The work can be greatly simplified if the oscillatory term is expressed in complex notation. Thus we write for the trial solution

$$v_C(t) = V_0 e^{-\alpha t} e^{j\omega t} \tag{I.7}$$

where both the constants α and ω are to be real numbers. We are to find the value of these constants for which Eq. (I.7) satisfies the differential equation.

The solution is certainly correct at $t = 0$, since the exponential terms both become equal to unity; so $v_C(t) = V_0$, the correct starting condition. And after a long time, the first factor $V_0 e^{-\alpha t}$, goes to zero, giving $v_C = 0$, as we expect. This factor is the exponential damping term we can expect from the discussions of transients in Chap. 11. The second factor is the sinusoidal term expressed in complex-number notation.

We now rewrite Eq. (I.7) in more concise form and take its derivatives as required for substitution in Eq. (I.6).

$$v_C(t) = V_0 e^{(j\omega - \alpha)t}$$

$$\frac{dv_C}{dt} = (j\omega - \alpha) V_0 e^{(j\omega - \alpha)t}$$

$$\frac{d^2 v_C}{dt^2} = (j\omega - \alpha)^2 V_0 e^{(j\omega - \alpha)t}$$

Substitution in Eq. (I.6) and simplification gives

$$-\omega^2 - 2j\omega\alpha + \alpha^2 + \frac{R}{L}(j\omega - \alpha) + \frac{1}{LC} = 0$$

This equation has both real and imaginary terms. But a complex number can equal zero only if both real and imaginary parts are zero. We therefore separate the equation into real and imaginary parts. The imaginary part gives

$$-2j\omega\alpha + \frac{L}{R} j\omega = 0 \qquad \text{or} \qquad \alpha = \frac{R}{2L}$$

The real part gives

$$-\omega^2 + \alpha^2 - \alpha \frac{R}{L} + \frac{1}{LC} = 0$$

Replacing α by $R/2L$ leads to

$$\omega^2 = \frac{1}{LC} - \frac{R^2}{4L^2}$$

These values of α and ω make the proposed solution satisfy the differential equation.

We now see the condition for critical damping of the LCR circuit. Since oscillatory motion requires ω to be real, oscillations occur only if

$$\frac{1}{LC} > \frac{R^2}{4L^2}$$

Otherwise ω in Eq. (I.7) becomes imaginary, the exponent in the term $e^{j\omega t}$ becomes real and negative, and the term becomes a damping term.

Whenever $1/LC$ exceeds $R^2/4L^2$ the voltage oscillates according to

$$v_C(t) = V_0 e^{-Rt/2L} e^{j\omega t}$$

where

$$\omega = \sqrt{\frac{1}{LC} - \frac{R^2}{4L^2}}$$

giving a voltage which varies with time, as shown in Fig. I.2.

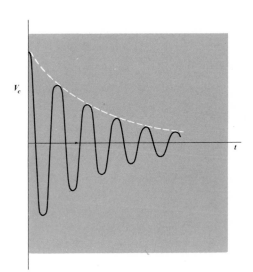

Fig. I.2 Voltage across the capacitor in an LCR circuit when 1/LC exceeds $R^2/4L^2$.

In extreme cases in which the resistance term is negligible compared with $1/LC$, the solution reduces to

$$v_C(t) = V_0 e^{j\omega_0 t}$$

where $\omega_0 = 1/\sqrt{LC}$, and the circuit oscillates without damping, at its resonance frequency ω_0. The effect of the resistance is to damp the oscillations and to shift the frequency toward a lower value.

If $1/LC$ just equals $R^2/4L^2$, ω is zero, and the circuit is *critically damped*, according to

$$v_C(t) = V_0 e^{-Rt/2L}$$

If the resistance term is so large that

$$\frac{R^2}{4L^2} > \frac{1}{LC}$$

ω becomes an imaginary quantity which we call ω'.

$$\omega' = j\sqrt{\frac{R^2}{4L^2} - \frac{1}{LC}} = j\sqrt{A}$$

where $\sqrt{A}$ is a real positive number. The voltage equation then becomes

$$v_C(t) = V_0 e^{-(\alpha - j\omega')t} = V_0 e^{-(\alpha + \sqrt{A})t}$$

$$= V_0 \exp - \left(\frac{R}{2L} + \sqrt{\frac{R^2}{4L^2} - \frac{1}{LC}} \right) t$$

If the term $1/LC$ can be neglected in comparison with the resistive term, the solution becomes

$$v_C(t) = V_0 e^{-Rt/L}$$

appendix J

dispersion; phase and group velocity

In a vacuum, plane electromagnetic waves of all frequencies travel with the same velocity. But in matter, the velocity depends on the frequency. The dependence of velocity on frequency is known as *dispersion*. The rainbow spectrum of white light which has traveled through a glass prism illustrates this effect, and we later show (Appendix M) that the velocity of microwaves in a hollow metal guide provides another example.

The traveling wave $A \cos (\omega t - kx)$ can be described by

$$A e^{j(\omega t - kx)} \tag{J.1}$$

Suppose, then, that there are two waves of equal amplitude A

$$A e^{j(\omega_1 t - k_1 x)} \qquad \text{and} \qquad A e^{j(\omega_2 t - k_2 x)}$$

where ω_1 and ω_2 are nearly the same and k_1 and k_2 have close to the same value. The result of superposing these two waves is the sum

$$A \exp [j(\omega_1 t - k_1 x)] + A \exp [j(\omega_2 t - k_2 x)] \tag{J.2}$$

where exp (x) is written for e^x, and the two waves are assumed to have equal amplitude.

This sum can be written in an equivalent form, which describes the combined wave.

The first term in Eq. (J.2) can be written

$$A \exp j \left(\frac{\omega_1 t}{2} + \frac{\omega_1 t}{2} + \frac{\omega_2 t}{2} - \frac{\omega_2 t}{2} - \frac{k_1 x}{2} - \frac{k_1 x}{2} - \frac{k_2 x}{2} + \frac{k_2 x}{2} \right)$$

Equal terms in ω_2 and in k_2 have been added and subtracted without affecting the result. The same kind of operation is performed on the second term in Eq. (J.2). When the two waves are added, the result is easily seen to be

$$A \exp \{ \tfrac{1}{2} j[(\omega_1 + \omega_2)t - (k_1 + k_2)x] \}$$
$$\times \{ \exp \tfrac{1}{2} j[(\omega_1 - \omega_2)t - (k_1 - k_2)x]$$
$$+ \exp - \tfrac{1}{2} j[(\omega_1 - \omega_2)t - (k_1 - k_2)x] \} \qquad (J.3)$$

Taking the real part of the complex expression,[1] we find

$$A \left\{ \cos \left[\left(\frac{\omega_1 + \omega_2}{2} \right) t - \left(\frac{k_1 + k_2}{2} \right) x \right] \right\}$$
$$\left\{ 2 \cos \left[\left(\frac{\omega_1 - \omega_2}{2} \right) t - \left(\frac{k_1 - k_2}{2} \right) x \right] \right\} \qquad (J.4)$$

This result shows very clearly what happens. There is a traveling wave which is very much like either of the original waves. It has a frequency $(\omega_1 + \omega_2)/2$, that is, the average of the two original waves, and a wave vector $(k_1 + k_2)/2$, that is, the average of the original wave vectors. Multiplying this wave, and therefore modifying its amplitude, or *modulating* it, is a low-frequency wave of frequency $(\omega_1 + \omega_2)/2$ and of wave vector $(k_1 - k_2)/2$. Such a combination wave looks like that shown in Fig. J.1. If there is no dispersion, the velocity of the high-frequency wave is the same as that of the lower-frequency modulation wave. But with dispersion, these two velocities are unequal.

The velocity of the high-frequency wave, given by the average values of ω and k, is called the *phase velocity* v_p. Equation (J.4) shows

---

[1] We have used

$$e^{jx} = \cos x + j \sin x$$
$$e^{-jx} = \cos x - j \sin x$$

in the evaluation of the real part of the difference frequency term.

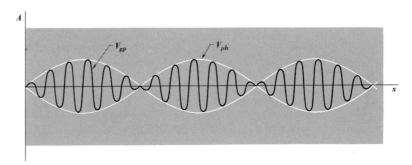

Fig. J.1 *Interference between two waves of slightly different fre-*
quencies gives a modulated wave. If the velocities of the two
waves are different as a result of dispersion, the group and phase
velocities are different. The same reasoning applies to a distribu-
tion of frequencies making a single wave packet. Energy is
propagated at the group velocity.

that here

$$v_p = \frac{\omega_1 + \omega_2}{k_1 + k_2}$$

As the two frequencies approach each other, the limiting value of the
phase velocity is

$$v_p = \frac{\omega}{k} \tag{J.5}$$

How fast does the modulation envelope move along the propagation direction? This is answered by examining the modulating term
in Eq. (J.4), which gives $(\omega_1 - \omega_2)/2$ and $(k_1 - k_2)/2$, the difference
terms, for the effective frequency and wave vector for the wave. This
velocity, called the *group velocity*, is

$$v_g = \frac{\omega_1 - \omega_2}{k_1 - k_2} \tag{J.6}$$

As the two waves come closer to the same frequency, the limit
approached in Eq. (J.6) is

$$v_g = \frac{d\omega}{dk} \tag{J.7}$$

Although the highest velocity at which information or energy can
move in electromagnetic radiation is c, the velocity of light, v_p can, and

in many circumstances does, exceed this value. However, the group velocity v_g represents the rate at which energy or information can be transferred, and v_g never exceeds c. It can be shown, in fact, that for electromagnetic waves in a vacuum (as in a waveguide)

$$v_p v_g = c^2 \tag{J.8}$$

The group velocity measures the time of travel of the front end of the wave after suddenly turning on an oscillating source of a wave. In a situation involving dispersion, this is a longer time than that for a particular oscillation to travel the same distance.

appendix K

short derivation of the electromagnetic wave equation

We illustrate here the great usefulness of the differential form of Maxwell's equations by showing how they give rise in free space to a traveling wave. We write

$$\text{curl } \mathbf{E} = -\frac{\partial \mathbf{B}}{\partial t} \quad \text{and} \quad \text{curl } \mathbf{B} = \mu_0 \epsilon_0 \frac{\partial \mathbf{E}}{\partial t}$$

We take the curl of the first equation, using the operator notation discussed earlier. This gives

$$\mathbf{\nabla} \times (\mathbf{\nabla} \times \mathbf{E}) = -\frac{\partial}{\partial t}(\mathbf{\nabla} \times \mathbf{B}) = -\mu_0 \epsilon_0 \frac{\partial^2 \mathbf{E}}{\partial t^2}$$

A well-known vector identity gives

$$\mathbf{\nabla} \times (\mathbf{\nabla} \times \mathbf{E}) = \mathbf{\nabla}(\mathbf{\nabla} \cdot \mathbf{E}) - \nabla^2 \mathbf{E} \tag{K.1}$$

In the absence of charge, $\mathbf{\nabla} \cdot \mathbf{E}$, the divergence of the field, is zero. Thus we arrive at

$$\nabla^2 E = \mu_0 \epsilon_0 \frac{\partial^2 \mathbf{E}}{\partial t^2} \tag{K.2}$$

In one dimension, as for a plane wave, this becomes

$$\frac{\partial^2 E_y}{\partial x^2} = \mu_0 \epsilon_0 \frac{\partial^2 E_y}{\partial t^2} \qquad (K.3)$$

This is the differential equation of a plane wave. Although this derivation hides the details of the argument given in Sec. 12.5, it is a remarkable example of concise mathematics covering a rather complicated set of phenomena.

appendix L

an electromagnetic wave in a conducting medium

In Sec. 12.11 we discussed the reflection of an electromagnetic wave incident on the plane boundary of a conducting medium, in the approximation that the resistivity is negligible. Here we consider the more complicated case where resistivity is important. In this case we investigate the transmission of the wave into the volume of the material. We find that there is appreciable penetration of the wave into the metal, but that the strength of the ac field attenuates exponentially. The depth of penetration depends on the resistivity of the metal.

Assuming an electromagnetic wave is incident normally at the plane surface of a metal, there are time-varying fields of amplitude E_0 and H_0 at the surface. Let the z axis be pointed into the metal, in the direction of propagation of the wave into the material. We assume the usual situation, that the metal obeys Ohm's law, or

$$\mathbf{J} = \sigma\mathbf{E} \tag{6.30}$$

where $\mathbf{J}$ = current density in any region in the metal
$\quad \sigma$ = conductivity
$\quad \mathbf{E}$ = field in the same region

This is the microscopic form of Ohm's law, as discussed in Chap. 6.

The next step is to write the second Maxwell equation in differential form for the relation between **E** and **H** in the presence of conductivity.

$$\text{curl } \mathbf{H} = \nabla \times \mathbf{H} = \mathbf{J} + \epsilon \frac{\partial \mathbf{E}}{\partial t}$$

$$= \sigma \mathbf{E} + \epsilon \frac{\partial \mathbf{E}}{\partial t} \tag{12.4a}$$

The relation between **E** and $\partial \mathbf{H}/\partial t$ comes from another Maxwell equation, and can be written in the form

$$\nabla \times \mathbf{E} = -\mu \frac{\partial \mathbf{H}}{\partial t} \tag{12.1a}$$

Using the vector identity

$$\nabla \times (\nabla \times \mathbf{E}) = \nabla(\nabla \cdot \mathbf{E}) - \nabla^2 \mathbf{E} \tag{K.1}$$

and noting that $\nabla \cdot \mathbf{E}$ is zero here if the net charge in any region of the metal is zero, and following the same argument as in Appendix K, we find

$$\nabla^2 \mathbf{E} - \mu\epsilon \frac{\partial^2 \mathbf{E}}{\partial t^2} - \mu\sigma \frac{\partial \mathbf{E}}{\partial t} = 0 \tag{L.1}$$

which is the same as Eq. (K.2) of Appendix K modified to accommodate the conductivity of the material. In order to get this result it was necessary to take the time derivative of **H** inside the curl. That is,

$$\frac{\partial}{\partial t} (\nabla \times \mathbf{H}) = \nabla \times \frac{\partial \mathbf{H}}{\partial t} = \sigma \frac{\partial \mathbf{E}}{\partial t} + \epsilon \frac{\partial^2 \mathbf{E}}{\partial t^2} \tag{L.2}$$

Equation (L.2) is the differential equation for a damped traveling wave. We therefore assume a solution of the form

$$E = E_0 e^{j(\omega t - kz)} \tag{L.3}$$

for a wave moving along the z direction. The wave vector **k** holds the key to the behavior of the wave within the metal. When **k** is complex, it can be written as $k = k_1 + jk'$. The real part, k_1, refers to the propagation of the wave as usual; that is, $k_1 = 2\pi/\lambda$. The imaginary part, k', refers to the attenuation of the wave, since it leads to a multiplying term

$$e^{k'z}$$

in the wave equation. This term implies an exponential decrease in wave amplitude with z.

We now substitute the trial expression (L.3) for the wave into the differential equation (L.2), which it must satisfy. When this is done we find

$$(-jk)^2\mathbf{E} - \mu\epsilon(j\omega)^2\mathbf{E} - \mu\sigma(j\omega)\mathbf{E} = 0 \tag{L.4}$$

This equation determines the values of k for which Eq. (L.3) satisfies the differential wave equation. In equivalent form

$$(-jk)^2 - \mu\epsilon(j\omega)^2 - \mu\sigma(j\omega) = 0 \tag{L.5}$$

must hold. This last equation can be solved for k^2. We find

$$k^2 = \mu\epsilon\omega^2 \left(1 - \frac{j\sigma}{\epsilon\omega}\right) \tag{L.6}$$

Thus k is in fact shown to be a complex quantity. The term involving unity in this equation refers to the displacement current, but this term is insignificant in a metal compared with the conductivity term. That is, for metals at radio frequencies,

$$\frac{\sigma}{\epsilon\omega} \gg 1$$

and we can write

$$k \approx \sqrt{-j\mu\sigma\omega}$$

We must now evaluate $\sqrt{-j}$.

$$-j = e^{-j\pi/2}$$

$$\text{so } \sqrt{-j} = e^{-j\pi/4} = \cos\frac{\pi}{4} - j\sin\frac{\pi}{4} = \frac{1}{\sqrt{2}} - \frac{j}{\sqrt{2}}$$

With this result, the complex expression for k becomes

$$k = \frac{1-j}{\delta}$$

where

$$\delta = \sqrt{\frac{2}{\mu\sigma\omega}}$$

Evidently, δ is a length. Substitution of the value of k into the proposed wave equation gives

$$E = E_0 e^{j(\omega t - z/\delta)} e^{-z/\delta} \tag{L.7}$$

The first exponential factor represents a traveling wave moving into the metal, but this is multiplied by the second exponential term which represents a damping factor. This equation shows that δ measures the exponential damping of the wave as it travels into the metal. δ is called the skin depth. The attenuation of an ac field in a conductor was discussed qualitatively in Chap. 9.

appendix M

an electromagnetic wave in a waveguide

We investigate here the nature of the dominant mode of an electromagnetic wave in a rectangular waveguide, as discussed in Chap. 12. This can be discussed most easily by looking at the boundary conditions on **E** in the guide. The top and bottom broad faces of the guide serve to limit the wave to the inner volume of the conducting rectangular guide, but do not affect **E** within the guide, since the vertically polarized **E** vector is normal to the top and bottom faces. But the **E** vector must go essentially to zero at the two side faces of the guide, since **E** is parallel to these conducting faces. An end view of the field in the guide was shown in Fig. 12.17.

It can be shown that the simple superposition of two polarized plane waves of the same wavelength gives a single modified wave which has a Poynting vector pointed along the guide and which can satisfy the zero **E** field boundary condition at the sidewalls of the guide. Since this combined wave is the sum of two free-space plane waves, and since it satisfies the boundary conditions, it is a solution to the problem.

Figure M.1 can be used to demonstrate the argument. Two plane waves with unit propagation vectors $\hat{\mathbf{n}}_1$ and $\hat{\mathbf{n}}_2$ are shown. They make

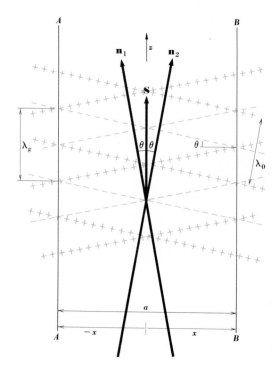

Fig. M.1 *An electromagnetic wave in a waveguide can be represented as the sum of two
plane waves, with propagation vectors* n_1
and n_2. *Successive wavefronts are shown.
The interference pattern of these two
waves produces zero E field at the sidewalls
AA and BB.*

angles θ and $-\theta$ with the z axis. The direction of the polarized **E** vectors
is normal to the figure. Wavefronts are shown, with successive crests
marked positive and successive valleys marked negatively. The sum of
the two waves gives a wave propagating in the z direction. Along the
center line of the figure the **E** fields add to give an amplitude $2E_0$,
where E_0 is the amplitude of either plane wave. But because of the tilt
in the direction of one wave with respect to the other, as we move
away from the center line the two waves become more and more out of
phase. Along the planes AA and BB, the two waves are just 180° out of
phase, which means that their sum is zero. Thus, if conducting planes
were placed along AA and BB, their only effect would be to limit the
wave to the space between them.

This combined wave is made up of two plane waves, each of which satisfies Maxwell's equations; so the sum satisfies them. It also meets the boundary conditions for a rectangular guide of width a. It can also be shown that the amplitude of the composite wave varies with the x coordinate across the guide, as shown in Fig. 12.19.

We can determine some other characteristics of this waveguide wave. If the free-space wavelength of the two plane waves is λ_0, we see that the wavelength of the guide wave is

$$\lambda_g = \frac{\lambda_0}{\cos \theta} \tag{M.1}$$

The fact that λ_g is greater than λ_0 does not mean that information travels down the guide at a velocity greater than c, the velocity of electromagnetic waves in free space. λ_g is related to the *phase velocity*, as discussed in Appendix J. The *group velocity*, with which information travels, is shown by the geometry of Fig. M.1 to be

$$v_g = c \cos \theta \tag{M.2}$$

From the last two equations it follows that

$$v_g v_p = c^2 \tag{M.3}$$

To show this last result we combine Eqs. (M.1) and (M.2) with the equations

$$
\begin{aligned}
f\lambda_0 &= c & &\text{free-space velocity} \\
f\lambda_p &= v_p & &\text{phase velocity} \\
f\lambda_g &= v_g & &\text{group velocity}
\end{aligned}
$$

The result of Eq. (M.3) follows immediately. In free space both group and phase velocities are the same as the free-space velocity.

It is useful to have the relationship between λ and λ_0 in terms of the width a of the guide. This relationship is available from Fig. M.1 when we note that

$$\frac{\lambda_0/2}{a} = \sin \theta \tag{M.4}$$

Combining this with Eq. (M.1) and eliminating θ by means of

$$\sin^2 \theta + \cos^2 \theta = 1$$

we find

$$\left(\frac{1}{\lambda}\right)^2 + \left(\frac{1}{2a}\right)^2 = \left(\frac{1}{\lambda_0}\right)^2 \tag{M.5}$$

or

$$\lambda = \frac{\lambda_0}{\sqrt{1 - (\lambda_0/2a)^2}} \tag{M.6}$$

This is the waveguide equation for the dominant mode in the rectangular guide. This equation shows at once that there is a minimum, or cutoff, frequency below which a waveguide will not transmit a wave. Thus, when λ_0, the free-space wavelength, becomes as long as $2a$, λ_g approaches infinity, and there is no longer a transmitted wave. Another way of seeing this is to note that as λ_0 is increased, by lowering the frequency, the angle θ increases, and becomes 90° when $\lambda_0 = 2a$. In this situation the two plane waves are pointed across the guide, and no energy travels down the guide.

In this appendix we chose to discuss only the electric-field components of the wave. The lines of **B** are also affected by the guide. It can be shown in fact that the **B** fields add to form the closed loops, as in Fig. 12.20. We chose to work with the **E** field rather than the **B** field because it is somewhat simpler to do so.

answers to selected problems

1.1A $Q_3 = 4Q_1$

1.1C (a) $F = 0$

     (b) $F = 9 \times 10^{11}Q^2$

        newtons

1.2B $2\mu_0 + 4$ coul

1.3A (a) $F = 0$

     (b) $F = 2.88 \times 10^7$

        newtons

1.4A (a) $F = \dfrac{1}{4\pi\epsilon_0}\dfrac{Q_1Q_2}{a^2}$

        newtons

     (b) $W = \dfrac{1}{4\pi\epsilon_0}\,Q_1Q_2$

        $\left(\dfrac{1}{b} - \dfrac{1}{a}\right)$ joules

1.6A (a) 6.65×10^{15} rps

     (b) 10.4×10^{-35} kg-m^2/

        rad sec^{-1}

     (c) 1.36×10^{27} m

2.1B (a) Q/ϵ_0 lines

     (b) $N = Q/32\pi\epsilon_0$ lines

     (c) 1 line/m^2

2.1D (a) $E = 0$

     (b) $E = \dfrac{12.5Q}{4\pi\epsilon_0}$

        newtons/coul

     (c) $E = \dfrac{25Q}{4\pi\epsilon_0}$ newtons/

        coul

     (d) $E = \dfrac{4Q}{4\pi\epsilon_0}$ newtons/

        coul

2.1F $E = \dfrac{Q}{4\pi\epsilon_0 2R^2}$ newtons/

     coul

2.1H $1.89 \times 10^{11}\,Q$ newtons/

     coul

2.2A 10^{-2} sterad

2.4A $\dfrac{40Q}{4\pi\epsilon_0}$ joules

2.5A $\dfrac{\sqrt{13}\,p}{8\pi\epsilon_0 r^3}$ newtons/coul

2.6B $F = KaQ = Kp$ newtons

3.1A $(a) = (b) = \dfrac{Q^2}{4\pi\epsilon_0 a}$ joules

3.2B (a) $V_S = \dfrac{p}{4\pi\epsilon_0(a^2 - l^2/4)}$ volts

   $W = QV_S$ volts

   (b) $V_S = \dfrac{p}{4\pi\epsilon_0 a^2}$ volts

   $E = \dfrac{2p}{4\pi\epsilon_0 a^3}$ volts

3.2D $V_{\text{in}} = \dfrac{\rho}{6\epsilon_0}(3R^2 - r^2)$ volts

   $V_{\text{out}} = \dfrac{\rho R^3}{3\epsilon_0 r}$ volts

   $E_{\text{in}} = \dfrac{\rho r}{3\epsilon_0}$ volts/m

   $E_{\text{out}} = \dfrac{\rho R^3}{3\epsilon_0 r^2}$ volts/m

3.2F $V = \dfrac{Q}{4\pi\epsilon_0 R}$ volts;

   $W = \dfrac{Q^2}{4\pi\epsilon_0 2R}$ joules

3.2H $V_{12} = \dfrac{Q}{2\pi\epsilon_0} \ln \dfrac{r_2}{r_1}$ volts

3.2J (b) $x = 32.3$ cm,
   -7.65 cm, -20 cm
   (c) Equilibrium at $x =$ -20 cm, stable for $-$ charge, unstable for $+$ charge

3.3B $E_x = (bx - a)(x^2 + y^2)^{-3/2} + 3\,ax^2(x^2 + y^2)^{-5/2}$ volts/m

$E_y = 3\,axy(x^2 + y^2)^{-5/2} + by(x^2 + y^2)^{-3/2}$ volts/m

3.4A $v = \left(\dfrac{2eV}{m}\right)^{1/2} = 0.59 \times 10^7$ m/sec
   $W = 1.6 \times 10^{-17}$ joule $= 1.6 \times 10^{-10}$ ergs $= 100$ electron volts

3.4C $V_1 = \dfrac{2d^2 V}{b^2}$ volts

3.6A (a) $E = \dfrac{1}{4\pi\epsilon_0 r^3} \sqrt{(2p\cos\theta)^2 + (p\sin\theta)^2}$

   (b) $\tan\phi = \frac{1}{2}\tan\theta$

4.1B $C = \dfrac{4\pi\epsilon_0}{\left(\dfrac{1}{a}+\dfrac{1}{c}\right) - \left(\dfrac{1}{b}+\dfrac{1}{d}\right)}$ farads

4.1D $C_2 = \dfrac{C_1 d}{d - a}$ farads

4.2A $C = \dfrac{(C_1 + C_2)C_3}{C_1 + C_2 + C_3}$ farads

4.2C $\dfrac{C_1}{C_2} = \dfrac{C_3}{C_4}$

4.4A $V_e = 5.56 \times 10^{-13}$ volt
   $V_p = 1.02 \times 10^{-9}$ volt

4.6A (a) $U = \dfrac{Q_2}{8\pi\epsilon_0 R}$ joules
   (b) $r = 2R$

4.6C $\Delta U = \dfrac{1}{2}Q_0^2 \dfrac{C_2}{C_1^2 + C_1 C_2}$ joules

4.6E $V_2 = 2V_1$, $U_2 = 2U_1$

4.7A $F = \dfrac{A\epsilon_0 V^2}{2d^2}$ newtons

5.1B $dQ_p = 2\pi r^2 P \sin\theta \cos\theta\, d\theta$
   $Q_p{}^+ = \pi r^2 P$ coul

5.2B $\phi_2 = 24°25'$

5.3B $\dfrac{C_b}{C_a} = \dfrac{4K_1 K_2}{(K_1 + K_2)^2}$

5.3D $P = -\sigma_f$

$\chi = \infty$

5.4A $V_2 = \dfrac{V_1}{K}$ volts

$U_2 = \dfrac{U_1}{K}$ joules

Slab pulled in

6.1B $v = 0.0625$ m/sec

6.1D $i = \frac{1}{2}\sigma\omega R^2$ amp

6.3B $R_2 = 1$ ohm

6.4A (a) $R = 8\frac{1}{3}$ ohms

(b) $P_1 = 2.88$ watts

$P_2 = 7.20$ watts

$P_3 = 0.854$ watt

$P_4 = 0.64$ watt

$P_5 = 0.426$ watt

6.4D $R_0 = (1 + \sqrt{3})R$ ohms

6.5A $i_1 = \frac{11}{13}$ amp

$i_2 = \frac{3}{13}$ amp

$i_3 = \frac{8}{13}$ amp

6.6A (a) $R_i = 0.05$ ohm

(b) $R_i = 0.15$ ohm

6.7A (a) $R_v = 9{,}990$ ohms

(b) $R_a = 1.111$ ohms

6.7C $R_1 = 0.0278$ ohm

$R_2 = 0.250$ ohm

$R_3 = 2.50$ ohms

7.1A $\tau = 2.09 \times 10^{-12}$ sec

8.1A $\dfrac{F}{l} = \dfrac{\mu_0 i i'}{2\pi a} = 2 \times 10^{-4}$

newton/m (attractive)

8.1C $F = \dfrac{\mu_0 N^2 i^2 a}{b}$ newtons

8.1E $T = IBa$ newtons

8.2B $B = \dfrac{\pi_0 jr}{2}$ webers/m^2

$r < a$

$B = \dfrac{\mu_0 a^2 j}{2r}$ webers/m^2

$r > a$

8.2D $B = \dfrac{\mu_0 i}{2\pi b} \ln \dfrac{b + a}{a}$

weber/m^2

8.2F (a) $j^s = \dfrac{Ni}{L} = 3 \times 10^4$

amp/m

(b) $B_1 = \dfrac{\mu_0 N i}{L} = 12\pi \times$

10^{-3} weber/m^2

(c) $B_2 = \dfrac{\mu_0 N i}{2L} = 6\pi \times$

10^{-3} weber/m^2

(d) $\Phi = B_1 A = 48\pi^2 \times$

10^{-7} weber

(e) $\Phi = B_2 A = 24\pi^2 \times$

10^{-7} weber

8.2H $B = \dfrac{\mu_0 \sigma \omega a^4}{8b^3}$ webers/m^2

$b \gg a$

8.2J $\Phi = 1.1 \times 10^{-7}$ weber

8.2L $B_b = \dfrac{\mu_0 i}{\pi r}$ webers/m^2

$B_a = \dfrac{\mu_0 i}{r}\left(\dfrac{1}{4} + \dfrac{1}{2\pi}\right)$

webers/m^2

8.2N $B = \dfrac{\mu_0 N i}{4r}$ webers/m^2

8.2P $B = 0.02$ weber/m^2

$= 200$ gauss

8.3B $m = 7.2 \times 10^{-26}$ kg

8.3D $R_H = 6.25 \times 10^{-10}$

$N = 10^{28}$ electrons/m^3

8.3F (a) $\omega = 4.8 \times 10^7$

rad/sec

(b) $W = 1.92 \times 10^{-12}$

joule

$= 1.2 \times 10^7$ ev

(c) $n = 300$ revolutions

8.4B $F = NI_0 2\pi r B_0 \cos\theta$

newtons, upwards

9.1B $\mathcal{E}_{max} = \omega BnA$ volts

9.2A (a) $F = evB$ newtons, upward on electrons

(b) $E = vB$ volts/m upward

(c) $V = vBL$ volts

(d) $i = \dfrac{vBL}{R}$ amp

(e) $\mathcal{E} = vBL$ volts

9.2C $v = \dfrac{mgR}{B^2 l^2}$ m/sec

$v' = 4v$ m/sec

9.3B $\Phi = 0.5 \times 10^{-7}$ weber

9.4A $L' = 3L$ henrys

9.4C $\mathcal{E} = \dfrac{\mu_0 i a b}{2\pi} \dfrac{V}{l(l+a)}$ volts

9.5A $U = 250$ joules

$\mathcal{E} = 900$ volts

9.5C $U = \frac{1}{3} \times 10^{-2}$ joule

10.1A (a) $j^s_{free} = 13{,}333$ amp/m

(b) $H = 13{,}333$ amp/m

(c) $\mu = 1.28 \times 10^{-6}$ weber/amp-m

(d) $M = 267$ amp/m

(e) $B = 17.1 \times 10^{-3}$ weber/m^2

10.1C $\chi = 3.28 \times 10^{-3}$

$p_m = 2.61 \times 10^{-3}$ amp-m^2

$M = 1.8 \times 10^6$ amp/m

$p_m = 18$ amp-m^2

$\tau = 1.8 \times 10^{-6}$ newton-m

$q_m = 180$ unit poles

10.2B $\dfrac{X_1}{X_2} = (2 \cot \theta)^{-\frac{1}{2}}$

10.4A Power density $= 12$ watts/m^3,

$P = 24 \times 10^{-5}$ watts

$i_{max} = 0.04$ amp

$L = 2.5 \times 10^{-3}$ henrys

L would decrease

10.5B $x = 3 \times 10^{-4}$ m

11.1B (a) $I = \dfrac{V_0}{[R^2 + (1/\omega C)^2]^{\frac{1}{2}}} \sin(\omega t + \Phi)$,

$\Phi = \tan^{-1} \dfrac{1}{\omega CR}$

(b) $\Delta\Phi = 0$

(c) $\Delta\Phi = 90°$ (V_R leads V_c)

(d) $V_R = \dfrac{V_0 R}{[R^2 + (1/\omega C)^2]^{\frac{1}{2}}}$ volts

$V_c = \dfrac{(V_0/\omega C)}{[R^2 + (1/\omega C)^2]^{\frac{1}{2}}}$ volts

11.1D (a) $N\Phi = NBA \sin\theta$ webers

(b) $\mathcal{E} = -N\omega BA \cos\omega t$ volts

(c) $\mathcal{E} = N\omega BA$

(d) $i = -N\omega BA \times \cos \dfrac{\omega t}{(R^2 + \omega^2 L^2)^{\frac{1}{2}}}$ amp

(e) $\Phi = \tan^{-1} \dfrac{\omega L}{R}$

(f) $\Phi = 0$

(g) I_L lags V_L by 90°

11.3A (a) $\omega_{max} = \dfrac{1}{(LC)^{\frac{1}{2}}}$ rad/sec

(b) $I_{max} = \dfrac{V_0}{R}$ amp

(c) $\omega = \dfrac{\sqrt{3}\, R \pm (3R^2 + 4L/C)^{\frac{1}{2}}}{2L}$ rad/sec

(d) $\omega = 0, \infty$

11.4A (b) $t = \dfrac{L}{R} \ln 2$ sec

     (c) $\tau = \dfrac{L}{R}$ sec

11.4C (a) $t = \dfrac{1}{RC} \ln 2$ sec

     (b) $i_{max} = \dfrac{V_0}{R}$ amp,

        at $t = 0$

     (c) $q_{max} = CV_0$ coul,

        at $t = \infty$

     (d) $t = \dfrac{1}{RC} \ln 2$ sec

11.5A $\dfrac{V_1}{V_2} = \dfrac{5n_1}{2n_2}$

12.2A (a) 3×10^5 cps

     (b) 3×10^8 cps

     (c) 10^{10} cps

     (d) 3×10^{12} cps

     (e) 6×10^{14} cps

     (f) 3×10^{19} cps

     (g) 3×10^{20} cps

12.4A (a) $\lambda = 300$ m

     (b) $E_0 = 122.6$ volts/m

        $H_0 = 0.325$ amp/m

12.6A $f = 1.5 \times 10^{10}$ cps

13.1A (a) 4.3×10^{-8}

     (b) 10.4 cm

13.1C 1.15×10^{-6} sec

13.2A $0.741c$; $0.99c$

13.2C (a) $0.51mc^2 = 7.67 \times 10^{-11}$ joule

     (b) $0.45c = 1.35 \times 10^8$ m/sec

     (c) $0.24mc^2 = 3.61 \times 10^{-11}$ joule

16.1A $\Delta v_p = 25$ volts

index

623